# THEORY OF CONVENTIONAL AND UNCONVENTIONAL SUPERCONDUCTIVITY IN THE HIGH-$T_{\mathrm{C}}$ CUPRATES AND OTHER SYSTEMS

# PHYSICS RESEARCH AND TECHNOLOGY

PHYSICS RESEARCH AND TECHNOLOGY

# THEORY OF CONVENTIONAL AND UNCONVENTIONAL SUPERCONDUCTIVITY IN THE HIGH-$T_\mathrm{C}$ CUPRATES AND OTHER SYSTEMS

DZHUMANOV SAFARALI

nova publishers

New York

For permission to use material from this book please contact us:
Telephone 631-231-7269; Fax 631-231-8175
Web Site: http://www.novapublishers.com

### NOTICE TO THE READER

The Publisher has taken reasonable care in the preparation of this book, but makes no expressed or implied warranty of any kind and assumes no responsibility for any errors or omissions. No liability is assumed for incidental or consequential damages in connection with or arising out of information contained in this book. The Publisher shall not be liable for any special, consequential, or exemplary damages resulting, in whole or in part, from the readers' use of, or reliance upon, this material. Any parts of this book based on government reports are so indicated and copyright is claimed for those parts to the extent applicable to compilations of such works.

Independent verification should be sought for any data, advice or recommendations contained in this book. In addition, no responsibility is assumed by the publisher for any injury and/or damage to persons or property arising from any methods, products, instructions, ideas or otherwise contained in this publication.

This publication is designed to provide accurate and authoritative information with regard to the subject matter covered herein. It is sold with the clear understanding that the Publisher is not engaged in rendering legal or any other professional services. If legal or any other expert assistance is required, the services of a competent person should be sought. FROM A DECLARATION OF PARTICIPANTS JOINTLY ADOPTED BY A COMMITTEE OF THE AMERICAN BAR ASSOCIATION AND A COMMITTEE OF PUBLISHERS.

Additional color graphics may be available in the e-book version of this book.

LIBRARY OF CONGRESS CATALOGING-IN-PUBLICATION DATA

Theory of conventional and unconventional superconductivity in the High-Tc cuprates and other systems / editor, Dzhumanov Safarali.
  p. cm.
 Includes bibliographical references and index.
 ISBN: 978-1-62081-554-0 (hardcover)
 1. Copper oxide superconductors. I. Safarali, Dzhumanov.
 QC611.98.C64T46 2011
 537.6'23--dc23
                          2012011768

*Published by Nova Science Publishers, Inc.* † *New York*

# Contents

# Preface

The study of superconductivity in solids was initiated in 1911 after the Kamerlingh-Onnes' discovery of this phenomenon in ordinary metals. Yet, we had to wait for a long time (until the seminal work by Bardeen, Cooper, and Schrieffer in 1957) to understand the physics of conventional superconductors. The discovery of unconventional superconductivity in the new classes of superconductors, such as in heavy-fermion and organic superconductors, and especially in high-$T_c$ cuprate superconductors ushered in a revolutionary era in condensed matter physics. This research completely changed our outlook on superconductivity and other electronic processes in solids. In particular, this discovery has led to an enormous experimental and theoretical effort to explore the novel superconductivity in cuprate superconductors. To date, as many as a thousand papers have been published on the high-$T_c$ cuprates without providing clear understanding of their normal and superconducting state properties which are significantly different from those conventional superconductors and are not well described by the existing theories of insulators, metals, and superconductors. Actually, the search for a new promising high-$T_c$ superconductor is still carried out empirically due to the absence of a successful and a predictive microscopic theory of high-$T_c$ superconductivity. There are many fundamental questions concerning the microscopic mechanism of novel (unconventional) superconductivity in high-$T_c$ cuprates, heavy-fermion and organic compounds, which cannot be settled only within the BCS-like $s$-, $p$-, and $d$-wave pairing theories in a convincing way. While the usual Bose-Einstein condensation (BEC) theory of an ideal Bose-gas of pre-formed Cooper pairs and real-space pairs is inapplicable for the explanation of the phenomenon of superconductivity. It follows that the understanding of the new physics of unconventional superconductivity in high-$T_c$ cuprates and other systems requires a more pertinent microscopic theory for describing not only the relevant pairing mechanisms but also the superfluid condensations of paired charge carriers underlying the superconductivity in these systems. We, therefore, feel that the time has come to write a book that describes not only the new ideas and concepts on novel superconductivity and superfluidity that have been developed in the last few years but also the more microscopic details of the normal and superconducting states in high-$T_c$ cuprates and other systems (e.g., heavy-fermion and organic superconductors and superfluid $^3$He).

This book presents the fundamentals of the modern microscopic theory of conventional and unconventional superconductivity in high-$T_c$ cuprates and other systems. It is desirable that the reader should be familiar with the quantum mechanics, statistical mechanics, solid state theory, BCS theory of superconductivity, and existing theories of quantum liquids. First, the applicability of the different BCS-like $s$-, $p$-, and $d$-wave pairing theories of superconductivity to high-$T_c$ cuprates and other systems is analyzed. Then, the applicability of the two-stage Fermi-Bose-liquid scenario for unconventional superconductivity in high-$T_c$ cuprates and other systems is discussed. According to this scenario, the precursor Cooper-like pairing of polaronic carriers above superconducting transition temperature $T_c$ and the subsequent condensation of tightly-bound (bosonic) Cooper pairs into a superfluid Bose-liquid state at $T_c$ result in the novel superconductivity in the pseudogap state of unconventional superconductors (such as underdoped, optimally doped and moderately overdoped cuprates, heavy-fermion and organic superconductors). In contrast, in BCS (fermionic) superconductors the Cooper pairing of carriers and the superfluidity of weakly bound Cooper pairs occur simultaneously at $T_c$. The basic concepts and principles of the theory of conventional superconductivity in BCS (fermionic) superconductors and of novel superconductivity in non-BCS (bosonic) superconductors are presented. In this book, many results of the theory of conventional superconductivity in BCS superconductors (including heavily overdoped cuprates) are given in juxtaposition with the respective results for the theory of unconventional superconductivity in underdoped; optimally doped and moderately overdoped high-$T_c$ cuprates. The theoretical results are compared with crucial experiments in many specific cases. The nature of the possible superconducting phases in high-$T_c$ cuprates and other unconventional superconductors is established and the existence of the BCS and non-BCS superconducting states in high-$T_c$ cuprates is demonstrated. The nature of the two superfluid phases of liquid $^3$He is also established. Conclusions which have been written since the book was prepared for publication and added in proof, provides a summary of important theoretical and experimental results on the unconventional superconductivity and superfluidity in various condensed matter.

I benefitted greatly from valuable and stimulating discussions with G. Baskaran, J.D. Fan, B.L. Oksengendler, E.M. Ibragimova, P.J. Baimatov, B.Ya. Yavidov, A.A. Abdujabbarov and M. Nadirbekov. Furthermore, I should like to thank U.S. Salikhbaev at the Institute of Nuclear Physics (in Tashkent) for his support in writing this book. I also thank U.T. Kurbanov, O.K. Ganiev, Z.S. Khudayberdiev, and E.X. Karimbaev for their assistance in preparing the manuscript.

Finally, I thank my family and relatives for their endless support and unselfish help during many years in my scientific research work. This book is devoted to bright memory of my mother (Alibek kizi Yanglish) who was my first teacher (inspirator).

S. Dzhumanov
March 2, 2012

# Chapter 1

# Conventional Superconductors

## 1.1.  Introduction

Superconductivity (resistanceless conductivity of materials) is one of the most unique phenomena that occurs in nature. In 1911, superconductivity was discovered by a Dutch physicist named Heike Kamerlingh-Onnes in mercury at about 4.2K [1]. Later this phenomenon was also observed in other metals. It turned out that many metals and alloys become superconducting (SC) when cooled down to very low temperatures. Superconductivity for these systems is characterized by the SC transition or critical temperature $T_c$ below which the electrical resistance is zero. Various materials undergo a phase transition from the metallic state to the SC one at different critical temperatures and conventional metals have relatively low critical temperatures $T_c \lesssim 10K$ (see Table 1.1). The highest SC transition temperature $T_c \gtrsim 23K$ is observed in the compound $Nb_2Ge$.

**Table 1.1. The critical temperature for the onset of superconductivity in some conventional superconductors**

| Material | Al | Ti | Ga | Hg | In | Pb |
|---|---|---|---|---|---|---|
| $T_c, K$ | 1.18 | 0.39 | 1.09 | 4.16 | 3.40 | 7.19 |
| Material | V | Nb | W | $V_3Si$ | $Nb_3Sn$ | $Nb_3Ge$ |
| $T_c, K$ | 5.4 | 9.20 | 0.01 | 17.10 | 18.05 | 23.20 |

Further, a number of general regularities were established [1, 2, 3, 4, 5]. Some of the important regularities are: (i) monovalent and ferromagnetic metals do not exhibit superconductivity at normal pressures; (ii) those metals which are characterized by appreciable electron-phonon coupling and are poor conductors, they undergo a transition to superconductivity at a certain critical temperature $T_c$; (iii) some metals such as noble metals and alkaline metals are good conductors and do not become superconductors until reaching very low temperatures; (iv) the transition to the SC state (in the absence of an external magnetic field) is the second-order phase transition that occurs without latent heat; (v) some elements (As, Se, Y, Sb, Te, Cs, Ba and others) and semiconductors (Si and Ge) become superconductors under pressure; (vi) critical temperature $T_c$ depends on crystal modification and atomic mass; and (vii) non-magnetic impurities do not destroy superconductivity and their effect on $T_c$ is weak enough. Outlined in this chapter, we briefly discuss the basic properties of conventional superconductors.

## 1.2.  Classification of Solids on Electrical Conductivity

Classification in the type of chemical bonds found in solids are evaluated next. Classification of solids is usually based either on the type of chemical bonds or on the electrical properties. Classification for the existing solids based on the character of the interaction between their atoms or molecules allows to analyze the nature of the chemical bonds in solids and provide the existence of a stable crystal lattice. According to this classification scheme all solids can be conditionally subdivided into six types [2, 6, 7, 8]: metallic crystals, covalent crystals, ionic crystals, molecular crystals, crystals with hydrogenic bond, quantum crystals. Another classification scheme based on electrical conductivity $\sigma$ of solids enables us to see the important distinctions between electronic structures and electronic properties of different solids. According to this classification the existing solids can be conductionally subdivided into four separate types: metals, semiconductors, insulators and superconductors. Metals are good conductors and their conductivity $\sigma$ at low temperatures changes from $10^4$ to $10^9 \Omega^{-1} cm^{-1}$ [8, 9]. On the contrary, insulators practically do not conduct an electric current and their conductivity $\sigma$ varies from $10^{-12}$ to $10^{-20} \Omega^{-1} cm^{-1}$. Further, solids having the intermediate values of $\sigma$ ranged from $10^4$ to $10^{-12} \Omega^{-1} cm^{-1}$ belong to a semiconductor class. Such distinctions between conductivities of metals, semiconductors, and insulators depend on the peculiarities of the electronic structure of these systems and the electric properties of solids which are determined by a mutual location of different energy bands and by distribution of electrons on these bands. In particular, the conduction band of the metals is partially filled. While the conduction band of the semiconductors and insulators at absolute zero temperature $T = 0$ is totally empty and separated from the totally filled valence band by the energy gap $E_g$ which is smaller than 2 eV in semiconductors. As distinct from semiconductors the energy gap $E_g$ separating the valence band from the conduction band in insulators is much greater than $2 eV$. At low temperatures any semiconductor becomes an insulator. In the case of increasing temperature $T$, the part of electrons in semiconductors are thermally excited from the valence band to the conduction band and the concentration of the thermally excited electrons given by $n_e = n \exp(-E_g/k_B T)$ (where $n$ is the concentration of the valence electrons) is much smaller than the concentration of conduction electrons in metals in which $E_g = 0$. The distinction between metals and semiconductors is clearly manifested in the temperature dependence of their electrical resistivities $\rho(T)$ as shown in Fig. 1.1.

The low temperature resistivity in pure metals follows the $T^2$ law $\rho = \rho_0 + A_1 T^2$ due to the dominating electron-electron scattering, whereas their high temperature resistivity shows $T$-linear dependence due to the dominating carrier-acoustic phonon scattering $\rho = \rho_0 + A_2 T$, where $\rho_0$ is the residual resistivity, $A_1$ and $A_2$ are constant coefficients. The temperature dependence of $\rho$ in semiconductors and insulators for the dominating carrier-acoustic phonon scattering is given by $\rho = A_3 exp(E_g/k_B T)$, where $A_3$ is the factor of proportionality.

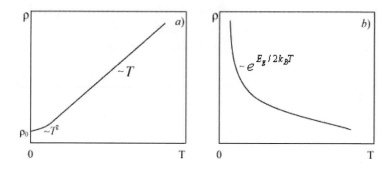

Figure 1.1. The characteristic temperature dependence of the resistivity in metals ($a$) and semiconductors ($b$).

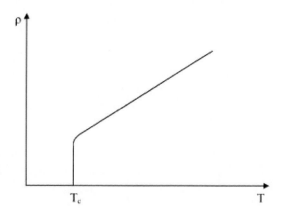

Figure 1.2. Resistance curve for a superconductor showing a drop in resistivity at about $T_c$.

At low temperatures, many materials and doped semiconductors as well as other materials become superconductors [3, 4, 5, 9, 10, 11] and below the SC transition temperature $T_c$, the electrical resistivity in these solids is practically vanishing (Fig. 1.2). In particular, the resistivity of the metallic superconductors is smaller than $10^{-23}\Omega cm$ [4, 9].

## 1.3.   One-Electron Band Theory of Solids

The stationary state of all particles of solids is described by the Schrödinger equation

$$\hat{H}\Psi = E\Psi, \tag{1.1}$$

where $\hat{H}$ is the Hamiltonian operator of the system composed of electrons and atomic nuclei, $\Psi$ is the wave function of the given system depending on coordinates of all particles, $E$ is the energy of the system.

The Eq.(1.1) cannot be solved exactly due to the enormous number of independent variables, and therefore, its solution is obtained by using the different simplifying assumptions. In particular, adiabatic approximation based on the large distinction of masses of nuclei $M$

and electrons $m_e$ allows to consider the independent motions of atomic nuclei and electrons [8, 12, 13]. However, for the solution of the Schrödinger equation of many electron system requires further approximations. Such important simplifying assumptions are: (i) the crystal lattice has the strict periodicity; (ii) the electron-electron interaction can be replaced by the averaged interaction $\tilde{U}(\vec{r})$ in the Hartree-Fock approximation; and (iii) the electron-lattice interaction is weak enough and it is considered as a small perturbation. These three assumptions underlying the one-electron band theory of solids enable to find the approximate solution of the electronic Schrödinger equation. The electronic band structure of solids is then determined from the equation

$$\left[-\frac{\hbar^2}{2m_e}\Delta + V(\vec{r})\right]\psi(\vec{r}) = E\psi(\vec{r}), \tag{1.2}$$

where $V(\vec{r}) = \tilde{U}(\vec{r}) + U(\vec{r})$ is the potential energy of an electron in the crystal, $U(\vec{r})$ is the potential energy of the electron in the field of all nuclei. It would be instructive to find the solutions of the Eq.(1.2) in two limiting cases, namely, in the nearly-free-electron model and tight-binding approximation. In the nearly-free-electron model the potential $V(\vec{r})$ is considered as a small perturbation and the solutions of the Eq.(1.2) are the Bloch functions

$$\psi_k(\vec{r}) = \frac{1}{\sqrt{\Omega}}U_k(\vec{r})exp(i\vec{k}\vec{r}), \tag{1.3}$$

where $U_k(\vec{r})$ is the periodic function with the period equal to the period of lattice $a_0$ (i.e., $U_k(r+a) = U_k(r)$), $\Omega = N \cdot \Omega_0$ is the volume of the crystal containing $N$ unit cells.

The Bloch functions (1.3) are normalized by the conditions

$$\int \psi_{k'}^*(\vec{r})\psi_k(\vec{r})d^3r = \delta_{kk'},$$

$$\frac{1}{\Omega_0}\int U_{k'}^*(\vec{r})U_k(\vec{r})d^3r = 1. \tag{1.4}$$

The periodic potential of the crystal in Eq.(1.2) may be expanded in Fourier series

$$V(\vec{r}) = \sum_{\vec{g}} V_{\vec{g}}e^{i\vec{g}\vec{r}}, \tag{1.5}$$

where $V_{\vec{g}}$ is the expanding coefficient, $\vec{g}$ is the reciprocal lattice vector. According to the perturbation theory, the energy of the nearly free electron is given by

$$E(\vec{k}) = E_0(\vec{k}) + \langle \psi_{\vec{k}}^{*0}|V|\psi_{\vec{k}}^0\rangle + \sum_{\vec{k}'\neq\vec{k}} \frac{|\langle \psi_{\vec{k}'}^{*0}|V|\psi_{\vec{k}}^0\rangle|^2}{E_0(\vec{k}) - E_0(\vec{k}')} \tag{1.6}$$

The matrix element $\langle \psi_{\vec{k}'}^{*0}|V|\psi_{\vec{k}}^0\rangle$ is nonzero only when $\vec{k} - \vec{k}' + \vec{g} = 0$. Thus, Eq.(1.6) can be written as

$$E(\vec{k}) = E_0(\vec{k}) + V_0 + \sum_{\vec{g}\neq 0} \frac{|V_{\vec{g}}|^2}{E_0(\vec{k}) - E_0(\vec{k}+\vec{g})} \tag{1.7}$$

The validity condition of the usual perturbation theory is not satisfied for $V_g \neq 0$ and $E_0(\vec{k}) \rightarrow E_0(\vec{k}+\vec{g})$ or $2\vec{k}\vec{g}+\vec{g}^2 \rightarrow 0$ (i.e., when $\vec{k}$ lies on the edges of the Brillouin zone). In this case, two unperturbated electronic states have nearly the same energies $(E_0(\vec{k}) \simeq E_0(\vec{k}+\vec{g}))$. Then Eq.(1.2) should be solved taking into account the degeneracy of these states and the wave function for degenerate states should be chosen in the form

$$\psi_{\vec{k}}(\vec{r}) = C_1 \psi_{\vec{k}}^0(\vec{r}) + C_2 \psi_{(\vec{k}+\vec{g})}^0(\vec{r}) \tag{1.8}$$

Inserting this expression into Eq.(1.2), multiplying by $\psi_{\vec{k}}^{*0}(\vec{r})$ and $\psi_{(\vec{k}+\vec{g})}^{*0}(\vec{r})$, and integrating over $\vec{r}$, we find

$$C_1[E_0(\vec{k}) - E + V_0] + V_g C_2 = 0$$
$$V_g^* C_1 + [E_0(\vec{k}+\vec{g}) - E + V_0] C_2 = 0 \tag{1.9}$$

Eliminating $C_1$ and $C_2$ from these equations and taking zero energy as $V_0 = 0$, we obtain a quadratic equation which have the solutions

$$E(\vec{k}) = \frac{1}{2}[E_0(\vec{k}) + E_0(\vec{k}+\vec{g})] \pm \frac{1}{2}[E_0(\vec{k})E_0(\vec{k}+\vec{g}) + 4|V_{\vec{g}}|^2]^{1/2} \tag{1.10}$$

Thus, we see that the potential of a periodic lattice leads to the splitting of the energy levels near the boundary of the Brillouin zone and the function $E(\vec{k})$ does undergo a discontinuity given by $E_g = 2|V_{\vec{g}}|$. At $g = 2\pi/a_0$ the boundaries of the first Brillouin zone correspond to $k = \pm\pi/a_0$. The energy spectrum of nearly free electrons acquires the band character, i.e., two allowed energy bands have to arise, which are separated by the forbidden energy band $E_g$ (Fig. 1.3). Owing to the periodic dependence of electronic energy on $\vec{k}$ (i.e., $E_0(\vec{k}) = E_0(\vec{k}+2\pi/a_0)$) all energy bands may be considered within the first Brillouin zone.

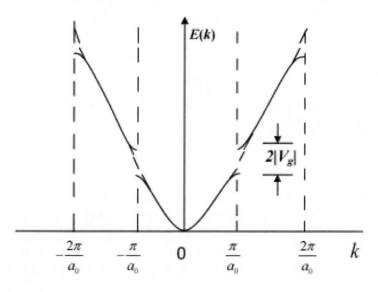

Figure 1.3. The energy spectrum of nearly free electrons in a one-dimensional case.

We shall now consider another limiting case in which the electronic shells of the atoms of crystalline solids weakly overlap and each electron belongs to one's own atom. This means that the electronic state in the isolated atom is changed slightly in the formation of the crystal from the atoms. Therefore, for describing the electronic states of the inner energy levels of atoms and the localized impurity (or defect) levels the approximation of nearly free electrons is inadequate. In this case, a better approximation is the tight-binding method and the overlapping of the electronic shells of atoms will be considered as a perturbation. In the tight-binding approximation, the wave function of an electron in the crystal is expressed as the linear combination of atomic wave functions $\varphi_a(\vec{r}-\vec{n})$

$$\psi_{\vec{k}}(\vec{r}) = \frac{1}{\sqrt{N}} \sum_n C_n \varphi_a(\vec{r}-\vec{n}), \qquad (1.11)$$

where $N$ is the number of atoms in the crystal, $\vec{n}$ is the radius vector of the $n-th$ atom. The coefficients $C_n$ are chosen so that the function $\psi_{\vec{k}}(\vec{r})$ should satisfy the translation condition

$$\psi_{\vec{k}}(\vec{r}+\vec{m}) = e^{i\vec{k}\vec{m}} \psi_{\vec{k}}(\vec{r}), \qquad (1.12)$$

so that $C_n = e^{i\vec{k}\vec{n}}$. If we use the notation $\vec{l} = \vec{n} - \vec{m}$, then Eq.(1.11) takes the form

$$\psi_{\vec{k}}(\vec{r}+\vec{m}) = \frac{1}{\sqrt{N}} \sum_n e^{i\vec{k}\vec{n}} \varphi_a(\vec{r}+\vec{m}-\vec{n}) = e^{i\vec{k}\vec{m}} \frac{1}{\sqrt{N}} \sum_l e^{i\vec{k}\vec{l}} \varphi_a(\vec{r}-\vec{l}), \qquad (1.13)$$

which is identical with the expression (1.12). Inserting (1.11) into the Schrödinger equation (1.2), multiplying by $\psi_{\vec{k}}^*(\vec{r})$ and integrating over $\vec{r}$, we obtain

$$E(\vec{k}) = \frac{1}{N} \sum_{\vec{n}} \sum_{\vec{m}} e^{i\vec{k}(\vec{n}-\vec{m})} \int \varphi_a^*(\vec{r}-\vec{m}) \hat{H}(\vec{r}) \varphi_a(\vec{r}-\vec{n}) d^3\vec{r}, \qquad (1.14)$$

After replacing $\vec{r}$ by $\vec{r}'+\vec{n}$, one obtains the following expression for $E(\vec{k})$:

$$E(\vec{k}) = \frac{1}{N} \sum_{\vec{n}} \sum_{\vec{l}} e^{i\vec{k}\vec{l}} \int \varphi_a^*(\vec{r}'+\vec{l}) \hat{H}(\vec{r}'+\vec{n}) \varphi_a(\vec{r}') d^3\vec{r}', \qquad (1.15)$$

According to the periodicity condition of the potential $V(\vec{r})$, it holds that $\hat{H}(\vec{r}'+\vec{n}) = \hat{H}(\vec{r}')$. Then Eq.(1.15) may be written as

$$E(\vec{k}) = \sum_l e^{i\vec{k}\vec{l}} I(\vec{l}), \qquad (1.16)$$

where $I(\vec{l}) = \int \varphi_a^*(\vec{r}+\vec{l}) \hat{H}(\vec{r}) \varphi_a(\vec{r}) d^3\vec{r}$ is the overlap energy integral.
Since the overlap integral $I(\vec{l})$ rapidly decreases with increasing $|\vec{l}|$, the terms in the sum (1.16) corresponding only to the nearest neighbors of the atom give the main contribution to the energy $E(\vec{k})$. Therefore, one may keep the terms $\vec{l} = 0$ and $\vec{l} = \vec{l}_1$ (where $\vec{l}_1$ is the vector connecting the neighboring sites of the lattice) in (1.16). In this case we obtain the following relation

$$E(\vec{k}) = \varepsilon(0) + \sum_{\vec{l}_1} e^{i\vec{k}\vec{l}_1} I(\vec{l}_1), \qquad (1.17)$$

where $\varepsilon(0)$ is the overlap energy integral for the lattice site $\vec{l} = 0$.

In a simple cubic lattice the vectors $\vec{l}_1$ have the coordinates $\vec{l}_1 = (\pm a_0, 0, 0), (0, \pm a_0, 0)$ and $(0, 0, \pm a_0)$. Then from (1.17), we obtain

$$E(\vec{k}) = \varepsilon(0) + 2I(a)(\cos k_x a_0 + \cos k_y a_0 + \cos k_z a_0) \qquad (1.18)$$

At $\varepsilon(a) < 0$, $E(\vec{k})$ varies from $E_{min} = \varepsilon(0) - 6|I(a)|$ (at $k_x = k_y = k_z = 0$) to $E_{max} = \varepsilon(0) + 6|I(a)|$ (at $\pm k_x = \pm k_y = \pm k_z = \pi/a_0$) and the values of the energy determined from (1.18) form the energy band with the bandwidth

$$W = 12|I(a)| = 2z|I(a)|, \qquad (1.19)$$

where $z = 6$ is the coordination number (or the number of the nearest neighbors of the atom) in the simple cubic lattice.

The Taylor expansion of $\cos k_x a, \cos k_y a$ and $\cos k_z a$ in (1.18) at $ka << 1$ gives

$$E(\vec{k}) = \varepsilon(0) + 6I(a) + \frac{\hbar^2 \vec{k}^2}{2m^*}, \qquad (1.20)$$

where $m^* = \hbar^2/2a_0^2|I(a)|$ is the effective mass of a carrier.

If $a_0 \to \infty$, then $I(a) \to 0$ (since the overlapping of the wave functions of neighboring atoms $\varphi_a(r + a_0)$ and $\varphi_a(r)$ tends to zero) and $W \to 0$. Thus, with decreasing the distance between atoms, the energy levels of the isolated atoms change positions and split into the energy bands due to the interaction of the atoms. The energy bands are separated by the energy gap $E_g$ (Fig. 1.4).

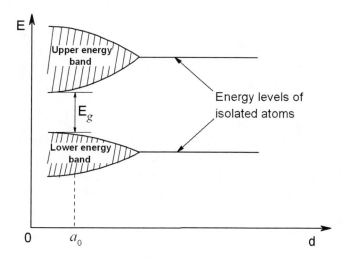

Figure 1.4. Splitting of the energy levels of atoms into the energy bands with decreasing the interatomic distance $d$ in the crystal. $a_0$ is the lattice constant.

## 1.4.   Simple Metals

The classical electron theory of metals was developed by Drude (1900) and Lorentz (1905), who applied the classical statistics of Maxwell and Boltzmann to the ideal electron gas in metals [6, 14, 15]. According to this theory, an electron having the effective mass $m_e$ will move with velocity $v$ in a crystal just as a molecule will move in a gas and the electron will make many collisions with the lattice imperfections (including lattice vibrations). The electrical conductivity $\sigma$ and thermal conductivity $k$ of the electron gas are then given by

$$\sigma = \frac{ne^2\bar{l}}{m_e v} \tag{1.21}$$

and

$$k = \frac{1}{3}\bar{l}vC_v = \frac{1}{3}v^2\tau C_v, \tag{1.22}$$

where $n$ and $\bar{l}$ are the concentration and the mean free path length of electrons, $C_v$ is the specific heat of the electron gas. The Drude-Lorentz theory was successful enough in explaining Wiedeman-Franz law. Indeed, assuming $m_e v^2 = 3k_B T$ and $C_v = \frac{3}{2}nk_B$, one can obtain the following relation for the ratio $k/\sigma$:

$$\frac{k}{\sigma} = \frac{3}{2}\left(\frac{k_B}{e}\right)^2 T = LT \tag{1.23}$$

which, as we know, represents the empirical law of Wiedemann and Franz where $L = (3/2)(k_B/e)^2$ is the Lorentz number. The deduced relation (1.23) was the triumph of the Drude-Lorentz theory. However, after this theory encountered a number of serious difficulties in describing the physical properties of metals. For example, the Wiedeman-Franz law is not always fulfilled (in particular, at low temperatures) [6, 14]. The classical electron theory is also faced with the difficulty of explaining the temperature dependence of the conductivity $\sigma$ of metals. As is well known, the average velocity $\bar{v}$ depends on temperature as $\bar{v} \sim T^{1/2}$. At the same time, experiments on conventional metals show [2] that at high temperatures $\sigma \sim 1/T$. So, assuming $n\bar{l} \sim T^{-1/2}$, one can obtain from Eq.(1.21) the observed temperature dependence of $\sigma$. However, the classical theory cannot substantiate such a dependence of $n\bar{l}$ on $T$. Further, according to the equipartition theorem the mean thermal energy of the free electron is equal to $3k_B T/2$ and hence the electron gas should make a contribution of $(3/2)nk_B$ to the specific heat of the metal. In reality, the contribution of free electrons to the specific heat at room temperatures is approximately 100 times smaller than the classical value $(3/2)nk_B$. Moreover, the classical theory predicts that the temperature dependence of the paramagnetic susceptibility of free electron gas is given by [6]

$$\chi_p = n\mu_B^2/k_B T, \tag{1.24}$$

where $\mu_B$ is the Bohr magneton.

In contrast, the observed paramagnetic susceptibility of simple metals is small and nearly independent of temperature [6, 16]. Some difficulties in the electron theory of metals were removed by Sommerfeld, who used the Fermi-Dirac statistics instead of Maxwell-Boltzmann statistics for the electron gas and derived the consistent theoretical results with the experiments [8, 12]. However, the theory of the degenerate electron gas proposed by Sommerfeld was still inadequate for the full description of the properties of metals. Now, we shall consider the degenerate electron gas in metals. The equilibrium Fermi-Dirac distribution function for the degenerate electron gas in metals is given by

$$f(\varepsilon) = \frac{1}{e^{(\varepsilon - \mu_F)/k_B T} + 1},$$  (1.25)

where $\varepsilon = \hbar^2 k^2 / 2m$ is the energy of electrons, $m$ is the mass of conduction electron, which may differ from $m_e$, $\mu_F$ is the chemical potential of the Fermi gas, which is equal to the Fermi energy $\varepsilon_F$ and determined from the equation

$$n = \frac{2}{(2\pi)^3} \int f(\varepsilon) d^3 k$$  (1.26)

At $T \to 0$, the function $f(\varepsilon)$ has the step-like character (Fig. 1.5)

$$f(\varepsilon) = \begin{cases} 1 & \text{at} \quad \varepsilon < \varepsilon_F \\ 0 & \text{at} \quad \varepsilon > \varepsilon_F \end{cases}$$  (1.27)

At $T \neq 0$, part of electrons would occupy the energy levels above $\varepsilon_F$.

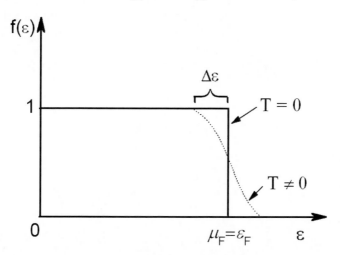

Figure 1.5. The Fermi-Dirac distribution function at $T = 0$ and $T \neq 0$.

In metals the Fermi level $\varepsilon_F$ lies in the conduction band and separates the occupied and empty electron states. At $T = 0$ the relation between the Fermi energy $\varepsilon_F$ and the electron density $n$ is obtained from (1.26) taking into account the approximation (1.27), and is given by

$$\varepsilon_F = \frac{\hbar^2}{2m} \left( 3\pi^2 n \right)^{2/3}$$  (1.28)

At $T \neq 0$, the states above $\varepsilon_F$ are occupied and at the same time the states below $\varepsilon_F$ are unoccupied due to transitions (or thermal excitations) of electrons from states with $\varepsilon < \varepsilon_F$ to states with $\varepsilon > \varepsilon_F$. As a consequence, the Fermi step is smeared (dotted curve in Fig. 1.5). The half-width of the smearing layer $\Delta\varepsilon$ is of the order of $k_BT$. Then the condition of degeneracy of the electron gas $\Delta\varepsilon << \varepsilon_F$ or $T << T_F = \varepsilon_F/k_B$ (where $T_F$ is the degeneracy temperature of the electron gas) in metals may be written as

$$n >> \frac{1}{3\pi^2}\left(\frac{2mk_BT}{\hbar^2}\right)^{3/2} \tag{1.29}$$

Only the electrons with density $n_T \approx n(k_BT/\varepsilon_F)$ take part in thermal motion and their contribution to the specific heat of the metal is small. For $T > 0$, the temperature-dependent chemical potential and the energy of the electron gas can be obtained from the equations

$$n = \frac{N}{\Omega} = A\int_0^\infty \frac{\varepsilon^{1/2}d\varepsilon}{e^{(\varepsilon-\mu_F)/k_BT}+1} \tag{1.30}$$

and

$$\frac{E}{\Omega} = A\int_0^\infty \frac{\varepsilon^{3/2}d\varepsilon}{e^{(\varepsilon-\mu_F)/k_BT}+1} \tag{1.31}$$

where $A = \sqrt{2}(m)^{3/2}/\pi^2\hbar^3$, $N$ is the number of conduction electrons. The integrals in these equations may be evaluated by using the function $\varphi(\varepsilon) = \varepsilon^\nu$ and the substitution $\varepsilon - \mu_F = k_BTx$ as follows [17]:

$$
\begin{aligned}
I &= \int_{-x_T}^\infty \frac{\varphi(\mu_F+k_BTx)}{e^x+1}k_BTdx \\
&= k_BT\left[\int_0^{x_T}\frac{\varphi(\mu_F-k_BTx)}{e^{-x}+1}dx + \int_0^\infty\frac{\varphi(\mu_F+k_BTx)}{e^x+1}dx\right] \\
&= k_BT\left[\int_0^{x_T}\left(1-\frac{1}{e^x+1}\right)\varphi(\mu_F-k_BTx)dx + \int_0^\infty\frac{\varphi(\mu_F+k_BTx)}{e^x+1}dx\right] \\
&= \int_0^{\mu_F}\varphi(\varepsilon)d\varepsilon - k_BT\left[\int_0^{x_T}\frac{\varphi(\mu_F-k_BTx)}{e^x+1}dx + \int_0^\infty\frac{\varphi(\mu_F+k_BTx)}{e^x+1}dx\right],
\end{aligned} \tag{1.32}
$$

where $x_T = \mu_F/k_BT$.

At $k_BT << \mu_F$, the range of integration in the second integral in Eq. (1.32) may be extended from 0 to $\infty$ and the function $\varphi(\mu_F \pm k_BTx)$ might be expanded as a Taylor series in powers of $x$ up to second-order terms:

$$\varphi(\mu_F \pm k_BTx) = \mu_F^\nu \pm k_BT\nu\mu_F^{\nu-1}x + \frac{1}{2}\nu(\nu-1)(k_BT)^2\mu_F^{\nu-2}x^2 \pm \cdots \tag{1.33}$$

Substituting (1.33) into (1.32) and performing the integration over $x$, we finally obtain (henceforth denoting $\mu_F$ through $\mu_F(T)$)

$$I_\nu = \frac{\mu_F^{\nu+1}(T)}{\nu+1} + 2\nu(k_BT)^2\mu_F^{\nu-1}(T)\frac{\pi^2}{12} \tag{1.34}$$

Inserting the expressions for $I_{1/2}$ and $I_{3/2}$ into (1.30) and (1.31), we obtain

$$\frac{N}{\Omega} \simeq \frac{2}{3} A \mu_F^{3/2}(T) \left[ 1 + \frac{\pi^2}{8} \left( \frac{k_B T}{\mu_F(T)} \right)^2 \right] \tag{1.35}$$

and

$$\frac{E}{\Omega} = \frac{2}{5} A \mu_F^{5/2}(T) \left[ 1 + \frac{5\pi^2}{8} \left( \frac{k_B T}{\mu_F(T)} \right)^2 \right] \tag{1.36}$$

In the small quadratic term $(\pi^2/8)(k_B T/\mu_F(T))^2$, after replacing $\mu_F(T)$ by $\mu_F(0) = (\hbar^2/2m)(3\pi^2 n)^{2/3}$, the Eq.(1.35) can be rewritten with an accuracy to the terms $\sim (k_B T/\mu_F(0))^2$ as

$$\mu_F(0) = \mu_F(T) \left[ 1 + \frac{\pi^2}{8} \left( \frac{k_B T}{\mu_F(0)} \right)^2 \right]^{2/3} \simeq \mu_F(T) \left[ 1 + \frac{\pi^2}{12} \left( \frac{k_B T}{\mu_F(0)} \right)^2 \right] \tag{1.37}$$

or

$$\mu_F(T) \simeq \mu_F(0) \left[ 1 - \frac{\pi^2}{12} \left( \frac{k_B T}{\mu_F(0)} \right)^2 \right] \tag{1.38}$$

Comparing (1.36) with (1.35), we obtain with an accuracy to the terms $\sim (k_B T/\mu_F(T))^2$

$$\frac{E}{N} \simeq \frac{3}{5} \mu_F(T) \left[ 1 + \frac{\pi^2}{2} \left( \frac{k_B T}{\mu_F(T)} \right)^2 \right] \tag{1.39}$$

Substituting (1.38) into (1.39), we obtain to second order in $(k_B T/\mu_F(0))$

$$E = \frac{3}{5} N \mu_F(0) \left[ 1 + \frac{5\pi^2}{12} \left( \frac{k_B T}{\mu_F(0)} \right)^2 \right] \tag{1.40}$$

Then, the electronic specific heat per unit volume is given by

$$C_e = \Omega^{-1} \frac{\partial E}{\partial T} = \frac{\pi^2}{2} (k_B T n/\mu_F(0)) = \gamma_e T, \tag{1.41}$$

where $\gamma_e = (\pi^2 k_B^2 n/2\mu_F(0)) = \frac{\pi^2}{3} k_B^2 g(\varepsilon_F = \mu_F(0))$,
$g(\varepsilon_F) = \sqrt{2} m^{3/2} \sqrt{\varepsilon_F}/2\pi^2 \hbar^3$ is the density of states at the Fermi level.

At temperatures much lower than the Debye temperature $\theta_D$, the total specific heat of the metal associated with the thermal motion of electrons and the lattice vibrations can be written as

$$C_v = \gamma_e T + \gamma_D T^3, \tag{1.42}$$

where $\gamma_D = 12\pi^4 k_B n_a/5\theta_D$, $n_a$ is the number of atoms in unit volume.

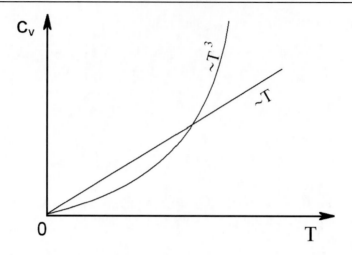

Figure 1.6. The specific heat of metals at low temperatures.

At sufficiently low temperatures the electronic specific heat becomes larger than the lattice specific heat (Fig. 1.6). Finally, the substitution of expressions (1.42) and $2\varepsilon_F/m$ for $C_v$ and $v^2$, respectively, and using the relations (1.21) and (1.22) give the familiar Sommerfeld formula for the ratio $k/\sigma$

$$k/\sigma = \frac{\pi^2}{3}(k_B/e)^2 T \tag{1.43}$$

which is more accurate and agrees very well with the experimental data [8, 14]. We now consider the equilibrium state of the electron gas in the presence of an external magnetic field $\vec{H}$. In this case the magnetic (spin) moment of the electron will be either parallel to $\vec{H}$ or antiparallel to $\vec{H}$ and there are two groups of electrons with energies $\varepsilon - \mu_B H$ (when the electron spin moment is parallel to $\vec{H}$) and $\varepsilon + \mu_B H$ (when the electron spin moment is antiparallel to $\vec{H}$). The magnetic moment of the electron gas is then given by [12]

$$M = \mu_B \int\limits_0^\infty [f(\varepsilon - \mu_B H) - f(\varepsilon + \mu_B H)] g(\varepsilon) d\varepsilon \tag{1.44}$$

For small $H$, the functions $f(\varepsilon \pm \mu_B H)$ may be expanded in a Taylor series in powers of $\mu_B H$. Retaining only the two terms of the expansion, we obtain from (1.44)

$$M \approx 2\mu_B^2 H \int\limits_0^\infty \left(-\frac{\partial f(\varepsilon)}{\partial \varepsilon}\right) g(\varepsilon) d\varepsilon \tag{1.45}$$

For the degenerate electron gas, the function $(-\partial f/\partial \varepsilon)$ at $T << \varepsilon_F/k_B$ can be approximated by the $\delta$-function $\delta(\varepsilon - \varepsilon_F(T))$. We then obtain

$$M = 2\mu_B^2 g(\varepsilon_F(T))H = \chi_p(T)H, \tag{1.46}$$

where $\chi_p(T) = 2\mu_B^2 g(\varepsilon_F(T))$ is the low-field paramagnetic susceptibility of the electronic gas, $\varepsilon_F(T) = \varepsilon_T \left[1 - \pi^2 (k_B T/\varepsilon_F)^2/12\right]$. For simple metals with $m \simeq m_e$, $n = 10^{22} cm^{-3}$, we find $\varepsilon_F \simeq 1.7 eV$ and at room temperature $(k_B T/\varepsilon_F)^2 \simeq 2.33 \cdot 10^{-4}$, so that $\chi_p$ is practically temperature-independent in accordance with the experiment. Note that the low-field diamagnetic susceptibility of the electron gas is one-third of the paramagnetic one [6]. The conductivity of the electron gas $\sigma$ in metal can be calculated with the use of the Boltzmann transport equation in the relaxation time approximation [16] and the expression for $\sigma$ may be written in the form:

$$\sigma = \frac{ne^2\tau}{m}, \tag{1.47}$$

where $\tau$ is the mean time between collisions or relaxation time of an electron moving in a crystal and making many collisions with the lattice imperfections.

In metals the scattering of the electron by acoustic phonons (which have the energy $\hbar\omega_q = \hbar v_s q$ and wave vector $\vec{q}$, where $v_s$ is the sound velocity) is dominant and the scattering probabilities of electrons $W_+$ (with phonon emission) and $W_-$ (with phonon absorption) both in the high temperature range and in the low temperature range are nearly the same [16, 18, 19]. We may, therefore, write the relaxation time in the form

$$\frac{1}{\tau(k)} = \frac{E_d^2 m}{4\pi\hbar^2\rho_M v_s k^3} \int_0^{2k} \frac{q^4 dq}{e^{\hbar v_s q/k_B T} - 1}, \tag{1.48}$$

where $E_d$ is the deformation potential, $\rho_M$ is the mass density of the material.

Making the substitution $y = \hbar v_s q/k_B T$ and integrating over $y$, we obtain (for the case $x_{max} = 2\hbar k v_s/k_B T \ll 1$)

$$\tau_1(\varepsilon) = \frac{2\pi\hbar^4\rho_M v_s^2}{E_d^2(2m)^{3/2}k_B T\sqrt{\varepsilon}} \tag{1.49}$$

At low temperatures, the upper limit of integration may be replaced by $\infty$. We then obtain

$$\frac{1}{\tau_2(\varepsilon)} = \frac{E_d^2 m\hbar(k_B T/\hbar v_s)^5}{4\pi\rho_M v_s(2m\varepsilon)^{3/2}} \int_0^{\infty} \frac{y^4 dy}{e^y - 1} = \frac{E_d^2 m\hbar(k_B T/\hbar v_s)^5}{4\pi\rho_M v_s(2m\varepsilon)^{3/2}}\Gamma(5)\xi(5), \tag{1.50}$$

where $\Gamma(5) = 4!$, $\xi(5) \simeq 1.037$ [15].

We thus obtain for the conductivity of simple metals at high and low temperatures the following relations:

$$\sigma_1(T) = \frac{2\sqrt{2m}e^2}{3\pi^2\hbar^3} \int_0^{\infty} \varepsilon^{3/2}\tau(\varepsilon)\left(-\frac{\partial f}{\partial \varepsilon}\right) d\varepsilon = \frac{2\hbar e^2\rho_M v_s^2\varepsilon_F}{3\pi m E_d^2 k_B T} \tag{1.51}$$

and

$$\sigma_2(T) = \frac{2\sqrt{2m}e^2}{3\pi^2\hbar^3} \int_0^{\infty} \varepsilon^{3/2}\tau(\varepsilon)\left(-\frac{\partial f}{\partial \varepsilon}\right) d\varepsilon = \frac{32\hbar m e^2\rho_M v_s^6\varepsilon_F^3}{3\pi E_d^2(k_B T)^5\Gamma(5)\xi(5)} \tag{1.52}$$

We see that $\sigma_1 \sim T^{-1}$ at high temperatures $(T > \theta_D)$ and $\sigma_2 \sim T^{-5}$ at low temperatures $(T << \theta_D)$. These results are in good agreement with the experimental findings in simple metals. This electron theory of metals, which was successful enough in describing the various properties of simple metals, does not explain the electronic properties of unusual metals, such as, for example, underdoped copper oxides (cuprates) [5, 20].

## 1.5.   Basic Properties of Conventional Superconductors

Superconductivity is one of most unique and intriguing phenomena in nature. This phenomenon was discovered first in simple metals and then in intermetallic compounds, since such materials were good electrical conductors. The SC behavior of these materials is closely tied to their electrical, magnetic, thermal and other properties, which are essentially different in the normal and SC states. A superconductor is a material which can carry an electrical current without any resistance. Conventional superconductors lose their resistivity at low enough temperatures and their normal state resistance is restored as the temperature exceeds some critical value $T_c$. The SC behavior of simple metals and alloys depends on other important parameters besides $T_c$, namely, the critical magnetic fields (i.e., $H_c$, $H_{c1}$ and $H_{c2}$) and the critical current density $I_c$ (passage of a large current produces a sufficient magnetic field to destroy the superconductivity). Many of the properties of conventional superconductors can be understood by the standard Bardeen-Cooper-Schrieffer (BCS) theory [21] which assumes that the electrons responsible for superconductivity are paired with antiparallel spins and the weak electron-phonon interaction binds electrons into the Cooper pairs. The BCS theory will be discussed in Chapter 3. The SC state of conventional superconductors has several characteristic properties. In this section, we briefly discuss the basic physical properties of conventional superconductors in the SC state. At the same time, some useful comments on the BCS theory is also discussed. Since, some questions remain open, although there is no doubt that many of the SC properties of conventional superconductors are consistent with the BCS theory.

### 1.5.1.   Electromagnetic Properties

The first characteristic feature of the SC state is that the flow of the current electrons below $T_c$ is resistanceless, that is, superfluid. Another fundamental property of conventional superconductors is their ability to expel a magnetic field completely from their interior below $T_c$. The complete exclusion of the magnetic flux from the bulk of a superconductor is called the Meissner effect (Fig. 1.7) which was discovered by Meissner and Ochsenfeld in 1933 [22]. It means that the superconductor exhibits perfect diamagnetism and the magnetic induction $\vec{B}$ inside the superconductor is zero (i.e., $\vec{B} = \vec{H} + 4\pi\vec{M} = 0$), where $\vec{H}$ is an external magnetic field, $\vec{M}$ is the magnetization of the material. The magnetic susceptibility of the superconductor is then given by

$$\chi = -\frac{1}{4\pi} \tag{1.53}$$

Superconductor in which the magnetic flux exclusion is complete for any applied magnetic field less than a critical value $H_c$ are called type I superconductors [2, 3, 23]. Above $H_c$ the

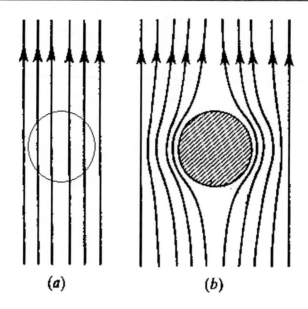

Figure 1.7. Magnetic flux density lines for (a) a normal metal and (b) a superconductor.

magnetic flux penetrates the superconductor completely and the normal state is restored. This means that superconductivity can be destroyed (with a return to a normal state) not only by increasing the temperature but also by either a large enough electric current $I > I_c$ or a large enough magnetic field $H > H_c$. The critical field $H_c$, at which superconductivity disappears, is decreased with increasing temperature. Empirically it was established that the temperature dependence of $H_c$ is well described by the formula [9, 23]

$$H_c(T) = H_c(0) \left[ 1 - (T/T_c)^2 \right], \tag{1.54}$$

which is illustrated in Fig. 1.8a. In reality, the magnetic induction is zero only deep inside the superconductor and the current flows in the surface layer, where $B \neq 0$.

Theoretical analysis of the response of a superconductor to an applied magnetic field was carried out by the brothers Fritz and Heinz London [24] (see for details, Chapter 2). They predicted that magnetic flux is excluded from a surface region of the superconductor and the magnetic induction at the surface decreases exponentially within a characteristic $\lambda_L$, called the London pentration depth, namely,

$$B(x) = B(0) \exp(-x/\lambda_L), \tag{1.55}$$

where $x$ measures distance into the superconductor from the surface.

It was found that the London penetration depth depends on temperature and at $T \to T_c$, $\lambda_L \to \infty$. The temperature dependence of $\lambda_L$ is well described by the empirical Gorter-Casimir formula

$$\lambda_L(T) = \lambda_L(0) \left[ 1 - (T/T_c)^4 \right]^{-1/2} \tag{1.56}$$

Note that the relation (1.56) was not derived earlier theoretically for a long time (see Ref. [25]). By considering a quantitative link between the London penetration depth $\lambda_L$ and the

SC carrier density $n_s$ expressed as $\lambda_L = (mc^2/4\pi n_s e^2)^{1/2}$ (where $c$ is the velocity of light), one can obtain from (1.56)

$$n_s(T) = n_s(0)\left[1 - (T/T_c)^4\right] \tag{1.57}$$

Experimental values of $\lambda_L(T)$ agree fairly with the empirical formula (1.56) and deviate

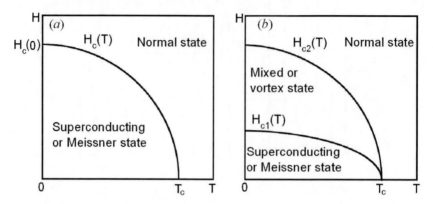

Figure 1.8. (a) Variation of $H_c$ with temperature in a type I superconductor. (b)Phase diagram for a type II superconductor.

from the exponential dependence predicted by the BCS theory (see Ref. [9]). The magnetic properties of SC alloys are more complicated. These SC compounds are characterized by the existence of a mixed or vortex state region in which the magnetic flux lines partially penetrates the superconductor at a certain lower critical field $H_{c1} < H_c$ but do not destroy the SC state and the normal state is not restored completely in the bulk of the material. If the magnetic field is increased, there is an upper critical value $H_{c2}$ ($> H_c$) for which the superconductivity is destroyed, the system returns to the normal state, and the magnetic flux penetrates the superconductor completely. Superconductors in which the mixed state exists in the intermediate region $H_{c1} < H < H_{c2}$, was called by Abrikosov [23] as type II superconductors. Type II superconductors, exclude the magnetic field completely up to the value $H_{c1}$ (i.e., in the Meissner state). Of course, both critical fields $H_{c1}$ and $H_{c2}$ depend on temperature and tend to zero at $T_c$ (Fig. 1.8b). In the mixed state, the magnetic flux penetrates the superconductor in the form of a regular array of regular flux lines and these magnetic flux tubes are thin normal lines, each carrying a flux quantum $\phi_0 = h/2e$. The effect of the magnetic flux quantization in units of $\phi_0$ was predicted first by F.London [26] and observed then experimentally by Deaver and Fairbank [27] and by Doll and Näbauer [28]. The SC currents circulate around the core of the normal tubular lines and the circulating currents form Abrikosov's vortices inside these tubes. The vortices quantized in units of $\phi_0$ form a peculiar vortex lattice similar to a crystal lattice. According to the Silsbee's rule, the critical current creating the critical magnetic field $H_c$ around the SC wire is given by [29]

$$I_c = cr_0 H_c/2, \tag{1.58}$$

where $r_0$ is the radius of the SC wire.

## 1.5.2.  Thermal Properties

The most important and distinctive property of the SC state of conventional superconductors is the behavior of their electronic specific heat $C_e$ below $T_c$ (Fig. 1.9). The total specific heat of the superconductor $C_v$ at constant volume is defined as the sum of the lattice and electronic specific heats. For the normal and SC phases of simple metals, the specific heat $C_v$ at $T \ll \theta_D$ may be expressed as

$$C_{vn} = C_{en} + \gamma_D T^3 \tag{1.59}$$

and

$$C_{vs} = C_{es} + \gamma_D T^3, \tag{1.60}$$

where $C_{en}$ and $C_{es}$ are the electronic specific heats of the superconductor in the normal and SC states, respectively.

One can assume that the lattice contribution to the specific heat $C_v$ is not changed at the transition of the system from the normal state to the SC one. This assumption seems to be reasonable enough, and it is also confirmed by the absence of noticeable changes in the lattice parameters (see Ref. [9]). Therefore, the quantity of $C_{es}$ can be determined from the relation

$$C_{es} - C_{en} = C_{vs} - C_{vn} \tag{1.61}$$

The observed electronic part of specific heat $C_{es}$ for the SC phase of some metals is approximately proportional to $T^3$ [30]. Whereas the temperature dependence of $C_{es}$ observed in other superconductors at $T > (0.2 \div 0.5)T_c$ is well described by the exponential law

$$C_{es}(T) = \gamma_s \exp(-\Delta/k_B T), \tag{1.62}$$

where $\gamma_s$ is the factor of proportionality, $\Delta$ is an energy gap in the excitation spectrum of superconductors. Note that the origin of the deviation of $C_{es}(T)$ from the simple exponential law (see Ref. [9]) still remains to be understood. This means that the ground and excited states of the superconductor is separated by the energy gap $\Delta$. We shall see in Chapter 3 that the existence of such a gap in the excitation spectrum of conventional superconductors is explained by the BCS theory. However, over many years (i.e., before the appearance of a new approach to superconductivity [25, 31]), the $T^3$ temperature dependence of $C_{es}$ in some superconductors remained as rather poorly understood. Eliashberg supposed [32] that a small additional term proportional to $T^3$ enters into the expression for $C_{es}$ and it is associated with the possible lattice contribution to the difference $C_{vs} - C_{vn}$. It is unlikely that such a small additional term in $C_{es}(T)$ can provide a quantitative explanation for the $T^3$-behavior of the $C_{es}(T)$ observed in several conventional superconductors.

Experimental results show that the SC transition in metals (in the absence of an external magnetic field) is the second-order phase transition without latent heat, and there is a sharp finite discontinuity (i.e., a step-like jump) in the electronic specific heat. Note that the step-like specific heat anomaly observed in the SC metals is quite different from the $\lambda$-like specific heat anomaly in liquid $^4H$.

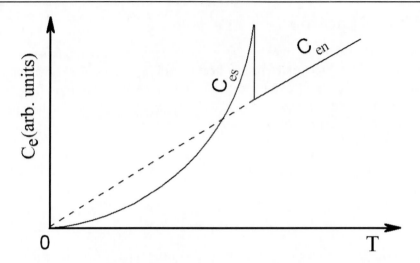

Figure 1.9. Schematic temperature dependence of the electronic specific heat of conventional superconductors in the SC state ($C_{es}$) and normal state ($C_{en}$).

For further understanding of the thermal properties of conventional superconductors, we discuss the distinctive feature of their thermal conductivity in the SC state. The total thermal conductivity of the superconductors $k$ is also defined by the sum of the electronic $k_e$ and lattice (or phonon) $k_{ph}$ thermal conductivities:

$$k = k_e + k_{ph}, \tag{1.63}$$

$k_e = \frac{1}{3}C_e v l = \frac{1}{3}C_e v^2 \tau_e$, $k_{ph} = \frac{1}{3}C_{ph} v_s l_{ph} = \frac{1}{3}C_{ph} v_s^2 \tau_{ph}$, $C_e$ and $C_{ph}$ are the electronic and lattice specific heats, respectively, $v$ is the velocity of the electron, $v_s$ is the sound velocity, $\tau_e$ and $\tau_{ph}$ are the relaxation times of the electron and phonon, $l$ and $l_{ph}$ are the mean free paths of electrons and phonons, respectively.

First, let us consider the thermal conductivity of metals in the normal state. At high temperatures ($k_B T >> \hbar\omega_D$), the change of the energy of electrons due to their collisions with the lattice vibrations is small, so that the collisions may be treated as elastic collisions. In this case, the number of phonons was considerable and varied with temperature linearly:

$$n_q = \frac{1}{e^{\hbar\omega_q/k_B T} - 1} \approx \frac{k_B T}{\hbar\omega_q} \tag{1.64}$$

The relaxation time in the scattering of electrons by lattice vibrations $\tau_e$ is proportional to $T^{-1}$ (see sec.1.4). For the degenerate electron gas one can assume that $v = v_F$. Then, let us consider the $k_e = const$. At low temperatures ($k_B T << \hbar\omega_D$), the phonons with energies $\hbar\omega_q \sim k_B T$ play an important role in scattering of electrons by lattice vibrations. Therefore, the energy $\varepsilon$ of electrons is changed markedly in each collision. Since the energy of electrons is changed by the quantity of the order of $k_B T$, each collision is effective for the thermal conductivity. In the present case, the different relaxation times $\tau_e$ and $\tau_t$ may be introduced for electrical and thermal conductivities, respectively [23]. Theoretical calculations show that $\tau_e \sim T^{-5}$, $\tau_t \sim T^{-3}$ and $\sigma \sim T^{-5}$, $k_e \sim T^{-2}$, $k_e/\sigma \sim T^3$.

It follows then, that the Wiedemann and Franz law is not fulfilled. According to (1.64), the probability of the collision of phonons $\tau_{ph}^{-1}$ is proportional to $n_q \approx k_B T / \hbar \omega_q$ at $k_B T >> \hbar \omega_D$. Then the thermal conductivity due to phonons $k_{ph}$ is proportional to $T^{-1}$ when $C_{ph}$ is constant. Whereas, at $k_B T << \hbar \omega_D$, the number of phonons is decreased exponentially $n_q \approx \exp(-\hbar \omega_q / k_B T)$ and $\tau_{ph} \sim \exp(\hbar \omega_q / k_B T)$, so that under the assumed condition, $C_{ph} \sim T^3$, $k_{ph} \sim T^3 \exp(\hbar \omega_q / k_B T)$. At very low temperatures, phonons are basically scattered by the crystal boundary and $l_{ph}$ becomes temperature-independent, so that $k_{ph} \sim T^3$. The phonon contribution to the thermal conductivity of simple metals is in general quite small. For example, if we take $C_{ph} \simeq 3nk_B$, $C_e = \pi^2 nk_B^2 T / 2\varepsilon_F$, $l_{ph}/l = 0.1$, $v_s/v_F \simeq 10^{-3}$, then we obtain $k_{ph}/k_e \approx (6\varepsilon_F / \pi^2 k_B T) \times 10^{-4}$ which, for $\varepsilon_F \simeq 3eV$ and $T = 300K$, yields $k_{ph}/k_e \simeq 0.7 \times 10^{-2}$. In the SC state of metals the contribution to $k_e$ comes only from the normal electrons and the electronic part of thermal conductivity is decreased with decreasing temperature. Since, according to the two-fluid model the number of the normal electrons decreases rapidly as the temperature is reduced. At the same time the number of the SC electrons increases with decreasing temperature and these carriers do not contribute to $k_e$. The electronic thermal conductivity of the SC phase $k_{es}$ of superconductors should be much smaller than that $k_{en}$ of their normal phase. A number of experiments showed that below $T_c$ the ratio $f(t = T/T_c) = k_{es}/k_{en}$ in pure samples of some metals decreases rapidly in proportion to $t^\nu$ with $\nu = 2 \div 4$ (see Ref. [9]). Moreover, a distinct $f(t)$ behavior had also been observed well below $T_c$ in conventional superconductors. It was later found that a rapid decrease of $f(t)$ well below $T_c$ can be described by the exponential law [33]. Such a behavior of $f(t)$ is assumed to be associated with the presence of an energy gap in the excitation spectrum of conventional superconductors. In contrast, the power-law behavior of $f(t)$ is indicative of the absence of such a gap and is not understood completely yet.

### 1.5.3. Thermodynamics of Superconductors

Metals in the normal and SC states have not only different electrical conductivities but also different values of thermodynamic parameters. Since the normal and SC states of metals represent different thermodynamical phase of matter. To evaluate the thermodynamics of superconductors, we first of all consider the change of their magnetic properties at the transition from the normal to the SC state. The free energy of the system in the external magnetic field is given by

$$F = U' - TS, \tag{1.65}$$

where $U' = U - MH$, $U$ is the internal energy of the superconductor at $H = 0$, $S$ is the entropy.

A small change in energy $U'$ arising from a small change in the magnetic field at constant volume of the system is given by

$$dU' = TdS - MdH \tag{1.66}$$

Then the differential of the free energy is

$$dF = -SdT - \vec{M}dH \tag{1.67}$$

At a fixed temperature, we have

$$F(T,H) = F(T,0) - \int_0^H \vec{M}dH \qquad (1.68)$$

In the normal state of the superconductor, the free energy $F_n$ does not depend on $H$, so that $F_n(T,H) = F_n(T,0)$. In the SC phase, the magnetization is given by $M = -H/4\pi$. We thus obtain from (1.68)

$$F_s(T,H) = F_s(T,0) + \frac{H^2}{8\pi} \qquad (1.69)$$

To find the thermodynamic critical magnetic field $H_c$, we equate the free energies $F_n$ and $F_s$ of the normal and SC phases. Then, $H_c$ is given by

$$F_n(T,0) - F_s(T,0) = \frac{H_c^2}{8\pi} \qquad (1.70)$$

At the phase boundary, $F_n = F_s$, and at $H = 0$ Eq.(1.67) can be written as

$$d(F_n - F_s) = -(S_n - S_s)dT, \qquad (1.71)$$

whence it follows that

$$S_s - S_n = \frac{1}{4\pi} H_c \frac{dH_c}{dT} \qquad (1.72)$$

One can see that at $T < T_c$, $H_c > 0$ and $dH_c/dT < 0$ (see Eq.(1.54)). This means that the entropy in the normal state is always larger than in the SC state and the SC phase is more ordered than the normal phase. At $T = T_c$ and $H_c = 0$, the latent heat $q = T(S_n - S_s)$ of the phase transition is equal to zero and we have dealt with the second-order phase transition. While, at $H_c > 0$, $q$ is positive and the transition from the normal state to the SC one is the first-order phase transition. The jump of the specific heat at $T_c$ is determined by expression

$$C_s - C_n = T\frac{d(S_s - S_n)}{dT} = \frac{T}{4\pi}\left[\left(\frac{dH_c}{dT}\right)^2 + H_c\frac{d^2H_c}{dT^2}\right] \qquad (1.73)$$

Taking into account that $H_c(T = T_c) = 0$, we obtain

$$C_s - C_n = \frac{T_c}{4\pi}\left(\frac{dH_c}{dT}\right)^2 > 0 \qquad (1.74)$$

The thermodynamic equations (1.68) and (1.69) can be also applied to the type II superconductors, for which the value of $H_c$ characterizes any auxiliary quantity or average critical magnetic field. Thus, this thermodynamical approach allows to find the important relationship between the magnetic and thermal properties of superconductors.

### 1.5.4. The Isotope Effect

Superconductivity after its discovery in simple metals remained obscure and mysterious phenomenon for a long time. Starting from the early 1950s, there have been great advances in understanding many key features of conventional superconductors. In particular, theoretical studies carried out by Fröhlich in 1950 [34] led to the prediction of the important role of the electron-phonon interaction in superconductivity. Fröhlich predicted very important property of the superconductors, namely, the dependence of the SC transition temperature $T_c$ on the isotope mass $M$ of the atomic nuclei of the superconductor. This is the so-called isotope effect, was also discovered experimentally in 1950 by Maxwell [35] and Reynolds et al., [36]. It was found that the mass of the isotopes is related with the SC transition temperature $T_c$ as follows

$$M^\alpha T_c = const,  \tag{1.75}$$

where $\alpha$ is the isotope effect exponent.

The isotope mass determines the frequency of lattice vibrations, $\omega \sim M^{-1/2}$. Experimentally, it was found that for most simple metals, $\alpha = 0.5$. Hence, it follows that superconductivity in metals is caused by the electron-phonon interaction. This discovery of the isotope effect allowed for the right starting point in developing an successful theory of superconductivity, commonly known as the BCS theory in which superconductivity results from the Cooper pairing mediated by the electron-phonon interaction. The BCS theory yields the excellent result for the isotope effect exponent $\alpha = 0.5$ in conventional metals. But the observed values of $\alpha = 0 \div 0.1$ [2, 9] in transition metals (Ru, Os, Zr, U) are much smaller than the value of $\alpha = 0.5$ or even negative $\alpha = -0.015$ (for Ir [37]) and $\alpha = -5$ (for U [38]). These features of conventional superconductors cannot be understood in terms of the standard BCS theory.

### 1.5.5. Optical Properties

The SC state of conventional metals is characterized by the existence of an energy gap in their electronic spectrum and superconductivity can be also destroyed by long-wave radiation. The presence of the energy gap between the ground and excited states of superconductors was conjectured first theoretically by F. London (see Refs. [37] and Ginzburg [39]). The determination for the possibility of the destruction threshold of superconductivity by using the electromagnetic radiation was already discussed in the 1930s [37, 40]. At that time the energy gap in the excitation spectrum of superconductors was not observed experimentally due to absence of the appropriate technique for absorption measurements of low-frequency radiation. The possibility of absorption measurements of electromagnetic radiation by superconductors in the region of the frequency $h\nu \sim k_B T_c$ appeared only in the middle of the 1950s [41]. Glover and Tinkham [42] succeeded in reaching the far-infrared region of the electromagnetic spectrum (i.e., the threshold of the low-frequency electromagnetic radiation for destruction of superconductivity) and observed an energy gap in the electronic spectrum of the superconductor. At the same time, Bardeen, Cooper, and Schrieffer [21] proposed a microscopic theory of superconductivity. The BCS theory accounted for many of the experimental observations; in particular, the existence of the energy gap

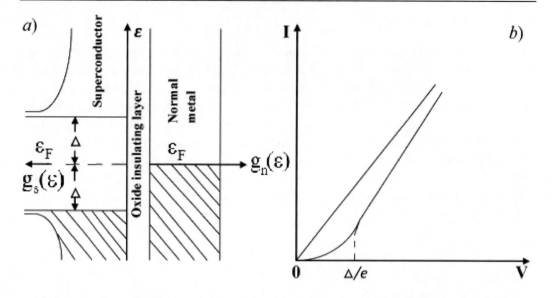

Figure 1.10. The density of states as a function of energy (*a*) and the current-voltage characteristics (*b*) for tunneling across superconductor-oxide insulator-normal metal junction at $T = 0$.

$E_g = 2\Delta$ between the ground and excited states of electrons. According to this theory, the electron-phonon interaction binds electrons into Cooper pairs and the binding energy of these pairs is manifested as a gap in the excitation spectrum of superconductors. Later, a large number of experiments confirmed the presence of such a BCS energy gap in conventional superconductors. For instance, the clear absorption edges were observed directly at frequencies corresponding to the width of the energy gap in superconductors [43, 44]. Nevertheless, in-gap states and precursor peaks beyond the absorption edges [9] (i.e., beyond the boundaries of the BCS energy gap) or above-the-gap structures [45] were also observed in conventional superconductors. Apparently, such unusual features of these old superconductors represent open questions waiting for an adequate physical explanation (see e.g., Ref. [31]) by going beyond the scope of the standard BCS theory. Another more simple and informative method of experimental detection of gap-like features in superconductors is the measurement of the tunnel current flowing across the superconductor-insulator-metal (or superconductor) contact (Fig. 1.10). In 1960, Giaeyer had observed [46] that the current-voltage characteristics of sandwiches consisting of a superconductor and either another superconductor or a normal metal, separated by a thin oxide insulating layer, were nonlinear, and that the nonlinearity is indicative of the existence of an energy gap in the excitation spectrum of the superconductor. At $T = 0$, the tunnel current is equal to zero up to a threshold voltage $V = E_g/2e = \Delta/e$. At $V \geq \Delta/e$, the tunnel current appears due to the destruction of Copper pairs and grows quickly approaching to the ohmic value with increasing voltage (Fig. 1.10b). At $T > 0$, the weak tunnel current appears even at low voltage due to the thermal excitation of some electrons from the states below $\varepsilon_F - \Delta$ to the states above $\varepsilon_F + \Delta$. The tunneling across superconductor-oxide insulator-superconductor junction (Fig. 1.11) can be explained in analogous manner.

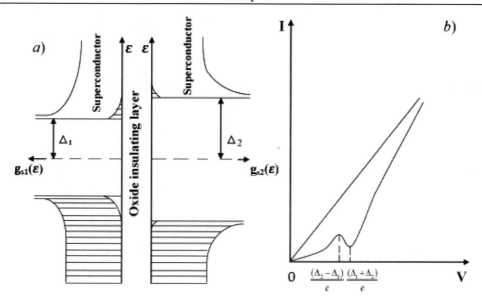

Figure 1.11. The density of states as a function of energy (a)and the current-voltage characteristics (b) for tunneling across superconductor-oxide insulator-superconductor junction
at $T \neq 0$.

In the equilibrium $(V = 0)$, the chemical potentials of two superconductors with the
energy gaps $\Delta_1$ and $\Delta_2 > \Delta_1$ are equal. For increasing $V$, the Fermi level of the second
superconductor shifts down by the quantity $eV$ and the energy of electrons in this superconductor decreases. As a consequence, the current increases until $V < (\Delta_2 - \Delta_1)/e$ because
of the increase of the thermally excited electrons which can tunnel from the first superconductor into the second superconductor. When $V > (\Delta_2 - \Delta_1)/e$, the number of free states
decreases in the right side of the tunnel junction with increasing $V$. Consequently, then the
current decreases. When $V = (\Delta_1 + \Delta_2)/e$ the upper limit of the lower band of the first superconductor coincides with the lower limit of the upper band of the second superconductor
and the current increases at $V > (\Delta_1 + \Delta_2)/e$ as shown in Fig. 1.11b. The observed $I - V$
curve like that of Fig. 1.11b and agrees well with the prediction of the BCS theory (see
e.g., Ref. [14]). Tunnelling was also used to study the so-called gapless superconductivity
and Josephson effect [9]. This phenomenon is associated with the presence of magnetic
impurities which destroy the Cooper pairs.

Experimental data on electromagnetic radiation absorption and electron tunneling in
some conventional superconductors indicate the presence of two energy gaps in their excitation spectrum (see, e.g., Ref. [9]), which was predicted theoretically by Suhl, Mattiass,
and Walker [47], and by Moskalenko [48]. Theoretical analysis of the properties of two-gap
superconductors was carried out by Geilikman, Zaitsev, and Kresin [49], that argued that
in the presence of two overlapping bands, each of them is characterized by its own energy
gap.

# References

[1] H. Kamerlingh Onnes, *Leiden Commun.* No. 119b, 120b, 122b, 124c (1911).

[2] C. Kittel, *Introduction to Solid State Physics* (Nauka, Moscow, 1978).

[3] D. R. Tilly and J. Tilly, *Superfluidity and Superconductivity* (Adam Hilger, Bristol, 1990).

[4] A. G. Zhilich, in: *Physics at the Threshold of New Discoveries*, (ed.), L. N. Labzovskii (Leningrad University press, Leningrad, 1990) chapter V.

[5] D. Pavuna, in: *The Symmetry and Fluctuations in High-$T_c$ Superconductors*, (eds.), J. Bok, G. Deutscher, D. Pavuna, and S. A. Wolf (Kluwer Academic Publishers, New York, 2002).

[6] S. V. Vonsovskii and M. I. Katsnelson, *Quantum Physics of Solid State* (Nauka, Moscow, 1983).

[7] A. M.Kosevich, *Physical mechanics of real crystals* (Naukova Dumka, Kiev, 1981).

[8] P. V. Pavlov and A. F. Khokhlov, *Solid State Physics* (Visshaya Shkola, Moscow, 1985).

[9] E. A. Lynton, *Superconductivity* (Mir, Moscow, 1971).

[10] P. J. Ford and G. A. Saunders, *Contemporary Phys.* 38, 63 (1997).

[11] H. Kawaji, H. Horie, Sh. Yamanaka, and M. Ishikawa, *Phys. Rev. Lett.* 74, 1427 (1995).

[12] A. Animalu, *Quantum Theory of Crystalline Solids* (Mir, Moscow, 1981).

[13] B. K. Ridley, *Quantum Processes in Semiconductors* (Mir, Moscow, 1986).

[14] N. W. Ashcroft and N. D. Mermin, *Solid State Physics.* V. 1 (Mir, Moscow, 1979).

[15] R. K.Pathria, *Statistical Mechanics.* 2nd ed. (Butterworth Heinemann, Oxford, 1996).

[16] A. Anselm, *Introduction to Semiconductor Theory* (Izd. Fiz. Math. Literature, Moscow, Leningrad, 1962).

[17] L. D.Landau and E. M. Lifshits, *Statical Physics.* Part I (Nauka, Moscow, 1976).

[18]  V. G. Levich, Yu. A. Vdovin, and V. A. Myamlin, *Course of Theoretical Physics.* V. 2 (Nauka, Moscow, 1971).

[19]  W. A. Harrison, *Solid State Theory* (Mir, Moscow, 1972).

[20]  P. W. Anderson, *The Theory of Superconductivity in the High-$T_c$ cuprates* (Princeton University Press, Princeton, 1997).

[21]  J. Bardeen, L. N. Cooper, and J. R. Schrieffer, *Phys. Rev.* 108, 1175 (1957).

[22]  W. Meissner and R. Ochscenfeld, *Naturwissenschaften* 21, 787 (1933).

[23]  A. A. Abrikosov, *Fundamentals of the Theory of Metals* (Nauka, Moscow 1987).

[24]  F. London and H. London, *Proc. Roy. Soc.* A149, 71 (1935); *Physica* 2, 341 (1935).

[25]  S. Dzhumanov and P. K. Khabibullaev, *Pramana J. Phys.* 45, 385 (1995).

[26]  F. London, *Superfluids.* V. 1 (John Wiley, N. Y., 1950).

[27]  B. S. Deaver and W. M. Faibank, *Phys. Rev. Lett.* 7, 43 (1961).

[28]  R. Doll and M. Näbauer, *Phys. Rev. Lett.* 7, 51 (1961).

[29]  M. Tinkam, *Introduction to Superconductivity* (Atomizdat, Moscow, 1980).

[30]  W. S. Corak and C. B. Satterthwaite, *Phys. Rev.* 99, 1660 (1954).

[31]  S. Dzhumanov, *Int. J. Mod. Phys.* B12, 1251 (1998).

[32]  G. M. Eliashber, *Zh. Eksp. Theor. Fiz.* 43, 1105 (1962).

[33]  B. B. Goodman, *Phys. Rev. Lett.* 6, 597 (1961).

[34]  H. Fröhlich, *Phys. Rev.* 79, 845 (1950).

[35]  E. Maxwell, *Phys. Rev.* 78, 477 (1950).

[36]  C. A. Reynolds, B. Serin, W. H. Wright, and L. B. Nesbitt, *Phys. Rev.* 78, 487 (1950).

[37]  L. M. Falicow, *IEEE Quantum Electronics.* 25, 2358 (1989).

[38]  M. L. Cohen, G. Gladstone, M. A. Jensen, and J. R. Scrieffer,*Superconductivity in Semiconductors and Transition Metals* (Mir, Moscow, 1972).

[39]  V. L. Ginsburg, *Zh. Eksp. Theor. Fiz.* 14, 134 (1944).

[40]  A.S. Davidov, *High Temperature Superconductivity* (Naukova Dumka, Kiev, 1990).

[41]  M. A. Bioni, M. P. Garfunkel, and A. O. McCoubrey, *Phys. Rev.* 101, 1427 (1956).

[42]  R. E. Glover and M. Tinkham, *Phys. Rev.* 104, 844 (1956); 108, 243 (1957).

[43]  P. L. Richards and M. Tinkham, *Phys. Rev.* 119, 575 (1960).

[44]  G. Richaysen, *Proc. Phys. Soc.* 89, 129 (1966).

[45]  A. Vaknin and Z. Ovadyahu, *Z. Phys.: Condens. Matter* 9, L303 (1997).

[46]  I. Giaever, *Phys. Rev. Lett.* 5, 147 (1960); 5, 464 (1960).

[47]  H. Suhl, B. Mattiass, and L. Walker, *Phys. Rev. Lett.* 3, 552 (1959).

[48]  V. Moskalenko, *Fizika Metal Metalloved.* 8, 503 (1959).

[49]  B. Geilikman, R. Zaitsev, and V. Kresin, *Sov. Phys. Solid State* 9, 642 (1967).

# Chapter 2

# Phenomenological Theories of Superconductivity

## 2.1. Introduction

Many properties of superconductors described in the previous chapter can be understood in terms of the phenomenological theories of superfluidity and superconductivity, which are based on the fundamental works of Landau, Gorter and Casimir, brothers F. London and H. London, Ginzburg and Landau, Pippard, Abrikosov, Saint-James and De Gennes and others (see e.g., Refs. [1, 2, 3]). The present chapter gives an introductory account of these theories. Actually, the phenomenon of superconductivity discovered by Kamerlingh Onnes [4] is very similar to superfluidity in liquid helium, $^4He$, discovered by Kapitza [5]. These two remarkable phenomena have one characteristic feature in common: the superconductivity is a frictionless flow of charged electrons through the crystal lattice, whereas the superfluidity is a frictionless flow of helium atoms through thin capillaries. The successful phenomenological theory of superfluidity was formulated by Landau [6], who derived the criterion for superfluidity. Any quantum fluid (including also electron fluid) will be a superfluid when the fluid flow velocity does not exceed some critical velocity determined by the Landau criterion. Therefore, superconductivity can be explained as the superfluidity of the electron liquid in solids. In 1934, Gorter and Casimir [7] proposed the so-called two-fluid model in which the electron gas within the superconductor is viewed as consisting of a mixture of two fluids. One fluid behaves like a normal fluid and the second fluid is a superfluid and carries the supercurrent. In 1935, F. London and H. London [8] derived their famous equations using the two-fluid model and Maxwell's equations. They gave an important phenomenological description of superconductivity. London's phenomenological theory was later generalized by Ginzburg and Landau (GL) [9] and by Pippard [10], who were introduced independently the concept of a coherence length $\xi$ which is different from the London penetration depth $\lambda_L$ and characterizes the spatial change of the SC order parameter. The starting point of the GL theory was the idea of the Landau's theory of second order phase transitions (without latent heat) and the introduction of the concept of a complex order parameter $\psi$ which is allowed to vary in space. This theory provides a good phenomenological description of superconductivity near the SC transition temperature $T_c$. Further, the GL theory was developed by Abrikosov [11] and by Saint-James and De Gennes [12], who predicted the existence of the mixed state (or vortex state in the type II superconductors) and the phenomena of surface superconductivity (or the formation of the germs of SC phases in a thin surface layer), respectively. Abrikosov subdivided all super-conductors into the two classes called as the type I and type II superconductors, using his own phenomenological theory and the concept of the surface energy of superconductors. In this chapter, we discuss the main features of the phenomenological theories of supercon-ductivity, which are very useful for description of many properties of superconductors.

## 2.2. Landau Criterion for Superfluidity

We have already mentioned that a quantum fluid flowing with velocity $v < v_c$ (where $v_c$ is the critical flow velocity of the fluid, determined from the Landau criterion for superfluid-ity) becomes superfluid. Landau formulated [6] that under the condition $v < v_c$ the quantum fluid should flow as a superfluid without any friction and the superfluidity is destroyed at $v > v_c$. We now discuss the question of the critical velocity of superfluid and consider the processes which might lead to the destruction of superfluidity (or superconductivity). We consider an excitation-free superfluid flowing through a long tube (or crystal lattice) with velocity $v$ relative to the immobile tube (or laboratory system of coordinates) at $T = 0K$. If we go over into the system of reference in which the superfluid is at rest, the walls of the tube are moving with respect to the superfluid with velocity -$v$. When the flow velocity of the fluid approaches to $v_c$ the drag friction between the tube and the superfluid arises. Therefore, the viscosity of the fluid will appear and the creation of an excitation in the superfluid becomes possible. This causes a loss of the superfluid's kinetic energy, which is ultimately converted into heat. As a consequence, the superfluid begins to slow down. We now determine the minimum value of the flow velocity at which a single excitation (or quasiparticle) can appear. Suppose that a single excitation with energy $\varepsilon(p)$ and momen-tum $p$ appeared in the superfluid. Because of the recoil, the velocity of the tube is then changed and become equal to $-v_1$. According to the principles of conservation of energy and momentum, one can write

$$\frac{Mv^2}{2} = \frac{Mv_1^2}{2} + \varepsilon(p) \tag{2.1}$$

and

$$-M\vec{v} = -M\vec{v}_1 + \vec{p}, \tag{2.2}$$

where $M$ is the mass of the tube.
Combining (2.1) and (2.2), we obtain

$$\varepsilon(p) + \vec{p}\vec{v} + \frac{p^2}{2M} = 0 \tag{2.3}$$

from which it follows that

$$\varepsilon(p) + \vec{p}\vec{v} = \varepsilon(p) + pv\cos\theta < 0, \tag{2.4}$$

where $\theta$ is the angle between $\vec{p}$ and $\vec{v}$.

The left-hand side of (2.4) is minimal when $\theta = \pi$ or $\vec{p}$ and $\vec{v}$ are antiparallel, so that $\varepsilon(p) - pv < 0$. Consequently, the condition for the appearance of an excitation in the superfluid is written as

$$v > \frac{\varepsilon(p)}{p} \tag{2.5}$$

The minimum value of $v$ at which an excitation can appear in the superfluid is equal to

$$v_c = \min \left[ \frac{\varepsilon(p)}{p} \right] \tag{2.6}$$

If $v < v_c$, the excitation cannot be appeared in the superfluid, which will flow through a tube or a crystal lattice with any dissipation. Thus, the Landau criterion for superfluity is written as

$$v < v_c = \min \left[ \frac{\varepsilon(p)}{p} \right] \tag{2.7}$$

Extremum of the function $\varepsilon(p)/p$ are determined from the equation

$$p \frac{d\varepsilon(p)}{dp} = \varepsilon(p) \tag{2.8}$$

These relations presented are also valid for $T \neq 0$. The Landau theory of superfluidity is based on the excitation spectrum of liquid $^4He$ and the equation (2.8) has two solutions corresponding to different regions of the spectrum (see, e.g., Ref. [3]). One solution corresponds to the origin and all points of the phonon region of the spectrum, whereas the second solution corresponds to the point near the minimum in the roton region. From Eq.(2.7) it follows that the critical velocity $v_c$ determines the threshold below which the existence of superfluidity in the system is possible. The theoretical calculations of $v_c$ for the quantum and electron liquids, which have the different energy-momentum relationships, are very important. According to (2.7), any liquid with the energy-momentum relationship of the form $\varepsilon(p) = v_s p$ (where $v_s$ is the sound velocity) is a superfluid (or superconducting (SC)). If the energy-momentum is given by the ideal-gas relationship $\varepsilon(p) = p^2/2m$, then the critical velocity would be zero. In this case, any velocity of the flowing fluid is greater than $v_c$. That is, the quantum (or electron) liquid would not be a superfluid (or SC). This is a very important result, for it brings out very clearly the fact that the specific interatomic and interelectron interactions in quantum and electron liquids, which give rise to an excitation spectrum different from the one characteristic of the ideal gas, play a key role in superfluidity and superconductivity. In particular, the criterion (2.7) can be satisfied when the excitation spectrum of the Fermi-and Bose-liquid has an energy gap at $p(= \hbar k) = 0$. Although, an ideal Bose-gas does undergo the phenomenon of Bose-Einstein condensation (BEC), it bears no a relation to the phenomenon of superfluidity and superconductivity [13, 14, 15, 16, 17]. As already pointed out by Landau [17], who argued that the BEC of an ideal Bose-gas should not be confused with the superfluidity. We shall discuss this question in more detail in chapters 5 and 8.

## 2.3.  London Equations for a Superconductor and Penetration Depth

In 1934, Gorter and Casimir put forward the idea of a two-fluid model [7] and developed the early phenomenological theory of superconductivity based on this model. In order to understand the behavior of a superconductor in an external electromagnetic field, just one year after F. London and H. London [8] used the Gorter-Casimir two-fluid model and derived their well-known equations. According to the two-fluid model, the electron liquid in superconductors can be divided into two components: SC component with density $n_s$ and normal component with density $n_n$. The total density of electrons is $n = n_s + n_n$. As the temperature decreases from $T_c$ to 0, the density $n_s$ increases from 0 to $n$. While at $T = T_c$ the SC component vanishes and the entire electron liquid is normal, $n_s = 0$, $n_n = n$. A similar two-fluid model has also been proposed for superfluidity in quantum liquid $^4He$. The SC and normal components are assumed to move freely through each other without any friction. The SC component sustains frictionless flow and leads to superconductivity. This component has zero entropy and does not transport heat. Only the normal component has all the entropy and carries heat. The two-fluid model is very useful for studying the thermodynamic and magnetic properties of superconductors. Detailed analysis have shown that this model gives a semiempirical description of the SC properties of the system. In particular, the temperature dependencies of the magnetic field $H_c$, the penetration depth of the magnetic field $\lambda$ and the SC carrier density $n_s$ predicted by the Gorter-Casimir two-fluid model are expressed in the forms (1.54), (1.56), and (1.57), respectively (see chapter 1).

Here, we shall now study the superconductor in an electromagnetic field. We will assume that the external electric and magnetic fields are so weak that they do not have any appreciable influence on the SC carrier density $n_s$. In addition, the spatial distribution of $n_s$ is assumed to be homogeneous. Under the assumed conditions the applied electric field $E$ will accelerate the electrons and the equation of motion for SC electrons is

$$m\frac{dv_s}{dt} = e\vec{E}, \tag{2.9}$$

where $m$ and $e$ are the electron mass and charge, respectively, $v_s$ is the velocity of superfluid electrons.

Introducing the supercurrent density $j_s = n_s e v_s$, Eq.(2.9) can be written as

$$\frac{d\vec{j}_s}{dt} = \frac{n_s e^2}{m}\vec{E} \tag{2.10}$$

Applying the *curl* operator to the both sides of (2.10) and using the Maxwell's first equation

$$curl\vec{E} = -\frac{1}{c}\frac{\partial\vec{H}}{\partial t}, \tag{2.11}$$

we obtain

$$\frac{\partial}{\partial t}\left[\frac{4\pi}{c}\lambda^2 curl\vec{j}_s + \vec{H}\right] = 0, \tag{2.12}$$

where $\lambda = (mc^2/4\pi n_s e^2)^{1/2}$, $c$ is the velocity of light. From Eq. (2.12), it can be seen that the quantity in the square brackets is conserved. According to the hypothesis of F. London and H. London, deep inside any superconductor, $\vec{j}_s = 0$ and $\vec{H} = 0$. Therefore, Eq. (2.12) can be rewritten as

$$\frac{4\pi}{c}\lambda^2 \, curl \, \vec{j}_s + \vec{H} = 0 \tag{2.13}$$

The second Maxwell equation has the form

$$curl \vec{H} = \frac{4\pi}{c}\vec{j}_s \tag{2.14}$$

Taking the *curl* of Eq. (2.14) and using the vector identity

$$curl \, curl \vec{H} = grad \, div\vec{H} - \Delta\vec{H}, \tag{2.15}$$

we can write Eq. (2.14) in the form

$$-\Delta\vec{H} + grad \, div\vec{H} = \frac{4\pi}{c} curl \, \vec{j}_s \tag{2.16}$$

When taking into account that $div\vec{H} = 0$ and combining Eqs. (2.13) and (2.16), we obtain

$$\Delta\vec{H} = \frac{1}{\lambda^2}\vec{H} \tag{2.17}$$

This is actually the London equation. We now apply the London equation to a bulk superconductor and examine how a magnetic field penetrates into the bulk superconductor. Consider a superconductor occupying half-space $x > 0$ and a magnetic field $\vec{H}$ lying parallel to the superconductor surface. In this case, the London equation (2.17) can be written as

$$\frac{d^2H}{dx^2} - \frac{1}{\lambda^2}H = 0 \quad \text{or} \quad H'\frac{dH'}{dH} - \frac{1}{\lambda^2}H = 0, \tag{2.18}$$

where $H' = dH/dx$.

The solution of this equation has the form

$$H(x) = H(0)\exp(-x/\lambda_F), \tag{2.19}$$

where $\lambda_F = \lambda$ is a characteristic length, which is called the London magnetic field penetration depth. The supercurrent density is then obtained from the Maxwell equation (2.14), which can be written as

$$j_s = -\frac{c}{4\pi}\frac{dH}{dx} \tag{2.20}$$

By substituting (2.19) into (2.20), we obtain

$$j_s = \frac{cH(0)}{4\pi\lambda_F}\exp(-x/\lambda_F) \tag{2.21}$$

¿From (2.19) and (2.21), we see that the far inside the superconductor magnetic field and supercurrent density vanish exponentially. The characteristic length $\lambda_F$ determines the thickness of the surface layer of a superconductor, where $H$ and $j_s$ essentially decreases from the surface to the interior of the superconductor. This length is temperature-dependent because it depends on $n_s$, which decreases with increasing temperature. The temperature dependence of $n_s$ is given by the empirical Gorter-Casimir formula (1.57). The magnetic field distribution in the superconductor and the temperature dependence of $\lambda_F$ described by the Gorter-Casimir formula (1.56) are shown in Figs. 2.1 and 2.2, respectively, Now we will

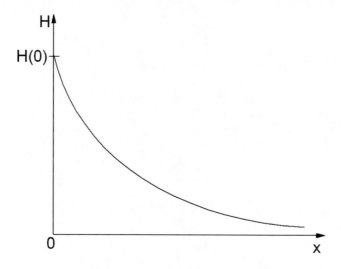

Figure 2.1. Magnetic field distribution in the surface layer of a superconductor.

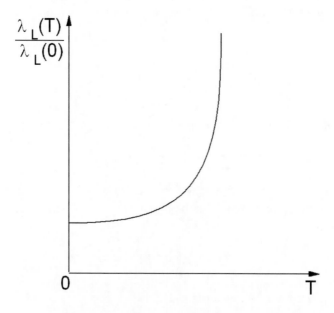

Figure 2.2. The variation of $\lambda_F$ with temperature.

**Table 2.1. The estimated values of SC carrier density and London penetration depth for some superconductors**

| Metal | Al | Ga | In | Zn | Cd | Pb | Sn |
|---|---|---|---|---|---|---|---|
| $n_s, 10^{22} cm^{-3}$ | 1.542 | 0.267 | 0.298 | 0.460 | 0.209 | 0.521 | 0.525 |
| $\lambda_L(0)$,Å | 521 | 785 | 1140 | 723 | 990 | 1034 | 824 |
| $\lambda_L^{exp}$,Å[1] | 500 | — | 640 | — | 1300 | 390 | 510 |

evaluate $\lambda_L(0)$ for conventional superconductors. In so doing, we will determine $n_s$ as the density of conduction electrons involved in the superconductivity (this question will be discussed in chapter 3). If the density of states near the Fermi surface is equal to $g(\varepsilon_F)$, then the value of $n_s$ is determined from the expression

$$n_s = g(\varepsilon_F)\hbar\omega_c, \tag{2.22}$$

where $g(\varepsilon_F) = (2m)^{3/2}\varepsilon_F^{1/2}/2\pi^2\hbar^3$, $\varepsilon_F$ is the Fermi energy, $\hbar\omega_c$ is the Coulomb cut-off energy for the electron-electron interaction, which is much larger than the characteristic Debye energy $\hbar\omega_D$ (more details about this situation can be found in chapter 3). It is reasonable to assume $\hbar\omega_c \simeq 10\hbar\omega_D$. The values of the effective mass $m$ of conduction electrons, the Fermi energy $\varepsilon_F$ and the characteristic Debye temperature $\theta_D = \hbar\omega_D/k_B$ for conventional metals are presented in [18]. The calculated values of $n_s$ and $\lambda_L(0)$ and the experimental values of $\lambda_L$ for some superconductors are given in Table 2.1

Introducing the vector potential $\vec{A}$ and using $\vec{H} = curl\vec{A}$, the London equation (2.13) can be written in the form

$$\vec{j}_s = -\frac{c}{4\pi\lambda_L^2}\vec{A} = -\frac{n_s e^2}{mc}\vec{A} \tag{2.23}$$

This equation is applicable only if the London penetration depth $\lambda_L$ is much larger than the so-called coherence length $\xi_0$ over which the current and vector potential are charged slowly. The length $\xi_0$ scale introduced by Ginzburg and Landau [9] and by Pippard [10] is different from $\lambda_L$ and represents the length scale affecting the behavior of a superconductor. It is a characteristic length which measures the spatial response of the superconductor to some perturbation. For pure metals, $\xi_0$ is of the order $\xi_0 \sim 10^{-4} cm$, as we shall see later in chapter 3. While the London penetration depth is about $\lambda_L \sim 10^{-5} - 10^{-6} cm$. This means that the local London electrodynamics is not applicable to pure superconductors. Since at $\lambda_L << \xi_0$ the magnetic field or vector potential $\vec{A}$ and current density $\vec{j}_s$ vary rapidly over the length $\xi_0$. In this case, the local London equation (2.23) should be replaced by a nonlocal one relating the supercurrent $\vec{j}_s$ to the vector potential $\vec{A}$ which is allowed to change rapidly over the length $\xi_0$. Such a nonlocal relation was proposed by Pippard [10], who reasoned that the current $\vec{j}_s(\vec{r})$ at a point $\vec{r}$ depends on $\vec{A}(\vec{r}')$ at all neighboring points $\vec{r}'$ satisfying the condition $|\vec{r} - \vec{r}'| < \xi_0$. In reality, the vector potential $\vec{A}$ is nonzero in the narrow region with thickness $\lambda_p$ (Pippard's penetration depth) and acts on a SC carrier of size $\xi_0$ only within the depth $\lambda_p << \xi_0$. Although the SC carrier still participates in creating the current density $\vec{j}_s$, the effect of $\vec{A}$ on it is reduced, because only part of it $\lambda_p/\xi_0$ feels the presence of the vector potential. Thus, the value of $\vec{j}_s$ will be reduced roughly by a factor $\xi_0/\lambda_p$ in comparison with the local case [19, 20, 21], i.e.,

$$\vec{j}_s(\vec{r}) = -\frac{\lambda_p}{\xi_0}\frac{n_s e^2}{mc}\vec{A}(\vec{r}) \tag{2.24}$$

Using the Maxwell's equation $curl\vec{H} = (4\pi/c)\vec{j}_s$ and applying the *curl* operator to the both sides of this equation and then when taking into account (2.13), we can write (2.24) in the London-like form

$$curl\,curl\vec{H} = \frac{4\pi}{c}curl\,\vec{j}_s = -\frac{\lambda_p}{\lambda_L^2\xi_0}\vec{H} \tag{2.25}$$

The solution of this equation has the form

$$H(x) = H(0)\exp(-x/\lambda), \tag{2.26}$$

where $\lambda = (\lambda_L^2\xi_0/\lambda_p)^{1/2}$ is a characteristic length which should be defined as Pippard penetration depth $\lambda_p$. Accordingly, we find

$$\lambda_p^3 = \lambda_L^2\xi_0 \tag{2.27}$$

A more accurate theoretical calculation yields $\lambda_p^3 = 0.62\lambda_L^2\xi_0$ (see Ref. [21]). One can see from (2.27) that $\lambda_p > \lambda_L$ at $\xi_0 > \lambda_L$.

In the opposite limit $\lambda_L \gg \xi_0$, Pippard modified the coherence length as $1/\xi(l) = (1/\xi_0) + (1/l)$ and the generalized London equation is then written as

$$\vec{j}_s(\vec{r}) = -\frac{n_s e^2}{mc}\frac{\xi(l)}{\xi_0}\vec{A}(\vec{r}), \tag{2.28}$$

where $\xi_0$ is the coherence length for pure superconductors, $\xi(l)$ is the coherence length for dirty superconductors which contain a large number of impurities, $l$ is the electron mean free path.

Since the relation Eq.(2.28) is the local London-type equation, the magnetic field penetration depth for dirty metals (where $l \ll \xi_0$) is determined from the expression

$$\lambda_p = \lambda_L\left(\frac{\xi_0}{l}\right)^{1/2} \tag{2.29}$$

Hence, in the limit $\lambda_L \gg \xi_0$, the dirty superconductors, SC alloys and high-$T_c$ cuprate superconductors fall into the category of the so-called London superconductors and they are described well by the local London equations. The numerical values of $\lambda_L$ for high-$T_c$ superconductors will be presented in chapters 4 and 8.

## 2.4. Quantization of Magnetic Field, Vortex State and Josephson Effect

It was already mentioned in chapter 1 that the supercurrent carriers in conventional superconductors are the Cooper pairs. Such carriers in high-$T_c$ cuprates are assumed to be Cooper-like polaron pairs [14, 15]. Below $T_c$ these pairs (which are composite bosons) condense into a superfluid state in which macroscopically large number of particles is described by the single wave function $\Psi(r)$ [22]. Therefore, the wave-function of carriers in the superfluid condensate can be written in the form $\Psi(\vec{r}) = (n_s/2)^{1/2} \exp(i\theta(r))$, where $n_s/2$ is the density of SC electron (or hole) pairs, $\theta$ is the phase of the wave-function. The quantity of $|\Psi|^2$ characterizes the degree of SC order: at $T = 0$, $|\Psi|^2 = n_s/2$ (full-ordered SC state) and full-disordered or normal state at $T = T_c$ corresponds $|\Psi|^2 = 0$. Consider a composite Bose particle of mass $2m$ and charge $2e$ moving in a magnetic field. The total momentum of this particle in a magnetic field is the sum of the free particle momentum $2m\vec{v}$ and the momentum $(2e/c)\vec{A}$ due to the magnetic field, i.e.,

$$\vec{P} = -i\hbar\nabla = 2m\vec{v} + \frac{2e}{c}\vec{A} \tag{2.30}$$

Then the supercurrent density is given by

$$\begin{aligned}
\vec{j}_s &= 2e|\Psi|^2\vec{v} = 2e\int \frac{1}{2}\left[\Psi^*(\vec{r}')\hat{\vec{v}}(\vec{r}')\Psi(\vec{r}') + \Psi(\vec{r}')\hat{\vec{v}}^*(\vec{r}')\Psi^*(\vec{r}')\right]\delta(r' - \vec{r}')dr' \\
&= e\left\{\frac{1}{2m}\left[\Psi^*(-i\hbar\nabla - \frac{2e}{c}\vec{A})\Psi + \Psi(i\hbar\nabla - \frac{2e}{c}\vec{A})\Psi^*\right]\right\} \\
&= \frac{c}{4\pi\lambda_L^2}\left\{\frac{\phi_0}{2\pi}\nabla\theta - \vec{A}\right\},
\end{aligned} \tag{2.31}$$

where $\phi_0 = \pi\hbar c/e$, $\nabla\theta$ is the change of the phase of the wave function $\Psi$.

Consider a superconductor with a hole and the contour $C$ inside the superconductor enclosing the hole, so that the distance from the contour to the internal surface of the hole is much larger than $\lambda_L$. Then at any point in the contour, the supercurrent is $\vec{j}_s = 0$ and, therefore, from (2.31) one obtains

$$\frac{\phi_0}{2\pi}\nabla\theta = \vec{A} \tag{2.32}$$

Line integration of (2.32) over the closed contour by using the Stokes theorem yields

$$\frac{\phi_0}{2\pi}\oint_C \nabla\theta dl = \oint_C \vec{A}dl = \int_S \nabla\vec{A}ds = \int_S \vec{H}ds = \phi, \tag{2.33}$$

where $\phi$ is the total magnetic-field flux through the surface $S$ enclosed by the contour $C$.

The wave function $\Psi$ must be single-valued. It follows that the change of $\theta$ for a full circle over the contour $C$ should be multiple of $2\pi$. Then taking into account

$$\oint_C \nabla\theta dl = 2\pi\nu, \qquad \nu = 0, 1, 2, \ldots, \tag{2.34}$$

Eq.(2.33) can be written as

$$\phi = \nu\phi_0 \tag{2.35}$$

One can see from (2.35) that the magnetic-field flux encircled by the contour $C$ is quantized in units of $\phi_0 \simeq 2.07 \times 10^{-7} G \cdot cm^2$. The magnetic flux quantization in superconductors is similar to the quantization of electron orbits in atom. This phenomenon was predicted by F. London in 1950 [23] before the concept of Cooper pairs. He believed that the supercurrent carriers are single electrons and the magnetic flux quantum should be $2\pi\hbar c/e = 2\phi_0$. At the same time Ginzburg and Landau assumed that the supercurrent carrier has the change $e^*$ [9]. Further, the BCS theory [24] predicted the value of $e^* = 2e$ and $\phi_0 = \pi\hbar c/e$ for conventional superconductors. Magnetic flux quantization was discovered experimentally in 1961 by Deaver and Fairbank [25] and by Doll and Näbauer [26]. Note, that the magnetic flux quantum appears also in the theory of normal metal and the spiral trajectory of electrons encircles the magnetic flux $\phi = 2\nu\phi_0$ [27]. In superconductors, the magnetic flux in the hole is produced by the supercurrent circulating around the hole is called the quantized vortex and the hole (around which the magnetic flux quantization occurs) represents the core of the quantized vortex lines. Such a vortex may appear only at a certain minimum velocity $v_s$ of the supercurrent circulation. Since the formation of the vortex requires the expenditure of energy and its kinetic energy is proportional to $v^2 \sim \nu^2$, so that only the vortices with $\nu = 1$ are formed. Therefore, the formation of two quantized vortices with $\nu = 1$ is more advantageous energetically than single vortex with $\nu = 2$. We assume that the paired carriers make the vortical motion with the constant velocity $\vec{v}$ over the internal surface of the above hole. Then the Bohr-Sommerfeld quantization rule for the motion of a carrier can be written as

$$\oint \vec{P}d\vec{l} = 2m \oint \vec{v}d\vec{l} = 2mv \cdot 2\pi r = 2\pi\nu\hbar, \tag{2.36}$$

from which we find the expression for $v_s$, namely,

$$v_s = \frac{\nu\hbar}{2mr}, \tag{2.37}$$

where $r$ is the radius of a closed ring of vortex line.

The relation (2.37) is valid for $\lambda_L \gg r \gg \xi_0$. The energy of the vortex line is basically determined by the kinetic energy of the circulating superfluid condensate. The energy per unit length of the vortex line is

$$\varepsilon_v = \frac{n_s}{2} \int_{\xi_0}^{\lambda_L} \frac{2mv_s^2}{2} 2\pi r dr = \frac{\pi n_s \nu^2 \hbar^2}{4m} \ln\frac{\lambda_L}{\xi_0}. \tag{2.38}$$

We now consider the structure of a single vortex line for the case $\chi = \lambda_L/\xi_0 \gg 1$. The radius of the vortex core is of the order of $\xi_0$. Using the Maxwell equation (2.14), we may write (2.31) in the form

$$\lambda_L^2 curl\vec{H} = \frac{\phi_0}{2\pi}\nabla\theta - \vec{A} \tag{2.39}$$

We next integrate (2.39) over the closed contour $C$ encircling the vortex line and use the Stokes theorem in the surface integrals. As a result, we have

$$\int (\vec{H} + \lambda_L^2 curlcurl\vec{H})d\vec{s} = \phi \qquad (2.40)$$

If the contour $C$ passes at the distance $r >> \lambda_L$ from the vortex line, where $\vec{H}$ already vanishes, the second integral in (2.40) may be omitted and $\phi_0$ is equal to the total magnetic flux through the contour $C$. Under these conditions, Eq. (2.40) becomes

$$\vec{H} + \lambda_L^2 curlcurl\vec{H} = \vec{H} - \Delta\vec{H} = \phi_0\delta(\vec{r}), \qquad (2.41)$$

where $\delta(\vec{r})$ is a two-dimensional $\delta$ function.

The solution of (2.41) in cylindrical coordinates (with $z$ axis along the vortex line) is [2, 21]

$$H(r) = \frac{\phi_0}{2\pi\lambda_L^2}K_0\left(\frac{r}{\lambda_L}\right), \qquad (2.42)$$

where $K_0$ is the zeroth order Bessel function of imaginary argument and $K_0(r/\lambda_L) \simeq \ln(\lambda_L/r)$ for $r << \lambda_L$.

The total energy of a vortex line including both the magnetic field energy and the kinetic energy of the supercurrent, is

$$\varepsilon = \frac{1}{8\pi}\int\left[\vec{H}^2 + \lambda_L^2(curl\vec{H})^2\right]dv, \qquad (2.43)$$

where $curl\vec{H} = \nabla \times \vec{H} = -\partial H_z/\partial r = -\partial H/\partial r$, $dv = rdrd\varphi dz$.

Second integral in (2.43) is logarithmically divergent at $r << \lambda_L$ and it is very large in comparison with the first integral. Substituting $curl\vec{H} = \phi_0/2\pi\lambda_L^2 r$ into (2.43), we obtain for the energy per unit length of the vortex line

$$\varepsilon = \left(\frac{\phi_0}{4\pi\lambda_L}\right)^2 \ln\frac{\lambda_L}{\xi_0}, \qquad \xi << r << \lambda_L. \qquad (2.44)$$

Thus, the $1/r$ divergence of the superfluid velocity $v_s = \hbar/2mr$ (at $v = 1$) ultimately destroys superconductivity in the vertex core where the value of $v_s$ exceeds the critical superfluid velocity $v_c$ determined by the Landau criterion and the pertinent microscopic theory should predict the values of $v_c, \lambda_L$ and $\xi_0$ (the physical significance of $v_c, \lambda_L$ and $\xi_0$ will become clear in the following chapters).

We now turn to the Josephson effects (i.e., interference effects) arising at the presence of a weak link between two superconductors. In chapter 1, we have considered the tunneling of separate electrons across superconductor-insulator-metal or superconductor-insulator-superconductor junction. In 1962, however, Josephson predicted [28] that besides this normal tunnel current should exist yet another component of the tunnel current, which is caused by the tunneling of paired carriers across Superconductor-Insulator or Normal metal-Superconductor junction. For the sake of simplicity, we consider two identical superconductors which are weakly connected by a thin insulating layer. For paired carriers this insulating layer represents a thin barrier and the bound pair of carriers can tunnel across the barrier. Since the wave functions of two weakly coupled superconductors will overlap and interfere. Both superconductors separated by a thin barrier become the one system described by the common wave function. This means that a finite supercurrent can flow through $S - I - S$ junction even in the absence of the applied voltage. If a finite voltage $V_0$ is applied to this junction and the tunneling probability of paired carriers across a thin barrier is $K$, two coupled Schrödinger equations for the wave functions $\Psi_1 = (n_s/2)^{1/2}e^{i\theta_1}$ and $\Psi_2 = (n_s/2)^{1/2}e^{i\theta_2}$ on both sides of the barrier can be written in the forms [29]

$$i\hbar\frac{d\Psi_1}{dt} = E_1\Psi_1 + K\Psi_2, \quad i\hbar\frac{d\Psi_2}{dt} = E_2\Psi_2 + K\Psi_1, \tag{2.45}$$

where $E_1 = eV_0$ and $E_2 = -eV_0$ are the energies of the system in the $\Psi_1$ and $\Psi_2$ states, respectively.

Substituting the expressions for $\Psi_1$ and $\Psi_2$ into (2.45), and equating the real and imaginary parts separately, we obtain Josephson equations

$$\hbar\frac{dn_s}{dt} = \pm 2Kn_s sin(\theta_2 - \theta_1), \quad \hbar\frac{d\varphi}{dt} = \hbar\frac{d(\theta_2 - \theta_1)}{dt} = 2eV_0 \tag{2.46}$$

One can see from (2.46) that the phase difference $\varphi$ between two weakly coupled superconductors produces a supercurrent flow between them given by

$$J_s = J_0 sin\varphi, \tag{2.47}$$

where $J_0 = 4eKn_s$.

The second equation in (2.46) gives $\varphi = \varphi_0 + (2eV_0/\hbar)t$, so that

$$J_s = J_0 sin(\varphi_0 + 2eV_0 t/\hbar) \tag{2.48}$$

The Josephson effect is closely related to the magnetic field quantization and the comparison of (2.34) and (2.35) yields $\varphi = 2\pi\phi/\phi_0$.

Finally, it should be noted that incoherent Cooper pairs may exist as an ideal Bose-gas and undergo a Bose-Einstein condensation without superconductivity above $T_c$ in high-$T_c$ superconductors [14, 15, 30, 31]. We assume that the normal (i.e., nonzero-voltage (non-SC)) currents of unpaired carriers $I_n$ and incoherent Cooper pairs must flow through pseudogapped Metal-Insulator-Pseudogapped metal junction, where the wave functions of Bose-Einstein condensates (see Ref. [22]) above $T_c$ on both sides of the barrier can be written as $\Psi_1 = (n_0/2)^{1/2}e^{i\theta_1}$ and $\Psi_2 = (n_0/2)^{1/2}e^{i\theta_2}$ with $\varphi_0 = 2\nu\pi = 0$ for $V_0 = 0$ and $\varphi \neq 0$ for $V_0 \neq 0$.

## 2.5.  Ginzburg-Landau Theory and Coherence Length

In the previous section, we discussed the idea of the SC state which represents some kind of macroscopic quantum state. In 1950, Ginzburg and Landau (G-L) [9] proposed the phenomenological theory of superconductivity using this idea and the idea of the second order phase transition theory developed earlier by Landau [32] (see also Ref. [33]). They assumed the existence of a macroscopic wave function, $\Psi$, which is considered as the order parameter associated with superconductivity. The order parameter is complex quantity and varied in space. G-L postulated that the density of SC carriers is proportional to $|\Psi|^2$, which is nonzero at $T \leq T_c$ and vanishes at $T \geq T_c$. We first consider a simple case of a homogeneous superconductor without external magnetic field. In this case, $\Psi$ does not depend on a coordinate. If the value of $\Psi$ is small near $T_c$, one can expand the free energy of a superconductor as

$$F_s = F_n + a_1|\Psi| + a_2|\Psi|^2 + a_3|\Psi|^3 + a_4|\Psi|^4 + \cdots ,    (2.49)$$

where $F_n$ is the free energy in the normal state (i.e., at $\Psi = 0$), $a_1, a_2, a_3$ and $a_4$ are the temperature-dependent coefficients.

The symmetry and stability of the system requires that the odd terms in Eq.(2.49), namely, $a_1$ and $a_3$ must be zero [33], so that

$$F_s(T) = F_n(T) + a_2(T)|\Psi|^2 + a_4(T)|\Psi|^4 + \cdots ,    (2.50)$$

where $a_2(T) = a(T - T_c)$, $a > 0$, $a_4(T) = a_4(T_c) = b/2 > 0$. The equilibrium values of $|\Psi|$ is determined by the condition $\partial F/\partial|\Psi| = 0$, from which we find $|\Psi| = 0$ for $T > T_c$ and $|\Psi|^2 = |\Psi_0|^2 = -a(T - T_c)/b = |a(T_c - T)|/b$ for $T < T_c$. Substituting the value of $|\Psi_0|^2$ into (2.50) and comparing the result with the well-known relation (1.69), we obtain

$$F_n(T) - F_s(T) = \frac{[a(T - T_c)]^2}{2b} = \frac{H_c^2(T)}{8\pi}    (2.51)$$

In the case of an inhomogeneous superconductor and in the presence of an external magnetic field, the wave function $\Psi$ is coordinate dependent. In this case, we must add the energy of the magnetic field $H^2/8\pi$ and the energy associated with the spatial inhomogeneity of the order parameter or the contribution of the kinetic energy of SC carriers $n_s m^* \vec{v}^2/4$ (where $m^*$ is the mass of the SC entity and $\vec{v} = -(i\hbar/m^*)\nabla - (e^*/cm^*)\vec{A}$ is the velocity of a SC carrier determined by (2.30)) to Eq. (2.50). Then the total free energy of the superconductor is

$$F = F_n^{(0)} + \int \left\{ a(T - T_c)|\Psi|^2 + \frac{1}{2}b|\Psi|^4 \right.$$
$$\left. + \frac{1}{2m^*}\left|\left[-i\hbar\nabla - \frac{e^*}{c}\vec{A}\right]\Psi\right|^2 + \frac{H^2}{8\pi} \right\} dV,    (2.52)$$

where $F_n^{(0)}$ is the free energy of the normal state without magnetic field.

The momentum operators $-i\hbar\nabla$ and $i\hbar\nabla$ operate on the wave functions $\Psi$ and $\Psi^*$, respectively, which enter the Eq. (2.52) in the form $\Psi\Psi^*$ and are independent variables. The minimization of (2.52) with respect to $\Psi^*$ yields

$$\delta F = \int \left\{ a(T - T_c)\Psi\delta\Psi^* + b|\Psi|^2\Psi\delta\Psi^* \right.$$
$$\left. + \frac{1}{2m^*}\left[-i\hbar\nabla - \frac{e^*}{c}\vec{A}\right]\Psi\left[i\hbar\nabla - \frac{e^*}{c}\vec{A}\right] \right\} \delta\Psi^* dV = 0    (2.53)$$

The term $[-i\hbar\nabla - (e^*/c)\vec{A}]\Psi i\hbar\nabla\delta\Psi^*$ can be integrated in parts, using the Gauss theorem. In doing so, we use the function $\varphi = [-i\hbar\nabla - (e^*/c)\vec{A}]\Psi$ and the identity $\varphi\nabla\delta\Psi^* = \nabla(\varphi\delta\Psi^*) - \delta\Psi^*\nabla\varphi$. Then the last integral in (2.53) can be written as

$$
\frac{1}{2m^*}\int\varphi\left[i\hbar\nabla - \frac{e^*}{c}\vec{A}\right]\delta\Psi^*dV
$$

$$
= \frac{1}{2m^*}\left\{i\hbar\int\nabla(\varphi\delta\Psi^*)dV - i\hbar\int\delta\Psi^*\nabla\varphi dV - \frac{e^*}{c}\vec{A}\int\delta\Psi^*\varphi dV\right\}
$$

$$
= \frac{i\hbar}{2m^*}\oint\delta\Psi^*\left[-i\hbar\nabla - \frac{e^*}{c}\vec{A}\right]\Psi dS
$$

$$
+ \frac{1}{2m^*}\int\delta\Psi^*\left[-i\hbar\nabla - \frac{e^*}{c}\vec{A}\right]^2\Psi dV, \tag{2.54}
$$

where we have used Gauss's theorem to transform the first volume integral into the surface one.

Substituting now (2.54) into (2.53), we obtain

$$
\delta F = \int\left\{a(T - T_c)\Psi + b|\Psi|^2\Psi + \frac{1}{2m^*}\left[-i\hbar\nabla - \frac{e^*}{c}\vec{A}\right]^2\Psi\right\}\delta\Psi^*dV
$$

$$
+ \frac{i\hbar}{2m^*}\oint\delta\Psi^*\left[-i\hbar\nabla - \frac{e^*}{c}\vec{A}\right]\delta\Psi^*dS = 0 \tag{2.55}
$$

For an arbitrary variation $\delta\Psi^*$, we can assume $\delta\Psi^* = 0$ at the surface of the superconductor. As a result, we obtain the first G-L equation

$$
\frac{1}{2m^*}\left[-i\hbar\nabla - \frac{e^*}{c}\vec{A}\right]^2\Psi(\vec{r}) + a(T - T_c)\Psi(\vec{r}) + b|\Psi(\vec{r})|^2\Psi(\vec{r}) = 0 \tag{2.56}
$$

The minimization of (2.52) with respect to $\Psi$ leads to the complex conjugate of Eq.(2.56). If the requirement $\delta\Psi^* = 0$ is satisfied at the surface, we obtain the boundary condition of the G-L equation

$$
\vec{n}\left[-i\hbar\nabla - \frac{e^*}{c}\vec{A}\right]\Psi = 0, \tag{2.57}
$$

where $\vec{n}$ is the unit vector normal to the surface of the superconductor.

The minimization of (2.52) with respect to $\vec{A}$ (using the relation $\vec{H} = curl\vec{A}$) yields

$$
\delta_{\vec{A}}F = \int\left\{\frac{1}{2m^*}\delta_{\vec{A}}\left[\left(-i\hbar\nabla - \frac{e^*}{c}\vec{A}\right)\Psi\left(i\hbar\nabla - \frac{e^*}{c}\vec{A}\right)\Psi^*\right]\right.
$$

$$
\left.+ \frac{curl\vec{A}curl\delta\vec{A}}{4\pi}\right\}dV = \int\left\{\frac{1}{2m^*}\left[-\frac{e^*}{c}\Psi\delta\vec{A}\left(i\hbar\nabla - \frac{e^*}{c}\vec{A}\right)\Psi^*\right.\right.
$$

$$
\left.\left.- \frac{e^*}{c}\Psi^*\delta\vec{A}\left(-i\hbar\nabla - \frac{e^*}{c}\vec{A}\right)\Psi\right] + \frac{curl\vec{A}curl\delta\vec{A}}{4\pi}\right\}dV = 0 \tag{2.58}
$$

We further use the identity $div(\delta\vec{A}curl\vec{A}) = curl\vec{A}curl\delta\vec{A} - \delta\vec{A}curlcurl\vec{A}$ and transform the volume integral of $div(\delta\vec{A}curl\vec{A})$ (by applying the Gauss theorem) into the surface integral which is zero because the magnetic field at the surface of the superconductor is fixed, and therefore, $\delta\vec{A} = 0$. Then, Eq. (2.58) can be written as

$$\delta_{\vec{A}}F = \int \left[ \frac{i\hbar e^*}{2m^*c}(\Psi^*\nabla\Psi - \Psi\nabla\Psi^*) \right.$$
$$\left. + \frac{e^{*2}}{m^*c^2}\vec{A}|\Psi|^2 + \frac{1}{4\pi}curlcurl\vec{A} \right]\delta\vec{A}dV = 0 \qquad (2.59)$$

Then by taking into account Maxwell's equation $curlcurl\vec{A} = curl\vec{H} = (4\pi/c)\vec{j}$, we obtain the second G-L equation from (2.59)

$$\vec{j}(\vec{r}) = -\frac{i\hbar e^*}{2m^*}[\Psi^*(\vec{r})\nabla\Psi(\vec{r}) - \Psi(\vec{r})\nabla\Psi^*(\vec{r})] - \frac{e^{*2}}{m^*c}|\Psi|^2\vec{A}(\vec{r}) \qquad (2.60)$$

Now, let us examine the solutions of the G-L equations. First, consider a simple case, namely, penetration of a weak magnetic field into the superconductor occupying the half-space $x > 0$. An external magnetic field $H$ is applied along the $z$ axis and the vector potential $A$ is oriented along the $y$ axis. Then $H$ depends only on the $x$ coordinate, i.e., $H(x) = dA_y/dx$. One can also consider that $\Psi$ is the function only of $x$. The vanishing of the cross term $i(\vec{A}\vec{\nabla}) = iA_x\nabla_x$ in the first G-L equation (2.56) due to the equality $A_x = 0$ allows us to choose $\Psi$ real. Under these conditions, the second G-L equation can be written as

$$j_y(x) = -\frac{e^{*2}}{m^*c}\Psi^2(x)A_y(x) \qquad (2.61)$$

In order to simplify the G-L equations the new dimensionless variable
$\Psi' = \Psi/\Psi_0$ and parameter $\chi = \lambda_L/\xi$ are usually introduced, where $\lambda_L = (m^*c^2/4\pi e^{*2}|\Psi_0|^2)^{1/2}$, $\xi = (\hbar^2/2m^*|a(T_c - T)|)^{1/2}$. Then the first and second G-L equations in terms of the new variable (where we will omit prime on the wave function) and parameter can be expressed as

$$\xi^2\left[-\nabla_x^2 + \left(\frac{e^*}{\hbar c}\right)^2\vec{A}^2\right]\Psi - \Psi + |\Psi|^2\Psi = 0, \quad \left.\frac{d\Psi}{dx}\right|_S = 0 \qquad (2.62)$$

and

$$\frac{d^2A}{dx^2} = \frac{1}{\lambda_L^2}|\Psi|^2A, \quad \frac{d^2H}{dx^2} = \frac{1}{\lambda_L^2}|\Psi|^2H \qquad (2.63)$$

Here, we have used the relations $curlcurl\vec{A} = (4\pi/c)\vec{j}$ and $\vec{H} = curl\vec{A}$. At $\lambda_L << \xi$, the order parameter $\Psi$ is effected by the magnetic field only over a small distance $\lambda_L$, while it can vary substantially over a much larger distance $\xi$. In this case, the deviation of $\Psi$ from its equilibrium value $\Psi = 1$ deep inside the superconductor is small and the effect of the magnetic field on $\Psi$ is insignificant. In the absence of a magnetic field $(\vec{A} = 0)$, the first G-L equation has the form

$$\xi^2\frac{d^2\Psi}{dx^2} = -\Psi + \Psi^3 \qquad (2.64)$$

For $\chi \ll 1$, we can write $\Psi \simeq 1 + \Psi_1$ and assume $\Psi_1 \ll 1$. Substituting this expression into (2.64) and keeping only linear terms in $\Psi_1$, we obtain

$$\xi^2 \frac{d^2\Psi_1}{dx^2} = 2\Psi_1 \tag{2.65}$$

Since $x \to \infty$, we have $\Psi = 1$ and $\Psi_1 = 0$, the solution of the equation (2.65) is

$$\Psi_1(x) = \Psi_1(0)e^{-\sqrt{2}x/\xi} \tag{2.66}$$

One can see that $\xi$ is the characteristic length scale over which the order parameter varies. This length scale is called the coherent length. At $\chi \ll 1$ the order parameter $\Psi$ is nearly constant and equal to unity in the bulk of the superconductor. Then the solution of (2.63) is

$$H = H(0)e^{-x/\lambda_L} \tag{2.67}$$

When both parameters $\lambda_L$ and $\xi$ near $T_c$ depend on temperature as $(T_c - T)^{-1/2}$, their ratio is called the G-L parameter, and is therefore temperature independent. Finally, using the above expressions for $\lambda_L$ and $\xi$ and (2.51), we obtain

$$\chi = \sqrt{2}\frac{e^*\lambda_L^2 H_c}{\hbar c} \tag{2.68}$$

## 2.6.   Critical Magnetic Fields and Mixed State

The G-L theory allows to take into account the existence of the surface energy (or surface tension) between a normal metal and a superconductor. This theory was further developed by Abrikosov for the limiting case $\chi \gg 1$ [11], who developed the concept of such a surface energy and predicted the existence of type I and type II superconductors. According to the Ginzburg-Landau-Abrikosov theory, the surface energy of the interface between a normal and a SC region, $\sigma_{ns}$, is positive for type I superconductors ($\chi \ll 1$) and negative for those of type II ($\chi \gg 1$). Since the order parameter $\Psi$ and the magnetic field $H$ vary substantially in the vicinity of the interface (Fig. 2.3), the surface energy per unit area of the interface in the type I superconductor is of the order of $\sigma_{ns} \sim \xi H_c^2$. Whereas the surface energy per unit aria of the interface in the type II superconductor is of the order of $\sigma_{ns} \sim -\lambda_L H_c^2$. The exact values of $\sigma_{ns}$ for type I and type II superconductors are $\sigma_{ns} = 1.89\xi H_c^2/8\pi$ and $\sigma_{ns} = -\lambda_L H_c^2/8\pi$, respectively [2, 21]. Clearly, by increasing $\chi$ the surface energy should decrease and at a certain value of $\chi$ the energy $\sigma_{ns}$ becomes zero. A detailed treatment of the surface tension based on the G-L equations (see Ref. [22]) shows that as $\chi \to 1/\sqrt{2}$ the surface energy $\sigma_{ns}$ tends to zero. Hence, it follows that the exact value of $\chi$ separating the type I superconductors with $\sigma_{ns} > 0$ from the type II superconductors with $\sigma_{ns} < 0$ is $\chi = 1/\sqrt{2}$. Type I superconductors are characterized by the single critical magnetic field $H_c$, while type II superconductors are characterized by two lower $H_{c1}$ and upper $H_{c2}$ critical magnetic fields. In a type I superconductor, the nucleation of the SC phase or SC domains and the coexistence of the normal and SC phases at magnetic fields slightly greater than $H_c$ is energetically unfavorable due to the positive surface energy of the interface between these phases. In contrast, the nucleation of the normal phase in type II superconductors at

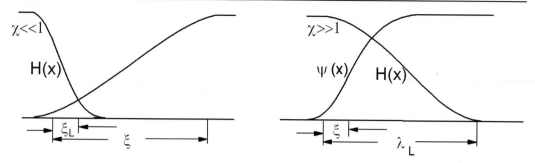

Figure 2.3. Spatial variation of $H$ and $\Psi$ near a normal metal-superconductor interface. The cases $\chi \ll 1$ and $\chi \gg 1$ refer to type-I and type-II superconductors.

$H < H_c$ becomes thermodynamically favorable due to the compensation of the increase of the volume energy by the negative energy of the surface of such a normal phase. These systems are unstable to the formation of multiple SC and normal domains with associated interfaces above some critical field called as the lower critical field $H_{c1}$. By increasing $H$ from $H_{c1}$ to the so-called upper critical field $H_{c2}$ the SC domains gradually decreases and the normal domains increases. At the same time the magnetic field partially penetrates the superconductor but does not destroy the SC state. The SC domains disappear completely at $H > H_{c2}$. Thus, for magnetic fields $H_{c1} < H < H_{c2}$ the SC and normal domains coexist in a type II superconductor and the regime $H_{c1} < H < H_{c2}$ represents a new thermodynamic SC state called the mixed or intermediate state. For magnetic fields which are slightly greater than $H_{c1}$, the magnetic field enters a type II superconductor as an array of quantized flux (or vortex) lines each carrying a flux quantum $\phi_0$ and the distance between two vortex lines is large. In this case the interaction energy between the lines can be neglected. Then the free energy of the superconductor per unit volume is given by

$$F(H) = F_s(0) + n_L \varepsilon - \int \frac{\vec{H}\vec{B}}{4\pi} dV, \tag{2.69}$$

where $\varepsilon$ is the energy of the vortex line given by (2.44), $n_L$ is the number of the vortex lines.

The supercurrent $\vec{j}_s$ inside the contour enclosing the vortex line is zero [11] and $curl\vec{H} = (4\pi/c)\vec{j}_s = 0$ from which it follows that $\vec{H} = const$. Using the Gauss theorem and the relation $\vec{H} = curl\vec{A}$, we carry out the integration in the last term of Eq.(2.69):

$$-\frac{H}{4\pi}\int \vec{B} dV = -\frac{Hn_L}{4\pi}\oint \vec{H} d\vec{s} = -\frac{n_L H}{4\pi}\int \vec{A} d\vec{l} = -\frac{n_L H}{4\pi}v\phi_0 \tag{2.70}$$

At $v = 1$ the condition for the nucleation of the vortex lines is

$$F(H_{c1}) - F_s(0) = \frac{\phi_0}{(4\pi\lambda_L)^2}\ln\frac{\lambda_L}{\xi} - \frac{H_{c1}}{4\pi} = 0, \tag{2.71}$$

where we used (2.44) for the energy of the vortex line. The lower critical magnetic field is then given by

$$H_{c1} = \frac{\phi_0}{4\pi\lambda_L^2}\ln\frac{\lambda_L}{\xi} = \frac{\phi_0}{4\pi\lambda_L^2}\ln\chi \tag{2.72}$$

Assuming $e^* = 2e$ and using the expression for the flux quantum $\phi_0 = \pi\hbar c/e$, we obtain from (2.68)

$$H_c = \frac{\phi_0}{2\sqrt{2}\pi\lambda_L^2}\chi = \frac{\phi_0}{2\sqrt{2}\pi\lambda_L\xi} \tag{2.73}$$

For magnetic fields slightly smaller than $H_{c2}$, the SC order parameter or the germs of the SC phase must be small and non-linear term in (2.52) can be omitted. Then the linearized first G-L equation has the form

$$\frac{1}{2m^*}\left(-i\hbar\nabla - \frac{e^*}{c}\vec{A}\right)^2\Psi = |a(T_c - T)|\Psi \tag{2.74}$$

This equation is the same as the Schrödinger equation for a particle with mass, $m^*$, charge $e^*$, and energy, $|a(T_c - T)|$, in a magnetic field (see Ref. [22]). Now the first and second G-L equations (2.74) and (2.63) for the one-dimensional case ($\vec{H}||z$, $\vec{A}||y$, $\Psi = \Psi(x) << 1$) can be written as

$$-\xi^2\frac{d^2\Psi}{dx^2} + \left[\left(\xi\frac{e^*}{\hbar c}A\right)^2 - 1\right]\Psi = 0 \tag{2.75}$$

and

$$\frac{d^2A}{dx^2} = 0 \tag{2.76}$$

Substituting the solution of Eq.(2.76), $A = Hx$, into Eq.(2.75), we obtain

$$-\frac{\hbar^2}{2m^*}\frac{d^2\Psi}{dx^2} + \frac{(e^*H)^2}{2m^*c^2}x^2\Psi = |a(T_c - T)|\Psi \tag{2.77}$$

Evidently, Eq.(2.77) is the Schrödinger equation of a harmonic oscillator with frequency $\omega = |e^*|H/m^*c$ and energies $\varepsilon_n = \hbar\omega(n+\frac{1}{2})$. The highest magnetic field $H = H_{c2}$ at which SC phase or domains can nucleate in type II superconductors corresponds to the minimum value of $\varepsilon_n$ (i.e., $\varepsilon_0 = \hbar\omega/2 = |a(T_c - T)|$). As a result, we find

$$H_{c2} = \frac{2m^*c|a(T_c - T)|}{\hbar e^*} = \frac{\phi_0}{2\pi\xi^2} = \sqrt{2}\chi H_c \tag{2.78}$$

In 1963, Saint-James and de Gennes showed [35] that the SC phase (i.e., SC domains) can nucleate in a thin surface layer (which has a thickness $\sim \xi$) even under the applied external magnetic field $H > H_{c2}$. Assuming that the magnetic field is parallel to the surface and applying the G-L equation (2.74) with the boundary condition $d\Psi/dx|_S = 0$, they predicted that the surface SC state may exist up to the critical magnetic field $H_{c3} = 1.695H_{c2}$. The exact theoretical estimations of $H_{c3}$ require somewhat tedious numerical calculations. However, other more simple variational methods (see e.g., Refs. [2, 27] for the details) yields quite good results for the critical magnetic field $H_{c3}$, which are in excellent agreement with the exact value of $H_{c3}$.

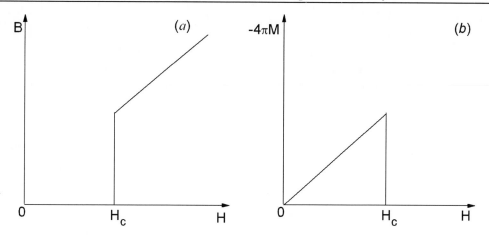

Figure 2.4. (a) magnetic induction $B$ versus magnetic field $H$, and (b) corresponding magnetization $-M$ versus $H$, for a type I superconductor.

## 2.7. Meissner Effect and Type II Superconductivity

We have already mentioned in chapter 1 that superconductors exhibit, for weak magnetic fields, perfect diamagnetism or Meissner effect. According to the Meissner effect, far inside the superconductor the magnetic induction $\vec{B}$ is zero, while outside it $\vec{B} = \vec{H}$. The magnetic induction $\vec{B}$ and the magnetic field $\vec{H}$ are related to each other by the well-known expression $\vec{B} = \vec{H} + 4\pi\vec{M}$, where $\vec{M}$ is the magnetization of the superconductor. As is well known from electrodynamics, the change in the internal energy of a system arising from a small change in the magnetic induction at constant volume of the system is given by

$$dU = T dS + \frac{\vec{H}}{4\pi} d\vec{B}, \tag{2.79}$$

where $S$ is the entropy density. The proper variables of the Helmholtz free energy density $F$ used in chapter 1 (see (1.65)) are the temperature $T$ and the magnetic field $\vec{H}$. Since $F$ is not continuous at the critical magnetic fields, we now use the Gibbs free energy density which is continuous at critical magnetic fields and whose proper variables are $T$ and $\vec{B}$. We know that the Gibbs free energy of a gas is $G = U + PV - TS$, where $P$ and $V$ are the pressure and volume of the gas. Replacing $P$ and $V$ accordingly by $-\vec{H}/4\pi$ and $\vec{B}$ (see Ref. [36]), we obtain the Gibbs free energy of the superconductor

$$G = U - TS - (1/4\pi)\vec{H}\vec{B} = F - (1/4\pi)\vec{H}\vec{B} \tag{2.80}$$

Using (2.79), we can write the differential of the Gibbs free energy in the form

$$dG = -S dT - B\frac{dH}{4\pi} \tag{2.81}$$

As we already know, superconductors are subdivided into type I and type II superconductors. The main difference between type I and type II superconductors is their different

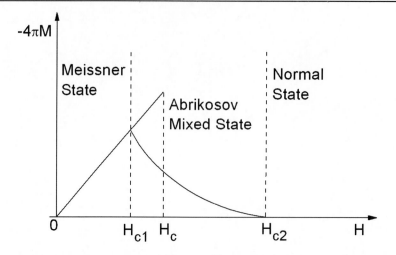

Figure 2.5. The magnetization curves for a type II superconductor.

response to an external magnetic field. Type I superconductors exhibit a complete Meissner effect up to the thermodynamic critical magnetic field $H_c$, above which they become normal metals. When the magnetic field penetrates the surface layer of a type I superconductor, an induced current arises which, according to Lenz's law, generates a magnetic field in the direction opposite to that of the external field. Therefore, at $H < H_c$ the magnetic flux lines is suddenly completely expelled from the interior of the superconductor. When taking into account that $B = 0$ at $H < H_c$ and $B = H$ at $H > H_c$, we carry out the integration of Eq.(2.81) at constant $T$. We then have

$$G(T) = G(T,0) - \frac{1}{4\pi} \int_{H_c}^{H} \vec{B} d\vec{H}$$

$$= G(T,0) - \frac{1}{8\pi}(H^2 - H_c^2) \quad \text{for} \quad H > H_c \qquad (2.82)$$

and

$$G(T,H) = G(T,0) \quad \text{for} \quad H < H_c, \qquad (2.83)$$

from which it follows that $G(T,H)$ is continuous at $H = H_c$. The dependence of the magnetic induction $B$ and the magnetization $-M$ on the magnetic field $H$ is shown in Fig. 2.4.

One can see that in type I superconductors the Gibbs free energy of the normal state is larger than that of the SC state by $(1/8\pi)H_c^2(T)$. The Meissner effect is only characteristic property of type I superconductors with $\chi < 1/\sqrt{2}$. The magnetic responses of type II superconductors with $\chi > 1/\sqrt{2}$ are more complex. The fact is that initially type II superconductors push all the magnetic flux out and display the Meissner effect (i.e., $\vec{B} = 0$ in the interior of the superconductor) at low magnetic fields. However, beginning from a certain value of the field $H = H_{c1}$ called the lower critical field, magnetic flux partially penetrates the superconductor, but the SC state is not destroyed completely. By a further increase in $\vec{H}$, the magnetization $-M$ increases continuously above $H_{c1}$, and becomes zero at a field

$H = H_{c2}$ (Fig. 2.5) called the upper critical magnetic field $H_{c2}$. In the region $H_{c1} < H < H_{c2}$, the magnetic induction $\vec{B} < \vec{H}$ appears inside the superconductor, and the normal and SC phases coexist. This region is called the Abrikosov mixed state [11]. At $H = 0$ ($B = 0$), we have $G_s = F_s$ and $G_n = F_n$. By taking into account that $F_n(T,0) - F_s(T,0) = H_c^2/8\pi$ (see (1.70)) and the Gibbs free energies of the phases are equal at $H = H_{c2}$, we find

$$\int_0^{H_{c2}} M dH = -\frac{H_c^2}{8\pi} \tag{2.84}$$

As can be seen from (2.84), the area under the magnetization curve in Fig. 2.5 depends only on $H_c$ and is equal to $-H_c^2/8\pi$. Thus, the value of $H_c$ can be found from the experimental curve of the magnetization of a type II superconductor. At $H = H_{c2}$, the normal state is restored and the superconductivity is destroyed completely in the bulk of the superconductor. However, in a thin surface layer the superconductivity will exist even at $H > H_{c2}$ (see Fig. 2.6), until $H = H_{c3} = 1.695 H_{c2}$, which is called the third critical field. For magnetic fields $H_{c2} < H < H_{c3}$, the SC layer is retained on the surface of a type II cylindrical superconductor.

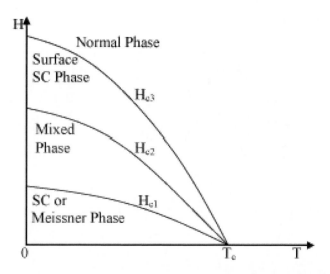

Figure 2.6. Schematic phase diagram for a type II superconductor.

## 2.8.   Critical Current

Another important parameter of superconductors is the critical current $I_c$ which destroys their superconductivity. We now consider the behavior of a SC wire with the radius $r_0$ carrying a current $I$, which creates a magnetic field $H$ around the wire. As soon as the current reaches the value of $I_c$, the magnetic field generated by it at the surface of the SC wire becomes equal to $H_c$ and the surface of a type I superconductor goes to the normal state. In order to find the relation between the critical magnetic field $H_c$ and the critical current $I_c$, we use the Maxwell equation $curl\vec{H} = (4\pi/c)\vec{j}$ and integrate this expression over surface of the circle with radius $r_0$. We then have

$$\int curl\vec{H}d\vec{s} = \frac{4\pi}{c}I(r_0) \tag{2.85}$$

The surface integral in the left-hand side of (2.85) can be converted into a contour integral, with the result

$$\int curl\vec{H}d\vec{s} = \oint \vec{H}d\vec{l} = 2\pi r_0 \cdot H \tag{2.86}$$

According to the Silsbee rule [37], the critical current $I_c$ cannot exceed the current creating the critical magnetic field $H_c$ around the superconductor. Consequently, equating (2.85) with Eq.(2.86), we obtain

$$I_c = \frac{c r_0 H_c}{2} \tag{2.87}$$

When the current $I$ exceeds the critical value $I_c$ the magnetic field $H(r_0)$ created by the current $I > I_c$ at the surface of the wire becomes larger than $H_c$. In this case, the superconductivity in the surface layer is destroyed and a normal layer of thickness $(r_0 - d)$ forms at the surface of the wire (Fig. 2.7).

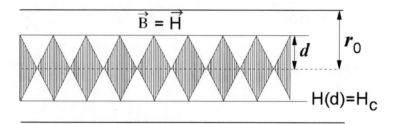

Figure 2.7. The structure of the intermediate state in a type I superconductor with the current $I > I_c$.

Then, all the SC current flows through the core of the wire having the radius $d < r_0$ and the magnetic field $H(d) = 2I/cd$ created by the current at the surface of this core becomes even larger than $H(r_0)$. As a consequence, the radius of the SC core $r$ tends to zero and the normal state may be restored completely in the interior of the wire. By taking into account that $I(r) = j\pi r^2$ and $I(r_0) = j\pi r_0^2$, we obtain for the magnetic field $H(r) = 2I(r)/cr = 2I(r_0)r/cr_0^2 = (r/r_0)H_c < H_c$.

It follows that the core of the SC wire cannot become completely normal and should remain partially SC (shaded regions in Fig. 2.7). Then, at $I > I_c$ the surface layer of the wire ($d < r < r_0$) is normal and its inner region ($0 < r < d$) should be in the intermediate state. The radius of the SC core of a type I superconductor is determined from the equation $H(d) = H_c$. The values of the critical current in a type II superconductor are determined in such a manner. At first, the current flows along the surface of the SC wire (Meissner effect) just like in the case of a type I superconductor. This critical current above which the resistance of a type II superconductor appears is determined from the expression

$$I_{c1} = \frac{cr_0 H_{c1}}{2} \tag{2.88}$$

Taking into account (2.72) and (2.73), we obtain for the lower critical magnetic field

$$H_{c1} = \frac{H_c}{\sqrt{2}\chi} \ln \chi \tag{2.89}$$

As soon as the field created by the surface current exceeds the critical value $H_{c1}$, the vortex rings will nucleate at the surface and vanish in the core of the wire. The formation of such vortices and their motion lead to the appearance of the resistance (see Ref. [27]). In the outer region ($d < r < r_0$) of the SC wire, $\vec{B} < \vec{H}$ and at the inner boundary of the surface layer $H(d) = H_{c1}$. By a further increase in current, the density of vortex rings increases and the SC domains in the interior of the wire decreases. When the current reaches the maximum value $I_{c2}$ and creates the magnetic field $H_{c2}$, the superconductivity is destroyed completely and $B = H$ at all values of the radius of the SC wire. This maximum current is equal to $I_{c2} = cr_0 H_{c2}/2$. We now consider a thin wire carrying a current $I$ and find the value of the critical current by using the G-L theory. Since the wire is thin, we can neglect the energy of the magnetic field created by the current and write the free energy expansion near $T_c$ in the form

$$F_s = F_n + a(T - T_c)|\Psi|^2 + \frac{b}{2}|\Psi|^4 + \frac{m^* v_s^2}{2}|\Psi|^2, \tag{2.90}$$

where the last term describes the kinetic energy of the SC carriers and $v_s$ is the velocity of these carriers.

Minimization of the expression (2.90) with respect to $\Psi$ yields

$$|\Psi|^2 = |\Psi_0|^2 - \frac{m^* v_s^2}{2b} = |\Psi_0|^2 \left[ 1 - \frac{m^* v_s^2}{2a(T_c - T)} \right] \tag{2.91}$$

The current density $I$ is given by

$$I = e^* v_s |\Psi|^2 = e^* |\Psi_0|^2 \left[ 1 - \frac{m^* v_s^2}{2a(T_c - T)} \right] \tag{2.92}$$

One can see that the current $I$ reaches its maximum value $I_m$ at $dI_s/dv_s = 0$. We then identify the value of $I_m$ as the critical current

$$I_c = I_m = e^* |\Psi_0|^2 \frac{2}{3} \left[ \frac{2a(T_c - T)}{3m^*} \right]^{1/2} \tag{2.93}$$

Substituting $|\Psi_0|^2 = m^* c^2/4\pi e^{*2}\lambda_L^2$ and $a(T_c - T) = (e^{*2}/m^* c^2)H_c^2\lambda_L^2$ into Eq.(2.93), we obtain

$$I_c = \frac{cH_c}{3\sqrt{6}\pi\lambda_L} \tag{2.94}$$

## 2.9.   Fluctuation Effects

The G-L theory neglects fluctuation effects and the order parameter $\Psi$ in this theory represents its most probable or equilibrium value at which the free energy $F$ of a system is a minimum. However, all thermodynamic quantities undergo fluctuations and fluctuation effects are expected to be important in a narrow range of temperature near the phase transition temperature. In particular, the SC order parameter (which is also thermodynamic variable) may fluctuate about its equilibrium value and the probability of such a fluctuation is proportional to $\exp(\Delta S_f)$, where $\Delta S_f$ is the change of the entropy given by $\Delta S_f = -W_{\min}/k_B T = -\Delta F/k_B T$ (at constant temperature $T = T_c$ and volume $V$), $W_{\min}$ is the minimum work required for taking out the system from the equilibrium state, which is equal to the changing its free energy $\Delta F$. To describe fluctuations in inhomogeneous superconductors (in which inhomogeneities arise in the presence of fluctuations), we write the G-L free energy density (in the absence of a magnetic field) in the form

$$F = V \left[ a(T - T_c)|\Psi(\vec{r})|^2 + \frac{b}{2}|\Psi(\vec{r})|^4 + \frac{\hbar^2}{2m^*}|\nabla\Psi(\vec{r})|^2 \right] \tag{2.95}$$

We consider the fluctuation effects above $T_c$. In this case $F$ is a minimum when $|\Psi| = 0$, so that $\Delta F = F$ and the fluctuation of the order parameter about the value $|\Psi| = 0$ is $\Delta\Psi = \Psi$. We expand $\Psi(\vec{r})$ in Fourier series:

$$\Psi(\vec{r}) = \sum_{\vec{k}} \Psi_{\vec{k}} \exp[i\vec{k}\vec{r}], \quad \Psi_{-\vec{k}} = \Psi_{\vec{k}}^* \tag{2.96}$$

When the deviation of the order parameter from its equilibrium value is small the fourth order term in Eq.(2.95) can be neglected. Substituting now (2.96) into (2.95) and carrying out the integration over unit volume using the orthogonality of the terms in a Fourier series, we obtain

$$\Delta F = V \sum_{k} \left[ a(T - T_c) + \frac{\hbar^2 k^2}{2m^*} \right] |\Psi_{\vec{k}}|^2 \tag{2.97}$$

The fluctuation probability near $T_c$ is written as

$$\omega_f \sim \exp\left\{ V \sum_{k} \left[ a(T - T_c) + \hbar^2 k^2/2m^* \right] |\Psi_{\vec{k}}|^2/k_B T_c \right\} \tag{2.98}$$

One can see that $\omega_f$ is the product of separate factors with different $\vec{k}$. Therefore, fluctuations of different $\vec{k}$ are statistically independent. Comparing (2.98) with the Gaussion distribution function, we find the mean-square fluctuation of the order parameter with a given $\vec{k}$

$$\langle|\Psi_k|^2\rangle = \frac{k_B T}{2V[a(T - T_c) + \hbar^2 k^2/2m^*]} = \frac{m^*}{V\hbar^2} \frac{k_B T}{[k^2 + 1/\xi^2(T)]} \tag{2.99}$$

It follows that at $T \to T_c$ long wavelength fluctuations with $k \sim 1/\xi(T)$ are rapidly increased. Since the divergence of (2.99) at $k \to 0$ as $T \to T_c$ is unphysical and the G-L theory is not valid for such rapid variations, a cutoff at $k \sim 1/\xi_0$ [2] is required to give a finite value for $|\Psi_k|^2$. Thermal fluctuations of $\Psi$ may lead to the existence of SC effects above $T_c$ because $\langle \Psi^2 \rangle \neq 0$ although $\langle \Psi \rangle = 0$. In particular, theoretical calculations show that both the heat capacity [21, 27] and diamagnetic susceptibility [20] is proportional to $\xi(T)$ and diverges as $(T - T_c)^{-1/2}$ at $T \rightarrow T_c$. The fluctuations of the order parameter for $T > T_c$ also contribute to the conductivity and lead to the fluctuation-enhanced conductivity called as paraconductivity. The fluctuation-induced conductivity $\sigma_f$ depends on the dimensionality $D$ of the system and the magnitude of $\sigma_f$ is given by [2, 27]

$$\sigma_f(T) = \begin{cases} (e^{*2}/128\xi_0)\sqrt{T_c/(T - T_c)} & \text{for a 3D case} \\ (e^{*2}/64\hbar d)[T_c/(T - T_c)] & \text{for a 2D film} \\ (\pi e^{*2}\xi_0/64\hbar S)[T_c/(T - T_c)]^{3/2} & \text{for a thin wire,} \end{cases} \tag{2.100}$$

where $\xi_0 = (\hbar^2/2m^*aT_c)^{1/2}$, $d$ is the thickness of a thin film ($d << \xi$), $S$ is the cross-section of a thin wire ($S << \xi^2$).

Finally, we examine the validity of the G-L theory and the region above $T_c$, where SC effects may arise from the fluctuations. The applicability of the G-L theory is limited by the condition $\langle (\Delta\Psi)^2 \rangle = \langle (\Psi - \Psi_0)^2 \rangle << |\Psi_0|^2$, where $|\Psi_0|^2$ is the equilibrium value of $|\Psi|^2$ below $T_c$. Since the characteristic length for variation of $\Psi$ is $\xi(T)$, the volume with $\Psi \neq 0$ is of the order of $V \sim \xi^3(T)$ and the difference in free energies of normal and SC states is equal to $\Delta F = [a(T - T_c)]^2 V/2b$. When $k = 0$, G-L theory is applicable at $T - T_c >> 2(k_B T_c b)^2 m^{*3}/a\hbar^6$. Whereas at $k^2 << 1/\xi^2$ the validity criterion for this fluctuation theory can be written as

$$\frac{\langle |\Psi_k|^2 \rangle}{|\Psi_0|^2} \approx \frac{k_B T}{[a(T - T_c)]^2 \xi^3} = \frac{k_B T}{4|\Delta F|} << 1, \tag{2.101}$$

from which it follows that the fluctuation-induced SC effects may exist above $T_c$ in the temperature range $T << 4|\Delta F|/k_B = 2N(\varepsilon_F)\Delta_{BCS}^2/k_B$, where $N(\varepsilon_F)$ is the density of state at the Fermi level, $\Delta_{BCS}$ is the BCS energy gap in the excitation spectrum of a superconductor or order parameter, which is comparable in energy to $k_B T_c$ (see chapter 3).

# References

[1] E. A. Lynton, *Superconductivity* (Mir, Moscow, 1971).

[2] M. Tinkam, *Introduction to Superconductivity* (Atomizdat, Moscow, 1980).

[3] D. R. Tilly and J. Tilly, *Superfluidity and Superconductivity* (Adam Hilger, Bristol, 1990).

[4] H. Kamerlingh Onnes, *Leiden Commun.* 120b, 122b, 124c (1911).

[5] P. L. Kapitza, *Nature* 141, 74 (1938).

[6] L. D. Landau, *J. Phys. (USSR)* 5, 71 (1941); 11, 91 (1947).

[7] C. J. Garter and H. B. G. Casimir, *Physica* 1, 306 (1934); *Phys. Z.* 35, 963 (1934); *Z. Techn. Phys.* 15, 539 (1939).

[8] F. London and H. London, *Proc. Roy. Soc.* A149, 71 (1935); *Physica* 2, 341 (1935).

[9] V. L. Ginzburg, and L. D. Landau, *Zh. Eksp. Theor. Fiz.* 20, 1064 (1950).

[10] A. B. Pippard, *Proc. Roy. Soc.* A203, 210 (1950); A216, 547 (1953).

[11] A. A. Abrikosov, *Zh. Eksp. Theor. Fiz.* 32, 1442 (1957).

[12] D. Saint-James and P. G. De Gennes, *Phys. Lett.* 7, 306 (1963).

[13] V. Z. Kresin and S. A. Wolf, *Fundamentals of Superconductivity* (Plenum Press, New York, 1990).

[14] S. Dzhumanov and P. K. Khabibullaev, *Pramana J. Phys.* 45, 385 (1995).

[15] S. Dzhumanov, A. A. Baratov and S. Abboudy, *Phys. Rev.* B54, 13121 (1996-II).

[16] R. K. Pathria, *Statistical Mechanics*. 2nd ed. (Butterworth-Heinemann, Oxford, 1996).

[17] L. D. Landau, *Zh. Eksp. Theor. Fiz.* 14, 112 (1944).

[18] C. Kittel, *Introduction to Solid State Physics* (Nauka, Moscow, 1978).

[19] De Gennes, *Superconductivity of Metals and Alloys* (Mir, Moscow, 1968).

[20] V. V. Schmidt, *The Physics of Superconductors. Introduction to Fundamentals and Applications* (Springer-Verlag, Berlin, Heidelberg, 1997).

[21] J. B. Ketterson and S. N. Song, *Superconductivity*(Cambridge Universirty Press, Campridge, 1999).

[22] L. D. Landau, E. M. Lifshitz and L. P. Pitaevskii,*Statistical Physics. Part 2. Theory of Condensed State* (Nauka, Moscow, 1978).

[23] F. London, *Superfluids*. V. 1 (John Wiley and Sons, New York, 1950).

[24] J. Bardeen, L. N. Cooper and J. R. Schrieffer, *Phys. Rev.* 157, 108 (1957).

[25] B. S. Deaver and W. M. Fairbank, *Phys. Rev. Lett.* 7, 43 (1961).

[26] R. Doll and M. Näbauer, *Phys. Rev. Lett.* 7, 51 (1961).

[27] A. A. Abrikosov, *Fundamentals of the Theory of Metals* (Nauka, Moscow, 1987).

[28] B. D. Josephson, *Phys. Lett.* 1, 251 (1962).

[29] R. P. Feynman, *Lectures on Physics*, Vol. 3 (Addison-Wisley, New York, 1965) chapter 21.

[30] S. Dzhumanov and P. K. Khabibullaev, *Izv. Akad. Nauk Uzb. SSR. Ser. Fiz. Mat. Nauk.* 1, 47 (1990).

[31] S. Dzhumanov, P. J. Baimatov, and P. K. Khabibullaev, *Uzb. Zh. Phys.* 6, 24 (1992).

[32] L. D. Landau, *Zh. Eksp. Teor. Fiz.* 7, 19 (1937).

[33] L. D.Landau and E. M. Lifshits, *Statical Physics*. Part I (Nauka, Moscow, 1976).

[34] I. N. Bronstein and K. A. Semendyaev, *Handbook of Mathematics* (Nauka, Moscow, 1981).

[35] D. Saint-James and P. G. de Gennes, *Phys. Lett.* 7, 306 (1963).

[36] Yu. B. Rumer and M. Sh. Rivkin, *Thermodynamics, Statistical Physics and Kinetics* (Nauka, Moscow, 1977).

[37] F. B. Silsbee, *J. Wash. Acad. Sci.* 6, 597 (1916).

# Chapter 3

# Microscopic Theory of Conventional Superconductivity

## 3.1. Introduction

As is clear from the chapter 2, the phenomenological theory of superconductivity developed prior to the microscopic one was independent of the mechanisms responsible for superconductivity in types I and II superconductors, and has been very useful in the study of a whole class of phenomena related to SC phase transitions in these systems. Nevertheless, this theory has limitations because it does not explain the microscopic origins of superconductivity (i.e., SC order parameters and entities). For a long time after the discovery of superconductivity, the nature of this phenomenon was not explained at the microscopic level. The first important step in understanding the microscopic mechanism of superconductivity in conventional metals was made by Cooper in 1956 [1], who put forward the idea of an instability of the normal ground state of an electron gas with respect to the formation of bound electron pairs. These so-called Cooper pairs are bound by an electron-phonon interaction. In 1957 Bardeen, Cooper, and Schrieffer (BCS) [2] produced their famous pairing theory of superconductivity, which was based on the idea of Cooper-pair formation. The BCS theory explains many experimental observations (such as, for example, the existence of an energy gap in the excitation spectrum, the isotope effect, the Meissner effect, a second-order phase transition at a temperature $T_c$) in conventional superconductors and deepens our understanding of the phenomenological theory by providing the framework for calculating the basic parameters of this theory (such as $T_c$, and specific heat jump at $T_c$, the SC order parameter, the coherence parameter $\xi$, the London penetration depth $\lambda_L$ and the critical magnetic field $H_c$). In particular, in 1959 Gor'kov showed [3] that the G-L theory can be derived from the BCS theory and in the reformulated G-L theory the charge and mass of a SC carrier emerge naturally as $e^* = 2e$ and $m^* = 2m$. In this chapter, we present the main results of BCS pairing theory with the use of a technique called second quantization.

## 3.2. Landau Fermi-Liquid Theory

Up to now we have treated the free electron model of a metal, which describes the behavior of the one electron in the averaged field of the lattice and other electrons (see chapter 1). However, in metals the interactions between the electrons in a degenerate electron gas are expected to be important and significantly change the properties of the system. We now consider the system of interacting electrons obeying Fermi statistics. The behavior of such a system in the low-temperature region can be understood in terms of the Landau theory of a Fermi liquid [4, 5, 6] (for comprehensive discussions, see, e.g., the review article by Abrikosov and Khalatnikov [7] and the book by Pines and Nozieres [8]) proposed for understanding the behavior of liquid $^3He$ well below the Fermi temperature $T_F$ given by $\varepsilon_F/k_B$ [9] (where $\varepsilon_F$ is the Fermi energy). Actually, this theory is applicable to the electron gas in metals when the energy spectrum of electrons in a crystal lattice does not differ from the energy spectrum of a Fermi liquid. It is important to note that a liquid consisting of fermions may not necessarily possess a spectrum of the Fermi type since the spectrum of a degenerate Fermi gas depends critically on the strength of the interelectron interactions. When the interactions between electrons are switched on, two things can happen: (i) Interactions between the electrons are slowly (adiabatically) switched on and weak enough. In this case, the ground state of the system is reformed by shifting the energy levels, but the character of the energy spectrum does not change, i.e., one-to-one correspondence between the states of the system with interaction and the system without interaction is retained. This is first and basic postulate of Landau's Fermi liquid theory. The properties of the interacting Fermi system may then be calculated by some form of perturbation approach. (ii) Interelectron interactions are such that they tend to bind electrons into pairs and lead to the radical change of the ground state and energy spectrum of the interacting system. This situation occurs when the interaction between electrons are attractive, as shown in the BCS theory [2] and bipolaron theory [10, 11, 12, 13, 14, 15]. In the present case, the perturbation approach is not applicable and the one-to-one correspondence between the energy spectra of the interacting and non-interacting Fermi systems does not exist. For instance, the BCS type energy spectrum of the interacting Fermi gas is quite different from the energy spectrum of the non-interacting Fermi gas and the Landau Fermi-liquid. In addition, a system consisting of composite bosons, such as tightly-bound Cooper pairs, is expected to have a Bose type spectrum [16, 17, 18]. In this section, we discuss the main results of the Landau theory of a Fermi liquid which corresponds to the previously mentioned situation (i). According to the first postulate of Landau's Fermi liquid theory, the Fermi type spectrum of an electron liquid is constructed as an analogy to the spectrum of a non-interacting Fermi gas. Obviously, the state of a Fermi liquid is then completely characterized by the distribution function $n(\vec{p})$ of the corresponding non-interacting Fermi gas [19]

$$n(\vec{p}) = \{\exp[(\varepsilon(\vec{p}) - \mu)/k_B T] + 1\}^{-1}, \qquad (3.1)$$

where $\varepsilon(\vec{p}) = p^2/2m$ is the energy of Fermi particles with momentum $\vec{p}$ and mass $m$, $\mu$ is the chemical potential or Fermi energy $\varepsilon_F = \mu$. In the ground state of the non-interacting Fermi gas, all single particle states with momentum $\vec{p}$ less than the Fermi momentum $p_F = \hbar k_F$ are occupied ($n(\vec{p}) = 1$) and all other states with $p > p_F$ are empty ($n(p) = 0$). At low temperatures, $T << T_F$ the excitations of a Fermi liquid correspond to the particle (with energy $\varepsilon > \varepsilon_F$) and hole (with $\varepsilon < \varepsilon_F$) excitations (referred to as "quasiparticles") whose number coincides with the number of particles in the liquid and which also obey Fermi statistics. In metals the quasiparticles represent the electrons interacting with other quasiarticles and therefore, clothed with the cloud of electron-hole pairs. They have the charge $\pm e$, spin $s = \pm 1/2$ and an effective mass $m^* > m$. Landau's second postulate is that the energy of a quasiparticle is a function of the momentum, $\vec{p}$ and the energy of the system is a functional of the distribution function $n(p)$. We are now in a position to write down an expression for the energy spectrum $\varepsilon(\vec{p})$ of the quasiparticles near the Fermi surface. These quasiparticles have energies in an energy interval of the order of $k_B T << \varepsilon_F$, so that at low temperatures $\varepsilon(\vec{p}) \simeq \varepsilon_F$. We can, therefore, write

$$\varepsilon(\vec{p}) = \varepsilon_F + \left\{ \frac{\partial \varepsilon}{\partial \vec{p}} \right\}_{p=p_F} (p - p_F) + \cdots = \varepsilon_F + v_F(p - p_F), \tag{3.2}$$

where $v_F$ is the velocity of the quasiparticles at the Fermi surface. The energy of a quasiparticle, $\varepsilon_\sigma(\vec{p})$ (where $\sigma$ is a spin coordinate), is defined as the amount of energy by which the total energy $E$ of the system increases when one quasiparticle is added to the unoccupied state $|p\sigma>$, or

$$\delta E = \sum_{p\sigma} \varepsilon_\sigma(\vec{p}) \delta n_{\sigma\sigma}(\vec{p}), \tag{3.3}$$

where $\delta n_{\sigma\sigma}$ is the corresponding change in the distribution function.

In a system of interacting quasiparticles, $\varepsilon_\sigma(\vec{p})$ depends on the state of all other quasiparticles and the change in the quasipartical energy as a function of a change of the quasiparticle distribution $\delta n(\vec{p})$ in zero magnetic field is given by

$$\delta \varepsilon(\vec{p}) = \sum_{\vec{p}'} f(\vec{p}, \vec{p}') \delta n(\vec{p}'), \tag{3.4}$$

where the spin index is omitted. The interaction of quasiparticles with the ground state of the system is taken care of by $m^*$. Then we may write the total energy of the interacting Fermi system in the form

$$\delta E = \sum_{\vec{p}\sigma} \varepsilon_\sigma(\vec{p}) \delta n_\sigma(\vec{p}) + \frac{1}{2} \sum_{\vec{p}\sigma;\vec{p}'\sigma'} f_{\sigma\sigma'}(\vec{p}, \vec{p}') \delta n_\sigma(\vec{p}) \delta n_{\sigma'}(\vec{p}'), \tag{3.5}$$

where $f_{\sigma\sigma'}(\vec{p}, \vec{p}')$ is the function of the Fermi liquid interaction introduced by Landau.

The function $f$ being a second functional derivative of $E$, plays an important role in the theory of the Fermi liquid. This Landau interaction function has the form [19, 20]

$$f_{\sigma\sigma'}(\vec{p}, \vec{p}') = f_1(\vec{p}, \vec{p}') + f_2(\vec{p}, \vec{p}') \vec{\sigma}\vec{\sigma}', \tag{3.6}$$

where $\vec{\sigma}$ and $\vec{\sigma}'$ are the Pauli matrices, $f_1(\vec{p}, \vec{p}')$ and $f_2(\vec{p}, \vec{p}')$ are the functions of the direct and exchange interaction, respectively. Since we are concerned only with the values of $\vec{p}$ and $\vec{p}'$ lying near the Fermi surface, $p \simeq p' \simeq p_F$. Hence, $f_1(\vec{p}, \vec{p}')$ and $f_2(\vec{p}, \vec{p}')$ are the functions only of the angle $\theta$ between $\vec{p}$ and $\vec{p}'$, so that Eq. (3.6) becomes [7]

$$f_{\sigma\sigma'}(\vec{p}, \vec{p}') = f_1(\theta) + f_2(\theta) \vec{\sigma}\vec{\sigma}' \tag{3.7}$$

It is convenient to introduce two dimensionless functions $F$ and $G$ defined as $F(\theta) = D(\varepsilon_F)f_1(\theta)$ and $G(\theta) = D(\varepsilon_F)f_2(\theta)$, where $D(\varepsilon_F) = 2g(\varepsilon_F)$(see chapter 1) is the density of states at the Fermi level and the factor 2 arises from the spin degeneracy. Further, one can expand these functions in Legendre polynomials

$$F = \sum_l (2l+1)F_l P_l(\cos\theta), \quad G(\theta) = \sum_l (2l+1)G_l P_l(\cos\theta) \tag{3.8}$$

For many cases, it is sufficient to keep the terms $l = 0$ and 1 only. The density of states is given by the usual formula with replacing $m$ by $m^*$:

$$D(\varepsilon_F) = m^* p_F / \pi^2 \hbar^3 \tag{3.9}$$

Then the specific heat is

$$C_v = (m^* p_F / 3\hbar^2)k_B^2 T \tag{3.10}$$

from which it follows that the measurements of $C_v$ determine $m^*$. The effective mass $m^*$ is directly related to the Landau parameter $F_1$ and the important relationship between $m$ and $m^*$ (or $F_1$) can be found by using the principles of the Galilean transformation (see, e.g., Refs. [8, 19, 20, 21]). Here, we use the method of the derivation of such a relationship discussed in [20] and present the revised version of this derivation procedure. We consider a Fermi liquid in equilibrium and at rest, and increase the momentum of each quasiparticles (which have an effective mass $m^*$) by an amount $\delta\vec{p}$. This effect leads to the motion of the whole system with a velocity $\delta\vec{p}/m^*$. According to the principles of the Galilean transformation, the energy of each quasiparticle will be increased by

$$\delta\varepsilon(\vec{p}) = \vec{p}\frac{\delta\vec{p}}{m^*}, \tag{3.11}$$

where the spin index is omitted in the absence of a magnetic field. On the other hand, using Eqs. (3.2) and (3.4) the change in the quasiparticle energy due to the increase of $\vec{p}$ by $\delta\vec{p}$ and due to the interaction of the quasiparticales is given by

$$\delta\varepsilon(\vec{p}) = (\partial\varepsilon(\vec{p})/\partial\vec{p})\delta\vec{p} + \sum_{\vec{p}'} f(\vec{p}, \vec{p}')\delta n(\vec{p}') \tag{3.12}$$

Combining (3.11) and (3.12) and replacing the sum by an integral, we have

$$\frac{\vec{p}}{m^*}\delta\vec{p} = \left\{\frac{\partial\varepsilon}{\partial p}\right\}\frac{\vec{p}}{p}\delta\vec{p} + \int f(\vec{p}, \vec{p}')\delta n(\vec{p}')d\tau', \tag{3.13}$$

where $d\tau' = 2(p')^2 dp' d\Omega/(2\pi\hbar)^3$, $\Omega$ is an element of solid angle.

For any degenerate Fermi gas, the function $\partial n/\partial p$ has a large value near the Fermi surface only and behaves as a delta function. Therefore, we can write the change in the distribution function resulting from the change in $\vec{p}$ as

$$\delta n(\vec{p}') = \frac{\partial n(\vec{p}')}{\delta\vec{p}'}\partial\vec{p}' = -\frac{\vec{p}'}{p'}\delta\vec{p}\delta(p' - p_F) \tag{3.14}$$

We can now substitute (3.14) into (3.13) and carry out the integration. Taking into account that the main contributions to the integral come from the values of $p \simeq p' \simeq p_F$, as before we may write $f(\vec{p}, \vec{p'}) = f(\theta)$. After the substitution of $v_F = \partial \varepsilon / \partial p = p_F/m$ into (3.13) and the integration with respect to $dp'$, we obtain

$$\frac{1}{m} = \frac{1}{m^*} + \frac{2p_F}{(2\pi\hbar)^3} \int f(\theta) \cos\theta d\Omega \tag{3.15}$$

We note that the derivation procedure of the relationship between $m^*$ and $m$ presented in [20] gives the negative and not positive second term on the right of Eq. (3.15). Expanding $f(\theta)$ in Legendre polynomials (see (3.8)) and taking into account that

$$\int_0^\pi \sin\theta \cos\theta P_l(\cos\theta) = 0 \quad \text{for} \quad l \neq 1$$

and

$$\int_0^\pi \sin\theta \cos\theta P_1(\cos\theta) = 2/3,$$

we find

$$m^*/m = [1 + (F_1/3)] \tag{3.16}$$

The transport properties of the degenerate Fermi system are determined by the distribution of those quasiparticles lying in the energy range $\Delta\varepsilon \sim k_B T$ close to the Fermi surface. The parameter $m^*$ is also related to the transport coefficients. In particular, the conductivity of the degenerate electron gas in pure metals at $T \ll T_F$ may be written as $\sigma = n_e e^2 \tau / m^*$, where $n_e$ and $\tau$ the density and relaxation time of conduction electrons, respectively. The relaxation of $\delta n(\vec{p})$ to its equilibrium value occurs as the result of quasiparticle-quasiparticle scattering and one can show that the scattering probability of quasiparticles is proportional to $(k_B T)^2$ and $\tau \sim T^{-2}$ (see Refs. [9, 21]). However, even in the low temperature region, the temperature dependence of the relaxation time in metals containing impurities and defects is determined by the scattering of electrons at impurities and acoustic phonons. The magnetic susceptibility $\chi_L$ of a Fermi liquid, like the specific heat, depends on the density of states at the Fermi surface or on $m^*/m$. Moreover, it is related to the other Landau parameter $G_0$. The expression for $\chi_L$ has the form [20, 22]

$$\frac{\chi_L}{\chi_g} = \frac{m^*}{m}[1 + G_0/4]^{-1}, \tag{3.17}$$

where $\chi_g$ is the magnetic susceptibility of a Fermi gas. It follows from Eq. (3.17) that when $G_0 < 0$ the exchange interaction enhances the spin paramagnetism and the ground state of the Fermi liquid would be ferromagnetic if $G_0/4 \leq -1$. This Landau Fermi liquid theory is well applicable to the liquid $^3He$ in the low temperature region (where $k_B T \gg \hbar/\tau$) and it may be also applicable to the heavy-fermion systems [23, 24]. In particular, experimental results show [9, 20, 25] that for liquid $^3He$, $m^*/m = 2.8$, $F_1 \simeq 5.4$, $\tau$ is proportional to $T^{-2}$ in the temperature range 3-40K and $G_0$ is indeed negative (i.e., $G_0/4 \simeq -0.7$).

## 3.3.  Electron-Phonon Interaction in Metals

One of the key fundamental problems in condensed matter physics is the interaction between charge carriers (electrons and holes) and lattice vibrations (or phonons). The electron-phonon interaction is responsible for many physical processes in solids, such as the scattering of electrons (hole) by phonons (this process determines the temperature dependence of the resistivity and other kinetic coefficients in solids), the polaron formation (a carrier is dressed with a cloud of virtual phonons just like it dressed with a cloud of electron-hole excitations in a Fermi liquid and the polaron is the quasiparticle consisting of the carrier and the induced lattice distortion, which moves as an entity in the crystal), the phonon-mediated pairing of carriers, which plays an important role in superconductivity, and the ultrasonic attenuation in solids. In metal and covalent semiconductors, the electron-phonon interaction is usually considered as a small perturbation for the energy of carriers. In these systems, the carriers interact with the longitudinal-acoustic phonons and the electron-phonon interaction can be described by means of deformation potential introduced by Bardeen and Shockly [26]. In undistorted cubic crystal, the electron energy band is assumed to have the spherical form described (in the effective mass approximation) by the expression

$$\varepsilon(\vec{k}) = \hbar^2 \vec{k}^2 / 2m, \tag{3.18}$$

where $m$ is the effective band mass of a carrier.

We now consider the interacting carrier-crystal lattice system. In the presence of a carrier, the lattice will be distorted and the polarization field of the lattice creates a potential well for the carrier. The attraction of the carrier to the distorted lattice reduces its energy. At small lattice distortions characterized by the deformation tensor $\Delta(\vec{r})$ (in the continuum approximation), the energy of the carrier interacting with acoustic phonons can be written as [27]

$$\varepsilon(\vec{k}, \Delta(\vec{r})) \simeq \varepsilon(\vec{k}) - E_d \Delta(\vec{r}), \tag{3.19}$$

where $E_d$ is the constant of deformation potential, $\Delta(\vec{r})$ is the relative change of the volume, $\Omega$.

One can show that the parameter $E_d$ is given by [27]

$$E_d = \frac{2}{3} \varepsilon_F \tag{3.20}$$

The potential energy of a carrier in a deformable isotropic crystal lattice is

$$V_d(\vec{r}) = -E_d \Delta(\vec{r}) = -E_d \, div U(\vec{r}), \tag{3.21}$$

where $U(\vec{r})$ is the displacement vector of the point $\vec{r}$ in the crystal.

The displacement vector $U(\vec{r})$ of an atom from the lattice site $\vec{n}$ in the second quantization representation is defined as

$$U(\vec{n}) = \sum_{s,\vec{q}} \left( \frac{\hbar}{2MN\omega_s(\vec{q})} \right)^{1/2} \vec{e}_s(\vec{q})(b_{\vec{q}s} + b_{-\vec{q},s}) e^{i\vec{q}\vec{n}}, \tag{3.22}$$

where $\omega_s(\vec{q}) = |\vec{q}|v_s$ is the longitudinal acoustic phonon frequency for the branch $s$, $b^+_{\vec{q}s}(b_{\vec{q}s})$ is the creation (annihilation) operator for a phonon with wave vector $\vec{q}$ and polarization $s$, $\vec{e}_s(\vec{q}) = \vec{e}_s(-\vec{q})$ is the unit polarization vector of phonons, $M$ is the mass of atoms of unit cell, $N$ is the number of unit cells in the crystal, $v_s$ is the acoustic phonon velocity along the polarization direction $s$. Substituting (3.22) into (3.21), we obtain

$$V_d(\vec{r}) = i\sum_{\vec{q}} (\hbar/2MN\omega_l(\vec{q}))^{1/2} |\vec{q}|(b_{\vec{q}l} - b^+_{-\vec{q}l})e^{i\vec{q}\vec{r}}, \tag{3.23}$$

where the index $l$ characterizes the longitudinal branch of acoustic vibrations (further on, we shall omit this index). We now introduce the operator functions

$$\Psi(\vec{r}) = \sum_{\vec{k}} c_{\vec{k}}\varphi_{\vec{k}}(\vec{r}), \quad \Psi^*(\vec{r}) = \sum_{\vec{k}} c^+_{\vec{k}}\varphi^*_{\vec{k}}(\vec{r}), \tag{3.24}$$

where $\varphi_{\vec{k}}(\vec{r}) = (1/\sqrt{V})\exp(i\vec{k}\vec{r})$ is the single-particle wave function, $c^+_{\vec{k}}(c_{\vec{k}})$ is the creation (annihilation) operator for a carrier with wave vector $\vec{k}$. Then the Hamiltonian operator of the electron-acoustic phonon interaction has the form

$$\begin{aligned} H_{e-L} &= \int \Psi^*(\vec{r})V_d\Psi(\vec{r})d^3r \\ &= i\sum_{\vec{k},\vec{q}} \left(\frac{\hbar}{2MN\omega_l(\vec{q})}\right)^{1/2} |\vec{q}|c^+_{\vec{k}+\vec{q}}c_{\vec{k}}(b_{\vec{q}} - b^+_{-\vec{q}}), \end{aligned} \tag{3.25}$$

where we used the relation (for the normal scattering)

$$\sum_q \exp[i(\vec{k}' - \vec{k} + \vec{q})\vec{r}] = \delta_{\vec{k}'-\vec{k},\vec{q}} \tag{3.26}$$

The terms in (3.25) characterize the scattering processes of electrons by phonons and the corresponding diagrams are shown in Fig. 3.1.

Figure 3.1. Feynman diagrams corresponding to the phonon emission and absorption by the electron.

The total Hamiltonian of the interacting electron-phonon system consists of an electronic part $H_e$, a lattice part $H_L$ and the interaction part:

$$H = H_e + H_L + H_{e-L}, \tag{3.27}$$

where

$$H_e = \sum_{\vec{k}} \varepsilon(\vec{k}) c_{\vec{k}}^+ c_{\vec{k}},$$

$$H_L = \sum_{\vec{q}} \hbar\omega(\vec{q}) \left(b_{\vec{q}}^+ b_{\vec{q}} + \frac{1}{2}\right).$$

We consider an electron in the conduction band of the metal and the change of the electronic energy and mass at the weak electron-phonon interaction. The stationary state of the interacting electron-phonon system in a first approximation of the perturbation theory is described by the wave function [27]

$$\Psi_{\vec{k}0} = |\vec{k},0\rangle - \sum_{\vec{k}',\vec{q}} \frac{\langle\vec{k}',\vec{q}|H_{e-L}|\vec{k},0\rangle}{D(\vec{k},\vec{q})} |\vec{k}',\vec{q}\rangle, \tag{3.28}$$

where $|\vec{k},0\rangle$ and $|\vec{k}',\vec{q}\rangle$ are the states of the electron with wave vector $\vec{k}$ (without phonon) and $\vec{k}' = \vec{k} - \vec{q}$ (with phonon $|\vec{q}\rangle$), respectively, $D(\vec{k},\vec{q}) = \varepsilon(\vec{k}-\vec{q}) + \hbar\omega(\vec{q}) - \varepsilon(\vec{k}) = (\hbar^2/2m)[\vec{q}(\vec{q}+\vec{Q}_a) - 2\vec{k}\vec{q}]$, $\vec{Q}_a = 2mv_s\vec{q}/\hbar|\vec{q}|$, $\varepsilon(\vec{k})$ is the unperturbed energy of the electron. Then the energy of the electron in the second-order perturbation theory is given by [27]

$$E(\vec{k}) = \varepsilon(\vec{k}) - \sum_{\vec{q}} \frac{|\langle\vec{k}',\vec{q}|H_{e-L}|\vec{k},0\rangle|^2}{D(\vec{k},\vec{q})} \tag{3.29}$$

where $\langle\vec{k}',\vec{q}|H_{e-L}|\vec{k},0\rangle = -iE_d(\hbar|\vec{q}|/2MNv_s)^{1/2}\delta_{\vec{k}',\vec{k}-\vec{q}}$.

By expanding $D^{-1}(\vec{k},\vec{q})$ in powers of $k \cdot \cos\theta/(q+Q_a)$ (where $\theta$ is the angle between $\vec{k}$ and $\vec{q}$) at $k \ll Q_a$ [27] and replacing the summation over $\vec{q}$ in a standard way by an integral over $\vec{q}$ according to the rule

$$\sum_q \cdots = \frac{\Omega N}{(2\pi)^2} \int_{-1}^{1} d(\cos\theta) \int_0^{q_m} \cdots q^2 dq, \tag{3.30}$$

and then performing the integrals, we obtain

$$E(\vec{k}) = \left[\frac{\hbar^2}{2m} - B\right]\vec{k}^2 - A, \tag{3.31}$$

where

$$A = \zeta\left[\frac{y^2}{2} - y + \ln(y+1)\right],$$

$$B = \frac{4\zeta}{3Q_a^2}\left[\frac{2}{y+1} - \frac{1}{2(y+1)^2} - \frac{3}{2} + \ln(y+1)\right],$$

$\zeta = \left(\frac{mE_d}{\pi\hbar}\right)^2 \frac{v_0 Q_a}{M}$, $Q_a = 2mv_s/\hbar$, $y = q_m/Q_a$, $q_m \approx \pi/a_0$, $a_0$ is the lattice constant, $v_0$ is the volume of unit cell. Here, some mistakes in the expression for $B$ presented in [27] are corrected. Thus, the weak electron-phonon interaction in metals leads to lowering the energy levels of conduction electrons by quantity $A$ and to increasing the effective mass of the electron, which is related to the effective band mass as

$$m^* = m/(1-\lambda), \qquad (3.32)$$

where $\lambda = 2mB/\hbar^2$.

We evaluate the values of $\zeta$, $A$, $B$ and $\lambda$ for metals. In the case of Pb, we take $\varepsilon_F = 9.37eV$ [28], $m \simeq 1.325 \times 10^{-27}g$, $a_0 = 4.94\text{Å}$ [29], $M/v_0 = 11.59g/cm^3$, $v_s \simeq 2.2 \times 10^5 cm/s$, $E_d = (2/3)\varepsilon_F = 6.25eV$, $Q_a = 5.53 \times 10^5 cm^{-1}$, $y = \pi/a_0 Q_a \simeq 115$. Then the estimated values of $\zeta$, $A$, $B$ and $\lambda$ are $4.77 \times 10^{-7}eV$, $3.1 \times 10^{-3}eV$, $6.8 \times 10^{-18}eV \cdot cm^2$ and $2.6 \times 10^{-2}$, respectively. It follows that the electron-phonon interaction in metals is weak enough and the charge carriers are quasifree electrons with $m^* \approx m$. Nevertheless, such a weak electron-phonon interaction plays an important role in the pairing of electrons in metals. In polar materials the electron-phonon interactions are strong enough and extremely important in the self-trapping and pairing of carriers (see chapter 4).

## 3.4. Cooper Pairing

In 1956, Cooper showed [1] that in metals the ground state of an electron gas with an arbitrarily small attraction between electrons is unstable with respect to the formation of the bound state of electron pairs. These pairs are called Cooper pairs and bound by an electron-phonon interaction. In the Cooper model, two electrons above the Fermi sea interact with each other via the potential $V(r_1 - r_2)$ independent of their spins, and the presence of $N-2$ other electrons, which occupy all the states below the Fermi level $(\vec{k} < \vec{k}_F, \varepsilon < \varepsilon_F)$. In addition, in the ground state two pairing electrons should have opposite momenta $(\vec{k}$ and $-\vec{k})$ and spins $(\uparrow, \downarrow)$, so that Cooper pairs are formed with zero orbital angular momentum $l = 0$ ($s$-wave pairing) and center-of-mass momentum $\hbar\vec{K} = 0$. The Schrödinger equation for two interacting electrons has the form

$$-\frac{\hbar^2}{2m}(\nabla_1^2 + \nabla_2^2)\Psi(\vec{r}_1, \vec{r}_2) + V(r_1 - r_2)\Psi(\vec{r}_1, \vec{r}_2) = (E + 2\varepsilon_F)\Psi(\vec{r}_1, \vec{r}_2), \qquad (3.33)$$

where $\Psi(\vec{r}_1, \vec{r}_2)$ is the two-electron wave function, $E$ is the energy of an electron pair measured relative to the energy of two unpaired electrons, i.e., twice the Fermi energy $\varepsilon_F$.

Defining the center of mass coordinate $\vec{R} = \frac{1}{2}(\vec{r}_1 + \vec{r}_2)$ and relative coordinate $\vec{r} = \vec{r}_1 - \vec{r}_2$, we can take the wave function $\Psi(\vec{r}_1, \vec{r}_2)$ in the form of a product of wave functions $\Phi(\vec{R})$ and $\psi(\vec{r})$:

$$\Psi(\vec{R}, \vec{r}) = \Phi(\vec{R})\psi(\vec{r}), \qquad (3.34)$$

where $\Phi(\vec{R})$ is simply a plane wave

$$\Phi(\vec{R}) = \exp(i\vec{K}\vec{R}), \qquad (3.35)$$

and the center of mass of the electron pair is assumed to be at rest. Then the Schrödinger equation becomes

$$\left[-2\frac{\hbar^2}{2m}\nabla_{\vec{r}}^2 + V(\vec{r})\right]\Psi(\vec{r}) = (E + 2\varepsilon_F)\psi(\vec{r}) \qquad (3.36)$$

We now expand $\psi(\vec{r})$ in a Fourier series

$$\psi(\vec{r}) = \frac{1}{\sqrt{\Omega}} \sum_{\vec{k}} a_{\vec{k}} \exp(i\vec{k}\vec{r}) \tag{3.37}$$

Substituting (3.37) into (3.36) and multiplying both sides of this equation by $\frac{1}{\sqrt{\Omega}} \exp(-i\vec{k}'\vec{r})$, and integrating the left-hand and right-hand sides of the equation over $\vec{r}$, we obtain

$$\left[ E - 2(\varepsilon(\vec{k}) - \varepsilon_F) \right] a_{\vec{k}} = \sum_{\vec{k}'} V(\vec{k}, \vec{k}') a_{\vec{k}'}, \tag{3.38}$$

where

$$V(\vec{k}, \vec{k}') = \frac{1}{\Omega} \int e^{-(\vec{k} - \vec{k}') \cdot \vec{r}} V(\vec{r}) d^3\vec{r}, \tag{3.39}$$

and we have used the orthogonality relation

$$\int \exp[i(\vec{k} - \vec{k}')\vec{r}] d^3\vec{r} = \Omega \delta_{kk'} \tag{3.40}$$

In order to simplify the solution of Eq. (3.38), the interaction potential $V(\vec{k}, \vec{k}')$ is usually assumed to be attractive within a thin layer over the Fermi surface of thickness $\hbar\omega_D << \varepsilon_F$:

$$V(\vec{k}, \vec{k}') = \begin{cases} -G & \text{for} \quad \varepsilon_F < \varepsilon(\vec{k}), \varepsilon(\vec{k}') < \varepsilon_F + \hbar\omega_D \\ 0, & \text{otherwise}, \end{cases} \tag{3.41}$$

where $\hbar\omega_D$ is a characteristic phonon energy, which reflects the main Cooper's idea that attraction between two electrons arises via exchange of virtual phonons.

Using the approximation (3.41) and solving (3.38) for $a_{\vec{k}}$, we have

$$a_{\vec{k}} = G \frac{\sum_{\vec{k}'} a_{\vec{k}'}}{2[\varepsilon(\vec{k}) - \varepsilon_F] - E} = G \frac{C}{2[\varepsilon(\vec{k}) - \varepsilon_F] - E}, \tag{3.42}$$

where

$$C = \sum_{\vec{k}'} a_{\vec{k}'} \tag{3.43}$$

The summation over $\vec{k}$ in both sides of Eq. (3.42) and the cancelation of $C$ from both sides gives

$$\frac{1}{G} = \sum_{k > k_F} \left[ 2(\varepsilon(\vec{k}) - \varepsilon_F) - E \right]^{-1} \tag{3.44}$$

Replacing the sum over $\vec{k}$ by an integral, we obtain

$$\frac{1}{GD(0)} = \int_{\varepsilon_F}^{\varepsilon_F + \hbar\omega_D} \frac{d\varepsilon}{2(\varepsilon - \varepsilon_F) - E} = \frac{1}{2} \ln \frac{E - 2\hbar\omega_D}{E}, \tag{3.45}$$

where $D(0)$ is the density of states at the Fermi surface for electrons of one spin orientation. Solving Eq. (3.45) for $E$, we have

$$E = -\frac{2\hbar\omega_D}{\exp[2/GD(0)] - 1} \tag{3.46}$$

In the weak-coupling limit, $GD(0) << 1$, we find

$$E = -2\hbar\omega_D \exp[-2/GD(0)], \tag{3.47}$$

from which it follows that the pair state of electrons will have a lower energy than the energy of the normal state of an electron gas. Thus, the electron pair always has a bound state and its binding energy with respect to the Fermi energy is $\Delta_b = |E|$. This means that the interaction between two electrons is attractive near the Fermi surface and the filled Fermi sea is unstable with respect to the formation of a bound electron pair. One may conclude that other $N - 2$ electrons filling the Fermi sea should pair up in this fashion. However, because of the Fermi statistics they cannot do so quite independently [22] and we must go beyond simple Cooper model and take into account that the ground state of the interacting many electron system should be different from the bound pair state in the Cooper problem.

## 3.5. The BCS Pairing Theory

The currently universally accepted theory of superconductivity in conventional metals, known as the BCS theory [2], was proposed in 1957 by Bardeen, Cooper, and Schrieffer, who generalized the Cooper pairing model to the case of a highly correlated many electron system. Since the Cooper model treats only the correlated two electrons quite differently from all the other electrons, the BCS pairing theory goes beyond this model and enables us to calculate the ground state energy of the interacting many electron system. The most convenient language used in many-electron theory is second quantization formalism, in which the occupied and empty states are specified by use of creation and annihilation operators. The creation (annihilation) operator $a_{\vec{k}\sigma}^+ (a_{\vec{k}\sigma})$ creates (annihilates) electron with momentum $\vec{k}$ and spin projection $\sigma(=\uparrow\ or\ \downarrow)$. Since electrons are Fermi particles, the creation $a_{\vec{k}\sigma}^+$ and annihilation $a_{\vec{k}\sigma}$ operators obey anticommutation relations of fermion operators

$$[a_{\vec{k}\sigma}, a_{\vec{k}'\sigma'}^+] = a_{\vec{k}\sigma}a_{\vec{k}'\sigma'}^+ + a_{\vec{k}'\sigma'}^+ a_{\vec{k}\sigma} = \delta_{\vec{k}\vec{k}'}\delta_{\sigma\sigma'}$$

$$[a_{\vec{k}\sigma}, a_{\vec{k}'\sigma'}] = [a_{\vec{k}\sigma}^+, a_{\vec{k}'\sigma'}^+] = 0 \tag{3.48}$$

The particle number operator pertaining to the state $\vec{k}\sigma$ is defined by

$$n_{\vec{k}\sigma} = a_{\vec{k}\sigma}^+ a_{\vec{k}\sigma} \tag{3.49}$$

The eigenvalue of the operator $n_{\vec{k}\sigma}$ is 0 (when $n_{\vec{k}\sigma}$ operates on an occupied state) or 1 (when $n_{\vec{k}\sigma}$ operates on an empty state). The Hamiltonian $H$ of the many electron system is taken as the sum of the kinetic energy of all the electrons and the potential energy of all electron-electron interactions. In this system the mean number of particles is controlled by the chemical potential $\mu$ (or Fermi energy $\varepsilon_F$) and the single particle energies $\varepsilon(\vec{k})$ are measured from $\varepsilon_F$. The Hamiltonian of the interacting many-electron system in the second-quantization representation may now be written in the form

$$H = \sum_{\vec{k}\sigma} \xi(\vec{k}) a_{\vec{k}\sigma}^+ a_{\vec{k}\sigma} + \frac{1}{2} \sum_{\vec{k}\sigma} \sum_{\vec{k}'\sigma'} \sum_{\vec{q}} V(\vec{q}) a_{\vec{k}+\vec{q}\sigma}^+ a_{\vec{k}'-\vec{q}\sigma'}^+ a_{\vec{k}'\sigma'} a_{\vec{k}\sigma}, \qquad (3.50)$$

where $\xi(\vec{k}) = \varepsilon(\vec{k}) - \mu$, $\varepsilon(\vec{k}) = \hbar^2\vec{k}^2/2m$, $V(\vec{q}) = V(\vec{k}' - \vec{k})$ is the potential of pair interaction between electrons.

In the BCS model, the electrons interact with each other by exchange of virtual phonons just as in the case of Cooper pairing. This electron-phonon coupling means that an electron with the momentum $\vec{k}'$ would emit a phonon carrying the momentum $\vec{q}$, which is absorbed by the other electron with the momentum $\vec{k}'$ (Fig. 3.2). The law of conservation of momen-

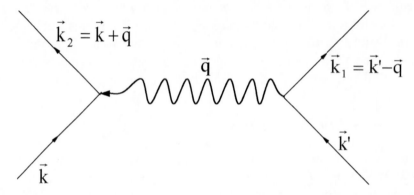

Figure 3.2. The phonon-exchange interaction between electrons.

tum requires $\hbar\vec{k} + \hbar\vec{k}' = \hbar\vec{k}_1 + \hbar\vec{k}_2 = \hbar\vec{K}$ (where $\vec{k}_1 = \vec{k}' - \vec{q}$, $\vec{k}_2 = \vec{k} + \vec{q}$) and the centers of the Fermi spheres of two electrons are distant from each other by the total momentum $K$ (Fig. 3.3). Since the momenta of the interacting electrons must lie within the layer of thickness $2\hbar\omega_D$ in energy, all possible values of $\vec{k}$, $\vec{k}'$ and $\vec{k}_1$, $\vec{k}_2$ satisfying the earlier condition lie in the shaded regions of Fig. 3.3. This means that the number of electron states involved in the interaction increases as $\vec{K}$ decreases, and has a sharp maximum at $\vec{K} \to 0$ when the energy layers of two Fermi spheres combine and the volume of the shaded region becomes maximum. In this connection, the BCS pairing theory states that in the momentum space the electrons in a thin energy layer near the Fermi surface interact attractively with each other and they will form the Cooper pairs with opposite momenta and opposite spins. Thus, we retain in (3.50) only the pair attraction between electrons with opposite momenta $(\vec{k}', -\vec{k}'$ and $\vec{k}, -\vec{k})$ and spins $(\sigma = \uparrow, \sigma' = \downarrow)$, and write the reduced or pair BCS Hamiltonian in the form (replacing $\vec{k}'$ by $-\vec{k}$ and $\vec{k} + \vec{q}$ by $\vec{k}'$)

$$H = \sum_{\vec{k}\sigma} \xi(\vec{k}) a_{\vec{k}\sigma}^+ a_{\vec{k}\sigma} + \sum_{\vec{k},\vec{k}'} V(\vec{k}' - \vec{k}) a_{\vec{k}'\uparrow}^+ a_{-\vec{k}'\downarrow}^+ a_{-\vec{k}\downarrow} a_{\vec{k}\uparrow}, \qquad (3.51)$$

where $V(\vec{k}' - \vec{k})$ is real and symmetric function of $\vec{k}' - \vec{k}$ [30]. The ground state energy of the interacting many-electron system is calculated by using this model BCS Hamiltonian. In

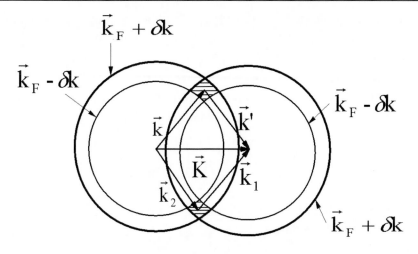

Figure 3.3. Possible electron states within a thin energy layer ($\varepsilon_F - \hbar\omega_D < \varepsilon < \varepsilon_F + \hbar\omega_D$) of the Fermi surface involved in forming the Cooper pairs with center-of-mass momentum $\hbar\vec{K}$.

so doing, different mathematical methods, such as variational method, method of canonical transformations, Green's function methods are applied to study the BCS problem. Here, we will use the method of canonical transformations proposed by Bogoluibov [31] and Valatin [32], since it is a more convenient and sophisticated modern method, which is well suited to consider the ground state and the lowest excited states of a superconductor.

One can assume that the deviations of the products of operators $a^+_{\vec{k}'\uparrow} a^+_{-\vec{k}'\downarrow}$ and $a_{-\vec{k}\downarrow} a_{\vec{k}\uparrow}$ in (3.51) from their average values $\langle a^+_{\vec{k}'\uparrow} a^+_{-\vec{k}'\downarrow} \rangle$ and $\langle a_{-\vec{k}\downarrow} a_{\vec{k}\uparrow} \rangle$ are small. Then one pair of operators, $a_{-\vec{k}\downarrow} a_{\vec{k}\uparrow}$ or $a^+_{\vec{k}'\uparrow} a^+_{-\vec{k}'\downarrow}$, can be replaced by its expectation value, so that we write the identity

$$a_{-\vec{k}\downarrow} a_{\vec{k}\uparrow} = F_{\vec{k}} + (a_{-\vec{k}\downarrow} a_{\vec{k}\uparrow} - F_{\vec{k}}), \tag{3.52}$$

where $F_{\vec{k}} = \langle a_{-\vec{k}\downarrow} a_{\vec{k}\uparrow} \rangle$.

This is a mean field approximation, and the quantity in brackets in (3.52) is the small fluctuation term. Substituting (3.52) and its Hermitian conjugate into the Hamiltonian (3.51) and dropping the term

$$\sum_{\vec{k},\vec{k}'} V(\vec{k}' - \vec{k})(a^+_{\vec{k}'\uparrow} a^+_{-\vec{k}'\downarrow} - F^*_{\vec{k}'})(a_{-\vec{k}\downarrow} a_{\vec{k}\uparrow} - F_{\vec{k}})$$

which is second-order in the fluctuations and is assumed to be very small, we write the mean-field Hamiltonian in the form

$$H_{MF} = \sum_{\vec{k}\sigma} \xi(\vec{k}) a^+_{\vec{k}\sigma} a_{\vec{k}\sigma} + \sum_{\vec{k},\vec{k}'} V(\vec{k}' - \vec{k}) \left[ a^+_{\vec{k}'\downarrow} a^+_{-\vec{k}'\downarrow} F_{\vec{k}} + a_{-\vec{k}\downarrow} a_{\vec{k}} F^*_{\vec{k}'} - F^*_{\vec{k}'} F_{\vec{k}} \right] \tag{3.53}$$

Now, we introduce the gap function

$$\Delta(\vec{k}) = -\sum_{\vec{k}'} V(\vec{k}' - \vec{k}) \langle a_{-\vec{k}'\downarrow} a_{\vec{k}'\uparrow} \rangle = -\sum_{\vec{k}'} V(\vec{k}' - \vec{k}) F_{\vec{k}'} \tag{3.54}$$

This function can be chosen as the real one [33]. Then the resulting Hamiltonian becomes

$$H_{MF} = \sum_{\vec{k}\sigma} \xi(\vec{k}) \left[ a^+_{\vec{k}\uparrow} a_{\vec{k}\uparrow} + a^+_{-\vec{k}\downarrow} a_{-\vec{k}\downarrow} \right] - \sum_{\vec{k}} \Delta(\vec{k}) \left[ a^+_{\vec{k}} a^+_{-\vec{k}} + a_{-\vec{k}} a_{\vec{k}} - F^*_{\vec{k}} \right] \qquad (3.55)$$

The mean-field Hamiltonian (3.55) is a bilinear form in the pair of operators and may be diagonalized by using the Bogoliubov transformation:

$$a_{\vec{k}\uparrow} = u_{\vec{k}} b_{\vec{k}\uparrow} + v_{\vec{k}} b^+_{-\vec{k}\downarrow}, \quad a_{-\vec{k}\downarrow} = u_{\vec{k}} b_{-\vec{k}\downarrow} - v_{\vec{k}} b^+_{\vec{k}\uparrow}$$
$$a^+_{\vec{k}\uparrow} = u_{\vec{k}} b^+_{\vec{k}\uparrow} + v_{\vec{k}} b_{-\vec{k}\downarrow}, \quad a^+_{-\vec{k}\downarrow} = u_{\vec{k}} b^+_{-\vec{k}\downarrow} - v_{\vec{k}} b_{\vec{k}\uparrow}, \qquad (3.56)$$

where $b^+_{\vec{k}}$ ($b_{\vec{k}}$) is the new creation (annihilation) operator for a quasiparticle, $u_{\vec{k}}$ and $v_{\vec{k}}$ are real functions satisfying the condition

$$u^2_{\vec{k}} + v^2_{\vec{k}} = 1 \qquad (3.57)$$

The new operators $b_{\vec{k}\sigma}$ and $b^+_{\vec{k}\sigma}$ just as the old operators $a_{\vec{k}\sigma}$ and $a^+_{\vec{k}\sigma}$ satisfy the anticommutation relations of Fermi operators:

$$[b_{\vec{k}\sigma}, b_{\vec{k}'\sigma'}] = [b^+_{\vec{k}\sigma}, b^+_{\vec{k}'\sigma'}] = 0, \quad [b_{\vec{k}\sigma}, b^+_{\vec{k}'\sigma'}] = \delta_{\vec{k}\vec{k}'} \delta_{\sigma\sigma'} \qquad (3.58)$$

Substituting (3.56) into (3.55) and taking into account (3.57) and (3.58), we obtain

$$\begin{aligned}
H_{MF} = \sum_{\vec{k}} \Big\{ &\left[ 2\xi(\vec{k}) v^2_{\vec{k}} - 2\Delta(\vec{k}) u_{\vec{k}} v_{\vec{k}} \right] + \left[ \xi(\vec{k})(u^2_{\vec{k}} - v^2_{\vec{k}}) + 2\Delta(\vec{k}) u_{\vec{k}} v_{\vec{k}} \right] \\
&\times \left( b^+_{\vec{k}\uparrow} b_{\vec{k}\uparrow} + b^+_{-\vec{k}\downarrow} b_{-\vec{k}\downarrow} \right) + \left[ 2\xi(\vec{k}) u_{\vec{k}} v_{\vec{k}} - \Delta(\vec{k})(u^2_{\vec{k}} - v^2_{\vec{k}}) \right] \\
&\times (b^+_{\vec{k}\uparrow} b^+_{-\vec{k}\downarrow} + b_{-\vec{k}\downarrow} b_{\vec{k}\uparrow}) + F^*_{\vec{k}} \Delta(\vec{k}) \Big\}
\end{aligned} \qquad (3.59)$$

We now choose $u_{\vec{k}}$ and $v_{\vec{k}}$ so that they are satisfied the condition

$$2\xi(\vec{k}) u_{\vec{k}} v_{\vec{k}} - \Delta(\vec{k})(u^2_{\vec{k}} - v^2_{\vec{k}}) = 0 \qquad (3.60)$$

Then the Hamiltonian (3.59) has the diagonal form and it includes the terms of the ground-state energy $E_0$ and the energy $E(\vec{k})$ of quasiparticles

$$H_{MF} = E_0 + \sum_{\vec{k}} E(\vec{k}) (b^+_{\vec{k}\uparrow} b_{\vec{k}\uparrow} + b^+_{-\vec{k}\downarrow} b_{-\vec{k}\downarrow}), \qquad (3.61)$$

where

$$E_0 = \sum_{\vec{k}} \left[ 2\xi(\vec{k}) v^2_{\vec{k}} - 2\Delta(\vec{k}) u_{\vec{k}} v_{\vec{k}} + F^*_{\vec{k}} \Delta(\vec{k}) \right], \qquad (3.62)$$

$$E(\vec{k}) = \xi(\vec{k})(u^2_{\vec{k}} - v^2_{\vec{k}}) + 2\Delta(\vec{k}) u_{\vec{k}} v_{\vec{k}} \qquad (3.63)$$

In (3.61), we have reduced the Hamiltonian (3.55) to the Hamiltonian of an ideal gas of non-interacting quasiparticles.

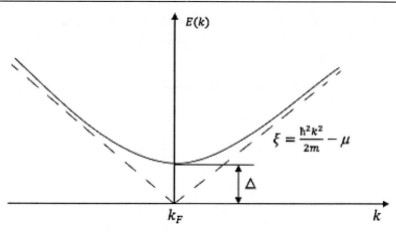

Figure 3.4. Energy spectrum of Bogoliubov quasiparticles. The dashed lines refer to the energy spectrum of a non-interacting electron gas.

Combining (3.57) and (3.60), and solving the quadratic equation, we have

$$u_{\vec{k}}^2 = \frac{1}{2}\left[1 + \frac{\xi(\vec{k})}{E(\vec{k})}\right], \quad v_{\vec{k}}^2 = \frac{1}{2}\left[1 - \frac{\xi(\vec{k})}{E(\vec{k})}\right] \tag{3.64}$$

Equations (3.62), (3.63), and (3.64) give

$$H_{MF} = \sum_{\vec{k}}\left\{\left[\xi(\vec{k}) - E(\vec{k}) + F_{\vec{k}}^*\Delta(\vec{k})\right] + E(\vec{k})\left[b_{\vec{k}\uparrow}^+ b_{\vec{k}\uparrow} + b_{-\vec{k}\downarrow}^+ b_{-\vec{k}\downarrow}\right]\right\}, \tag{3.65}$$

where $E(\vec{k}) = \sqrt{\xi^2(\vec{k}) + \Delta^2(\vec{k})}$, $\Delta(\vec{k})$ is the energy gap in the excitation spectrum of quasiparticles (Fig. 3.4), $\xi(\vec{k}) = (\hbar^2\vec{k}^2/2m) - \mu$ is the single-particle energy in the absence of a gap ($\Delta(\vec{k}) = 0$) relative to the chemical potential.

### 3.5.1. The BCS Ground and Excited States At Zero Temperature

This solution of the BCS problem for the energy spectrum of the interacting electron gas depends on the gap function or order parameter, $\Delta(\vec{k})$ given by (after replacing the $a_{\vec{k}\sigma}$ operators by the $b_{\vec{k}\sigma}$ operators)

$$\Delta(\vec{k}) = -\sum_{\vec{k}'}V(\vec{k}' - \vec{k})\left[\left(u_{\vec{k}'}b_{-\vec{k}'\downarrow} - v_{\vec{k}'}b_{\vec{k}'\uparrow}^+\right)\left(u_{\vec{k}'}b_{\vec{k}'\uparrow} + v_{\vec{k}'}b_{-\vec{k}'\downarrow}^+\right)\right] \tag{3.66}$$

¿From (3.65), we see that the Bogoliubov quasiparticles are independent fermions described by the Fermi distribution function

$$f(E(\vec{k})) = \left[e^{E(\vec{k})/k_B T} + 1\right]^{-1} \tag{3.67}$$

Since $\Delta(\vec{k})$ is real (or $c$-number), then the expectation values of the products of off-diagonal operators $b_{\vec{k}\sigma}b_{\vec{k}'\sigma'}$, is zero and only the products of diagonal operators $b_{\vec{k}\sigma}^{+}b_{\vec{k}\sigma}$ yield nonzero averages. Using the relations

$$\langle b_{\vec{k}\sigma}^{+}b_{\vec{k}\sigma}\rangle = f_{\vec{k}\sigma}, \quad \langle b_{\vec{k}\sigma}b_{\vec{k}\sigma}^{+}\rangle = 1 - f_{\vec{k}\sigma}, \quad \langle b_{\vec{k}\sigma}b_{\vec{k}'\sigma'}\rangle = \langle b_{\vec{k}\sigma}^{+}b_{\vec{k}'\sigma'}^{+}\rangle = 0, \tag{3.68}$$

the gap equation (3.66) may be written as

$$\Delta(\vec{k}) = -\sum_{\vec{k}'}V(\vec{k}'-\vec{k})u_{\vec{k}'}v_{\vec{k}'}(1-2f_{\vec{k}'}) \tag{3.69}$$

At $T = 0$, there are no quasiparticles; so that, $f_{\vec{k}} = 0$. By using (3.64), we find the functions $u_{\vec{k}}$ and $v_{\vec{k}}$, which are smeared significantly in the vicinity of the Fermi energy $\varepsilon_F = \mu$ as shown in Fig. 3.5. The smearing of these functions near $\varepsilon_F$ is a consequence of the pairing

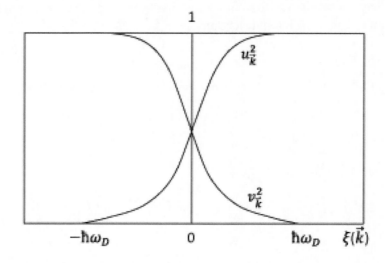

Figure 3.5. The occupation amplitudes of ground pair state $v_{\vec{k}}^2$ and excited pair state $u_{\vec{k}}^2$ in the vicinity of the Fermi energy.

interaction between electrons. At $T = 0$, the Eq. (3.69) is written as

$$\Delta(\vec{k}) = -\sum_{\vec{k}'}V(\vec{k}'-\vec{k})u_{\vec{k}'}v_{\vec{k}'} \tag{3.70}$$

We now evaluate the ground-state energy $E_0$ at $T = 0$ using the relation

$$E_0 = \sum_{\vec{k}}\left[\xi(\vec{k}) - E(\vec{k}) + F_{\vec{k}}^{*}\Delta(\vec{k})\right] \tag{3.71}$$

Substituting (3.70) and $F_{\vec{k}}^{*} = \langle a_{\vec{k}\uparrow}^{+}a_{-\vec{k}\downarrow}^{+}\rangle = u_{\vec{k}}v_{\vec{k}}$ into (3.71) and using (3.64), we obtain

$$E_0 = \sum_{\vec{k}}\left[\xi(\vec{k}) - E(\vec{k}) + \frac{\Delta(\vec{k})}{2E(\vec{k})}\Delta(\vec{k})\right] = \sum_{\vec{k}}\left[\xi(\vec{k}) - \frac{\xi^2(\vec{k})}{E(\vec{k})} - \frac{\Delta^2(k)}{2E(\vec{k})}\right] \tag{3.72}$$

Using the BCS model potential,

$$V(\vec{k}' - \vec{k}) = \begin{cases} -V_{ph}, & |\xi(\vec{k})| \quad \text{and} \quad |\xi(\vec{k}')| \leq \hbar\omega_D, \\ 0, & \text{otherwise}, \end{cases} \tag{3.73}$$

we have $\Delta(\vec{k}) = \Delta(\vec{k}') = \Delta$, and Eq. (3.72) may be written as

$$E_0(\Delta) = D(0) \int_{-\hbar\omega_D}^{\hbar\omega_D} \left[ \xi - \frac{\xi^2}{E(\xi)} - \frac{\Delta^2}{2E(\xi)} \right] d\xi$$

$$= -2D(0) \int_0^{\hbar\omega_D} \left[ \frac{\xi^2}{\sqrt{\xi^2 + \Delta^2}} + \frac{\Delta^2}{2\sqrt{\xi^2 + \Delta^2}} \right] d\xi \tag{3.74}$$

At $\Delta = 0$, $E(\vec{k}) = |\xi(\vec{k})|$ and Eq. (3.72) gives the normal state energy

$$E_N = E_0(\Delta = 0) = \sum_{|\vec{k}| < k_F} 2\xi(\vec{k}) = 2D(0) \int_{-\hbar\omega_D}^{0} \xi d\xi = -2D(0) \int_0^{\hbar\omega_D} \xi d\xi \tag{3.75}$$

Using (3.64) and (3.73), we may rewrite the gap equation (3.70) for $T = 0$ as

$$1 = \frac{V_{ph}}{2} \sum_{\vec{k}} \frac{1}{E(\vec{k})} = \frac{D(0)V_{ph}}{2} \int_{-\hbar\omega_D}^{\hbar\omega_D} \frac{d\xi}{\sqrt{\xi^2 + \Delta^2(0)}}, \tag{3.76}$$

which gives

$$\frac{\Delta(0)}{\hbar\omega_D} = [\sinh(1/D(0)V_{ph})]^{-1} \tag{3.77}$$

In the weak-coupling limit, $D(0)V_{ph} \ll 1$, we can approximate (3.77) as

$$\Delta(0) \simeq 2\hbar\omega_D \exp[-1/D(0)V_{ph}] \tag{3.78}$$

Evaluating the integrals in Eqs. (3.74) and (3.75), we find the difference in energies $E_0(\Delta)$ and $E_N$ at $\hbar\omega_D/\Delta \gg 1$:

$$E_0(0) - E_N = -D(0)\Delta^2 \left( \frac{\hbar\omega_D}{\Delta} \right) \sqrt{\left( \frac{\hbar\omega_D}{\Delta} \right)^2 + 1} + D(0)(\hbar\omega_D)^2$$

$$= -\tfrac{1}{2}D(0)\Delta^2 \tag{3.79}$$

Thus, the BCS ground-state energy of the interacting many-electron system is lower than the normal-state energy of the system. The second term in (3.65) is the sum of the energies of excited quasiparticles. At $\xi(\vec{k}) \geq 0$ the spectrum of quasiparticle states begins from the minimum value $E_{min}(\vec{k}) = \Delta(\vec{k})$ of excitation energy, i.e., the lowest-energy level corresponds to the $E(0) = |\Delta(0)|$ which is the energy gap separating the excited state from the ground state. The excitation energy of each quasiparticle is equal to $E(\vec{k})$ and the one-particle excited state is called the "broken pair" state [22]. While the energy required for exciting both comnponents of Cooper pairs is $2E(\vec{k})$ and the minimum value of the energy gap (which separates the so-called excited pair state from the ground pair state) is equal to $2|\Delta(0)|$.

## 3.5.2.    The BCS Ground and Excited States at Finite Temperatures

The BCS pairing theory is readily generalized to finite temperature $T$. At $T > 0$, a certain fraction of Cooper pairs will be broken into single-particle excitations; so that, the probality of Cooper pair formation will be reduced. Above some critical temperature $T_c$ Cooper pairs cannot exist in thermal equilibrium state. The temperature dependence of the energy gap $\Delta(\vec{k})$ is given by equation (3.69), which with the use of Eqs. (3.64) and (3.67) becomes

$$
\begin{aligned}
\Delta(\vec{k}, T) &= -\sum_{\vec{k}'} V(\vec{k}' - \vec{k}) \frac{\Delta(\vec{k}', T)}{2E(\vec{k}')} \left[ 1 - 2f(E(\vec{k}')) \right] \\
&= -\sum_{\vec{k}'} V(\vec{k}' - \vec{k}) \frac{\Delta(\vec{k}', T)}{2E(\vec{k}')} \tanh\left( \frac{E(\vec{k}')}{2k_B T} \right),
\end{aligned}
\tag{3.80}
$$

where $E(\vec{k}) = \sqrt{\xi^2(\vec{k}) + \Delta^2(\vec{k}, T)}$ is also temperature-dependent.

Using the BCS model potential (3.73) and replacing the sum in Eq. (3.80) by an integral just as at $T = 0$ (see Eq. (3.76)), we obtain an equation for $\Delta(T)$:

$$
\frac{1}{\lambda_{ph}} = \int_0^{\hbar\omega_D} \frac{d\xi}{\sqrt{\xi^2 + \Delta^2(T)}} \tanh\left[ \sqrt{\xi^2 + \Delta^2(T)}/2k_B T \right],
\tag{3.81}
$$

where $\lambda_{ph} = V_{ph} \cdot D(0)$ is the BCS coupling constant.

This equation can be solved numerically and the result of numerical determination of $\Delta(T)$ is shown in Fig. 3.6. However, the analytical solution of Eq. (3.81) can be obtained

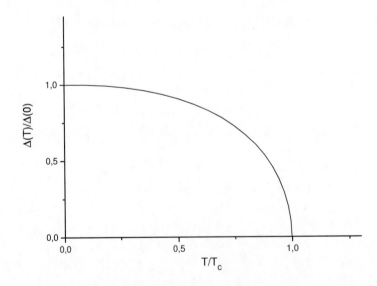

Figure 3.6. Temperature dependence of the BCS pairing gap $\Delta$.

for the cases $T \to 0$ and $T \to T_c$. At $T \to 0$, the Eq. (3.81) may also be written as

$$\frac{1}{\lambda_{ph}} = \int\limits_{-\hbar\omega_D}^{\hbar\omega_D} \frac{1 - 2f(E(\xi))}{2E(\xi)} = \int\limits_0^{\hbar\omega_D} \frac{d\xi}{\sqrt{\xi^2 + \Delta^2(T)}} - 2 \int\limits_0^{\hbar\omega_D} \frac{f(E(\xi))}{\sqrt{\xi^2 + \Delta^2(T)}}, \tag{3.82}$$

Then, using (3.78), we obtain

$$\ln \frac{2\hbar\omega_D}{\Delta(0)} = \ln \frac{2\hbar\omega_D}{\Delta(T)} - \int\limits_0^{\hbar\omega_D} \frac{d\xi}{\left[\exp\left(\sqrt{\xi^2 + \Delta^2(T)}/k_B T\right) + 1\right] \sqrt{\xi^2 + \Delta^2(T)}} \tag{3.83}$$

In view of the rapid convergence of the integral, the upper limit can be taken to infinity. Taking into account that $\Delta(T)/k_B T \to \infty$ for $T \to 0$, we have

$$\ln \frac{\Delta(0)}{\Delta(T)} \approx \frac{2}{\Delta^*(T)} \int\limits_0^\infty e^{-\Delta^*(T)[1 + (x/\sqrt{2}\Delta^*(T))^2]} dx = \sqrt{\frac{2\pi}{\Delta^*(T)}} e^{-\Delta^*(T)}, \tag{3.84}$$

where $\Delta^*(T) = \Delta(T)/k_B T$.

Since $\Delta^*(T \to 0) \gg 1$, we obtain from (3.84)

$$\Delta(T) = \Delta(0) \left[1 - \sqrt{2\pi k_B T / \Delta(0)} e^{-\Delta(0)/k_B T}\right] \tag{3.85}$$

When $T \to T_c$ we have $\Delta(T)/k_B T \to 0$ and the integral in (3.83) is calculated by performing some algebraic transformation and expanding the integrand in powers of $\Delta(T)/k_B T$ up to the first-order term (for details, see [19, 33]). Hence, in this case we have

$$\ln \frac{\Delta(0)}{\Delta(T)} = \ln \frac{\pi k_B T}{\gamma \Delta(T)} + \frac{7\zeta(3)\Delta^2(T)}{8\pi^2 (k_B T)^2} \tag{3.86}$$

from which it follows that $\Delta(T)$ goes to zero at $T = T_c$

$$T_c = \frac{\gamma \Delta(0)}{\pi k_B}, \tag{3.87}$$

where $\ln \gamma = C \approx 0.5772$ is Euler's constant, $\zeta(v) = \sum_{n=1}^\infty n^{-v}$ is the Reimann zeta function (for $v = 3$, $\zeta(3) \simeq 1.202$). Inserting $\Delta(0) = \pi k_B T_c / \gamma$ into (3.86), we obtain

$$\ln \frac{T}{T_c} = -\frac{7\zeta(3)}{8\pi^2} \left(\frac{\Delta(T)}{k_B T}\right)^2 \quad \text{or} \quad \frac{T}{T_c} = \exp\left[-\frac{7\zeta(3)}{8\pi^2} \left(\frac{\Delta(T)}{k_B T}\right)^2\right] \tag{3.88}$$

For small $\Delta(T)$, Eq. (3.88) becomes

$$\Delta(T) = 2\pi k_B T_c \sqrt{\frac{2}{7\zeta(3)} \left(1 - \frac{T}{T_c}\right)} \simeq 3.0633 k_B T_c \sqrt{1 - T/T_c} \tag{3.89}$$

At $T = T_c$, $E(\xi) = |\xi|$ and Eq. (3.82) has the form

$$\frac{1}{\lambda_{ph}} = \int\limits_0^{\hbar\omega_D} \frac{d\xi}{\xi} \tanh \frac{\xi}{2k_B T_c} \tag{3.90}$$

Performing first the integration by parts then replacing the upper limit of the rapidly converging integral by infinity, we obtain

$$\frac{1}{\lambda_{ph}} = \ln z \cdot \tanh z \Big|_0^{\hbar\omega_D/2k_BT_c} - \int_0^{\infty} \frac{\ln z}{\cosh^2 z} dz \simeq \ln \frac{\hbar\omega}{2k_BT_c} - \ln \frac{\pi}{4\gamma}, \quad (3.91)$$

where we have taken into account that $\hbar\omega_D \gg 2k_BT_c$ in the weak-coupling limit and $\tanh(\hbar\omega_D/2k_BT_c) \to 1$. From Eq. (3.91), we have

$$k_BT_c = \frac{2\hbar\omega_D}{\pi}\gamma e^{-1/\lambda_{ph}} \approx 1.135\hbar\omega_D e^{-1/\lambda_{ph}} \quad (3.92)$$

Combining (3.78) and (3.92), we find

$$\frac{2\Delta(0)}{k_BT_c} \simeq 3.52 \quad (3.93)$$

which is the characteristic quantity measured in experiments. The BCS value of the ratio $2\Delta(0)/k_BT_c$ is close to the experimental values of this ratio for many conventional superconductors, such as Al, Sn, Ta, In, Ga, Tl and V [28, 34, 35]. However, the BCS value of $2\Delta(0)/k_BT_c$ is small enough in comparison with the values of $2\Delta(0)/k_BT_c$ observed in other conventional superconductors (for example Hg, Nb, Pb), in which deviations from the BCS value of 3.52 seemingly is caused either by the low value of $\hbar\omega_D$ (i.e., the condition $\hbar\omega_D \gg 2k_BT_c$ is not well satisfied for Hg and Pb) or by the precursor BCS-like pairing above $T_c$ (see chapter 7). Moreover, the temperature dependence of the SC order parameter observed in Sn is also somewhat different from the temperature dependence of the BCS order parameter (see Fig. 3.7). It is seen that Eq. (3.92) contains the isotope effect, since

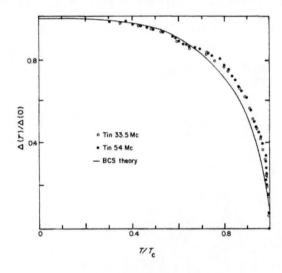

Figure 3.7. The ratio $\Delta(T)/\Delta(0)$ as a function of $T/T_c$ in Sn. The solid curve is the prediction of BCS theory. The points are the ultrasonic attenuation data of Morse and Bohm (taken from [36]).

$\omega_D$ is proportional to $(\beta/M)^{1/2}$, where $\beta$ is an elastic constant of lattice, $M$ is the mass of the atoms in the metal. The attractive interaction potential $V$ is assumed to be independent of $M$, so that Eq. (3.92) predicts $T_c \sim M^{-1/2}$. One can assume that deviations from the simple $M^{-1/2}$ law in various superconductors are caused by the presence of a static lattice distortions in the strong electron-phonon interactions (which will be discussed in chapters 6 and 7). At $T = 0$, all quasiparticle states with energies $E(\vec{k}) \geq \Delta(0)$ are unoccupied. While, at $T \neq 0$ part of free quasiparticle states (i.e., excited states) with energies $E(\vec{k}) \geq \Delta(T)$ are occupied according to the Fermi distribution (3.67) of quasiparticles. In this case, the energy gap $\Delta(T)$ separates the broken pair and excited states of a superconductor from its ground state, and the broken pair and excited pair states are given relative to the ground pair states by $E(\vec{k},T) = \sqrt{\xi^2(\vec{k}) + \Delta^2(T)}$ and $E(\vec{k},T) = 2\sqrt{\xi^2(\vec{k}) + \Delta^2(T)}$, respectively just as in the case $T = 0$.

### 3.5.3. Density of States

In a normal metal, all one-electron states with $\varepsilon(\vec{k}) \leq \mu = \varepsilon_F$ are occupied by pairs of electrons with opposite spins. In the SC state, all electrons within a narrow energy layer $\mu - \hbar\omega_D \leq \varepsilon(\vec{k}) \leq \mu + \hbar\omega_D$ take part in BCS pairing and form Cooper pairs at the chemical potential $\mu$. The excitation energy $E(\vec{k})$ of quasiparticles has important consequences for their density of states $D(E)$ which is determined so that $D(E)dE$ is the number of quasiparticle levels (disregarding spin) with energy between $E$ and $E + dE$. Since both $E$ and $\xi$ depend on $\vec{k}$, the one-to-one correspondence exists between the values of $E$ and $\xi$. Therefore, we can determine the density of states $D(E)$ by equating the number of quasiparticle levels in the BCS state with the number of quasiparticle levels in the normal state

$$D(E)dE = D(\xi)d\xi \tag{3.94}$$

When the energy $\xi$ is measured from the Fermi energy, we can take $\mu = 0$. We now assume that the density of states $D(\xi)$ varies in a narrow range of energies $-\hbar\omega_D \leq \xi \leq \hbar\omega_D$ very little and can be replaced by its value at the Fermi surface, $D(\varepsilon_F)$. We may then write (3.94) in the form

$$D(E) = D(0)\frac{d\xi}{dE} = D(0)\frac{E}{\sqrt{E^2 - \Delta^2}} \tag{3.95}$$

By taking into account that there are also quasiparticle states with negative energies $E < -\Delta$ below the Fermi surface and no states exist in the gap $|\Delta|$, Eq. (3.95) can be written as

$$D(E) = \begin{cases} \frac{D(0)E}{\sqrt{E^2-\Delta^2}}, & E > \Delta \\ -\frac{D(0)E}{\sqrt{E^2-\Delta^2}}, & E < -\Delta \\ 0, & -\Delta < E < \Delta \end{cases} \tag{3.96}$$

According to the BCS pairing model, the excited (i.e., unpaired) quasiparticles have energy levels separated from the ground state by a gap of width $\Delta$. In the BCS ground state

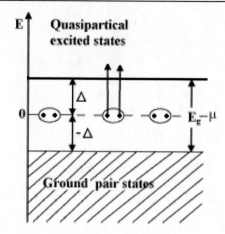

Figure 3.8. BCS ground state of a superconductor, which has all bound pairs of quasi-particles at the Fermi level $\varepsilon_F = \mu$. Excited states occur by breaking a pair to form two quasiparticles, each with excitation energy $E(\vec{k})$.

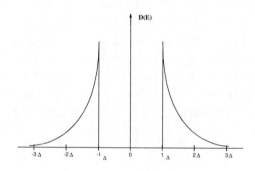

Figure 3.9. Density of states of a BCS superconductor.

quasiparticles are paired. For breaking a pair of quasiparticles, one must excite both quasi-particles to the excited pair state, so that it requires energy $E(\vec{k}) + E(\vec{k}') \geq E_g = 2\Delta$ (Fig. 3.8).

The density of states $D(E)$ for excitations of quasiparticles has a divergent singularity just at $E = \pm\Delta$, as shown in Fig. 3.9. In the BCS ground state, all Cooper pairs have zero center-of-mass momentum $\vec{K} = 0$ and their superfluidity is often determined from the crite-rion $v_c = \min[E(\vec{k})/\hbar\vec{k}] > 0$, where $v_c$ is the critical velocity of independent quasiparticles and are not moving Cooper pairs. We shall discuss this subject in chapter 8. The energy gap and the density of states $D(E)$ are directly measured experimentally by electron tunneling. The most important verifications of the BCS pairing theory came from the electron tun-neling and the coherent Cooper-pair tunneling (predicted by Josephson [37]) experiments, which provide an excellent verification of the BCS theory in conventional superconductors [34, 35].

### 3.5.4. Thermodynamic Properties of Conventional Superconductors

The existence of the energy gap in the excitation spectrum of superconductors leads to thermal activated behavior of all thermodynamic quantities below $T_c$. We now calculate the thermodynamic quantities of the interacting electron gas in superconductors. The entropy of a Fermi gas of quasiparticles is given by

$$S = -2k_B \sum_{\vec{k}} \left[ f(E(\vec{k})) \ln f(E(\vec{k})) + (1 - f(E(\vec{k}))) \ln(1 - f(E(\vec{k}))) \right], \qquad (3.97)$$

where the factor 2 arises from the spin degeneracy.

The electronic specific heat below $T_c$ is easily calculated from the expression

$$C_{es} = T \frac{\partial S}{\partial T} = 2k_B T \sum_{\vec{k}} \frac{\partial f(E(\vec{k}))}{\partial T} \ln \frac{1 - f(E(\vec{k}))}{f(E(\vec{k}))} \qquad (3.98)$$

Substituting $f(E(\vec{k}))$ from (3.67) into (3.98), replacing the summation by an integration from $-\hbar \omega_D$ to $\hbar \omega_D$, and taking the lower and upper limits of the rapidly converging integral to $-\infty$ and $+\infty$, respectively, we obtain

$$C_{es} = \frac{2}{k_B T} D(0) \int_{-\infty}^{+\infty} f(E)(1 - f(E)) \left[ E^2 - \frac{T}{2} \frac{d\Delta^2(T)}{dT} \right] d\xi \qquad (3.99)$$

At low temperatures for $k_B T << \Delta(0)$, $f(E) \simeq \exp(-E/k_B T) << 1$, and $d\Delta^2(T)/dT \cong 0$, the specific heat $C_{es}$ takes the form

$$C_{es} = \frac{4}{k_B T^2} D(0) \int_0^\infty E^2 e^{-E/k_B T} d\xi \qquad (3.100)$$

Since the main contribution to the integral (3.100) comes from the region of small $\xi << \Delta(0)$, we can replace $E^2$ by $\Delta^2(0)$ and expand in the exponent $E(\xi)$ in powers of $(\xi/\Delta(0))$. We then have

$$C_{es} = \frac{4D(0)\Delta^2(0)}{k_B T^2} \int_0^\infty e^{-\Delta(0)/k_B T} e^{-\xi^2/2\Delta(0)k_B T} d\xi$$

$$= 2\sqrt{2\pi} k_B D(0)\Delta(0) (\Delta(0)/k_B T)^{3/2} e^{-\Delta(0)/k_B T}, \qquad (3.101)$$

As is seen from (3.101), the specific heat tends to zero exponentially at $T \to 0$ due to the existence of the gap $\Delta$ in the excitation spectrum. Using (3.97), we have

$$S_s(T) \simeq 2D(0)k_B \left( \frac{2\pi\Delta^3(0)}{k_B T} \right)^{1/2} e^{-\Delta(0)/k_B T} \qquad (3.102)$$

Comparing (3.101) with Eq. (1.41) (see chapter 1), and by taking into account $g(\varepsilon_F) = 2D(0)$ and (3.87), we obtain

$$\frac{C_{es}(T)}{C_{en}(T_c)} = \frac{3}{\gamma} \sqrt{\frac{2}{\pi}} \left( \frac{\Delta(0)}{k_B T} \right)^{3/2} e^{-\Delta(0)/k_B T}, \qquad (3.103)$$

where $C_{en}(T_c)$ is the specific heat in the normal state (i.e., at $T = T_c$). Near $T_c$ the energy gap $\Delta(T)$ tends to zero and one can replace $E(\vec{k})$ by $\xi(\vec{k})$ in Eq.(3.99). Then Eq. (3.99) has the form

$$C_{en}(T = T_c) = \frac{4}{k_B T^2} D(0) \int_0^\infty \xi^2 \frac{e^{\xi/k_B T}}{(e^{\xi/k_B T} + 1)^2} d\xi$$

$$= 4D(0) k_B^2 T \int_0^\infty \frac{x^2 e^x}{(e^x + 1)^2} dx,$$

which can be expressed as

$$C_{en}(T = T_c) = 4D(0) k_B^2 T \int_0^\infty \frac{x^2 e^{-x}}{(e^{-x} + 1)^2} \tag{3.104}$$

Expanding the denominator of the integrand in powers of $e^{-x}$ and evaluating the integrals, we obtain the usual normal-state specific heat

$$C_{en}(T = T_c) = 4D(0) k_B^2 T \int_0^\infty x^2 \left[ e^{-x} - 2e^{-2x} + 3e^{-3x} - 4e^{-4x} + \cdots \right] dx$$

$$= 4D(0) k_B^2 T \left[ 2 \left( 1 - \frac{1}{2^2} + \frac{1}{3^2} - \frac{1}{4^2} + \cdots \right) \right] = 4D(0) k_B^2 T_c \frac{\pi^2}{6}$$

$$= \gamma_e T_c, \tag{3.105}$$

where $\gamma_e = 2\pi^2 D(0) k_B^2/3 = \pi^2 k_B^2 g(\varepsilon_F)/3$.

The first term in the integral (3.99) determines the normal-state specific heat and the second term involving $\partial \Delta^2(T)/\partial T$ gives rise to a discontinuity $\Delta C_e$ in electronic specific heat at $T_c$. Using the relation $f(E)(1 - f(E)) = f(|\xi|)(1 - f(|\xi|)) = -k_B T \partial f/\partial \xi$, we obtain

$$\Delta C_e = (C_{es} - C_{en})|_{T_c} = 2D(0) \frac{d\Delta^2(T)}{dT} \int_0^\infty \frac{\partial f}{\partial \xi} d\xi$$

$$= 2D(0) \frac{d\Delta^2(T)}{dT} f(\xi) \Big|_0^\infty = -D(0) \frac{d\Delta^2(T)}{dT} \Big|_{T_c} \tag{3.106}$$

Using the expression (3.89) for $\Delta(T)$ near $T_c$, we obtain

$$\Delta C_e \simeq 9.4 k_B^2 T_c \cdot D(0) \tag{3.107}$$

Comparing (3.107) with (3.105), we find the relative magnitude of the discontinuity $\Delta C_e$

$$\frac{\Delta C_e}{\Delta C_{en}} \Big|_{T_c} = \frac{9.384 \cdot 3}{2\pi^2} \simeq 1.426 \tag{3.108}$$

The temperature dependencies of $C_{es}$ and $C_{en}$ are shown in Fig. 3.10.

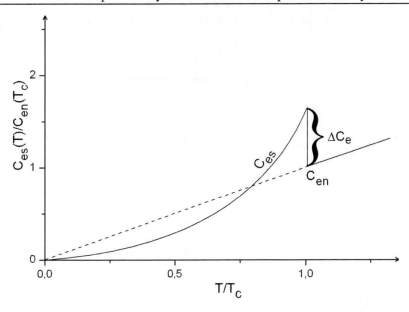

Figure 3.10. Temperature dependence of the electronic specific heat of conventional super-conductors in the BCS model.

These predictions of the BCS pairing theory of thermodynamic properties, such as the specific heat behavior at $T \to 0$ and $T \to T_c$ are in reasonable agreement with experimental results for many conventional superconductors [34, 39]. At the same time, the specific heat in various metals below $T_c$ is found to vary as $T^3$ rather than exponentially (see Refs. [34, 38]). Note that the thermodynamic quantities are most key parameters characterizing the SC state of superconductors.

### 3.5.5.  Magnetic Properties of Conventional Superconductors

The free energy of a superconductor may be written as

$$F = U - TS = H_{MF} - TS,  \tag{3.109}$$

where $U$ is the total energy of the system.

At $T = 0$, we can take the normal-state free energy $F_n(0) = 0$ and determine the critical magnetic field $H_c(0)$ from the relation

$$F_n(0) - F_s(0) = E_N - E_0(\Delta(0)) = \frac{1}{2}D(0)\Delta^2(0) = \frac{H_c^2(0)}{8\pi},  \tag{3.110}$$

where $F_s$ is the free energy of the system in the SC state.

The change in free energy $F_n(T)$ with increasing temperature from zero is given by

$$F_n(T) - F_n(0) = -\int S_n(T)dT = -\int \gamma_e T dT = -\frac{\gamma_e T^2}{2},  \tag{3.111}$$

where $S_n$ is the normal-state entropy, $\gamma_e = 2\pi^2 D(0)k_B/3$.

Using Eq.(3.102), we find the change in free energy $F_s(T)$ with increasing temperature from zero

$$
F_s(T) - F_s(0) = -\int S_s(T)dT = -\gamma_s \int_0^{k_B T} \frac{dt}{\sqrt{t}} e^{-\Delta/t}
$$

$$
= -2\gamma_s \sqrt{\Delta} \int_{\sqrt{\Delta/t}}^{\infty} \frac{e^{-x^2}}{x^2} dx
$$

$$
= 2\gamma_s \sqrt{t} \left[ e^{-\Delta/t} + \sqrt{\frac{\pi \Delta}{t}} \left( 1 - \Phi(\sqrt{\Delta/t}) \right) \right], \tag{3.112}
$$

where $\gamma_s = 2\sqrt{2\pi}D(0)\Delta^{3/2}(0)$, $t = k_B T$, $\Phi(\sqrt{\Delta/t}) = \frac{2}{\sqrt{\pi}} \int_0^{\sqrt{\Delta/t}} e^{-x^2} dx$ is the error function.

At low temperatures, $\Delta/k_B T \gg 1$, and temperature contribution to $F_s(0)$ given by (3.112) is exponentially small, i.e., $F_s(T) \simeq F_s(0)$. The thermodynamic critical magnetic field is then determined from the expression

$$
\frac{H_c^2(T)}{8\pi} = F_n(T) - F_s(T) \simeq -\frac{\pi^2 D(0)(k_B T)^2}{3} + \frac{1}{2}D(0)\Delta^2(0) \tag{3.113}
$$

Using Eq.(3.110) and the BCS relation $\Delta(0) = 1.76 k_B T_c$, we find

$$
H_c(T) = H_c(0)\sqrt{1 - \frac{2\pi^2}{9.2928}\left(\frac{T}{T_c}\right)^2} \simeq H_c(0)\left[1 - 1.062\left(\frac{T}{T_c}\right)^2\right] \tag{3.114}
$$

In order to determine the temperature dependence of $H_c(T)$ near $T_c$, we use the BCS approximation (3.73) and write the second (interaction) term in (3.51) in the form

$$
H_{int} = -V_{ph} \sum_{k,k'} a_{\vec{k}'\uparrow}^+ a_{-\vec{k}'\downarrow}^+ a_{-\vec{k}\downarrow} a_{\vec{k}\uparrow} \tag{3.115}
$$

Expressing the products of operators $a_{\vec{k}'\uparrow}^+ a_{-\vec{k}'\downarrow}^+$ and $a_{-\vec{k}\downarrow} a_{\vec{k}\uparrow}$ through the quasiparticle operators (3.56) and taking thermally averaged values of such productors, we can write (3.115) as

$$
H_{int} = -\frac{V_{ph}}{4} \sum_{k,k'} \frac{\Delta(\vec{k})\Delta(\vec{k}')}{E(\vec{k})E(\vec{k}')} \left[ 1 - f(E(\vec{k})) \right] \left[ 1 - f(E(\vec{k}')) \right] \tag{3.116}
$$

where we have used the relations (3.64) and (3.68) to write the products $u_{\vec{k}}v_{\vec{k}}$, $b_{\vec{k}\uparrow}^+ b_{\vec{k}\uparrow}$ and $b_{-\vec{k}\downarrow} b_{-\vec{k}\downarrow}^+$.

Using Eq.(3.80) together with the BCS approximation (3.73), we obtain from (3.116), $-\Delta^2(T)/V_{ph}$. According to statistical physics, the derivative of the averaged values of the total energy (Hamiltonian) with respect to any parameter $\eta$ is expressed through the derivative of the free energy with respect to the same parameter [40]

$$
\left\langle \frac{\partial H}{\partial \eta} \right\rangle = \left( \frac{\partial F}{\partial \eta} \right)_{T,V,\mu} \tag{3.117}
$$

It is convenient to take the interaction constant $V_{ph}$ appearing in the second term in (3.51) as the same parameter. Then differentiating $H$ with respect to $V_{ph}$, we have $\partial F/\partial V_{ph} = -\Delta^2(T)/V_{ph}^2$. Since the gap $\Delta$ tends to zero for $V_{ph} \to 0$, we can integrate this equation over $V_{ph}$ to get

$$F_s(T) - F_n(T) = -\int_0^{V_{ph}} \frac{\Delta^2}{V_{ph}^2} dV_{ph} \qquad (3.118)$$

Further, differentiating Eqs. (3.78) and (3.86) with respect to $V_{ph}$, we find

$$\frac{dV_{ph}}{V_{ph}^2} = \frac{7\zeta(3)D(0)}{4\pi^2(k_B T)^2}\Delta d\Delta \qquad (3.119)$$

Substituting this expression into (3.118), we obtain

$$F_s(T) - F_n(T) = -\frac{7\zeta(3)D(0)}{4\pi^2(k_B T)^2}\int_0^\Delta \Delta^3 d\Delta \qquad (3.120)$$

At $T \to T_c$, we obtain from (3.120) using the relation (3.89)

$$F_s(T) - F_n(T) = -\frac{4\pi^2 D(0)}{7\zeta(3)}(k_B T_c)^2\left[1 - \frac{T}{T_c}\right]^2, \qquad (3.121)$$

so that

$$\frac{H^2(T)}{8\pi} = F_n(T) - F_s(T) = \frac{8\pi^2}{7\zeta(3)}\left(\frac{k_B T_c}{\Delta(0)}\right)^2 H^2(0)\left[1 - \frac{T}{T_c}\right]^2 \qquad (3.122)$$

from which, we have finally

$$H_c(T) = 1.74H_c(0)\left[1 - \frac{T}{T_c}\right] \qquad (3.123)$$

We note that the approximate parabolic temperature dependence of $H_c$ presented in (3.114) does not fully coincide with the curve $H_c(T)$ as measured experimentally in conventional superconductors (see Refs. [34, 38]). However, such a deviation of $H_c(T)$ from the parabolic dependence is small and the asymptotic expressions (3.114) and (3.123) for $T \ll T_c$ and $T \to T_c$ are close enough to the empirical dependence of $H_c(T)$.

Superconductivity is often considered as the superfluidity of a Fermi-gas. In this case the Cooper pairs are regarded as the fermions. One can assume that the various deviations of the observed SC properties of superconductors from the BCS predictions are rather involved with this assumption. In this section, we discuss the superconductivity of Cooper pairs in the context of the original BCS pairing theory based on the concept of a superfluid Fermi-liquid. According to the two-fluid model, the Fermi-gas with the BCS pairing interaction is characterized by separation of its density into the normal and superfluid parts. The density of the normal part of a Fermi-liquid is given by [19]

$$\rho_n = -\frac{8\pi}{3(2\pi\hbar)^3}\int p^4\frac{df}{dE}dp = -\frac{p_F^4}{3\pi^2\hbar^3 v_F}\int_{-\hbar\omega_D}^{+\hbar\omega_D}\frac{df}{dE}d\xi, \qquad (3.124)$$

where $p_F$ is the Fermi momentum.

The total density of the Fermi gas with the number of electrons $N_e$ is

$$\rho = mN_e/\Omega = 2\frac{4\pi p_F^3}{3(2\pi\hbar)^3}m = \frac{mp_F^3}{3\pi^2\hbar^3}. \tag{3.125}$$

When comparing this relation to Eq.(3.124), we find

$$\frac{\rho_n}{\rho} = -2\int_0^{+\hbar\omega_D}\frac{df}{dE}d\xi = \frac{2}{k_BT}\int_0^{\infty}\frac{e^{E/k_BT}}{(e^{E/k_BT}+1)^2}d\xi \tag{3.126}$$

Here, we replaced the upper limit of the rapidly converging integral by infinity. At low temperatures, $\Delta/k_BT \gg 1$ and

$$\frac{\rho_n}{\rho} \simeq \frac{2}{k_BT}\int_0^{\infty}e^{-\sqrt{\xi^2+\Delta^2}/k_BT}d\xi$$

$$= \frac{2}{k_BT}\int_0^{\infty}e^{-\Delta/k_BT}e^{-\xi^2/2\Delta k_BT}d\xi = \sqrt{2\pi\Delta/k_BT}e^{-\Delta/k_BT}. \tag{3.127}$$

Whereas at $T \to T_c$, $E \to |\xi|$, and $\partial f/\partial E \simeq \partial f/\partial|\xi|$, so that Eq. (3.126) becomes

$$\frac{\rho_n}{\rho} \simeq -2\int_0^{\infty}\frac{df}{d|\xi|}d\xi = -2f(\xi)\,|_0^{\infty} = 1, \tag{3.128}$$

This means that $\rho_n/\rho \to 1$ and the superfluid density $\rho_s$ becomes negligible, i.e., $\rho_s/\rho \to 0$ as $T \to T_c$. At low temperatures, the temperature dependence of the London penetration depth has the form

$$\lambda_L(T) = \lambda_L(0)\left[1 - \rho_n/\rho\right]^{-1/2} = \lambda_L(0)\left[1 - \sqrt{2\pi\Delta/k_BT}e^{-\Delta/k_BT}\right]^{-1/2} \tag{3.129}$$

Using (3.126) and the relation $\xi = \sqrt{E^2 - \Delta^2}$, we obtain an expression for $\lambda_L(T)$ that holds at all temperatures $T \le T_c$:

$$\lambda_L(T) = \lambda_L(0)\left[1 - 2\int_{\Delta}^{\infty}\left(-\frac{df}{dE}\right)\frac{E}{\sqrt{E^2-\Delta^2}}dE\right]^{-1/2} \tag{3.130}$$

It is seen that at $T > T_c$, $\Delta = 0$ (normal state) and $\lambda_L(T) \to \infty$, corresponds to the absence of the Meissner effect. When $\Delta$ becomes non-zero, the value of $\lambda_L(T)$ below $T_c$ is finite and the behavior of the system becomes significantly different from the normal state and is characterized by Meissner effect. The experimental dependence of $\lambda_L(T)$ in classic super-conductor rather follows a power law dependence than an exponential dependence [34, 35].

### 3.5.6. Bogoliubov and Eliashberg-McMillan Pairing Theories

The BCS pairing theory is only a simplified theory, that ignored all, with the exception of a very special type of pairing interaction between electrons in metals. The BCS theory, which was developed for simple metals, explains quite satisfactorily the basic SC properties of these classic superconductors. Nonetheless, experimental studies on conventional superconductors have shown that various SC properties of some materials deviate from the predictions of the BSC theory. In particular, although the isotope effect exponent $\alpha$ is about 0.5 for a few conventional superconductors, experiments on other metals are often inconsistent with this BSC value of $\alpha$, which is highly reduced or even negative in these systems and varies from material to material [34, 41, 42]. Such deviations of $\alpha$ from the value 0.5 can be explained in terms of a more detailed theory of pairing interaction between electrons developed by Bogoliubov, Tolmachev, and Shirkov [30], Eliashberg [43], and McMillan [44]. In reality, the net electron-electron interaction is the sum of the attractive phonon-mediated interaction and the repulsive Coulomb interaction between electrons. Therefore, Bogoliubov et al. [30] have considered a more realistic model in which the interaction potential is chosen in the form

$$V(\vec{k}-\vec{k}') = \begin{cases} -V_{ph} + V_c, & \xi(\vec{k}), \xi(\vec{k}') < \hbar\omega_D = \varepsilon_D, \\ V_c, & \hbar\omega_D < \xi(\vec{k}), \xi(\vec{k}') < \hbar\omega_c \\ 0, & \xi(\vec{k}) \text{ or } \xi(\vec{k}') > \hbar\omega_c. \end{cases} \quad (3.131)$$

This model potential contains the attractive part $-V_{ph}$ and the repulsive part $V_c$, and the Coulomb cut-off energy $\hbar\omega_c$ of order $\mu = \varepsilon_F$. Using the Bogoliubov model potential (3.131), we obtain the following expression for $T_c$ (see Appendix A):

$$k_B T_c \simeq 1.135 \hbar\omega_D e^{-1/\lambda}, \quad (3.132)$$

where $\lambda = D(0)\tilde{V}_A = \lambda_{ph} - \mu_c$, $\tilde{V}_A = V_{ph} - V_c/[1 + D(0)V_c \ln(\varepsilon_F/\varepsilon_D)]$, $\mu_c = D(0)V_c/[1 + D(0)V_c \ln(\varepsilon_F/\varepsilon_D)]$, $\varepsilon_F \gg \varepsilon_D$.

The same expression for $\mu_c$ or $\tilde{V}_A$ was also obtained by Morel and Anderson [45]. Hence, the effect of the Coulomb repulsion is greatly reduced at $\mu_c \ll D(0)V_c$. According to the BCS theory, for a pure electron-phonon interaction the isotope effect exponent is determined from the relation

$$\frac{\delta T_c}{T_c} = \frac{\delta\omega_D}{\omega_D} = -\alpha\frac{\delta M}{M} = -0.5\frac{\delta M}{M}, \quad (3.133)$$

where $\omega_D \sim M^{-1/2}$, $M$ is the ionic mass, $\alpha = -d\ln T_c/d\ln M$.

However, for an effective electron-phonon interaction, the SC transition temperature $T_c$ and the isotope effect exponent $\alpha$ are affected by the frequency dependence of the Coulomb interaction. From Eq. (3.132), it follows that:

$$\frac{\delta T_c}{T_c} = \frac{\delta\omega_D}{\omega_D}\left[1 - \frac{\mu_c^2}{(\lambda_{ph} - \mu_c)^2}\right] = -\frac{1}{2}\frac{\delta M}{M}\left[1 - \frac{\mu_c^2}{(\lambda_{ph} - \mu_c)^2}\right] \quad (3.134)$$

We see that $\alpha \leq 0$ for $\lambda_{ph} \geq 2\mu_c$.

The expression (3.134) for the isotope effect exponent $\alpha$ is in reasonable agreement with the experiments for conventional superconductors [34, 42, 46]. Later, modifications of the BCS and Bogoliubov pairing theories were done by Eliashberg [43] and McMillan [44], using the precise experimental information about the crystal lattice vibrations. In the Eliashberg theory, the dimensionless electron-phonon coupling constant is defined as:

$$\lambda_{ph} = 2 \int_0^{\omega_D} \alpha^2(\omega) F(\omega) \frac{d\omega}{\omega}, \tag{3.135}$$

where $F(\omega)$ is the phonon density of states, $\alpha^2(\omega)$ is an effective electron-phonon coupling function of energy $\omega$.

Further, McMillan generalized the Eliashberg theory taking into account the Coulomb interaction and obtained the following semiempirical expression for $T_c$ [44]:

$$k_B T_c = \frac{\hbar \omega_D}{1.45} \exp\left[ -\frac{1.04(1 + \lambda_{ph})}{\lambda_{ph} - \mu_c(1 + 0.62\lambda_{ph})} \right] \tag{3.136}$$

Usually, the estimated values of $\mu_c$ for conventional superconductors are $\mu_c \simeq 0.1 - 0.2$ [41]. While the values of $\lambda_{ph}$ for various metals and alloys vary from 0.2 to 1.0 [41, 47, 48]. For these superconductors, the values of the Debye phonon frequency $\omega_D$ vary from $70K$ to $560K$ [41, 46, 47].

The Eliashberg-McMillan equations contain the effects of renormalization of SC quasiparticle excitations, which are not simply single electrons from broken Cooper pairs but dressed quasiparticles [41, 48]. These approaches serve as a basis for understanding the anomalous behaviors of the various conventional superconductors, mostly transition metals [42, 47, 49], in which significant deviations from the BCS was observed. Most of the researchers believe (see Refs. [42, 48]) that the BCS and Eliashberg-McMillan theories can be also used to examine the SC properties of the high $T_c$ oxides. Another view is that these theories are inappropriate for the high-$T_c$ superconductors and other unconventional superconductors for which a new state of matter, with radically different properties should be postulated (see, e.g., Refs. [18, 42, 48, 50, 51, 52, 53, 54]). The different approaches to the mechanisms of high-$T_c$ superconductivity and other unconventional superconductivity will be discussed fully in chapters 5 and 8.

# References

[1] L. N. Cooper, *Phys. Rev.* 104, 1189 (1956).

[2] J. Bardeen, L. N. Cooper and J. R. Schrieffer, *Phys. Rev.* 108, 1175 (1957).

[3] L. P. Gor'kov, *Zh. Eksp. Teor. Fiz.* 36, 1918 (1959).

[4] L. D. Landau, *Zh. Eksp. Teor. Fiz.* 30, 1058 (1956).

[5] L. D. Landau, *Zh. Eksp. Teor. Fiz.* 32, 59 (1957).

[6] L. D. Landau, *Zh. Eksp. Teor. Fiz.* 35, 97 (1958).

[7] A. A. Abrikosov and I. M. Khalatnikov, *Rep. Prog. Phys.* 22, 329 (1959).

[8] D. Pines and P. Nozieres, *Theory of Quantum Liquids*, Vol. I (Benjamin, New York, 1966).

[9] S. G. Lipson, *Quantum Fluids: Proceedings of the Batsheva Seminar held at the Technion-Israel Institute of Technology, Haifa* (Gordon and Breach, Science Publishers, Inc., New York, 1970) p. 101.

[10] V. L. Vinetskii, *Zh. Eksp. Teor. Fiz.* 40, 1459 (1961).

[11] S. G. Suprun and B. Ya. Moizhes, *Fiz. Tverd. Tela* 24, 1571 (1982).

[12] D. Emin and M. S. Hillery, *Phys. Rev.* B39, 6575 (1989).

[13] J. Adamowski, *Phys. Rev.* B39, 3649 (1989).

[14] G. Verbist, F. M. Peeters and J. T. Devreese, *Physica Scripta.* T39, 66 (1991).

[15] S. Dzhumanov, A. A. Baratov and S. Abboudy, *Phys. Rev.* B54, 13121 (1996-II).

[16] J. R. Schrieffer, *Theory of Superconductivity* (Benjamin, New York, 1964).

[17] S. Fujita, *J. Superconduct.* 5, 83 (1992).

[18] S. Dzhumanov, P. J. Baimatov, A. A. Baratov and N. I. Rahmatov, *Physica* C 235-240, 2339 (1994).

[19] E. M. Lifshitz and L. P. Pitaevskii, *Statistical Physics*. Part 2 (Nauka, Moscow, 1978).

[20] J. Wilks, *The Properties of Liquid and Solid Helium* (Clarendon Press, Oxford, 1967).

[21] J. B. Ketterson and S. N. Song, *Superconductivity* (Cambridge University Press, Cambridge, 1999).

[22] A. J. Leggett, *Rev. Mod. Phys.* 47, 331 (1975).

[23] D. Rainer, *Physica Scripta.* T23, 106 (1988).

[24] H. R. Ott, *Int. J. Mod. Phys.* B6, 25 (1992).

[25] E. R. Dobbs, *Helium Three* (Oxford University Press, Oxford, 2000).

[26] J. Bardeen and W. Shockly, *Phys. Rev.* 80, 72 (1950).

[27] A. S. Davidov, *Solid State Theory* (Nauka, Moscow, 1976).

[28] C. Kittel, *Introduction to Solid State Physics* (Nauka, Moscow, 1978).

[29] S. V. Vonsovskii and M. I. Katsnelson, *Quantum Physics of Solid State* (Nauka, Moscow, 1983).

[30] N. N. Bogoliubov, V. V. Tolmachev and D. V. Shirkov, *A New Method in the Theory of Superconductivity* (Izd. AN USSR, Moscow, 1958).

[31] N. N. Bogoliubov, *Nuovo Cimento* 7, 794 (1958); *Zh. Eksp. Teor. Fiz.* 34, 58 (1958).

[32] J. G. Valatin, *Nuovo Cimento* 7, 843 (1958).

[33] Yu. B. Rumer and M. Sh. Rivkin, *Thermodynamics, Statistical Physics and Kinetics* (Nauka, Moscow, 1977).

[34] E. Lynton, *Superconductivity* (Mir, Moscow, 1971).

[35] D. R. Tilly and J. Tilly, *Superfluidity and Superconductivity* (IOP Publishing Ltd, Bristol, 1990).

[36] G. D. Mahan, M*any Particle Physics* (Plenum Press, New York, 1991).

[37] B. D. Josephson, *Phys. Lett.* 1, 251 (1962).

[38] M. Tinkham, *Introduction to superconductivity* (Atomizdat, Moscow, 1980).

[39] W. S. Corak, B. B. Goodman, C. B. Satterthwaite and A. Wexler, *Phys. Rev.* 96, 1442 (1954); 102, 656 (1956).

[40] L. D. Landau and E. M. Lifshitz, *Statistical Physics.* Part 1 (Nauka, Moscow, 1976).

[41] A. S. Davidov, *High Temperature Superconductivity* (Naukova Dumka, Kiev, 1990).

[42] L. M. Falicov, *IEEE Quantum Electronics* 25, 2358 (1989).

[43] G. M. Eliashberg, *Zh. Eksp. Teor. Fiz.* 38, 966 (1960).

[44]  W. L. Mcmillan, *Phys. Rev.* 167, 331 (1968).

[45]  P. Morel and P. W. Anderson, *Phys. Rev.* 125, 1263 (1962).

[46]  P. G. de Gennes, *Superconductivity of Metals and Alloys* (Mir, Moscow, 1968).

[47]  R. M. White and T. H. Geball, *Long Range Order in Solids*(Mir, Moscow, 1982).

[48]  M. L. Cohen, *Int. J. Mod. Phys.* B5, 1495 (1991).

[49]  M. L. Cohen, G. Gladstone, M. A. Jensen and J. R. Schrieffer, *Superconductivity in Semiconductors and Transition Metals* (Mir, Moscow, 1972).

[50]  P. W. Anderson, *Fiz. Niz. Temp.* 32, 381 (2006).

[51]  K. Friedberg and T. D. Lee, *Phys. Rev.* 40, 6745 (1989).

[52]  C. M. Varma, *Phys. Rev.* 55, 14554 (1997).

[53]  D. Pines, cond-mat/0404151.

[54]  S. Dzhumanov and P. K. Khabibullayev, *Izv. Akad. Nauk Uzb. SSR, Ser. Fiz. Mat. Nauk.* 1, 47 (1990); *Pramana-J. Phys.* 45, 385 (1995).

# Chapter 4

# High-$T_C$ and Other Unconventional Superconductors

## 4.1. Introduction

Since the discovery of superconductivity in Hg by Kamerlingh Onnes (1911), the search for superconducting (SC) materials with the highest SC transition temperatures $T_c$ has continued. But advances in finding new superconductors with higher $T_c$ values from 1911 to 1973 were achieved very slowly. Systematic studies were done not only on the simple metals but also on the metallic alloys (e.g., A15 compounds), the ternary Chevral phases and the oxide superconductors [1, 2, 3, 4]. Only the superconductor $Nb_3Ge$ which was discovered in 1973 by Gavaler (see Ref. [4]) among all these compounds had the highest $T_c = 23.3K$. As can be seen from Fig. 4.1, during the 75 years (i.e., from 1911 to 1986), the value of $T_c$ was increased only by about $19K$. So slow progress in obtaining substantially higher $T_c$ values inclined most of physicists to think that superconductivity was confined only to low temperatures. This pessimistic conclusion was also confirmed by the BCS expression for $T_c$. The discovery of superconductivity at $30K$ in the ceramic hole-doped copper oxides (cuprates) $La_{2-x}Ba_xCuO_4$ by Bernorz and Müller [5] in 1986 has changed this viewpoint completely. Shortly after, Chu and his colleagues discovered the new cuprate superconductors $YBa_2Cu_3O_{7-\delta}$ with $T_c = 93K$ [6]. Later, other families of the hole-doped cuprate superconductors with an even higher $T_c$ were also discovered [4, 7]. While the electron-doped cuprate superconductors $Nd_{2-x}Ce_xCuO_4$ and $Pr_{2-x}Ce_xCuo_4$ were discovered in 1989 [8]. Currently, the cuprate superconductor $HgBa_2Ca_2Cu_3O_{8+\delta}$ has the record $T_c$ values of 133 [9, 10] and $135K$ [11]. The observed physical properties of the hole-doped high-$T_c$ cuprates in the underdoped and optimally doped regimes are unconventional in many respects, in both the normal and SC states; since the behaviors of these high-$T_c$ cuprates strongly deviate from the standard Fermi liquid and BCS descriptions of the normal and SC states.

For many years (until 1986) there have been many attempts to obtain the highest SC transition temperatures in organic compounds [12, 13, 14]. The first organic superconductor $(TMTSF)_2X$ (where $X = PF_6$, $ClO_4$, etc., TMTSF is tetramethyltetrasenafulvalene) with $T_c \simeq 1K$ was discovered by Jerome et al. [15]. Then other organic superconductors (including fullerene superconductors $K_3C_{60}$ with $T_c = 18K$ [16] and $Cs_2RbC_{60}$ with the

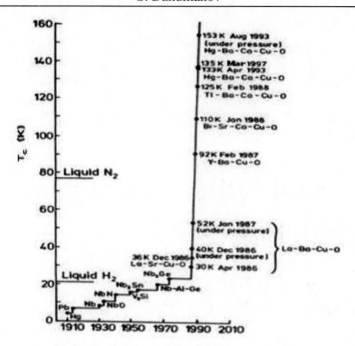

Figure 4.1. The highest achieved SC transition temperature $T_c$ as a function of year (From Ford and Saunders [4]).

highest $T_c \simeq 33K$ [17]) were discovered (see Ref. [18]). The organic materials are assumed to be exotic unconventional superconductors [18, 19]. There is also another class of exotic materials, such as $CeCu_2Si_2$, $UBe_{13}$, $UPt_3$, etc., which are known as the heavy-fermion superconductors [20]. In the end, during the 1970s and in the early 1980s, superconductivity in $CeCu_2Si_2$ (with $T_c \simeq 0.65K$), $UBe_{13}$, (with $T_c \simeq 0.95K$) and $UPt_3$ (with $T_c \simeq 0.54K$) were discovered by Steglich et al. [21], Ott et al. [22] and Stewart et al. [23]. Although the SC transition temperatures of these compounds are exceedingly low, their other properties are very interesting. In particular, they process huge values in critical magnetic fields. The unusual properties of the organic and heavy-fermion superconductors have many aspects in common with high-$T_c$ cuprates [19, 24]. Therefore, we will discuss the true essence of the common features of high-$T_c$, organic and heavy-fermion superconductors in this and other chapters.

## 4.2.  Resistive Transitions, Crystal Structure, and Phase Diagrams of the Cuprates

In 1986, Bernorz and Müller observed superconductivity in the hole-doped copper oxide composed of lanthanum and barium, which has the formula $La_{2-x}Ba_xCuO_4$ and the SC transition temperature $T_c$ of about $30K$ [5]. In this compound, the trivalent $La^{3+}$ ions are partially substituted by divalent $Ba^{2+}$ ions and there is the resistive transition from a metallic state to a SC one at $T_c$. Later, it was found (for references see [1]) that doping the parent compound $La_2CuO_4$ with Sr raised the SC transition temperature $T_c$ in the hole-doped cuprate $La_{2-x}Sr_xCuO_4$ (LSCO) to $40K$ at which the resistive transition occurs from the metallic state to the SC one. Soon after Chu and his colleagues [6] substituted yttrium for lanthanum and observed superconductivity in the new hole-doped copper oxide $YBa_2Cu_3O_7$ (YBCO) at $T_c \simeq 93K$. Resistive transitions from metallic state to SC ones in LSCO and YBCO are shown in Fig. 4.2. Further, other hole- and electron-doped cuprate

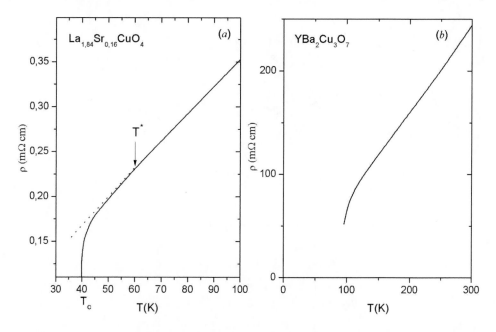

Figure 4.2. Temperature dependence of the bulk resistivity of (a) LSCO (taken from [25]) and (b) YBCO (taken from [26]). $T^*$ is the pseudogap temperature.

superconductors were discovered. The high-$T_c$ cuprates have a perovskite-type structure ($K_2NiF_4$ or $SrTiO_3$ type) shown in Fig. 4.3, and all of them have one or more $CuO_2$ planes in their structure, which are separated by layers of other atoms. The two-dimensional $CuO_2$ layers are assumed to play a crucial role in high-$T_c$ superconductivity, while the layers between these conduction layers are considered as the charge reservoirs [3, 4, 7]. The structure of $La_2CuO_4$ is simple and has one $CuO_2$ layer. The structure of the high-$T_c$ compound $YBa_2Cu_3O_{7-\delta}$ has chains of alternating $Cu^{2+}$ and $O^{2-}$ ions, as well as double $CuO_2$ layers. Other cuprate superconductors, such as $Bi_2Sr_2Ca_2Cu_3O_{10}$ (with highest $T_c \simeq 110K$), $Tl_2Ba_2Ca_2Cu_3O_{10}$ (with highest $T_c \simeq 125K$) and $HgBa_2Ca_2Cu_3O_{8+x}$ (with $T_c \simeq 135K$) containing three $CuO_2$ layers per unit cell have even more complicated structures [3, 4]. The undoped cuprates are charge-transfer (CT) insulators with antiferromagnetic (AF) long-range order [27]. These CT insulators undergo several phase transitions as a function of doping and temperature. The phase diagrams of $La_{2-x}Sr_xCuO_4$ and $YBa_2Cu_3O_{7-\delta}$ are shown in Figs. 4.4 and 4.5.

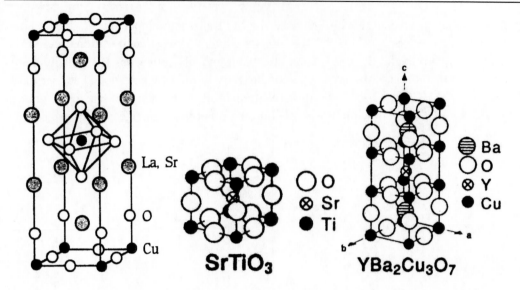

Figure 4.3. The crystal structures of SrTiO$_3$, La$_2$CuO$_4$ and YBa$_2$Cu$_3$O$_7$.

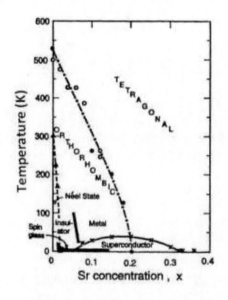

Figure 4.4. The phase diagram of La$_{2-x}$Sr$_x$CuO$_4$ in the plane of the doping $x$ and temperature $T$, showing the Neel state, spin glass, insulating, metallic and SC states, transition temperature between tetragonal and orthorhombic phases [28].

## 4.3. Normal-State Properties of High-$T_c$ Cuprates

The layered cuprates in the underdoped regime are strongly anisotropic materials and they can be considered as a stack of weakly bound conducting planes [29]. In addition, they are typical ionic (polar) materials, which are quite different from the conventional metals, and

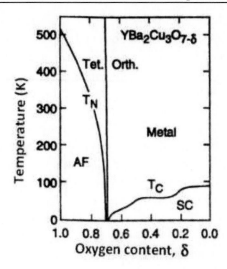

Figure 4.5. The phase diagram of $YBa_2Cu_3O_{7-\delta}$ in the plane of the doping $\delta$ and temperature $T$, showing AF phase, insulating, metallic and SC phases, transition transition line between tetragonal and orthorhombic phases [7].

non-polar semiconductors. Therefore, the physical properties of the doped high-$T_c$ cuprates are highly anomalous and are not well understood now. In particular, the question whether the electronic system in these materials is really two-dimensional (2D) or anisotropic three-dimensional (3D) is still under debate [27, 28]. Actually, the doped cuprates are anisotropic 3D systems [29, 30, 31] and the problem is in describing the anisotropy. One might argue that the anisotropy of the electronic system can be described by a mass anisotropy and the system turns out to be anisotropic three-dimensional, even if the mass is renormalized by a strong interaction [32]. Another important aspect of the doped cuprates is the polarizability of their crystal lattice in the presence of the charge carriers introduced by doping. Since the self-trapping of carriers is favorable in anisotropic polar materials and is responsible for the observed unusual properties of such systems. The most striking features of the anisotropic high-$T_c$ cuprates are their unusual normal state properties. In this section, we discuss distinctive features of the observed normal-state properties of the cuprates.

### 4.3.1. Optical Properties and Pseudogap Features

Infrared photoemission and optical spectroscopies and other experimental techniques have been used for studies of the characteristic features of the electronic states in the cuprate superconductors [27, 33, 34, 35]. The photoemission and optical experiments indicate that in the undoped cuprates, a strong Coulomb repulsion $U \simeq 6 - 10$ eV at the copper Cu site [27, 33] produces the Hubbard splitting of the Cu $3d$ levels and the CT gap $\Delta_{CT}$ between the oxygen $2p$ level and splitted upper Cu $3d$ level is much smaller than $U$. Therefore, the oxygen $2p$ band in the undoped cuprates lies within the Mott-Hubbard gap $U$ and the Fermi level $E_F$ is located at the center of the CT gap. Experiments on optical absorption show that the optical gap (or CT gap) in the underdoped compound $La_2CuO_4$ is of the order of $\Delta_{CT} = 1.5 - 2.0 eV$ [33] and upon doping the spectral weight location near the CT gap edge is transferred to low-energy excitations and the new states (the so-called in-gap or mid-gap states) are introduced in the CT gap. These in-gap states are distributed above the top of the oxygen valence band of hole-doped cuprates [27], coming from the doped holes themselves (probably due to the self-trapping of hole carriers, see chapter 6). Formation of such in-gap states on doping is also observed in the original CT gap $\Delta_{CT} \simeq 1.5 - 2.0 eV$ of electron-doped cuprates $Nd_{2-x}Ce_xCuO_4$ and $Pr_{2-x}Ce_xCuO_4$ [27]. There are different views on the origin and distribution of the in-gap states in the CT gap, the position of the Fermi level $E_F$ or chemical potential $\mu$ of the doped cuprates with respect to the CT gap, and the possible shift of $\mu$ by doping [27, 33, 34, 35]. Over the past two decades, photoemission spectroscopy, especially angle-resolved photoemission spectroscopy (ARPES) has contributed significantly to the understanding of the in-gap states and gap-like features in the doped high-$T_c$ cuprates [35]. The photoemission and ARPES experiments show (for review, see, e.g., [27, 35, 36]) that the $\mu$ is shifted up to the top of the valence band with hole doping and the presence of the two in-gap bands of width $\sim$0.1-0.2 eV each, occupying the energy range of $\sim$0.5 eV up to $\mu$ in the underdoped regime. The mid-infrared absorption observed in the cuprates is assumed to be associated with the optical transition between these two in-gap bands [36]. The CT excitation spectrum provides strong evidence that free holes and electrons in doped cuprates form large polarons and two in-gap bands have different origins [28]. Since the one band at $\sim 0.5 eV$, found in the lightly doped cuprates is nearly temperature independent and the second band, at $0.13 eV$ is sensitive to temperature. The nature of these in-gap bands is still poorly understood [27, 28, 35].

One of the most important features of the underdoped and optimally doped cuprates is the normal-state gap or so-called pseudogap (PG) observed in many experimental probes, such as ARPES, tunneling spectroscopy, optical measurements, and other experiments at temperatures between some characteristic temperature $T^*$ and the SC transition temperature $T_c$ [35, 37, 38, 39]. In particular, ARPES has the ability to measure the momentum dependence of the density of states (DOS) and the spectra taken in the momentum region near the $(\pi, 0)$ for an underdoped $Bi_2Sr_2CaCu_2O_{8+\delta}$ (Bi2212 with $T_c = 79K$) as a function of temperature (Fig. 4.6) show two different peaks at $T < T_c$ [40, 41]: a broad feature near 100-150 meV and a sharp peak at around 40 meV. ARPES spectra of two Bi2212 samples with $T_c = 79K$ (underdoped) and $86K$ (overdoped) show [40] that the sharp peak position (or energy gap) in both samples decreases slightly as $T \rightarrow T_c$ (Fig. 4.7) and this excitation gap does not close at $T_c$ (i.e., there is not any signature of the SC phase transition at $T_c$ in the gap magnitude). As first predicted theoretically [42, 43], the energy gap $\Delta$ observed in ARPES experiments [37, 40] eventually vanishes at $T^* \gg T_c$, and the SC order parameter and transition temperature $T_c$ are determined by other factors (i.e., condensation of Cooper pairs into a superfluid Bose-liquid state below $T_c$ and disappearance of the superfluid condensate or coherence (SC order) parameter at $T_c$). The PG opening in the excitation spectrum of the underdoped, optimally doped and some slightly overdoped cuprates above $T_c$ were also detected by optical experiments [38, 44]. Among spectroscopic probes, electron tunneling has proven to be powerful tool in the study of quasiparticle DOS both above and below $E_F$. Therefore, ARPES and tunneling spectroscopy are complementary probes of the gap-like structure in the cuprates above $T_c$. Scanning tunneling spectroscopy (STS) studies on superconductor-insulator-normal metal (S-I-N) tunneling showed that in Bi2212

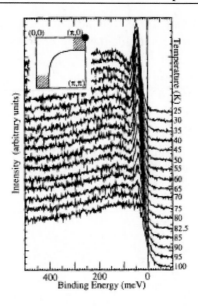

Figure 4.6. Temperature dependence of ARPES spectra, taken at $(\pi, 0)$ [40].

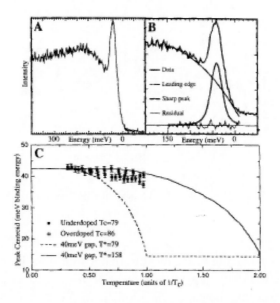

Figure 4.7. Temperature dependence of the sharp peak positions observed in two samples of Bi2212 [40]. Note that such a BCS-like temperature dependence of the gap magnitude $\Delta$ was first predicted in [42].

the PG exists not only in the underdoped regime, but also in the optimally doped and over-doped regimes [45, 46]. At zero temperature $(T = 0)$ and voltage $(V = 0)$, the chemical potentials of the two systems separated by a thin insulating layer are equal and no current flows through the S-I-N junction. When an external positive voltage $V > \Delta/e$ is applied to the normal metal, electrons tunnel from the metal through the junction to the free states of the superconductor. In this case, a tunneling current flows through the junction and its magnitude is proportional to the DOS in the superconductor just above the gap edge. One can assume that the sharp peak observed in the tunneling conductance at $V = \Delta/e$ [45, 46] is related to the BCS-like PG [42, 43]. If the negative voltage $V < -\Delta/e$ is applied to the superconductor, the breaking of Cooper pairs occurs and the tunneling current flows from the superconductor to the metal. The tunneling spectra of a slightly underdoped Bi2212 ($T_c = 83K$) measured at negative voltage have two gap-like features below $T_c$ [45] (Fig 4.8); a sharp peak at low gap-like bias and a broad peak (hump) at high bias, which is separated from the sharp peak by a dip. Similar peak-dip-hump structure is also observed in ARPES

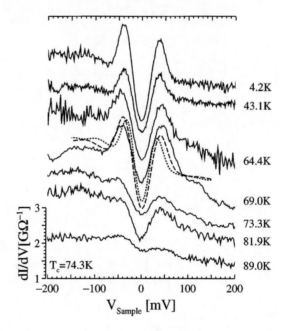

Figure 4.8.  Temperature dependence of the SIN tunneling conductance of underdoped Bi2212 [45].

spectra [40, 41, 47]. The broad hump and the dip are not seen at positive bias. The tunneling spectra of Bi2212 have the sharp asymmetric peaks at the gap edges ($\pm\Delta$) and significant quasipartical excitations filling the gap [45]. Another striking feature is that the magnitude of the gap $\Delta$ at $T \lesssim T_c$ does not change. Furthermore, as the doping level is increased, the gap $\Delta$ decreases, while the SC transition temperature is reduced. Thus, the ratio $2\Delta/k_B T_c$ changes from a value $\sim 6$ for overdoped Bi2212 (with $T_c = 62K$) to values approaching $\sim 14$ in the underdoped region [48]. For $YBa_2Cu_3O_{7-\delta}$ the values of $2\Delta/k_B T_c$ lie between 4 and 8 [2, 25]. While the energy gap $\Delta$ observed in many experiments is proportional to $T^*$ and the relation $2\Delta/k_B T^* \simeq 3.52$ holds for various high-$T_c$ cuprates, as was predicted theoretically in [24, 42]. This means that the normal-state gap $\Delta$ is the BCS-like pairing PG. Interestingly, ARPES and tunneling spectra of Bi2212 (Fig. 4.8) exhibit the peak-dip-hump structure both above and below $T_c$ (see Refs. [35, 49]). This peak-dip-hump structure in the S-I-N tunneling conductance appears only at negative bias [45]. The origin of the peak-dip-hump structure in the ARPES and tunneling spectra of underdoped and slightly overdoped Bi2212, and the temperature dependence of this structure are still unclear and controversial [35, 45, 49]. In superconductor-insulator-superconductor (S-I-S) tunneling spectra, two symmetric peak-dip-hump structures are observed at negative and positive bias voltages [48, 50] (Fig. 4.9a). It is believed that the peak and hump observed in ARPES and tunneling spectra correspond to the small and large pseudogaps, respectively [35, 50]. It was clearly demonstrated [46, 49] that the peak-dip-hump structure persists above $T_c$ and is unrelated to $T_c$. There have been different views regarding the origins of the small PG, large PG and SC gap. In particular, some experiments [37, 45] suggest that the small PG is a precursor of the SC gap. However, other experiments indicate [39, 46, 51] that the SC gap is distinct from the small PG which coexists with SC gap below $T_c$, as predicted before in [42, 43, 52]. Most importantly, accurate experimental data [46] show that the SC fluctuation and PG formation are independent phenomena. Finally, the zero-bias conductance

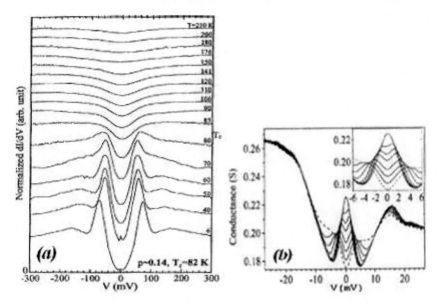

Figure 4.9. (a) Temperature dependence of the S-I-S tunneling conductance on optimally doped Bi2212 [50]. (b) Tunneling characteristics of an In/YBCO junction on a (110)-oriented film at increasing magnetic fields of up to T (main panel) and at decreasing fields (inset) [54].

peaks (ZBCPs), reflecting the DOS at the Fermi level, are often observed in the tunneling spectra of various normal metal-cuprate superconductor (N-S) and N-I-S and S-I-S junctions below $T_c$ [53, 54] (Fig.4.9b). In some experiments, ZBCPs are also observed above $T_c$ [55] (in Bi2212) and even well above $T_c$ [56] (in $(Bi, Pb)_2Sr_2Ca_2Cu_3O_{10+\delta}$). These experimental observations of ZBCPs could be due either to the Andreev reflection effect arising from the Cooper pair formation in the intermediate region (with the thickness of the order of coherence length $\xi(T)$) near the N-S interface or to other tunneling effects arising from the presence of impurity states and the surface roughness (see Ref. [54]).

### 4.3.2.  Thermal Properties

One of the most informative method for studying the SC and normal-state properties of high-$T_c$ cuprates is the specific heat probe. Above $T_c$, it is difficult to separate the electronic contribution from the experimentally observed total specific heat $C$. (Typical values of the linear specific heat coefficient $\gamma_e$ and the Debye temperature $\theta_D$ are $\gamma_e = 4.9 - 7.3 \, mJ/mole \, K^2$ and $\theta_D = 320 - 450 \, K$ for $La_{1.85}Sr_{0.15}CuO_4$ [57]). At $T > T_c$, the specific heat of high-$T_c$ cuprates is dominated by phonons. Nevertheless, the $T$ dependence of the specific heat $C(T)$ and anomalies in $C(T)$, which give indication for the phase transitions in the electronic subsystem above $T_c$ have been experimentally established. The earliest experimental observations of the specific heat anomalies above $T_c$ have been reported by Dunlap et al. [57], Inderhees et al. [58] and Fossheim et el. [59]. Specific heat anomaly observed in $La_{1.85}Sr_{0.15}CUO_4$ [57] is indicative of a phase transition at about $T \sim 80K$. The evidence for a small PG in the normal state of $La_{2-x}Sr_xCuO_4$ (LSCO) came from the observations of the electronic specific heat jumps (anomalies) at different doping levels $x = 0.10 - 0.20$. [44, 60] (Fig. 4.10a). The specific heat anomalies observed in LSCO at $T^* \simeq 60 - 100K$ can be caused by the formation of a small BCS-like pairing PG [42, 43] (see also chapter 7). Indeed, LSCO samples with $x \leq 0.2$, exhibit a small PG effect at $T = T^* > T_c$ and the anomaly in the electronic specific heat $C_e$ is rather BCS-like [44]. Such a BCS-like specific heat jump was also observed in the normal state of the optimally doped $YBa_2Cu_3O_{7-\delta}$ (YBCO) (with $T_c = 89K$) at $T^* = 93K$ [58] (Fig. 4.10b). Another specific

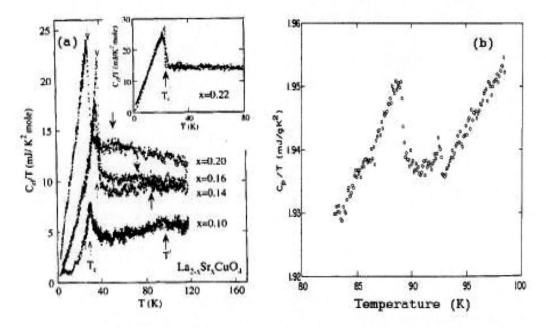

Figure 4.10.  (a) Electronic specific heat $C_e$ for $La_{2-x}Sr_xCuO_4$ $(0.1 \leq x \leq 0.2)$ plotted as $C_e/T$ vs $T$ [60]. (b) Specific heat anomaly in a single crystal of $YBa_2Cu_3O_{7-\delta}$ in the temperature range between $80K$ to $100K$ [58].

heat anomaly corresponding to a phase transition in YBCO (with $T_c \approx 91K$) is observed at

$T = 229K$ [59] (Fig. 4.11). The origin of this anomaly is not clear, but experimental studies of the thermopower of YBCO (with $T_c = 93K$) show [61] that the anomaly observed at $T \sim 215K$ is indicative of a phase transition in the electronic subsystem. Temperature and doping dependences of the electronic specific heat coefficient $\gamma_e$ for high-$T_c$ cuprates has been extensively studied by Loram et al. [62] by using the differential technique. Although the previously mentioned anomalies in the electronic specific heat $C_e(T)$ have not been found in these experiments, the PG effect in the underdoped YBCO is seen clearly in the depression of $\gamma_e$ in the normal state below some PG temperature (Fig. 4.11b), which seems to be different from the large PG temperature $T_0$ (Fig. 4.12). Whereas overdoped

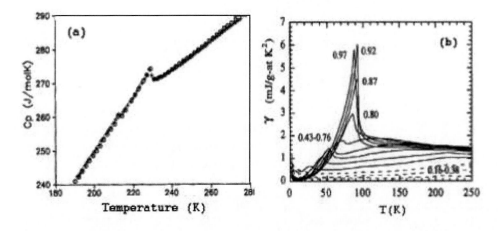

Figure 4.11. (a) Specific heat anomaly in a single crystal of $YBa_2Cu_3O_{7-\delta}$ in the temperature range $180K$ to $280K$ [59]. (b) Temperature dependence of $\gamma_e$ for $YBa_2Cu_3O_{6+x}$ [62].

samples YBCO ($0.92 \leq \delta \leq 0.97$) show typical metallic behavior and $\gamma_e$ is temperature independent. Tallon and Loram [39] discovered experimentally the so-called quantum critical point (QCP) in the electronic phase diagram of YBCO (Fig. 4.12) and such a QCP was also discovered theoretically [63, 64, 65]. The PG observed in the specific heat measurements [39] is similar to the large PG seen in ARPES and tunneling spectra of Bi2212. This PG temperature scale is much higher in LSCO than in YBCO and the PG appears in the overdoped region. The PG temperature $T_0$ falls to zero at the critical doping level $x_c = 0.19$ in YBCO [39].

## 4.3.3. Metal-insulator Transitions, Charge Transport, Phase Separation and Stripe Formation

The undoped cuprates are AF insulators and a small level of doping (e.g., $x = 0.02$ in LSCO) results in the disappearance of AF order, the material undergoes a transition from an AF insulator to an unusual insulator. By further doping, these compounds undergo insulator-to-metal transitions and they exhibit an anomalous metallic behavior in the underdoped region. The resistivity of the underdoped cuprates begins to show metallic behavior and its magnitude decreases with increasing doping $x$ (Fig. 4.13). In these systems the SC state

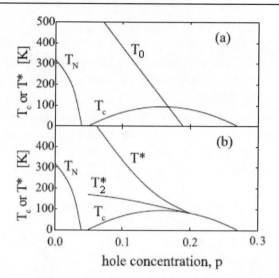

Figure 4.12. Two different electronic phase diagrams of high-$T_c$ cuprates proposed in Ref. [39]. (a) The phase diagram proposed by Tallon and Loram on the basis of their specific heat data. (b) The phase diagram obtained from the analysis of other experimental data. $T_0$ and $T^*$ are large and small PG temperatures, respectively, $T_N$ is the Neel temperature.

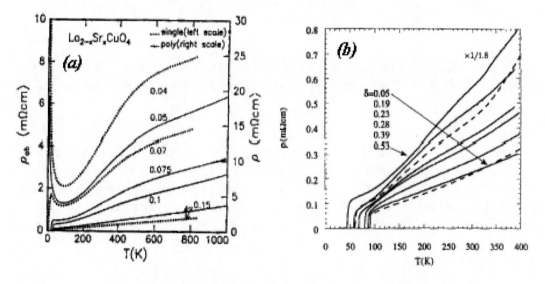

Figure 4.13. (a) Temperature dependence of the in-plane resistivity of $La_{2-x}Sr_xCuO_4$ single and poly crystals at various doping levels (taken from [38]). (b) In-plane resistivity vs. temperature for thin-film samples of YBCO with $0.53 \leq \delta \leq 0.05$. The dashed lines show $\rho(T)$ data for single crystals with $\delta = 0.0$ and $0.4$ [68].

arises under conditions of proximity of the metal-insulator transitions (MITs) and their normal state shows various anomalous properties. The Mott criterion for MIT, $n_c^{1/3}a_H \simeq 0.25$ predicts that $La_{2-x}Sr_xCuO_4$ at $a_H \simeq 8\text{Å}$ [28] should be metallic for $x \simeq 0.0057$ which is not satisfied in cuprates, since the LSCO system is still insulating for $x < x_c = 0.05 - 0.07$ [28, 66, 67] (see Fig. 4.4). For $x < x_c = 0.05 - 0.07$, the resistivity $\rho$ of LSCO increases with decreasing temperature and begins to show an insulating behavior. This indicates that the charge carriers become localized at low temperatures. At $T = 0$, the MIT takes place around $x = x_c$ as a superconductor-insulator transition. The charge transport properties of high-$T_c$ cuprates are unusual in terms of a Fermi-liquid theory. According to the Fermi-liquid theory, the resistivity $\rho(T)$ should be proportional to $T^2$ at low temperatures. In contrast, the in-plane resistivity $\rho_{ab}$ of high-$T_c$ cuprates in the optimally doped regime is approximately proportional to $T$ down to $T_c$ and $\rho_{ab}(T)$ gradually evolves towards a $T^2$ behavior with doping in the overdoped region [67]. The temperature dependence of $\rho_{ab}(T)$ at $T < T_c$ was studied by suppressing the superconductivity using pulsed high magnetic fields [69]. Interestingly, $\rho_{ab}(T)$ in the cuprates LSCO and $Bi_2Sr_{2-x}La_xCuO_{4+\delta}$ (BSLCO) shows insulating behavior at low temperatures, and MITs in these systems take place at different doping levels. In particular, the MIT occurs at optimum doping in LSCO, while the metal-to-insulator crossover in BSLCO takes place in the underdoped region around $x = 1/8$ [69]. It is believed that the insulating behavior of $\rho_{ab}(T)$ in LSCO may be caused by the charge ordering since the optimally doped composition is located in the vicinity of $x = 1/8$ where charge ordering or segregation (which manifests itself in the form of nanoscale phase separation and stripe formation) takes place in all hole-doped cuprates and the superconductivity is markedly suppressed [70]. This "magic" doping level is called 1/8 anomaly and is assumed to be related to the segregation of doped carriers into metallic and insulating domains or stripes driven by the charge inhomogeneities in underdoped and some optimally doped cuprates. The onset of the MIT and phase separation corresponds to the MIT-QCP [63, 65] located around $x = 1/8$, which is different from the PG-QCP [64, 65]. Another QCP at $x_c = 0.05 - 0.07$ corresponds to the MIT ending near lightly doped region. Note that the origin of the 1/8 anomaly in the underdoped cuprates is not yet fully understood. The in-plane resistivity $\rho_{ab}(T)$ in some underdoped cuprates (e.g., LSCO and $La_{2-x}Ba_xCuO_4$) [71, 72] shows a substantial deviation from $T$-linear behavior at a crossover temperature $T^*$ far above $T_c$. In other underdoped cuprates, $\rho_{ab}(T)$ deviates downward from its high-temperature $T$-linear dependence below $T^*$ [38, 39, 68]. Sometimes anomalous resistive transitions (i.e., a sharp drop and a small jump in $\rho_{ab}(T)$) are observed at $T^*$ [72, 73]. The crossover temperature $T^*$ systematically shifts to lower temperatures with increasing doping $x$, and finally merges with $T_c$ in the optimally doped cuprates. The origin of these anomalies in $\rho_{ab}(T)$ is not clear enough, but it is possible that they are associated with the opening of the small pairing PG at $T^*$ in the underdoped cuprates. Another unusual charge transport property of these systems is the strong anisotropy of the resistivity. In the underdoped regime, $\rho_{ab}(T)$ shows a metallic behavior, while the $c$-axis resistivity $\rho_c(T)$ exhibits an insulating temperature dependence and the ratio $\rho_c/\rho_{ab}$ ranges from 50 to 100 [71]. The resistivity anisotropy $\rho_c/\rho_{ab}$ decreases with increasing doping $x$ and temperature $T$. This ratio is nearly increased exponentially with decreasing $T$.

### 4.3.4. Magnetic Properties

High-$T_c$ cuprate superconductors have also unusual magnetic properties. Experimental results show [74, 75, 76] that the magnetic susceptibility $\chi$ in the normal state of these materials exhibits an anomalous temperature dependence and a strong doping dependence (Fig. 4.14). In LSCO the $\chi(T)$ for $x \lesssim 0.2$ decreases with lowering $T$ at low temperatures, and

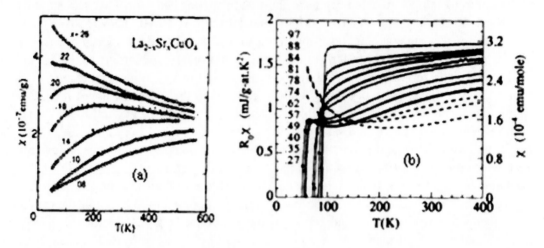

Figure 4.14. (a) Temperature dependence of the magnetic susceptibility $\chi$ of $La_{2-x}Sr_xCuO_4$ for various $x$ [75]. (b) Temperature dependence of $R_0\chi$ and $\chi$ in $YBa_2Cu_3O_{6+x}$ for $0.27 \leq x \leq 0.97$. $R_0 = S/\chi T = (\pi^2/3)(k_B/\mu_B)^2$ is the Wilson ratio for weakly interacting fermions having the entropy $S$ [76].

exhibits a broad peak at high temperatures of around $T^{max}$. When $x \geq 0.2$ susceptibility $\chi$ increases with lowering $T$ over the entire $T$ range below $600K$ [75]. Such a $T$-dependence of $\chi$ for $x > 0.2$ may be associated with a Curie-like contribution to $\chi$ coming from the spins localized on the impurities. The $T$-dependence of $\chi$ for $x = 0.2$, exhibiting a broad peak, is also described by taking a small Curie term into account. For $x < 0.2$, the $\chi(T)$ decreases largely below a temperature $T_\chi$, while the $T$ dependence of $\chi$ is almost linear and much weaker above $T_\chi$ (Fig. 4.14a). The crossover temperature $T_\chi$ decreases with increasing $x$ and its doping dependence is similar to the PG temperature $T^*$, where the resistivity shows a deviation from $T$-linear behavior, as discussed earlier. The strong temperature dependence of $\chi(T)$ below $T_\chi$ is also observed in YBCO [74] (Fig. 4.14b). However, there is no broad peak and Curie-like behavior in $\chi(T)$ at high doping levels. So far, there are no detailed theoretical predictions with which to compare the observed temperature and doping dependencies of $\chi$ in LSCO, YBCO, and other high-$T_c$ cuprates.

## 4.3.5.   Elastic Properties

Ultrasonic experiments indicated [2, 77] that the crystal lattice is also involved in the electronic phase transitions above $T_c$ in high-$T_c$ cuprates, where the strong electron-lattice interaction causes simultaneously the changes in the electron and lattice subsystems. In particular, two distinctly different kinks (or anomalies) in the longitudinal and shear sound velocities are observed at $T_c$ and $T_s > T_c$ in $La_{1.8}Sr_{0.2}CuO_{3.9}$ and $YBa_2Cu_3O_{6.9}$ in which $T_s$ values are about $93K$ and $120K$, respectively [2]. Several elastic anomalies have observed in the normal state of high-$T_c$ cuprates. In YBCO, the ultrasonic attenuation and the internal friction $Q^{-1}$ exhibit well defined peaks at approximately $120K$, $140-160K$, and $220-240K$ (see Refs. [77, 78, 79]). In optimally doped $YBa_2Cu_3O_{6.9}$ (with $T_c = 90K$), there are two internal friction peaks near $T_c$, which are similar to the specific heat heat anomalies observed in YBCO (with $T_c = 89K$) near $T_c$ [58]. By increasing oxygen content, the internal friction peak observed in optimally doped $YBa_2Cu_2O_{6.96}$ (with $T_c = 92.7K$) around $230K$ disappears in overdoped $YBa_2Cu_2O_{6.99}$ [78]. While other experiments show [79] that the internal friction peaks disappear at doping level $x_c = 0.21$ in $YBa_2Cu_2O_{6.94}$. The internal friction peak observed at $T \simeq 220-240K$ in YBCO is also similar to the specific heat peak observed at $T \sim 230K$ in this system. These elastic anomalies in high-$T_c$ cuprates seem to be associated with the (bi)polaronic effects and the precursor BCS-like pairing of large polarons above $T_c$ [77, 79].

## 4.4. Superconducting State Properties of High-$T_c$ Cuprates

Since the discovery of high-$T_c$ cuprate superconductors and other unconventional super-conductors, the peculiar SC state properties of these materials have been intensively studied using different experimental techniques. These experimental studies have shown that the high-$T_c$ cuprates are particularly puzzling and exhibit a variety of different unconventional behaviors. Experimental investigations have also demonstrated that heavy-fermion (HF) and organic superconductors share some common features with the high-$T_c$ cuprates [19, 80]. Despite much progress in experimental research, there is still no consensus on the nature of the SC state and SC transition in these materials. In this section, we discuss the basic experimental results which provide valuable informations relevant to the true SC state and offer important clues on the precise nature of the SC transition and for unveiling the microscopic mechanism of unconventional superconductivity in high-$T_c$ cuprates, HF and organic superconductors.

### 4.4.1. Superconducting Order Parameter, Low-lying Excitations and Zero-bias Conductance Peak

In conventional superconductor the BCS order parameter serves as the SC order parameter. However, the SC order parameter in high-$T_c$ cuprates could be different from the BCS-like ($s$-, $p$- and $d$- wave) order parameter and is likely associated with the coherence parameter of a superfluid Bose-condensate of Cooper pairs [42, 43, 52]. Several early experiments that aimed at clarification in the nature of SC order parameter in high-$T_c$ cuprates have been made [81, 82, 83]. They have shown that something novel occurs in these systems. Actually, the variation of the SC order parameter $\Delta_{SC}$ with temperature does not follow the BCS temperature dependence and $\Delta_{SC}(T)$ shows a steep downward deviation from the BCS dependence at higher temperatures or a kink-like behavior near a characteristic temperature $T_c^* \simeq (0.5-0.7)T_c$ [81, 82, 83] (Fig. 4.15). Such a $T$-dependence of $\Delta_{SC}(T)$ is similar to the kink-like $T$-dependence of the coherent parameter of superfluid bosons (Cooper pairs) [24, 42, 52]. Later, the doping and temperature dependencies of the gap-like features were investigated by various experimental techniques (see Refs. [35, 38, 48, 84]). It was found that the ratio $2\Delta_{SC}(0)/k_BT_c$ varies from 0.7 to 14 in different experiments and the doping dependence of "SC gap" is similar to that of small PG temperature, $T^*$, and the assumed "SC gap" increases with decreasing doping level. While the SC transition temperature $T_c$ is reduced with decreasing doping. The assumed "SC gap" smoothly merges with the small PG

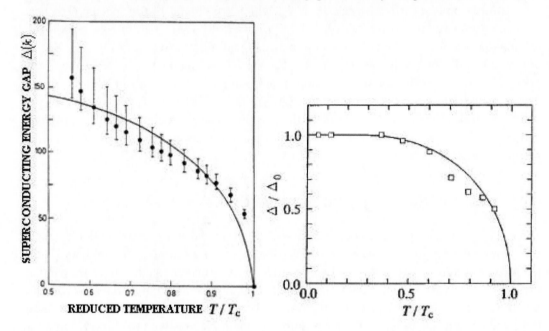

Figure 4.15. (a) Temperature dependence of the superconducting gap extracted from thermal conductivity measurements on EuBa$_2$Cu$_3$O$_{7-x}$ [81]. (b) Temperature dependence of the reduced gap in Bi2212(square) [83]. Solid line represents the BCS relation.

at $T_c$ and does not at all close at $T_c$. These experimental observations led to many controversial assumptions. It is often speculated that the "SC gap" and the PG have a common origin, and the PG is related to superconductivity [37, 45, 48, 50]. But this assumption contradicts with the thermodynamics of superconductors. Since the second-order SC phase transition at $T_c$ led to the vanishing of the SC order parameter ($\Delta_{SC}(T = T_c) = 0$) and to the observed discontinuity in $C_e$, which is not present in the "SC gap" data inferred from the ARPES and tunneling results. In this respect, measurements of the thermodynamic quantities are more sensitive probe of the SC gap and the SC transition. However, the SC properties of high-$T_c$ cuprates have been less explored than that of the normal state properties and the problem of the experimental determination of the SC gap and its precise temperature dependence stays surprisingly inscrutable as in the early stage of high-$T_c$ physics. Further, there is still no consensus on the nature of the low-lying excitations and ZBCP in the cuprates [53, 54]. Various experiments have evidenced (see Refs. [3, 53, 54, 84, 85]): (a) the existence of gapless excitations at $T \ll T_c$ and their nonexistence down to temperatures of order $T_c/2$, as first predicted in Refs. [24, 42, 52] on the basis of a superfluid Bose-liquid model (see also chapter 8); (b) the appearance of a zero-bias tunneling conductance; (c) the splitting of the ZBCPs under an applied magnetic field and without such a magnetic field; (d) the ZBCP shows different trends depending on temperature and material of the counter electrode and it becomes sharper and dips beside the peak grow at low temperatures when the counter electrode is a normal metal; (e) the suppression of the ZBCP with the onset of the superconductivity in the counter electrode of the S-I-S junction, and the single peak recovers when the applied magnetic field breaks the superconductivity in the counter electrode; (f) most experiments indicate that the ZBCP disappears above $T_c$.

The origins of the gapless excitations and ZBCPs in high-$T_c$ cuprates are often attributed to the nodes of a $d$-wave order parameter and the zero-energy Andreev surface bound states, which are formed at the nodes of the $d$-wave gap [53, 54]. However, for many reasons (see, e.g., Refs. [19, 35, 54, 86]), the d-wave model is inconsistent with the experimental observations and its validity is questionable [84]. Note that many researchers confuse the s-and d-wave pairing states of fermionic carriers in the cuprates with the novel SC state. In reality, the gapless excitations in high-$T_c$ superconductors can be naturally attributed to the presence of the gapless excitations of a superfluid Bose condensate of Cooper pairs [24, 42, 52] below a characteristic temperature $T_c^* << T_c$ and $T_c^* \simeq (0.5 \div 0.7)T_c$ (see also chapter 8). Also the precise measurements of tunneling conductance spectra of $La_{0.67}Sr_{0.33}MnO_3/YBCO$ and $Ag/YBCO$ junctions indicate [87] that the so-called broken time-reversal symmetry states, which led to the splitting of the ZBCP in zero magnetic field, are not induced at the surface of YBCO and the ZBCP consists of spin-dependent and -independent components. It is also found that the ZBCP does not exhibit the Zeeman splitting under the applied magnetic field value of $7T$. One possible scenario for the appearance of the ZBCP is the conversion of the electron (or hole) carriers into Cooper pairs at the N-S interface. One can assume that when the incoming carrier from N side, with energy smaller than the pairing gap energy $\Delta$, reaches a N-S interface, it cannot enter the superconductor, as a quasiparticle since there are no states below the gap $\Delta$. Instead, the carrier together with a second carrier from the normal metal can experience the pairing interaction at the N-S interface and form Cooper pair which enters the superfluid Bose condensate of Cooper pairs in the S side, while the missing carrier as a newly formed quasiparticle in the normal metal will move back inside N. As a result, the supercurrent flows through the N-S junction and the ZBCP is observed inside the gap $\Delta$.

### 4.4.2. Coexistence of the Pseudogap and Superconducting Gap

The existence of the normal-state gap (i.e., BCS-like pairing PG) below a characteristic temperature $T^* > T_c$) and the coexistence of the SC gap and the pairing PG below $T_c$ in high-$T_c$ cuprates have been postulated in [42, 43, 52], where it was argued that the SC order parameter is distinct from the PG. Later, such a PG was observed in ARPES and tunneling measurements [37, 40, 45, 48]. As predicted in [24, 42, 43, 52], the observed normal-state PG evolves smoothly across $T_c$ into the SC state gap. However, some experimental observations led to the conclusion that the PG is a precursor of the SC gap and has the SC origin (see, e.g., Refs. [37, 45, 50]). This confusion has hindered a detailed experimental investigation of the origins of novel high-$T_c$ superconductivity and the true SC order parameter. Nevertheless, a number of experimental works have been carried out for identification of the precise nature of the PG and the SC gap in high-$T_c$ cuprates [39, 46, 51, 88, 89]. In these experiments, it was reported that the PG and the SC gap coexist below $T_c$ and their origins are different. So far such statements about the origins and coexistence of two distinct gaps below $T_c$ and their temperature dependencies for different doping levels are partly controversial. Because, more contradictory results were reported in some tunneling experiments

[88, 89], where the PG and the true SC gap were not clearly distinguished. According to the new Fermi-Bose-liquid approach [42, 43, 52], the PG has its origin in a phenomenon different from superconductivity and the SC order parameter appears below $T_c$ within the BCS-like pairing PG which coexists with SC gap down to $T = 0$. Further studies of the doping and especially temperature dependencies of the PG and SC order parameter using the sophisticated and more informative experimental techniques may shed an important light on the distinctive properties of the PG and SC gap in high-$T_c$ cuprates.

### 4.4.3.    Thermodynamic Properties and λ-like Superconducting Properties

The electronic specific heat $C_e$ is one of most key thermodynamic properties of superconductors, since specific heat measurements are particularly sensitive to their low energy excitations and anomalies in $C_e(T)$ are, in principle, a proof of the bulk nature of the SC state. Therefore, this property of high-$T_c$ cuprates provides thermodynamic evidence for a SC phase transition at $T_c$. In contrast, ARPES and tunneling experiments are sensitive to the gap-like features, which may have nothing to do with the electronic phase transitions at $T_c$ and below $T_c$. One of the interesting anomalies characterizing the nature of the SC state in the high-$T_c$ cuprates is the λ-like jump in $C_e(T)$ observed at $T_c$ [44, 58, 59, 60] (Figs. 4.10 and 4.16a). The anomalies of $C_e(T)$ around $T_c$ in LSCO for $x = 0.10 - 0.2$ are different from BCS-like specific heat anomaly. Such anomalies in $C_e(T)$ were already

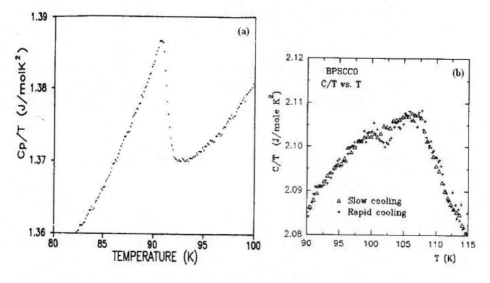

Figure 4.16. (a) Specific heat of the monocrystal YBCO (with $T_c = 90.8K$) plotted as $C_p/T$ vs. $T$ [59]. (b) Specific heat of $(BiPb)_2Sr_2Ca_2Cu_3O_{10-y}$ as $C/T$ vs. $T$ [90].

predicted theoretically in [24, 52] and resemble the λ-transition in $^4He$. Note that the λ-like specific heat anomaly was observed first in YBCO [59] (see Fig. 4.16a). While the anomaly of $C_e(T)$ in overdoped LSCO samples ($x \geq 0.22$) [44, 60] is similar to the BCS-like (i.e., step-like) jump in $C_e(T)$ observed in conventional superconductors. The high-$T_c$ cuprates show the specific heat jumps $\Delta C_e(T)/\gamma_e T_c \simeq 2 - 10$ [2, 57] at $T_c$, which are larger than the BCS value of $\Delta C_e(T)/\gamma_e T_c = 1.43$. The entropy decreases rapidly below $T_c$ [62, 76] and shows a clear signature of the SC phase transition in these materials at $T_c$. Surprisingly, a second anomaly in $C_e(T)$ in some high-$T_c$ cuprates was observed somewhat below $T_c$ (i.e., at $T_c^* < T_c$) [90, 91]. The existence of such a specific heat jump in high-$T_c$ superconductors at $T_c^* < T_c$ was also predicted within the framework of the theory of a superfluid Bose-liquid of Cooper pairs [24, 42, 52]. Thus, measurements of the specific heat behavior in the cuprates showed considerable deviation from BCS behavior, including a sharp $\lambda$-like jump at $T_c$ and a $T$-linear term in $C_e(T)$ at low-temperatures [3, 57, 92]. Below $T_c$ the temperature dependence of $C_e(T)$ is much stronger (see Figs. 4.11b and 4.16a); it can be fitted either with a power law $T^n$ (with $n \simeq 3$) or by a non-BCS exponential law [24]. The $T$-linear term at low temperatures is observed in YBCO and LSCO [92] and apparently absent in the Bi compounds [3, 92]. It could arise from a variety of sources. It might be attributed to the presence of some impurity phases [3] or unpaired carriers [24].

### 4.4.4. Electrodynamic Properties: Penetration Depth, Critical Magnetic Fields and Mixed State

The electrodynamic properties of superconductors are especially sensitive to the nature of their SC state. In particular, the temperature dependence of the London penetration depth $\lambda_L(T)$ is sensitive to the form of the excitation spectrum of a superfluid Fermi-liquid (in conventional superconductors) or Bose-liquid (in high-$T_c$ superconductors) (see chapter 8). Whereas the critical magnetic fields ($H_{c1}$, $H_c$, and $H_{c2}$) depend on the SC order parameter $\Delta_{SC}$. It is believed [42, 52] that the high-$T_c$ cuprates are the non-BCS superconductors (which is called as the boson superconductors), where the energy gap $\Delta_{SF}$ (see chapter 8) opens in the excitation spectrum of the two (2D)- and three (3D)-dimensional superconductors at $T > 0$ and $T > T_c^*$, respectively. Therefore, the behavior of $\lambda_L(T)$ is indicative of the presence or absence of the energy gap $\Delta_{SF}$ in the excitation spectrum of a superfluid Bose-liquid of Cooper pairs. Some early experiments (muon spin rotation ($\mu SR$) measurements) (see, e.g., Ref. [93]) performed on YBCO show a temperature dependence of $\lambda_L(T)$ which is well described by the empirical law $\lambda_L(T)/\lambda_L(0) = [1 - (T/T_c)^4]^{-1/2}$ which is now established theoretically within a 3D superfluid Bose-liquid model [24, 42, 52], (see chapter 8). While, other experiments (e.g., magnetization and surface impedance measurements) [93] indicated a power law dependence $\lambda_L(T) \sim T^2$ at low temperatures (Fig. 4.17).

In all probability such a dependence of $\lambda_L(T)$ can arise from a 2D superfluid Bose condensation of boson-like carriers (e.g., Cooper pairs). Since in this case the gap $\Delta_{SF}$ tends to zero as $T \to 0$ [42, 94]. The observed temperature dependence of the lower and upper critical magnetic fields $H_{c1}(T)$ and $H_{c2}(T)$ in high-$T_c$ cuprates are also very unusual. For example, the temperature dependence of $H_{c1}(T)$ does not show a BCS-like behavior. Instead, the upturn in $H_{c1}$ below a temperature $T_c^* \simeq (0.5 - 0.9)T_c$ was observed in YBCO [95, 96]. Similar behavior in the temperature dependence of $H_{c2}$ was observed in YBCO and $HgBa_2Ca_2Cu_3O_8$ (Hg-1223) at $T_c^* \simeq (0.64 - 0.88)T_c$ [97, 98]. The bending behavior of $H_{c1}(T)$ and $H_{c2}(T)$ (with a positive curvature $\partial^2 H_{c2}/\partial T^2 > 0$) near $T_c^*$ indicates that the kink-like change in the SC order parameter occurs around $T_c^*$ as in boson superconductors [24, 52]. The unusual behavior of $H_{c1}(T)$ has also been observed in other cuprates (see Ref. [95]). One can assume that the twin boundaries which are already present in YBCO system [99] stimulate superconductivity. Because the twin boundaries stimulate a

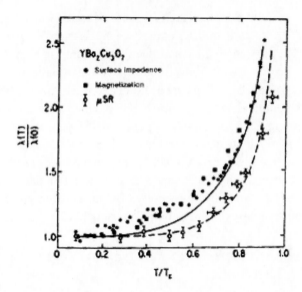

Figure 4.17. Temperature dependence of the reduced penetration depth of $YBa_2Cu_3O_{7-\delta}$ as evaluated from magnetization, muon spin rotation and surface impedance measurements [93]. The solid and dashed lines represent calculations using the Mattis-Bardeen theory and the Gorter-Casimir empirical formula.

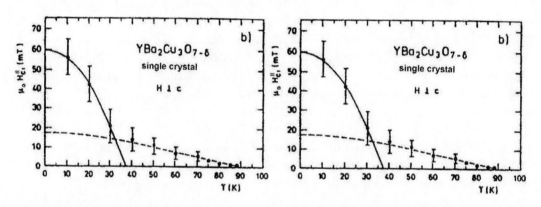

Figure 4.18. (a) Temperature dependence of $H_{c1}(T)$ of a single crystal $YBa_2Cu_3O_{7-\delta}$ for $H$ parallel to the $c$-axis [95]. The solid and dashed lines are parabolic fits to the low and high temperature data. (b) Temperature dependence of $H_{c1}(T)$ for the YBCO single crystals [96].

$3D \rightarrow 2D$ crossover in a superfluid Bose-liquid of Cooper pairs, which is accompanied by the appearance of the kink-like anomalies in $H_{c1}(T)$ and $H_{c2}(T)$ at more lower temperatures (e.g., $T_c^* \leq 0.5T_c$) [24]. According to the superfluid 3D Bose-liquid theory [24, 42, 52], the anomalous behavior of $H_{c1}(T)$ observed at $T_c^* \simeq 40K$ [95] is seemingly associated with a first-order phase transition in the SC state. Experimental observations of a resistive transition hysteresis and anomalous behavior of $H_{c1}(T)$ below $T_c$ in YBCO system also indicate

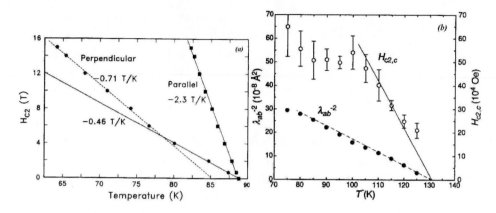

Figure 4.19. (a) Temperature dependence of $H_{c2}(T)$ for YBCO single crystal [97]. (b) Temperature dependencies of the in-plane penetration depth $\lambda_{ab}^{-2}(T)$ and the $H_{c2}(T)$ for HgBa$_2$Ca$_2$CU$_3$O$_8$ (with $T_c \simeq 133K$) superconductor for $H \| c$ [98].

the existence of a first-order phase transition at $T_c^* \simeq 40K$ [100]. The conventional mixed state is formed when the applied magnetic field $H$ exceeds a lower critical field $H_{c1}$ and superconductivity persists to an upper critical field $H_{c2}$, and below $T_c$ the complete 100% expulsion of magnetic flux from a superconductor occurs at $H < H_{c1}$. However, such a complete expulsion of magnetic flux from the interior of a superconductor is not characteristic for the cuprate superconductors [2, 101]. Since these high-$T_c$ cuprates show the incomplete or fractional Meissner effect and this is indicative in the presence of normal regions in the material below $T_c$. Actually, several types of charge carriers (e.g., large polarons and polaron Cooper pairs) may coexist in high-$T_c$ cuprates [24, 52] and the formation of a new type of mixed state is possible even in the absence of an applied magnetic field. This new mixed state is formed when the SC and non-SC charge carriers coexist below $T_c$. If below $T_c$ two types of SC carriers (with the SC transition temperatures $T_{c1}$ and $T_{c2}$) coexist, the new mixed state may exist in the temperature range $T_{c2} < T < T_{c1}$ [24, 102]. Such a new mixed state is also formed in the temperature range $0 < T < T_c$ when the unpaired and paired charge carriers coexist in high-$T_c$ cuprates.

### 4.4.5.  Vortex States, Integer and Half-Integer Magnetic Flux Quantization

The vortex state in high-$T_c$ cuprates is quite different from that in conventional superconductors. Different experiments [103] have shown that the vortex phase diagram of these materials is very complex and is composed of several vortex phase, such as Bragg glass, Bose glass, vortex glass, and vortex liquid phases. The vortex lattice (or glass) structure was observed at low enough temperature and the ordered vortex phase changes to the vortex liquid phase at the first-order vortex lattice melting transition temperature $T_m^* < T_c$. The vortex-lattice melting transition in YBCO (with $T_c \approx 92K$) has a complete 3D nature and the two dimensionally is not essential for such a first-order melting transition. The melting transition temperature $T_m^*$ is similar to the characteristic temperature $T_c^*$ where the anomalies in $C_e(T)$, $H_{c1}(T)$, and $H_{c2}(T)$ are observed. A number of experiments on the Nernst effect in high-$T_c$ cuprates have revealed the existence of vortex-like excitation in the temperature interval between $T_c$ and $T_v$ in the normal state (see, e.g., Refs. [104, 105]). The origin of these vortices is not yet well understood. Some Nernst effect studies show that the new characteristic temperature $T_v$ varies like $T_c$ with increasing doping and the interval between $T_c$ and $T_v$ is increased with the presence of controlled defects [105, 106, 107]. Moreover, the Nernst effect has strict 2D character. So, one can assume that the existence of vortices above $T_c$ can be associated with the 3D-2D crossover near the planar defects (e.g., twin boundaries (TBs)) or grain boundaries (GBs), where $T_c^{2D}(=T_v)$ is larger than $T_c^{3D}(=T_c)$ in the bulk of a SC material [24], and the local circulating supercurrent persists above $T_c$. The SC vortices is pinned by such structural defects and the local vortex states can exist in the temperature interval $T_c < T < T_v$. Although superconductivity is nucleated in the 2D localized regions (e.g., GBs or TBs) surrounded by a non-SC matrix at $T_v$, the local supercurrent circulating in these localized regions cannot flow through the whole sample. Since the global onset of superconductivity in the bulk of these superconductor occurs at $T_c$. Another remarkable feature of high-$T_c$ cuprates is that below $T_c$ the magnetic flux $\phi$ is quantized in units of $\phi_0/2$ (where $\phi_0 = \hbar/2e$) at the GBs [108, 109]. Experimental results indicate that in high-$T_c$ cuprates vortices at the GBs have half-integer flux quantum $\phi_0/2$, while all other situations correspond to the vortices with the integer flux quantum $\phi_0$ [109]. Some authors argue that the observed half-integer quantization effect is caused by a phase shift of $\pi$ at the Josephson junction and the $d$-wave pairing symmetry [109]. Such arguments seem to be inadequate. First, the half-integer quantization effect was also observed in heavily twinned crystals (or films) of YBCO for s-wave symmetry [108]. Secondly, the superfluid Bose condensation of Cooper pairs in the 3D-2D crossover regime provides a natural explanation for the half-integer quantization effect observed in the cuprates [24, 42, 52] (see chapter 8).

### 4.4.6.  Critical Current and Superfluid Density

The critical current density $I_c$ in high-$T_c$ cuprates depends on the GBs, the misorientation angle between adjacent GBs, and the vortex pinning. In particular, the $I_c$ decreases rapidly with increasing misorientation angle and it is governed by the links between the SC grains. Bulk high-$T_c$ materials have many GBs and characterized by $I_c \approx 10^3 A/cm^2$ at 77K [4, 101]. The value of $I_c$ is high enough in textured samples, where the misorientation angle between adjacent GBs is greatly reduced [4]. The values of $I_c$ within the grains are extremely high ($I_c \geq 10^7 A/cm^2$), while $J_c$ across the GBs is very low [101]. High quality YBCO films on SrTiO$_3$ substrates have much better current densities $I_c = 4 \times 10^6 A/cm^2$ at $T = 77K$ and $H = 0$ [110]. Further, irradiation by fast neutrons of YBCO single crystals to fluences of $5 \times 10^{18} cm^{-2}$ has led to a large increase of $I_c$ (i.e., $I_c$ increases 100 times and exceeds the value of $10^5 A/cm^2$ at $T = 40K$ and $H = 7T$) and pinning forces [111]. Because the defects created by neutron irradiation become very effective pinning centers. The observed temperature dependence of $I_c(T)$ just like $H_{c1}(T)$ shows a kink-like behavior near $T_c^* \simeq 0.5T_c$ [101, 112] (Fig. 4.20). The superfluid density $n_s$ is directly associated with the London penetration depth $\lambda_L$, i.e., $n_s(T) \sim (1/\lambda_L(T))^2$. Initially, it was speculated [113] that high-$T_c$ cuprates are characterized by a linear relation between $T_c$ and $n_c$ corresponding to an interacting Fermi-gas or a non-interacting Bose-gas. This assumption is questionable and contradicts with other experimental observations [51, 114]. According to the experimental

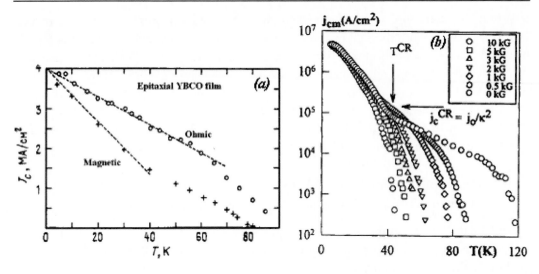

Figure 4.20. (a) Temperature dependence of the magnetic and ohmic critical current densities for some YBCO epitaxial films on $SrTiO_3$ substrates [101]. (b) Temperature dependencies of the critical current densities $j_{cm}$ for different fixed applied magnetic fields [112].

results [115], it was concluded that the $n_s$ in YBCO varies as $n_s \sim [1 - (T/T_c)^4]$, which is well described by a superfluid 3D Bose condensation model of Cooper pairs [24, 42, 52].

### 4.4.7. Gapless and Type II and III Superconductivity

The power law temperature dependence of the specific heat $C_e(T)$, the penetration depth $\lambda_L(T)$ and other SC properties observed in high-$T_c$ superconductors at low temperatures is considered as the direct evidence for the unconventional superconductivity of a gapless nature. There is now controversy about these experiments and the origin of the gapless superconductivity. For example, many authors often claim that the gapless superconductivity is associated with gapless spectrum of a Fermi-liquid, namely with the d-wave nodes. In principle, any BCS-like $d$-wave or $s$-wave pairing model cannot describe consistently the experimental observations of the existence of gapless excitations below some characteristic temperature $T_c^* << T_c$ and their nonexistence above $T_c^*$ up to $T_c$ in high-$T_c$ cuprates (for references, see, e.g., [85]). In contrast, such a gapless superconductivity can be naturally described by the gapless spectrum of a superfluid 3D Bose-liquid of Cooper pairs below $T_c^*$ [24, 42, 52].

Many experimental results indicate that the high-$T_c$ cuprates have unusual mixed state and they are extreme type-II superconductors [2, 4, 101, 102, 103]. Since Meissner flux expulsion of these materials is incomplete even at low temperatures and $H < H_{c1}$. In YBCO single crystals, the full Meissner effect is observed at applied fields $H \simeq 0.001 - 1.0 Oe$ (see Ref. [116]); while in LSCO, such a full Meissner effect was not found down to $H = 0.01 Oe$ [117]. Thus, experimental observations of the magnetic flux expulsion in high-$T_c$ cuprates have led to the conclusion [2, 24] that below $T_c$ the type II superconductivity with the full Meissner effect and type III superconductivity with the fractional Meissner effect may exist in these exotic superconductors; where novel SC vortex phases were also discovered (see Ref. [103]). An important difference between the cuprates and conventional type II superconductors is that the first-order phase transition in a quasi-3D vortex system was clearly observed at some characteristic temperature $T_s = T_c^* < T_c$ [118]. It was found that the magnetization step (above $T_s$) changes to a kink (below $T_s$). As mentioned earlier, the first-order phase transition in the quasi-3D vortex system observed in high-$T_c$ cuprates at $T_s$ is related to the first-order phase transition occurring in a 3D superfluid Bose-liquid state of Cooper pairs at $T_c^* < T_c$ [24, 42, 52].

### 4.4.8. One- and Two-bell-shaped Doping Dependences of $T_c$ with the Plateau or Local Minimum between Two Superconducting Domes

One of the universal features of high-$T_c$ cuprates is the nearly inverse parabolic (or bell-shaped) dependence of $T_c$ on the doped carrier concentration [119]. Note that such a parabolic concentration dependence of $T_c$ is incompatible with the theoretical approaches based on the 2D Hubbard model and d-wave pairing scenario [27, 104, 109]. Since these theoretical models consider purely 2D systems and predict a linear relation between $T_c$ and carrier concentration (i.e., $T_c \sim n_c/m^*$, where $m^*$ is effective mass of SC carriers). In high-$T_c$ cuprates, the $T_c$ has the maximum around the optimum doping concentration $x_0$ and the doping dependence of $T_c$ shows both the one-bell-shaped behavior [119] and the two-bell-shaped behavior with the plateau or local minimum between two SC domes [120, 121, 122] (Fig. 4.21). In $La_{2-x}Ba_xCuO_4$, the local minimum of $T_c$ observed near $x = 0.125$ shifts

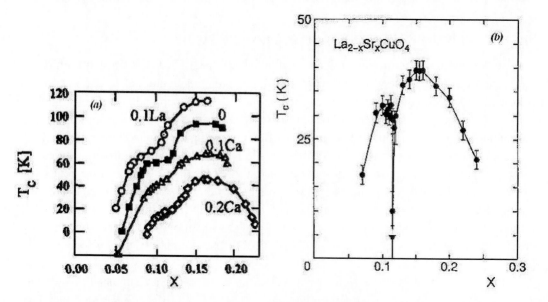

Figure 4.21. (a) Variation of $T_c$ with the reduced carrier concentration $x$ in La-and Ca-substituted YBCO [122]. (b) $x$-dependence of $T_c$ for LBCO [121].

to $x = 0.145$ with the partial substitution of $Ce$ for La; namely in $La_{1.98-x}Ce_{0.02}Ba_xCuO_4$ [120]. This two-bell-shaped behavior of $T_c(x)$ with the $60K$ plateau in YBCO [122] or the local minimum in $La_{2-x}(Sr,Ba)_xCuO_4$ near $x = 0.115$ is attributed to different phenomena (electronic phase separation, structural phase transition and magnetic ordering of Cu spin moments). We believe that the two-component scenario for unconventional superconductivity (which is driven by the superfluid condensation of distinctly different polaron Cooper pairs) proposed in [24, 42, 52, 123] may explain the two-bell-shaped doping dependence of $T_c$ in the cuprates.

## 4.5. Isotope Effect on the Superconducting Transition Temperature

Since the discovery of the high-$T_c$ cuprates superconductors a lot of experiments on isotope shift of $T_c$ have been performed in these materials (see Refs. [124, 125, 126]). These experiments indicate that the high-$T_c$ cuprates exhibit various anomalous isotope effects on $T_c$ and different values of oxygen isotope effect exponent $\alpha_o$ varying from $\alpha_o = -0.013$ to $\alpha_o \simeq 1.0$. Actually, the following general trends are observed in the families of high-$T_c$ cuprates [125, 126]: (1) changes in $T_c$ and $\alpha_o$ are correlated with the doping level, and $\alpha_o$ decreases with increasing $T_c$; (2) the values of $\alpha_o$ are quite different for different systems (e.g., $\alpha_o \simeq 0.1 - 1.0$ in LSCO ($10K < T_c < 40K$), $\alpha_o \simeq 0.02 - 0.05$ in YBCO (with $T_c = 91K$) and $\alpha_o = -0.013$ in Bi-2223 (with $T_c \simeq 108K$)); (3) the magnitude of $\alpha_o$ reaches a minimum value in each system when $T_c$ is at a maximum, and increases with decreasing doping and becomes larger than 0.5 in the underdoped LSCO (with $x \leq 0.125$). The anomalous isotope effects observed in high-$T_c$ cuprates clearly show that the electron-phonon coupling plays an important role in high-$T_c$ superconductivity. Consequently, the origins of the anomalous isotope effects on $T_c$ and the anticorrelation between doping dependencies of $\alpha_o$ and $T_c$ in the high-$T_c$ cuprates are still poorly understood. Further, these experimental observations of the substantial oxygen isotope shifts of $T_c$ in the cuprates cast doubts on the theoretical models which are based on non-phononic mechanisms for high-$T_c$ superconductivity.

## 4.6. Basic Physical Properties of Heavy-Fermion Superconductors

The heavy-fermion (HF) superconductors are mainly $Ce$- and $U$-based compounds, and their unusual SC and normal state properties are similar to those of high-$T_c$ cuprates [19, 20, 127]. The HF compounds are also the extreme type II superconductors and exhibit unconventional superconductivity and power law temperatures dependencies of various SC properties (e.g., specific heat, ultrasonic attenuation, and London penetration depth) [19, 20, 128]. Here, we briefly discuss the unusual physical properties of these materials, which are very similar to those of high-$T_c$ cuprate superconductors. The linear coefficient $\gamma_e$ of the electronic specific heat in the HF materials has an enormous value (e.g., $\gamma_e \simeq 450mJ/moleK^2$ [23] in $UPt_3$ and $\gamma_e \simeq 1000mJ/moleK^2$ in [129]) corresponding to a large electron effective masses $m^* \sim (10^2 - 10^3)m_e$. For the HF system $CeCu_2Si_2$, the electronic specific heat in the SC state has the following temperature dependence $C_{es}(T) \approx (T/T)^\beta C_{en}$ [20], where $\beta = 2.4 - 3$. Non-exponential $T$ dependencies of $C_{es}(T)$, $\lambda_L(T)$, ultrasound attenuation, and thermal conductivity are also observed in UBe$_{13}$ and UPt$_3$ [130]. Note that the shape of the specific heat $C_e$ anomalies in UBe$_{13}$ and UBe$_{12.97}$B$_{0.03}$ around $T_c$ are different from BCS behavior and has a $\lambda$-shaped anomaly [130]. In addition, the discontinuity $\Delta C_e$ at $T_c$ is almost twice as large as that expected from BCS prediction. The HF superconductors UPt$_3$ and Th-doped UBe$_3$ just like high-$T_c$ cuprates exhibit an unconventional superconductivity and the anomaly of the specific heat $C_e(T)$ in these materials at $T_c = T_{c1}$ is followed by a second anomaly at $T_c^*(= T_{c2})$, somewhat below $T_c$ (Fig. 4.22a). Specific heat measurements in various external magnetic fields

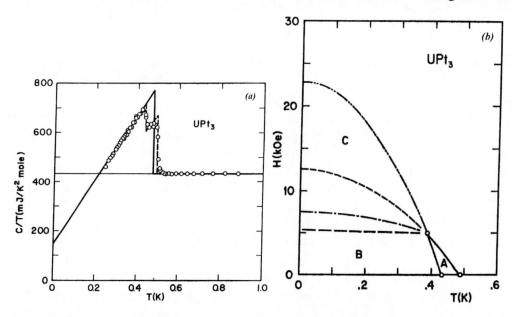

Figure 4.22. (a) Two distinct anomalies of $C_e(T)$ observed in UPt$_3$ at $T_{c1}$ and $T_{c2} < T_{c1}$ [130]. (b) Schematic $(H - T)$ phase diagram of superconducting UPt$_3$ [130]. Phase A is obtained from $C_e(T)$ measurements in zero and non-zero magnetic field. The lines separating B and C phases depend on the field orientation with respect to the crystal lattice and on the propagation direction of the sound waves.

show that these two anomalies merge into one at $H \approx 1T$ [130] and at least two distinct SC phases exist below $T_c$. The $H - T$ phase diagram of UPt$_3$ based on specific heat, ultrasonic attenuation and other measurements, has three distinctive SC phases (Fig. 4.22b).

Further, there are other similarities between HF superconductors and high-$T_c$ cuprates. Such similarities are: (a) $H_{c1}(T)$ and $H_{c2}(T)$ curves show upward curvature or a kink near $T^* = T_{c2}$; (b) HF systems have also gapless excitation spectrum at low temperatures; (c) The temperature-pressure (T-P) phase diagram of some HF superconductors with a QCP under a narrow SC dome [131] resembles that of $T - x$ phase diagram of high-$T_c$ cuprates; (d) The HF compounds UPd$_2$Al$_2$ and UPt$_3$ show a clear pseudogap feature in the normal state [132]. Many fundamental questions of HF superconductivity could not be settled solely by the existing BCS-like $s$-, $p$-, and $d$-wave pairing theories in a convincing way [128]. Since these theories contradict each other and give no insight into the underlying mechanism of superconductivity, and none of them fail to explain many observed details of HF superconductivity. A full understanding of unconventional superconductivity in HF systems requires a theory describing not only magnetically mediated BCS-pairing of heavy fermions but also superfluid Bose condensation of Cooper pairs. Apparently, such a non-standard one is the two-stage Fermi-Bose-liquid theory [24, 42, 52] which can provide a complete description of the SC properties of HF systems in terms of the precursor BCS-like pairing of heavy fermions and the superfluid Bose condensation of Cooper pairs.

## 4.7.    Basic Physical Properties of Organic Superconductors

The first organic superconductor $(TMTSF)_2PF_6$ undergoes a SC phase transition at $T_c = 1.4K$ under pressure ($6.5kbar$) [15], while the compound $(TMTSF)_2ClO_4$ showed the superconductivity at the same temperature $T_c = 1.4K$ under an ambient pressure [18] and the properties of this material in the SC state do not follow the BCS temperature dependence (for references, see Ref. [133]). Other organic compounds $k - (BEDT - TTF)_2Cu(NCS)_2$ and $k - (BEDT - TTF)_2Cu[N(CN)_2]Br$ have the highest SC transition temperatures $T_c = 10.4K$ and $11.6K$, respectively, at ambient pressure [18]. These compounds have a layered structure consisting of alternating donor BEDT-TTF sheets, each of which is separated by insulating anion ($X = Cu(NCS)_2$, $Cu[N(CN)_2]Br$) layers, and are characterized by quasi-two-dimensionality of the electronic state. Highly anisotropic organic BEDT-TTF based superconductors and high-$T_c$ cuprates may be considered as a stack of SC layers (BEDT-TTF and $CuO_2$ layers, respectively). The alkali-metal-doped $C_{60}$ compounds (i.e., fullerenes $A_xC_{60}$) are the new 3D high-$T_c$ organic superconductors, where the SC transition temperature is higher for larger dopants: $T_c = 18 - 19.3K$ for $K_xC_{60}$, $T_c = 28 - 30K$ for $Rb_xC_{60}$, and $T_c = 33K$ for $Rb_xCs_yC_{60}$ [135, 136]. These organic materials belong to the family of type II superconductors [18, 19, 134]. Experimental results [18, 19, 133, 136, 137] give evidence that the superconductivity in the organic compounds is also unconventional as in high-$T_c$ cuprates. Actually, the electronic specific heat $C_e$ of the quasi-2D organic superconductors shows a power-law temperature dependence [137] and a $\lambda$-like anomaly at $T_c$ [18, 138]. In particular, the quadratic or rather cubic (see Fig. 3 in Ref. [137]) temperature dependence of $C_e(T)$ was observed in $k - (BEDT - TTF)_2 Cu[N(CN)_2]Br$ well below $T_c$. In this system, $C_e(T)$ has also a finite linear term $\gamma_{res}T$, where the value of $\gamma_{res} = 1.2mJ/moleK^2$ at $T \to 0$ is very small compared with the normal state $\gamma_e$ value (i.e., $\gamma_{res}(T=0)/\gamma_e = 0.05$) and the Debye temperature is $212K$. The values of the ratio $\Delta C_e/\gamma_e T_c$ in quasi-2D organic superconductors are about $1.5 - 1.7$ [18, 138]. The coefficient of the $T$-linear specific heat in the $A_xC_{60}$ compounds is large enough ($\gamma_e \simeq 50 - 100mJ/moleK^2$) [134]. The temperature dependence of the London penetration depth $\lambda_L(T)$ observed in $k - (BEDT - TTF)_2Cu(NCS)_2$ and $k - (BEDT - TTF)_2Cu[N(CN)_2]Br$ compounds was found to follow a power law at low temperatures [133, 136], instead of an exponential behavior expected in the BCS theory. In $k - (BEDT - TTF)_2Cu(NCS)_2$ the $\lambda_L(T)$ is well approximated by the $T^n$ law at $T/T_c < 0.6$ and the exponent $n$ lies in the range of $1.7 - 2.2$ [133]. So, the experimental results give an evidence that the superconductivity in the quasi-2D organic compounds has a gapless nature just like in the high-$T_c$ cuprates and HF superconductors. Other analogies between organic superconductors and high-$T_c$ cuprates are: (a) the upward curvature of $H_{c2}(T)$ near $T_c$ [18]; (b) the ratio $2\Delta/k_BT_c \simeq 0.18$ [137] is much smaller than the BCS value 3.52; (c) weak isotope effect [18, 19]; (d) the existence of the familiar signatures of the pseudogap in the NMR, thermoelectric power and conductivity above $T_c$ [139, 140]. Further, as was first predicted in [24, 42, 52], several experiments indicate (see Ref. [140]) that in the organic superconductors $k - (BEDT - TTF)_2X$ with $X = Cu(NCS)_2$ and $Cu[N(CN)]Y$ ($Y = Br$ and $Cl$) a second-order phase transition takes place at a pseudogap formation temperature $T^* > T_c$. Thus, the comprehensive understanding of the unusual SC and normal state properties of high-$T_c$ cuprates, HF and organic superconductors may be achieved by analyzing crucial experiments in terms of very fundamental theories which combine the pairing theory with a proper theory of the superfluid Bose condensation of composite bosonic Cooper pairs. Such a new and more consistent theoretical approach has been suggested in [24, 42, 52] and will be presented in chapters 7 and 8.

# References

[1] K. A. Müller, J. G. Bednorz, and D. Tarnowski, *La Recherche,* N195, Janvier, 52 (1988).

[2] J. C. Phillips, *Physics of High-$T_c$ superconductors*(Academic Press, Boston, 1989).

[3] D. M. Ginsberg, in: *Physical Properties of High Temperature superconductors I*, ed., D.M. Ginsberg (Mir, Moscow, 1990) chapter 1.

[4] P. J. Ford and G.A. Saunders, *Contemporary Physics* 38, 63 (1997).

[5] J. G. Bednorz and K. A. Müller, *Z. Phys.* B64, 189 (1986).

[6] M. K. Wu, J. R. Ashburn, C. J. Torng, P. H. Hor, R. L. Meng, L. Gao, Z. J. Huang, Y. Q. Wang, and C. W. Chu, *Phys. Rev. Lett.* 58, 908 (1987).

[7] E. Dagotto, *Rev. Mod. Phys.* 66, 763 (1994).

[8] Y. Takura, H. Takagi, and S. Uchida, *Nature (London)* 337, 345 (1989).

[9] S. N. Putilin, E.V. Antipov, O. Chmaissem, and M. Marezio, *Nature* 362, 323 (1993).

[10] A. Schilling, M. Cantoni, J. D. Guo, and H. R. Ott, *Nature* 363, 56 (1993).

[11] A. Fukuoka, A. Tokiwa-Yamamoto, M. Itoh, R. Usami, S. Adachi, and K. Tanabe, *Phys. Rev.* B55, 6612 (1997-II).

[12] W. A. Little, *Phys. Rev.* 134A, 1416 (1964).

[13] V. L. Ginsburg, *Zh. Eksp. Teor. Fiz.* 47, 2318 (1964); *Phys. Lett.* 13, 101 (1964).

[14] V. L. Ginzburg and D. A. Kirzhnitz. eds.,"*Problems of High Temperature Supercon-ductivity*", (Nauka, Moscow, 1977).

[15] D. Jerome, A. Mazaud, M. Ribault and K. Bechgaard, *J. Phys. Lett.* 41, L95 (1980).

[16] A. F. Hebard, M. J. Rosseinsky, R. C. Haddon, D. W. Murphy, S. H. Glarum, M. Palstra, A. P. Ramirez, and A. R. Kortan, *Nature* 350, 600 (1991).

[17] K. Tanigaki, T. W. Ebbessen, S. Saito, J. Mizuki, J. S. Tsai, Y. Kubo, and S. Kuroda, *Nature* 352, 222 (1991).

[18] H. Mori, *Int. J. Mod. Phys.* B8, 1 (1994).

[19] B. H. Brandow, *Int. J. Mod. Phys.* B8, 3859 (1994).

[20] A. S. Davidov, *High Temperature Superconductivity* (Naukova Dumka, Kiev, 1990).

[21] F. Steglich, J. Aarts, C. D. Bredl, W. Liecke, D. Meschede, W. Franz, and H. Schafer, *Phys. Rev. Lett.* 43, 1892 (1979).

[22] H. R. Ott, H. Rudiger, Z. Fisk, and J. L. Smith, *Phys. Rev. Lett.* 50, 1595 (1983).

[23] G. R. Stewart, Z. Fisk, J. O. Willis, and J. L. Smith, *Phys. Rev. Lett.* 52, 679 (1984).

[24] S. Dzhumanov, *Int. J. Mod. Phys.* B12, 2151 (1998).

[25] T. Nakano, N. Momono, M. Oda, and M. Ido, *J. Phys. Soc. Jpn.* 67, 2622 (1998).

[26] K. Semba, T. Ishii, and A. Matsuda, *Physica* C185-189, 1303 (1991).

[27] M. Imada, A. Fujimori and Y. Tokura, *Rev. Mod. Phys.* 70, 1039 (1998).

[28] M. A. Kastner, R. J. Birgeneau, G. Shirane, and Y. Endoh, *Rev. Mod. Phys.* 70, 897 (1998).

[29] H. Shibata and T. Yamada, *Phys. Rev.* B56, R14275 (1997-II).

[30] A. N. Lavrov and V. F. Gantmakher, *Phys. Usp.* 41, 223 (1998).

[31] N. E. Hussey and J. R. Cooper, Research Review 1998.*High Temperature Superconductivity*, ed., W. Y. Liang (Cambridge Univesity Press, Cambridge, 1998) p. 52.

[32] S. Tajima, J. Schützmann, S. Miyamoto, I. Terasaki, Y. Sato, and R. Hauff, *Phys. Rev.* B55, 6051 (1997-I).

[33] M. Tachiki and H. Matsumoto, *J. Mag. Mag. Mater.* 90-91, 597 (1990).

[34] S. Uchda, *Physica* C185-189, 28 (1991).

[35] A. Damascelli, Z. Hussain, and Z.-X. Shen, *Rev. Mod. Phys.* 75, 473 (2003).

[36] J. Ashkenazi and C. G. Kuper, *Physica* C162-164, 767 (1989).

[37] H. Ding, T. Yokoya, J. C. Campuzano, T. Takahashi, M. Randeria, M. R. Norman, T. Mochiku, K. Kadowaki, and J. Giapintzakis, *Nature* 382, 51 (1996).

[38] T. Timusk and B. Statt, *Rep. Prog. Phys.* 62, 61 (1999).

[39] J. L. Tallon and J.M. Loram, *Physica* C349, 53 (2001).

[40] A. G. Loeser, Z.-X. Shen, M. C. Schabel, C. Kim, M. Zhang, and A. Kapitulnik, *Phys. Rev.* B56, 14185 (1997-I).

[41] M. R. Norman, H. Ding, J. C. Campuzano, T. Takeuchi, M. Randeria, T. Yokoya, T. Takahashi, T. Mochiku, and K. Kadowaki, *Phys. Rev. Lett.* 79, 3506 (1997).

[42] S. Dzhumanov, *Physica* C235-240, 2269 (1994).

[43] S. Dzhumanov and P. K. Khabibullaev, *Izv. Akad. Nauk Uzb. SSR, Ser. Fiz. Mat. Nauk* 1, 47 (1990).

[44] T. Matsuzaki, M. Ido, N. Momono, R. M. Dipasupil, T. Nagata, A. Sakai, and M. Oda, *J. Phys. Chem. Solids* 62, 29 (2001).

[45] Ch. Renner, B. Revaz, J.-Y. Genoud, K. Kadowaki, and O. Fischer, *Phys. Rev. Lett.* 80, 149 (1998).

[46] A. Matsuda, S. Sugita, T. Fujii, and T. Watanabe, *J. Phys. Chem. Solids* 62, 65 (2001).

[47] Z.-X. Shen and J. R. Schrieffer, *Phys. Rev. Lett.* 78, 1771 (1997).

[48] N. Miyakawa, P. Guptasarma, J. F. Zasadzinski, D. G. Hinks, and K. E. Gray, *Phys. Rev. Lett.* 80, 157 (1998).

[49] S. Rast, B. H. Franzer, M. Onellion, T. Schmauder, M. Abrecht, O. Touzelet, H. Berger, G. Margaritondo, and D. Pavina, *Europhys. Lett.* 51, 103 (2000).

[50] R. M. Dipasupil, M. Oda, N. Momono, and M. Ido, *J. Phys. Soc. Jpn.* 71, 1535 (2002).

[51] J. L. Tallon, J. W. Loram, J. R. Cooper, C. Panagopoulos, and C. Bernhard, *Phys. Rev.* B68, 180501 (2003).

[52] S. Dzhumanov and P. K. Khabibullaev, *Pramana J. Phys.* 45, 385 (1995).

[53] S. Kashiwaya and Y. Tanaka, *Rep. Prog. Phys.* 63, 1641 (2000).

[54] G. Deutscher, *Rev. Mod. Phys.* 77, 109 (2005).

[55] H.-S. Chang, H.-J. Lee and M. Oda, *Phys. Rev.* B64, 134504 (2001).

[56] T. Ekino, S. Hashimoto, T. Takasaki, and H. Fujii, *Phys. Rev.* B64, 092510 (2001).

[57] B. D. Dunlap, M. V. Nevitt, M. Slaski, T. E. Klipper, Z. Sungaila, A. G. McKale, D. W. Capone, R. B. Poeppel, and B. K. Flandermeyer, *Phys. Rev.* B35, 7210 (1987).

[58] S. E. Inderhees, M.vB. Salamon, N. Goldenfeld, J. P. Rice, B. G. Pazol, D. M. Ginsberg, J. Z. Liu, and G. W. Crabtree, *Phys. Rev. Lett.* 60, 1178 (1998).

[59] K. Fossheim, O. M. Nes, T. Laegreid, C. N. W. Darlington, D. A. O'Connor, and C. E. Gough, *Int. J. Mod. Phys.* B1, 1171 (1988).

[60] T. Matsuzaki, N. Momono, M. Oda, and M. Ido, *J. Phys. Soc. Jpn.* 73, 2234 (2004).

[61] V. N. Morgun, N. N. Chebotaev, and A. V. Bondarenko, *Fiz. Niz. Temp.* 16, 264 (1990).

[62] J. W. Loram, K. A. Mirza, J. M. Wade, J. R. Cooper, and W. Y. Liang, *Physica* C235-240, 134 (1994).

[63] C. Castellani, C. Di Castro, and M. Grilli, *Phys. Rev. Lett.* 75, 4650 (1995); *J. Phys. Chem. Solids.* 59, 1694 (1998).

[64] C. M. Varma, *Phys. Rev.* B55, 14554 (1997).

[65] S. Dzhumanov, *Superlattices and Microstructures* 21, 363 (1997); *Solid State Commun.* 115, 155 (2000).

[66] J. Fink, N. Nücker, M. Alexander, H. Romberg, M. Knupfer, M. Merkel, P. Adelmann, R. Clacssen, G. Mante, T. Buslaps,S. Harm, R. Manzke, and M. Skibowski, *Physica* C185-189, 45 (1991).

[67] H. Takagi and N. E. Hussey, *Proc. Intern. School of Physics "Enrico Fermi" Course* CXXXVI, eds., G. Iadonisi, J. R. Schrieffer, and M. L. Chiofalo (IOS Press, Amsterdam, 1998) p. 227.

[68] A. Carrington, D. J. C. Walker, A. P. Mackenzie, and J. R. Cooper, *Phys. Rev.* B48, 13051 (1993-I).

[69] S. Ono, Y. Ando, T. Murayama, F. F. Balakirev, J. B. Betts, and G. S. Boebinger, *Physica* C357-360, 138 (2001).

[70] M. Akoshima and Y. Koike, *J. Phys. Soc. Jpn.* 67, 3653 (1998).

[71] T. Adachi, T. Noji, and Y. Koike, *J. Phys. Chem. Solids.* 63, 1097 (2002).

[72] P. B. Allen, Z. Fisk, and A. Migliori, in: *Physical Properties of High Temperature Superconductors I*, ed., D. M. Ginsberg (Mir, Moscow, 1990).

[73] A. Ulug, B. Ulug, and R. Yagbasan, *Physica* C235-240, 879 (1994).

[74] D. C. Jonhston, *Phys. Rev. Lett.* 62, 957 (1989); *J. Mag. Mag. Mater.* 100, 218 (1991).

[75] T. Nakana, M. Oda, C. Manabe, N. Momono, Y. Miura, and M. Ido, *Phys. Rev.* B49, 16000 (1994-II).

[76] J. W. Loram, K. A. Mirza, and J. R. Cooper, Research Review 1998. *High Temperature Superconductivity.* ed., W. Y. Liang (Cambridge University Press, Cambridge, 1998) p. 77.

[77] L. Sun, Y. Wang, and Z. Yu, *Physica* C185-189, 1373 (1991).

[78] S. G. Titova, V. A. Fotiev, A. V. Pashenko, A. M. Burhanov, V. V. Gudkov, I. V. Zhevstovskih, A. V. Tkach, and V. V. Ustinov, *Superconductivity: Physics, Chemistry, Technika* 4, 1010 (1990).

[79] S. Dzhumanov and T. Khaidarov, in: *Abs. 5th Int. Conf. On Magnetic and Superconducting Materials* (Khiva, Uzbekistan, 2007) p. 38.

[80] T. Moriya and K. Ueda, *Rep. Prog. Phys.* 66, 1299 (2003).

[81] M. A. Izbizky, M. Nunez Regueiro, P. Esquinazi, and C. Fainstein, *Phys. Rev.* B38, 9220 (1988).

[82] B. A. Aminov, M. V. Pedyash, D. K. Petrov, H. T. Rakhimov, K. Sethupathi, M. V. Sudakova, and Ya. G. Ponomarev, *Physica* C185-189, 2533 (1991).

[83] N. Tsuda, E. Arai, A. Mottate, T. Kogawa, N. Numasaki, and D. Shimada, *Physica* C235-240, 1889 (1994).

[84] Ch. Thomsen and M. Cardona, in: *Physical Properties of High Temperature Super-conductors I*, ed., D. M. Ginsberg (Mir, Moscow, 1990) chapter 8.

[85] M. Granath, V. Oganesyan, S. A. Kivelson, E. Fradkin, and V. J. Emery, *Phys. Rev. Lett.* 87, 167011 (2001).

[86] A. Sacuto, R. Combescot, N. Bontemps, P. Momod, V. Viallet, and D. Colson, *Euro-Phys. Lett.* 39, 207 (1997).

[87] A. Sawa, S. Kashiwaya, H. Kashiwaya, H. Obara, H. Yamasaki, M. Koyanagi, I. Kurosawa, and Y. Tanaka, *Physica* C357-360, 294 (2001).

[88] V. M. Krastnov, A. Yurgens, D. Winkler, P. Delsing, and T. Claeson, *Phys. Rev. Lett.* 84, 5860 (2000).

[89] M. Suzuki and T. Wantanabe, *Phys. Rev. Lett.* 85, 4787 (2000).

[90] J. E. Gordon, S. Prigge, S. J. Collocott, and R. Driver, *Physica* C185-189, 1351 (1991).

[91] H. Mayama, Y. Okajima, and K. Yamaya, *Phys. Rev.* B57, 14470 (1998-II).

[92] N. E. Phillips, J. P. Emerson, R. A. Fisher, J. E. Gordon, B. F. Woodfiel, and D. A. Wright, *Physica* C235-240, 1737 (1994).

[93] J. Carini, L. Drabeck, and G. Grüner, *Mod. Phys. Lett.* B3, 5 (1989).

[94] M. J. Rice and Y. R. Wang, *Phys. Rev.* B37, 5893 (1988).

[95] H. Adrian, W. Assmus, A. Höhr, J. Kowalewski, H. Spille, and F. Steglich, *Physica* C162-164, 329 (1989).

[96] N. Kobayashi, H. Iwasaki, S. Terada, K. Noto, A. Tokiwa, M. Kikuchi, Y. Syono, and Y. Muto, *Physica* C153-155, 1525 (1988).

[97] T. Worthington, W. J. Gallagher, and T. R. Dinger, *Phys. Rev. Lett.* 59, 1160 (1987).

[98] A. Schilling, O. Jeandupeux, S. Büchi, H. R. Ott, and C. Rossel, *Physica* C235-240, 229 (1994).

[99] L. I. Burlachkov and L. I. Glasman, *Physica* C166, 75 (1990).

124                                     S. Dzhumanov

[100] J. M. Barbut, D. Bourgault, N. Schopohl, A. Sulpice, and R. Tournier, *Physica* C235-240, 2855 (1994).

[101] A. P. Malozemoff, in: *Physical Properties of High Temperature Superconductors I*, ed., D. M. Ginsberg (Mir, Moscow, 1990) chapter 3.

[102] E. J. Pakulis, *Phys. Rev.* B42, 10746 (1990).

[103] N. Kobayashi, T. Nishizaki, K. Kasuga, and S. Okayasu, *Physica* C460-462, 1204 (2007).

[104] P. A. Lee, N. Nagaosa, and X.-G. Wen, *Rev. Mod. Phys.* 78, 17 (2006).

[105] G. Bridoux, P. Pedrazzini, F. De la Cruz, and G. Nieva, Physica C460-462, 841 (2007).

[106] Y. Wang, Lu Li, N. P. Ong, *Phys. Rev.* B73, 024510 (2006).

[107] F. Rullier-Albenque, R. Tourbot, H. Alloul, P. Lejay, D. Colson, and A. Foeget, *Phys. Rev. Lett.* 96, 067002 (2006).

[108] R. Kleiner, A. S. Katz, A. G. Sun, R. Summer, D. A. Gajewski, S. H. Han, S. I. Woods, E. Dantsker, B. Chen, K. Char, M. B. Maple, R. C. Dynes, and J. Clarke, *Phys. Rev. Lett.* 76, 2161 (1996).

[109] C. C. Tsuei and J. R. Kirtley, *Rev. Mod. Phys.* 72, 969 (2000).

[110] H. Adrian, C. Tome-Rosa, G. Jakob, A. Walkenhorst, M. Maul, M. Paulson, M. Schimitt, P. Przyslupski, G. Adrian, M. Huth, and Th. Becherer, *Supercond. Sci. Technol.* 4, S166 (1991).

[111] T. Terai, Y. Nagamoto, T. Kubo, N. Chikumoto, and K. Sawa, *Physica* C460-462, 293 (2007).

[112] V. V. Metlushko, V. V. Moschalkov, Y. Bruynseraede, G. Güntherodt, H. Thomas, and K. Winzer, *Physica* C235-240, 2793 (1994).

[113] Y. J. Uemura, *Physica* C185-189, 733 (1991).

[114] F. Rullier-Albenque, H. Alloul, and R. Tourbot, *Phys. Rev. Lett.* 91, 047001 (2003).

[115] D. van der Marel, M. Bauer, E. H. Brandt, H.-U. Habermeier, D. Heitmann, W. König, and A. Wittlin, *Phys. Rev.* B43, 8606 (1991).

[116] V. G. Fleisher, R. Laiho, E. Lähderanta, Yu. P. Stepanov, and K. B. Traito, *Physica* C272, 26 (1996).

[117] A.S. Sherbakov, V. E. Startsev, E. G. Valiulin, V. L. Kozhevnikov, *Mod. Phys. Lett.* B4, 129 (1990).

[118] T. Hanaguri, T. Tsuboi, A. Maeda, T. Nishizaki, N. Kobayashi, Y. Kotaka, J.-I. Shimoyama, and K. Kishio, *Physica* C256, 111 (1996).

[119] C. N. R. Rao and A. K. Ganguli, *Physica* C235-240, 9 (1994).

[120] Y. Koike, T. Kawaguchi, S. Hosoya, N. Watanabe, T. Noji, and Y. Saito, *Physica* C185-189, 791 (1991).

[121] K. Kumagai, K. Kawano, H. Kagami, G. Suzuki, Y. Matsuda, I. Watanabe, K. Nishiyama, and K. Nagamine, *Physica* C235-240, 1715 (1994).

[122] J. L. Tallon, G. V. M. Williams, N. E. Flower, and C. Bernhard, *Physica* C282-287, 236 (1997).

[123] S. Dzhumanov, B. Yavidov, and N. A. Makhmudov, Superlattices and Microstructures 21, 325 (1997).

[124] K. A. Müller, *Z. Phys.* B80, 193 (1990).

[125] H. J. Bornemann, D. E. Morris, and H. B. Liu, *Physica* C182, 132 (1991).

[126] G.-M. Zhao, H. Keller, and K. Conder, *J. Phys.: Condens. Matter* 13, R569 (2001).

[127] D. S. Hirashima and T. Matsuura, *J. Phys. Soc. Jpn.* 59, 24 (1990).

[128] D. Rainer, *Physica Scripta* T23, 106 (1988).

[129] E.-W. Scheidt, T. Schreiner, P. Kumer, and G. R. Stewart, *Phys. Rev.* B58, 15153 (1998-II).

[130] H. R. Ott, *Int. J. Mod. Phys.* B6, 473 (1992).

[131] F. Steglich, *Physica* C460-462, 7 (2007).

[132] M. Dressel, N. Kasper, K. Petukhov, B. Gorshunov, G. Grüner, M. Huth, and H. Adrian, *Phys. Rev. Lett.* 88, 186404 (2002).

[133] K. Kanoda, K. Akiba, K. Suzuki, T. Takahashi, and G. Saito, *Phys. Rev. Lett.* 65, 1271 (1990).

[134] B. Batlogg, *Physica* C185-189, xviii (1991).

[135] S. Saito and A. Oshiyama, *Physica* C185-189, 421 (1991).

[136] T. Takahashi, K. Kanoda, and G. Saito, *Physica* C185-189, 366 (1991).

[137] Y. Nakazawa and K. Kanoda, *Phys. Rev.* B55, R8670 (1997-II).

[138] D. Jerome and H. J. Schulz, *Adv. Phys.* 31, 299 (1982).

[139] E. B. Park, J. W. Shim, H. Park, Y. W. Park, K. B. Lee, H. S. Kim, Z. Iqbal, and R. H. Bauchman, *Physica* C185-189, 409 (1991).

[140] T. Sasaki, N. Yoneyama, A. Matsuyama, and N. Kobayashi, *Phys. Rev.* B65, 060505 (2002).

# Chapter 5

# Different Theoretical Approaches to the Unconventional Superconductivity

## 5.1. Introduction

After the discovery of high-$T_c$ superconductivity in the ceramic copper oxides (cuprates) [1, 2], a large number of distinctly different theoretical models has been proposed to explain this remarkable phenomenon. Because the BCS pairing theory, which had been so successful in describing conventional superconductors, turned out to be inadequate for the description of high-$T_c$ superconductivity in the cuprates. A weak isotope effect observed initially in high-$T_c$ cuprates and the strong correlations found in the undoped cuprates favored some trends in theories to orientate themselves towards electronic (non-phononic) and magnetic mechanisms of high-$T_c$ superconductivity. Such trends are quite difficult to understand, even so, since from the very beginning of the era of high-$T_c$ superconductivity there was ample experimental evidence that indicated the important role played by the electron-phonon interaction in the basic physics of the cuprate superconductors. At the same time, a number of proposed theoretical models which were considered more relevant to the high-$T_c$ superconductivity in the cuprates were based on the strong electron-phonon interactions. Although there is increasing experimental evidence for a strong electron-phonon coupling in these polar materials (see e.g., Refs. [3, 4, 5, 6]), most of the experimental data are still inconclusive to convincingly confirm or rule out of the existing speculative theories. So far the proposed new theoretical models, which are based on the pairing mechanisms of carriers in real $(r)$-and momentum $(k)$-space, and on the Bose-Einstein condensation (BEC) of an ideal Bose-gas of real- and $k$-space pairs are mostly inconsistent and conflict with one another. Theoretical research on high-$T_c$ superconductivity is now an enormous field and it would be quite difficult to discuss the vast literature related to the subject. It is important, however, to discuss some specific theoretical models and ideas, which are often considered as the possible candidates to explain high-$T_c$ superconductivity in the cuprates, and the main merits and shortcomings of these theories and speculations.

## 5.2.    Bipolaronic Mechanism of Superconductivity

One of the early ideas of high-$T_c$ superconductivity was the so-called bipolaronic mechanism of superconductivity. The first idea of high-$T_c$ superconductivity was put forward by Ogg [7], who in 1946, conjectured that dimers in frozen metal-ammonia solutions were mobile and could be responsible for superconductivity, which is associated with the BEC and superfluidity of electron pairs. But these results were not confirmed. Another mechanism of superconductivity based on the BEC of an ideal Bose-gas of electron quasimolecules was proposed by Schafroth [8] before the BCS pairing theory [9]. Actually, in some polar materials, the superconductivity of electron or hole quasimolecules (bipolarons), proposed by Schafroth and then discussed by Chakraverty, Ranninger, Alexandrov, and others (see Refs. [10, 11]), might be expected at low carrier densities. Since the $r$-space pairing of carriers, in contrast to their pairing in $k$-space takes place in a dilute Fermi gas and leads to the formation of tightly bound electron or hole pairs. In polar materials with strong electron-phonon coupling, a moving charge carrier with its polarization cloud becomes a self-trapped quasiparticle (polaron). The idea of carrier self-trapping was first predicted by Landau [12] and the polaron problem has been discussed by Pekar, Fröhlich, Feynman, Mott, Holstein, Toyozawa, Emin, and others (see Refs. [13, 14]). The so-called small and large polarons (bipolarons) may exist in polar materials. The small (bi)polaron is localized but the large one can be mobile. Moreover, one distinguishes between Anderson (intrasite)-type small bipolarons or negative $U$-centers [15] and quasimolecular (intersite)-type small bipolarons [16]. Chakraverty [16] explored the analogy between bipolarons and Cooper pairs by extending the BCS-like approximation to the $r$-space bipolarons which are considered as localized Cooper pairs in the strong electron-phonon coupling limit. The temperature-electron-phonon coupling constant ($T - \lambda$) phase diagram proposed by Chakraverty has promoted the discovery of high-$T_c$ cuprate superconductors. Before this discovery the possiblity of $r$-space pairing and high-$T_c$ superconductivity of small and large bipolarons was discussed by Alexandrov and Ranninger [17], and Bishop and Overhauser [18]. In the small polaron theory the half-bandwidth $W$ of the free electron (hole) band is renormalized exponentially with the electron-phonon coupling strength and the polaronic half-bandwidth $W_p$ is given by [11, 19].

$$W_p = W \exp(-g^2) \tag{5.1}$$

In this case, the BCS-like coupling constant $\lambda_{BCS}$ is determined as $\lambda_{BCS} = zg^2 \hbar \omega_0 / 2W$, where $z$ is the number of nearest neighbors or coordination number, $\omega_0$ is the optical phonon frequency.

The superconducting (SC) transition temperature $T_c$ depends on the effective mass $m_B$ and density $n_B$ of bipolaronic carriers. In the low bipolaron-density limit, the dependence of $T_c$ on $n_B$ is given by the formula for BEC temperature $T_{BEC}$ of an ideal gas of free bosons [11, 19, 20]

$$T_c = T_{BEC} = 3.31 \hbar^2 n_B^{2/3} / k_B m_B \tag{5.2}$$

According to the theory of the small-bipolaronic superconductivity [11, 17], the excitation spectrum of bipolarons in the low bipolaron-density limit (when $n_B$ is less than some critical value $n_c$) is gapless (i.e., sound-wave like) and similar to the excitation spectrum of superfluid Bose liquid $^4He$, so that small bipolarons might be superconducting. The existence of linear sound-wave-like excitations in the SC state of small bipolarons change qualitatively the thermodynamic and electromagnetic properties of the bipolaronic superconductor from those predicted by BCS theory. In particular, at low enough temperatures, the specific heat varies as $C_v(T) \sim T^d$ [11] (where $d$ is the dimensionality of the system). But at higher temperatures, $C_v(T) \sim T^{d/2}$ in the SC state. The temperature dependencies of the London penetration depth $\lambda_L$, upper and lower critical magnetic fields $H_{c2}$ and $H_{c1}$ are also nonstandard [11], namely, one obtains an upward curvature of $H_{c2}(T)$ near $T_c$, with $H_{c2}(T) \sim [1 - (T/T_c)^{3/2}]^{3/2}$ and for $T << T_c$ the $\lambda_L(T)/\lambda_L(0)$ and $H_{c1}(T)/H_{c1}(0)$ are proportional to $(T/T_c)^{d+1}$. With increasing temperature these dependencies change to $\lambda_L(T)/\lambda_L(0) \simeq [1 - (T/T_c)^{d/2}]^{-1/2}$ and $H_{c1}(T)/H_{c1}(0) \approx 1 - (T/T_c)^{d/2}$. Note that in the strong electron-phonon coupling limit the possibility of obtaining small-bipolaronic high-$T_c$ superconductivity becomes unrealizable. Since the small bipolarons have very large effective masses $m_B \gtrsim 100m_e$ [20, 21] (where $m_e$ is the free electron mass). Therefore, some authors believe that either such small bipolarons are strongly localized [22] or their BEC temperature is vanishingly small [23]. Indeed, for the orthothombic high-$T_c$ cuprate superconductor $La_{2-x}Sr_xCuO_4$, the density of lattice atoms is $n_a = 1/V_a \simeq 5.3 \times 10^{21} \, cm^{-3}$ (where $V_a \simeq 190 Å^3$ is the volume per $CuO_2$ unit) and the carrier density in the optimally doped regime is about $n_p = 0.15 \cdot 5.3 \times 10^{21} \, cm^{-3} \simeq 0.8 \times 10^{21} \, cm^{-3}$, so that using appropriate values of $m_B = 100m_e$ and $n_B = n_p/2$, we obtain $T_c \simeq 15 \, K$. It follows that the small bipolarons can become SC at much lower temperatures. In this connection, Chakraverty et al. [23] have proposed the formation of the so-called peroxitons ($O - Cu^+ - O$) in the cuprates and demonstrated that the peroxiton will have an effective mass $m^* \simeq 10m_e$, which is sufficient to yield the BEC temperature $T_{BEC} \gtrsim 100 \, K$. Further, Alexandrov et al. [24] have considered the formation of the superlight Fröhlich-Holstein-type small bipolaron with the effective mass $m_B \sim 10m_e$ for explaining the high-$T_c$ superconductivity in the cuprates. It is believed that the normal-state pseudogap is half of the bipolaron binding energy and the temperature-doping phase diagram does not include any metallic state [25]. The small bipolaron model was also used to explain the anomalous normal-state properties of high-$T_c$ cuprates (see, e.g., Ref. [26]). It follows from this consideration that the small bipolaron theories encounter serious difficulties due to the very large effective mass and poor mobility of small bipolarons. Therefore, the large bipolarons due to their multisite extension and relatively small effective masses or high BEC temperatures are assumed to play an important role in high-$T_c$ superconductivity in the cuprates and the mechanism of the BEC of large bipolarons was proposed by Emin and Hillery [22] to explain this phenomenon in these materials. While the superfluid single particle and pair condensation of an interacting Bose-gas of large bipolarons in $k$-space was proposed in [27, 28] as a possible mechanism for novel high-$T_c$ superconductivity in these materials. According to this superfluid Bose-liquid approach, the pair condensation of attracting large bipolarons leads to the formation of Cooper-like pairs of large bipolarons. At the same time, a phonon-mediated attraction between two large bipolarons leading to the formation of their bound state in $r$-space was studied by Emin [29, 30], who argued that large bipolarons will condense into a liquid at sufficiently low temperatures. Actually, large bipolarons may exist only in the lightly doped cuprates (see Chapter 6), which are non-superconducting. Finally, we note that in most of bipolaronic models the Landau criterion for superfluidity is often examined within the Bogoliubov model of a repulsive Bose-gas (see Refs. [11, 20, 30]) and the $T_c$ is determined from the relation (5.2). However, the Bogoliubov model is inadequate for describing the superfluid properties of Bose-liquid $^4$He [31] and the BEC temperature of an ideal Bose-gas is not at all the SC transition temperature of bipolarons [27, 28].

## 5.3. Electronic Mechanisms of BCS-like Pairing

Before the discovery of high-$T_c$ superconductors, some theorists were exploring the possibility of obtaining high-$T_c$ superconductivity within the BCS-like pairing model due to the exchange of excitations other than phonons. In the initial stage, Little [32] and Ginzburg [33] hypothesized the existence of high-$T_c$ superconductors due to the interaction of electrons with electronic excitations whose energy is much higher than the phonon energy. Little put forward the idea of the excitonic mechanism of BCS-like pairing in a quasi-one-dimensional organic conductors with a side-branch. (The chain was assumed to be metallic, while the side-branch perhaps provided the excitons.) At the same time, Ginzburg suggested another possibility of obtaining high-$T_c$ superconductivity at the metal-insulator boundary due to the electron-exciton pairing interaction. In so doing, he considered the sandwich-type superconductor (with alternating layers of a metal and an insulator) in which the existence of excitons in the insulating layers was favored. Further, it was assumed that the mechanism of the BCS-like pairing of $\pi$ electrons in the complex organic molecules is also similar to the mechanism of superconductivity in the Little model [34]. In the electronic models, the role of excitations in causing the pairing of conduction electrons is similar to that of phonons [35]. In 1973, Allender, Bray, and Bardeen [36] proposed the specific excitonic model for a metal-semiconductor interface and speculated that a narrow gap semiconductor could be used as a polarizable excitonic medium. The possibility of the BCS-like pairing of carriers due to the exchange of electronic excitations has also been discussed by other authors (see Ref. [37]). Before 1986, a more detailed review of the electronic mechanisms of high-$T_c$ superconductivity based on the BCS-like pairing of carriers has been given by Ginzburg and Kirzhnits [38]. For attractive electron-mediated electron-electron pairing, the Debye energy $\hbar\omega_D$ in the expression for $T_c$ given by the BCS relation is replaced by the exciton energy $E_e$, i.e., the BCS-like expression for $T_c$ has the form [39].

$$k_B T_c \simeq 1.14 E_e \exp(-1/\lambda_{BCS}), \tag{5.3}$$

where $\lambda_{BCS}$ is the BCS-like electron-exciton coupling constant. Assuming that $E_e \simeq 1eV$ and $\lambda_{BCS} \simeq 0.2$, we obtain $T_c \simeq 78K$. For plasmon-mediated pairing mechanism, the exciton energy $E_e$ in Eq. (5.3) is replaced by $\hbar\Omega_p$ [40], where $\Omega_p$ is the plasma frequency. The value of $\Omega_p$ can be estimated as $\Omega_p = (4\pi n e^2/m^*)^{1/2}$, where $n$ and $m^*$ are the density and effective mass of carriers, respectively. For $n \simeq 10^{21} cm^{-3}$, $m^* \simeq m_e$ and $\lambda_{BCS} \simeq 0.2$, Eq. (5.3) yields $T_c \simeq 92K$. Indeed, the excitonic and plasmonic mechanisms of BCS-like pairing may give enhancement of $T_c$ in unconventional superconductors. However, extensive experimental research efforts till 1986 were not successful in raising the $T_c$ appreciably. Interest in exciton-mediated pairing mechanisms was largely increased after the discovery of layered high-$T_c$ cuprate superconductors. As a result, many different electronic (including hybrid (phonon-electronic)) mechanisms of BCS-like pairing have been suggested (see Refs. [10, 35, 37, 39, 41]). The new alternative approaches based on the localized electron-bag, spin-bag and correlation-bag mechanisms have been proposed by Weinstein [42], Schrieffer et al. [43], and Goodenough and Zhou [44]. In the combined phonon-electronic models, the exciton or plasmon energy and $\lambda_{BCS}$ in (5.3) are replaced by $\hbar\tilde{\Omega}$ and $\lambda_{BCS} = 2(\lambda_{ph} + \lambda_e)$, where $\tilde{\Omega} = \sqrt{\Omega_{ph}\Omega_p}$, $\Omega_{ph}$ is the characteristic phonon frequency, $\lambda_{ph}$ and $\lambda_e$ are the electron-phonon and electron-exciton (plasmon) coupling constants, respectively. While in the spin-bag model [43] based on the condition $U < W$ (where $U$ is the on-site Coulomb interaction energy, $W$ is the bandwidth of dressed carriers with the effective mass $m^*$), the BCS-like expressions for the energy gap $\Delta_{SC}(= \Delta_{BCS})$ and $T_c(= T_{BCS})$ have the forms

$$\Delta_{SC} = 2\sqrt{\varepsilon_F \hbar\omega_0}\exp\left[-\frac{1}{\lambda_{BCS}}\right]$$

and

$$k_B T_c \simeq 1.14\sqrt{\varepsilon_F \hbar\omega_0}\exp\left[-\frac{1}{\lambda_{BCS}}\right], \tag{5.4}$$

where $\varepsilon_F \simeq 0.1$ eV is the Fermi energy relative to the top of the valence band, $\lambda_{BCS} = V_0 N(0)$, $V_0$ is the pairing interaction potential between carriers, $N(0) = 1/W$ is the density of states, $W = 2\pi\hbar^2/m^*a^2$, $a$ is the lattice constant, $\hbar\omega_0$ is the effective cutoff energy for the pair interaction potential.

The correlation-bag model [44] based on the condition $U > W$ provides a similar expression for $T_c$. It is suggested that two carriers tend to share their spin or correlation bags and produce BCS-like pairing which can lead to superconductivity. Unfortunately, the electronic theories of BCS-like pairing encounter several problems [39, 41, 45] (apart from the experimental contradictions such as the $\lambda$-like SC transition [46] and the inconstant ratio $2\Delta_{SC}/k_B T_c$ and specific heat jump $\Delta C/\gamma_e T_c$ [41, 45])

## 5.4.   BCS-Bose-Einstein-Condensation Crossover Approach

Another alternative approach to high-$T_c$ superconductivity in the cuprates is based on the crossover from BCS condensation to BEC. Before the discovery of high-$T_c$ cuprates superconductors, Chakraverty [16], Leggett [47], Nozieres and Schmitt-Rink [48] have discussed the problem of the crossover from a weak-coupling BCS pairing regime to a strong-coupling $r$-space pairing or BEC regime. In particular, Leggett argued that the BCS formalism can describe the SC ground state over the entire coupling range encompassing weakly bound Cooper pairs as well as tightly bound pairs. Later the crossover from a BCS condensation to a BEC of tightly bound pairs was studied by Nozieres and Schimitt-Rink (NSR), who followed the evolution between these two limits in terms of the coupling strength of an effective fermionic attractive pair interaction. The BCS weak-coupling superconductivity has been viewed as BEC of Cooper pairs (since the structure of the BCS wave function is the same, characteristic of BEC). While the superconductivity of strongly bound pairs in the NSR theory is described by BEC of an ideal Bose of tightly bound pairs. After 1986, the crossover from BCS-like pairing to BEC of tightly bound pairs has been studied by many authors (see Refs. [11, 49, 50, 51, 52, 53, 54]). It is believed that the high-$T_c$ cuprates are characterized by relatively short coherence length and may be in an intermediate coupling regime (where no reliable approximations yet exist) between the weak-and strong-coupling limits. It is quite possible that the formation of large polarons and Cooper pairs of large polarons occurs in this intermediate region [54]. Earlier, it was argued [51] that high-$T_c$ cuprates belong to the transition region from the small polaronic BCS-like superconductors to the charged small bipolaronic Bose-liquid and such a crossover from BCS to BEC regime occurs at $\lambda_{BCS} = V_p/W_p = 1$, where $V_p$ is the polaron-polaron attraction energy.

The NSR theory describes a smooth crossover from BCS type superconductivity to BEC of small $r$-space pairing. According to this approach, $T_c$ in the weak-coupling regime is controlled by Cooper pair breaking and is determined as the usual BCS expression for $T_c$ (see chapter 3), whereas in the strong-coupling regime the bound pairs exist well above $T_c$ and the SC transition is driven by center of mass excitations of the pairs and $T_c$ is determined by usual BEC temperature $T_{BEC}$ of an ideal Bose-gas of tightly bound pairs. Note that there is some confusion in the literature concerning the characteristic SC transition, Cooper pair dissociation and BEC temperatures. Many authors argue (see Refs. [28, 48, 52, 54, 55]) that Cooper pair dissociation temperature $T^*$ is much larger than $T_c$. (Some of them [11, 48, 52] confuse the $T_c$ with the BEC temperature of an ideal Bose-gas of Cooper pairs). By contrast Hirsch [50] argued that the SC transition temperature is described by BCS theory over the entire coupling range and the BEC temperature $T_{BEC}$ is much larger than $T_c$, and no bound pairs exist above $T_c$. The NSR approach to the problem of the BCS-BEC crossover has been reexamined by some authors in terms of the BCS-like coupling constant $\lambda_{BCS}$, the product $k_F \xi$ (where $k_F$ is the Fermi wave vector and $\xi$ is the coherence length for the Fermi system) and the carrier concentration instead of the strength of the interaction potential. In [53], it has been shown that the crossover from BCS pairing to BEC of tightly bound pairs occurs at $k_F \xi = 2\pi$ and the SC transition is expressed in terms of $k_F \xi$ by the relation $k_B T_c = 0.4\varepsilon_F/k_F\xi$ for $k_F\xi \geq 2\pi$, i.e., all superconductors lie in the region $k_F\xi > 2\pi$. The description of the high-$T_c$ superconductivity and the formation of a pseudogap at temperature $T^*$ well above $T_c$ in the cuprates as the crossover from the BCS condensation to the BEC of an ideal Bose-gas of tightly bound preformed pairs was also proposed in different physical contexts (see e.g., Refs. [11, 52, 55]). However, such a BEC description is incompatible with the Landau criterion for superfluidity (since an ideal Bose-gas cannot be superfluid (Ref. [28]) and the mean-field-like (i.e., $\lambda$-like) SC transition in high-$T_c$ cuprates [56].

## 5.5. Boson-Fermion Models

Somewhat different approach which treats a mixture of preformed local pairs or $r$-space pairs (bosons) and free electrons (holes), and the effects resulting from boson-fermion interactions, was proposed by Ranninger and Robaszkiewicz [57] in the framework of the small (bi)polaron model and then rediscovered in a phenomenological approach by Friedberg and Lee [58]. Such a two-component model combines the BCS-like pairing ideas with the BEC of an ideal Bose-gas of preformed pairs. The superconductivity of mixed boson-fermion systems is described by using a two-band model consisting of a broad electronic (fermionic) band and a narrow bosonic band. Various versions of the boson-fermion model have been discussed by many authors in different physical contexts (see Refs. [56, 59, 60] and works quoted therein).

The SC properties of the boson-fermion system are determined by the relative position of the bosonic and and fermionic bands, the charge carrier density $n$ and the boson-fermion coupling strength $g_{BF}$. The preformed pairs (composite bosons) are assumed to be in a bound state (when the bosonic level is below the fermionic band and $n$ is smaller than a critical density $n_c$) or resonant state (when the bosonic level lies inside the fermionic band and coincides with the Fermi level for $n = n_c$) in which preformed pairs spontaneously decay into pairs of electrons (holes). It is speculated that for $n \geq n_c$ localized bosons (preformed pairs) due to a boson-fermion pair-exchange coupling can acquire itinerancy as the temperature is lowered towards $T_c$ and then Bose condense in the background of a Fermi-liquid [56, 59]. In this case, a BCS-like superconductivity is induced simultaneously in the fermionic subsystem and the localized composite bosons play the role of phonons in standard BCS theory. Below $T_c$, both bosons and fermions are assumed to be superfluid, with the energy gap $\Delta$ of the fermion system now related to the macroscopic zero-momentum occupation number $N_0$ of the bosons. In the opposite case (i.e., when the bosonic level is low compared with the Fermi level and $n < n_c$) the fermions will flow into the bosonic band forming bosons and the superconductivity in the entire system occurs due to the BEC of preformed pairs. The model Hamiltonian of a mixture of localized bosons and free fermions interacting with each other via the charge-exchange term $H_{BF}$, can be written as [58]

$$H = \sum_{\vec{q}} \left[ \varepsilon_B + \hbar^2 \vec{q}^2 / 2m_B \right] b_{\vec{q}}^+ b_{\vec{q}} + \sum_{\vec{k}\sigma} [\varepsilon(\vec{k}) - \mu] a_{\vec{k}\sigma}^+ a_{\vec{k}\sigma}$$
$$+ \frac{1}{\sqrt{\Omega}} \sum_{\vec{k}\sigma,\vec{q}} \left[ g_{BF}(k) b_{\vec{q}}^+ a_{\frac{\vec{q}}{2}+\vec{k}\sigma} a_{\frac{\vec{q}}{2}-\vec{k}\sigma} + H.C. \right], \tag{5.5}$$

where $\varepsilon_B = E_B - 2\mu$, $E_B$ denotes the relative position of the bosonic band with respect to the fermionic band, $m_B$ is the mass of the boson, $\varepsilon(k)$ is the kinetic energy of the fermions measured relative to the chemical potential $\mu$ (this chemical potential is common to bosons and fermions in order to guarantee charge conservation), $b_{\vec{q}}^+ (b_{\vec{q}})$ and $a_{\vec{k}\sigma}^+ (a_{\vec{k}\sigma})$ are the creation (annihilation) operators of bosons and fermions, respectively; $\sigma$ is the spin of the electron, $\Omega$ is the volume of the system.

For $g_{BF} = 0$, both the bosonic number $N_B$ and the fermionic number $N_F$ are separately conserved. While, for $g_{BF} \neq 0$, only the total particle number $N = N_F + 2N_B$ is conserved. The SC transition at $T_c$ is described as a BEC which occurs only because bosons become coherent due to the exchange of fermions. Further, the operators $b_0^+$ in the boson-fermion interaction term is replaced by $N_0^{1/2}$ according to the Bogoliubov approximation. In this approximation, the Hamiltonian $H$ can be easily diagonalized by using the Bogoliubov transformation of Fermi operators (see Eq.(3.56) in chapter 3) and the BCS-like excitation spectrum for the fermions is given by [58]

$$E(k) = \sqrt{(\varepsilon(k) - \mu)^2 + \Delta^2(k)}, \tag{5.6}$$

where $\Delta^2(k) = g_{BF}^2(k) N_0 / \Omega$.

The Friedberg and Lee model predicts the following temperature dependencies of $N_0$ and $\Delta$ [58]:

$$N_0(T) \approx N_0(0) \left[ 1 - (T/T_c)^{3/2} \right], \quad \Delta(T) \approx \Delta(0) \left[ 1 - (T/T_c)^{3/2} \right]^{1/2} \tag{5.7}$$

Whereas the SC transition temperature $T_c$ is determined by the BEC temperature of bosons $T_c \simeq 3.31\hbar^2 n_B^{2/3}/k_B m_B$, where $n_B$ is the density of bosons. In the boson-fermion model of Ranninger et al. [57, 59], $T_c$ depends on the total number of carriers $N$ and superconductivity is controlled by the BEC of bosons and a concomitantly driven BCS-like state of the fermionic subsystem. In such a boson-fermion model [56, 59], the pseudogap formation is explained by the presence of localized preformed pairs above $T_c$. The previously discussed boson-fermion models may have some relevance to the problem of high-$T_c$ cuprates. However, in judging the relevance of these approaches, one should consider their compatibility (without vague speculations) with the experimentally observed $\lambda$-like SC transition, first-order phase transition in the SC state, kink-like temperature dependence of the SC order parameter, critical current and magnetic fields.

## 5.6. Resonating Valence Bond Model

Shortly after the discovery of high-$T_c$ cuprate superconductors, the area of very active research was stimulated by the Anderson's suggestion [61] that the so-called resonating valence bond (RVB) state may exist in the undoped La$_2$CuO$_4$ compound with a layered perovskite structure. The RVB state was originally proposed in 1973, by Anderson [62], as a possible ground state for the $s = 1/2$ antiferromagnetic (AF) Heisenberg model on a triangular layer lattice. The RVB model has received considerable attention and further developed by many theorists (see, e.g., Refs. [10, 63, 64, 65, 66, 67, 68, 69, 70]). Anderson and other advocates of the idea of RVB state strongly believe that the essential physics of the cuprates would be captured by the one-band Hubbard model given by [63]

$$H = -t \sum_{\langle ij \rangle, \sigma} (c_{i,\sigma}^+ c_{j\sigma} + H.C.) + U \sum n_{i\downarrow} n_{i\uparrow}, \tag{5.8}$$

where $ij$ are copper sites with holes of spin $\sigma$, $t$ is the nearest-neighbor hopping integral, $U$ is the on-site Coulomb repulsive interaction, $n_{i\sigma} = c_{i\sigma}^+ c_{i\sigma}$ is the number operator.

By using the canonical transformation at $U \gg t$ the Hubbard Hamiltonian reduces to the $t - J$ Hamiltonian which is defined only in the non-doubly occupied subspace (see Refs. [63, 66]),

$$H = -t \sum_{\langle ij \rangle, \sigma} \left[ (1 - n_{i,-\sigma}) c_{i\sigma}^+ c_{j\sigma} (1 - n_{j,-\sigma}) + H.C. \right] - \mu \sum_{i\sigma} n_{i\sigma}$$
$$+ J \sum_{\langle ij \rangle} (\vec{s}_i \vec{s}_j - \frac{1}{4} n_i n_j), \tag{5.9}$$

where $s_i = c_{i\uparrow}^+ c_{i\downarrow}$ is the spin $\frac{1}{2}$ operator at the site $i$ of a two-dimensional (2D) square lattice, $J$ is the AF coupling between nearest neighbor sites $\langle ij \rangle$, $\mu$ is the chemical potential, $n_i = n_{i\downarrow} + n_{i\uparrow} = 1$.

The term $-\frac{1}{4} n_i n_j$ in (5.9) appears spontaneously in the strong-coupling expansion of the Hubbard model [71]. RVB model with a mean-field treatment was developed by Baskaran et al. [63]. The Hamiltonian (5.9) may be rewritten in terms of the valence bond singlet pair creation (annihilation) operators $b_{ij}^+ (b_{ij})$, as [63, 69]

$$H = -t \sum_{\langle ij \rangle, \sigma} (1 - n_{i,-\sigma}) c_{i\sigma}^+ c_{j\sigma} (1 - n_{j,-\sigma}) - \mu \sum_{i\sigma} n_{i\sigma} - J \sum_{\langle ij \rangle} \Delta_{ij} b_{ij}^+, \tag{5.10}$$

where $\Delta_{ij} = \langle b_{ij} \rangle$ is the pairing amplitude in the bond $ij$, $b_{ij}^+ = \frac{1}{\sqrt{2}}(c_{i\uparrow}^+ c_{j\downarrow}^+ - c_{i\downarrow}^+ c_{j\uparrow}^+)$ and the identity $(\vec{s}_i \cdot \vec{s}_j - \frac{1}{4}n_i n_j) = b_{ij}^+ b_{ij}$ is used. By transforming to momentum space, $H$ can be expressed as [63, 66]

$$H_{MF} = \sum_{\vec{k}\sigma}[\varepsilon(\vec{k}) - \mu]c_{\vec{k}\sigma}^+ c_{\vec{k}\sigma} - \sum_{\vec{k}}[\Delta(\vec{k})c_{\vec{k}\uparrow}^+ c_{-\vec{k}\downarrow}^+ + \Delta^*(\vec{k})c_{-\vec{k}\downarrow}c_{\vec{k}\uparrow}], \tag{5.11}$$

where $\Delta(\vec{k}) = \sum_{\vec{k}'}J(\vec{k}-\vec{k}')\langle c_{-\vec{k}'\downarrow}c_{\vec{k}'\uparrow}\rangle$, $\varepsilon(k) = -tx(\cos k_x + \cos k_y)$, $x = 1 - n$ describes the deviation from half-filled band.

The Hamiltonian $H_{MF}$ is similar to the BCS type one. Diagonalizing this Hamiltonian by using Bogoliubov transformations of Fermi operators gives quasiparticle energy spectrum

$$E(\vec{k}) = \sqrt{(\varepsilon(\vec{k}) - \mu)^2 + |\Delta(k)|^2} \tag{5.12}$$

The BCS-like gap $\Delta(k)$ and the chemical potential $\mu$ are determined from the equations

$$\Delta(k) = \sum_{\vec{k}'}J(\vec{k}-\vec{k}')\frac{\Delta(\vec{k}')}{2E(\vec{k}')}\tanh\frac{E(\vec{k}')}{2k_BT} \tag{5.13}$$

$$\frac{1}{N}\sum_{\vec{k}}\frac{\varepsilon(\vec{k})-\mu}{E(\vec{k})}\tanh\frac{E(\vec{k})}{2k_BT} = x \tag{5.14}$$

Initially, it was assumed that the order parameter $\Delta(\vec{k})$ has the form $\Delta(\vec{k}) = \Delta(\cos k_x + \cos k_y)$ which corresponds to the extended s-wave RVB solution [66]. The formation of singlet pairs explains the decrease of the uniform spin susceptibility, the creation of the spin pseudogap above $T_c$ and a linear term in the specific heat (when $E(k)$ becomes gapless). The elementary electronic excitations in the RVB state were first studied by Kivelson et al. [64], who developed the important concept of spinons and holons and spin-charge separations. In so doing, the spin-half neutral fermion excitation was called the spinon, while the second kind of excitation is termed a holon, which represents a spinless charged hole localized on the Cu-site (i.e., $Cu^{3+}$ states) in the hole-doped cuprates. Spin-charge separation creates spinons with zero charge and holons with zero spin. These two kinds of excitations are shown in Fig. 5.1. Since there are spinless holons (bosons) above $T_c$, the RVB model predicts a normal metal state with no Fermi surface, i.e., it is not a Fermi-liquid [10]. Equation (5.13) determines the spin gap $\Delta_{SC}$ (the pseudogap is associated with this spin gap) and the RVB mean-field onset temperature $T_{RVB}$ of spinon pairing. It is speculated that the doping of the pure $La_2CuO_4$ would destroy AF phase and stabilize the RVB state with creation of boson "hole" excitations and a SC state. One view is that a quasi-two-dimensional Bose gas of holons of mass $m_h$ and density $n_h$ Bose condense at $T_c \simeq 2\pi\hbar^2 n_h/k_B m_h$ to form the SC state [72, 73]. Another possibility is that the holon-holon interaction would lead to the pair condensation of holons and to the high-$T_c$ superconductivity of these charged bosons in the cuprates [74, 75, 76]. The original RVB theory of single layer superconductivity was replaced by the interlayer pair tunneling model [68, 74]. But this interlayer tunneling model

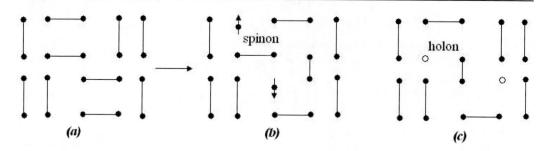

Figure 5.1. (a) The RVB ground state (solid lines represent spin-singlet pairs or valence bonds). (b) Two $s = \frac{1}{2}$ spins (or spinons) are formed by breaking a single valence bond. (c) The electrons are removed from the $CuO_2$ layer of the cuprates with the creation of holes (holons) on the Cu-sites.

has been seriously questioned or falsified by experiments [77]. The alternative pair condensation theory of a quasi-two-dimensional Bose gas of attracting holons was developed by Rice and Wang [75, 76] by analogy with the BCS pairing theory. It is shown that the temperature ($T$) dependencies of the critical magnetic field $H_c(T)$ and pair potential $\Delta_h(T)$ are also similar to those of a conventional superconductor, although the excitation spectrum of the holon superconductor $E_h(k) = \sqrt{(\varepsilon(k) + |\mu_h|)^2 - \Delta_h^2}$ (where $\varepsilon(k) = \hbar^2 k^2 / 2m_h$, $\mu$ is the chemical potential of a holon gas) is different from that of a BCS fermionic superconductor. It is also found that the $T$ dependence of the London penetration depth $\lambda_L(T)$ is in good agreement with some experimental results for $YBa_2Cu_3O_{7-\delta}$ and the specific heat, $C_v(T)$ is linear in $T$ for all $T < T_c$ and falls exponentially to zero for $T << T_c$, as in the BCS case. Quantitative comparison with experiments based on RVB theory have also been attempted by other authors (see Refs. [67, 69, 70, 78]). In particular, the RVB theory attributes the pseudogap observed in the normal state of high-$T_c$ cuprates to the singlet pairing of spinons [67, 69].

Although the ideas of the RVB state and spinon-holon phenomenology are highly attractive, there are unresolved theoretical problems [10, 41, 54, 79, 80] (aside from the experimental contradictions such as the isotope effect [81], the specific heat [82], the absence of the $Cu^{3+}$ state [10] (i.e., holes on the $Cu^{2+}$ lattice) in the cuprates, the absence of the holon-like bosons with the charge $e$ in the SC and normal states of these materials [83, 84]). For example, some theoretical results (see Ref. [10]) have shown that the two-dimensional Habbard model does not support superconductivity (i.e., a doped Mott insulator cannot become superconductor) and the AF or Neel state is the ground state of the undoped cuprates.

## 5.7.   Superconducting Fluctuation Approach

Starting from the early 1990s, other fundamentally different approaches to the theory of high-$T_c$ cuprate superconductors have also been proposed in [85] and [28, 86, 87]. According to these approaches, the SC transition temperature $T_c$ in these materials will not always coincide with the Cooper-pair formation or BCS-like pairing temperature $T_{BCS}$. One possible scenario based on the SC fluctuations has been first proposed by Doniach and Inui [85] and then reexamined by Emery and Kivelson (EK) [88], and actively pursued by other authors [70, 80, 89, 90, 91, 92]. Another approach based on the precursor BCS-like non-SC pairing (i.e., incoherent Cooper pairs begin to form at a mean-field transition temperature $T_{BCS} > T_c$) and the superfluid Cooper-pair condensation (at $T_c$) scenarios has been proposed by Dzhumanov and Khabibullaev [27, 28, 86, 87] (this theory of pseudogap phenomena and novel superconductivity will be presented in chapters 7 and 8). Here, we discuss the so-called precursor superconductivity models associated with SC fluctuations. According to the theories of the SC fluctuations [80, 85, 88], incoherent Cooper pairs begin to form at a higher temperature $T^*$ than the $T_c$ at which they Bose condense as an ideal Bose gas. EK phenomenologically assumed [88] that the superfluid density $n_s$ controls the phase stiffness of the SC order parameter $\Delta = |\Delta| e^{i\theta}$ and the layered high-$T_c$ superconductors with small superfluid density are characterized by the SC phase fluctuation (or superfluid phase stiffness) temperature $T_\theta^{max} \approx \hbar^2 n_s (T=0) d / 4 m^*$ at which the SC order parameter would disappear and by the mean-field transition temperature $T^{MF}$ below which pairing correlations become important, where $d$ is the spacing between the $CuO_2$ layers in the cuprates, $m^*$ is the effective mass of a hole or an electron. They proposed a phase diagram for high-$T_c$ cuprates based on SC phase fluctuations illustrated in Fig. 5.2. According to EK, at $T_c \ll T_\theta^{max}$, SC

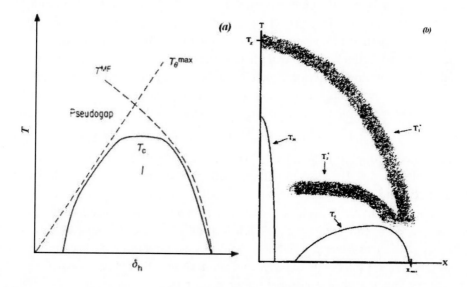

Figure 5.2. (a) Phase diagram of high-$T_c$ superconductors as a function of temperature $T$ and doping $\delta_h$ [88]. (b) A schematic phase diagram for a high-$T_c$ superconductor in the doping-temperature plane [93]. $T_N$ marks the Neel temperature. $T_1^*$ marks the upper crossover temperature below which the charge carriers are confined to the metallic stripes separated by insulating AF stripes. $T_2^*$ marks the pairing temperature of carriers within a stripe.

phase fluctuations are relatively unimportant; and, $T_c$ will be close to the meal-field transition temperature, $T^{MF}$, predicted by BCS theory. However, if $T_\theta^{max} \sim T_c$, then the SC phase fluctuations depress $T_c$ substantially below $T^{MF}$ or the $T_c$ is predominantly determined by

SC phase fluctuations (i.e., $T_c \simeq T_\theta^{max}$). In this case, the region between $T_{MF} = T^*$ and $T_c$ is characterized by the pseudogap formation identified as the SC pairing fluctuations. Emery et al. [93] have also suggested the phase diagram for a high-$T_c$ cuprate superconductor, as shown in Fig. 5.2b, where two crossover temperatures exist above $T_c$. The upper crossover temperature $T_1^*$ characterizes the aggregation of charge carriers into stripes, and the lower crossover temperature $T_2^*$ corresponds to the SC pairing temperature of carriers in the individual charge stripes. Whereas $T_c$ in underdoped materials is determined by the superfluid phase stiffness, and hence by the Josephson coupling between stripes i.e., by the onset of global phase coherence, rather than by the pairing temperature. In some theoretical models, the pseudogap is caused by the SC fluctuations and evolves smoothly into the SC gap, i.e., pseudogap is a precursor to the SC gap [70, 80, 88]. At the same time, some authors argue [70, 80] that except for the close vicinity of $T_c$ (where the picture based on SC phase fluctuations may be valid), the pseudogap region is not characterized by strong SC fluctuations, but rather behaves as a metal, and the SC phase fluctuations cannot explain a pseudogap phenomenon which extends to a large temperature range. On the other hand, Lee et al. [70] believed that in the underdoped cuprates the SC phase fluctuations exist in a wide range of temperature above $T_c$ and the observed vortices (or a large Nernst effect) in this temperature range may be associated with the SC fluctuations. A somewhat different microscopic approach to the precursor superconductivity [89, 90] has been proposed on the basis of a particular diagrammatic theory developed by Kadanoff and Martin [94], and by Patton [95], as applied to conventional SC fluctuation effects. In the present scenario along with the quasiparticles of the usual BCS theory, there are also incoherent (but not preformed) pair excitations of finite center-of-mass momentum and the physical process which generates the pseudogap is resonant pair scattering (above $T_c$). The structure of the gap equation is formally identical to that in BCS theory and the quasiparticle energy dispersion $E(\vec{k}) = \sqrt{\varepsilon^2(\vec{k}) + \Delta^2 \varphi(k)}$ contains the full excitation gap $\Delta = \sqrt{\Delta_{SC}^2 + \Delta_{PG}^2}$, where $\varphi(k)$ is associated with pairing symmetry. The excitation gap $\Delta$ is finite at $T_c$ and the SC gap $\Delta_{SC}$ is established at $T \leq T_c$, while the pseudogap coexist with SC gap below $T_c$ and decreases to zero at $T \to 0$. According to this microscopic theory of SC fluctuations, the physical quantities which characterize the SC state depend on the quasiparticle excitations and on the low lying pair excitations (which introduce new low temperature power law dependencies with ideal Bose gas character into physical quantities). The authors of this theory believe [89, 90] that some experiments support their theoretical predictions. However, other experimental observations of the vanishing of phase coherence well below $T^*$ [96], the different magnetic field dependencies of $T_c$ and pseudogap [97] and the distinct SC gap and pseudogap below $T_c$ and at $T = 0$ [98] cast doubts on theoretical models which rely on SC fluctuation scenarios. Moreover, there is another kind of pseudogap (with the energy scale $\sim 100 meV$ or beyond) which is surely not associated with the pairing amplitude [70]. The origin of this pseudogap is still controversial.

## 5.8.  The Marginal and Nearly Antiferromagnetic Fermi-Liquid Models

In addition to the theoretical scenarios discussed in the previous sections, there are also two different classes of theories proposed by Varma et al. [99, 100, 101] and Pines et al. [102, 103, 104] for the explanation of the anomalous properties of high-$T_c$ cuprate superconductors. The unusual normal state properties of these materials led to the idea that the underdoped and optimally doped cuprates are well described by a Fermi-liquid which is quite different from the standard Landau Fermi-liquid and is called the singular or marginal Fermi-liquid (MFL) [100, 101]. A fundamental characteristic of these systems is that the low-energy properties in a wide range of their electronic phase diagram are dominated by singularities as a function of energy and temperature [101]. It is believed that the breakdown of the Landau's Fermi-liquid theory occurs in this region of the phase diagram around the quantum critical point (QCP) where the phase transition temperature tends to zero as a function of some parameters, such as doping $x$ and pressure (Fig. 5.3). According to the

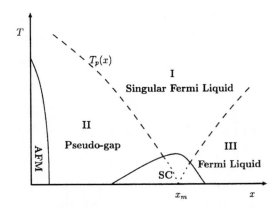

Figure 5.3. Schematic phase diagram of the cuprates for hole doping [101]. $x$ is the density of holes. $x_c$ is the critical hole concentration or QCP at which a quantum phase transition occurs. The AF phase and SC phase, are shown inside solid lines. Crossovers between different Fermi-liquid phases are shown through dashed lines.

MFL model, the anomalous normal state of region $I$ in Fig. 5.3 (as well as superconductivity) is controlled by fluctuations around the QCP, $x = x_c$ (i.e., a singularity at $T = 0$) and the SC region in the $T - x$ phase diagram is surrounded by three distinct regions [100, 101]: a region marked (III) with properties characteristic of a Landau Fermi-liquid, a region marked (I) in which the Landau Fermi-liquid theory and the quasiparticle concept are inapplicable, and a region marked (II), the so-called pseudogap region with a broken symmetry, in which the concept of a Fermi surface itself is lost and a four-fold pattern of circulating current (CC) flows in each unit cell (in the basal $a - b$ plane) between the copper and oxygen ions consecutively opposite directions. The CC phase terminates ($T^* \rightarrow 0$) at a QCP, $x_c$, within the SC region of the $T - x$ phase diagram. In the MFL phase, the normal-state resistivity $\rho$ follows a $T$-linear dependence. It is assumed that in region II the resistivity drops below the linear extrapolation from region I. Theoretical calculations of the specific heat $C_v$ and

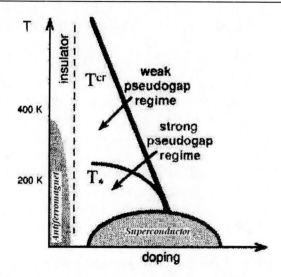

Figure 5.4. Schematic phase diagram of underdoped cuprates [104]. $T^{cr}$ marks upper crossover temperature characterizing the onset of sizable AF correlations. $T^*$ marks the lower crossover temperature characterizing the onset of a considerable loss of low energy spectral weight in the quasiparticle spectrum leading to a minimum of the characteristic spin-fluctuation energy $\omega_{sf}$.

magnetic susceptibility $\chi$ show that $C_v$ and $\chi$ in the CC phase are proportional to $T^{3/2}$ and $T^{1/2}$, respectively. Further, Chakravarty et al. [105] have proposed a similar scenario and argued that the pseudogap is characterized by the development of a new order parameter, a so-called $d_{x^2-y^2}$ density wave (DDW) state (see also Ref. [106]). At temperatures below $T^*$, circulating currents associated with the time-reversal breaking DDW phase produce local magnetic fields that point along the c-direction at the apical oxygen sites [106]. Like the CC phase, the DDW phase vanishes at $x = x_c$ under the SC dome.

Another class of approaches to the theory of high-$T_c$ cuprates based on the idea of the occurrence of AF correlations in the Fermi-liquid was proposed by Pines and collaborators [102, 103, 104]. Such a Fermi-liquid approach deals essentially with a nearly AF metal where charge carriers are dominantly scattered by spin fluctuations. In this nearly AF Fermi-liquid (NAFL) model, the AF spin fluctuations are responsible for the pseudogap phase in the underdoped cuprates. The NAFL model predicts the existence of the two distinct pseudogap regimes and crossover temperatures $T^{cr}$ (the upper crossover temperature marks the onset of AF correlations) and $T^*$ (the lower crossover temperature associated with the opening of a spin pseudogap) in the normal state [104] (Fig. 5.4). It was argued [104, 107] that above $T^{cr}$, in the mean-field regime, in which the pseudoscaling (pseudogap) behavior is absent and the characteristic energy of the spin fluctuations, $\omega_{sf}$, would be proportional to the inverse square of the AF correlation length, $\xi$ and $\omega_{sf}\xi^2 = const$. An AF correlation pseudoscaling or the weak pseudogap regime is assumed in the intermediate temperature region where $T^* < T < T^{cr}$ and $\omega_{sf}$ would be proportional to $\xi^{-1}$ and $\omega_{sf}\xi = const$. Whereas the strong pseudogap regime is assumed to exist in the temperature region where $T_c < T < T^*$ and $\xi$ becomes independent of temperature but $\omega_{sf}$, after exhibiting a minimum near $T^*$, rapidly increases as $1/T$ as $T$ decreases towards $T_c$. In the NAFL model, the dominant interaction between quasiparticles arises from spin fluctuations, as characterized in the dynamical spin susceptibility $\chi(\vec{q}, \omega)$. Since $\chi(\vec{q}, \omega)$ peaks at the momentum transfer $\vec{q}$ of the spin fluctuations close to the AF wave vector $\vec{Q} = (\pi, \pi)$, two different kinds of quasiparticles emerge [104]: hot quasiparticles which are located near $(0, \pi)$, connected to each other by $\vec{Q}$, and cold quasiparticles which are not strongly connected by AF spin fluctuations. The behavior of the hot quasiparticles is highly anomalous and non-Landau Fermi-liquid-like, while cold quasiparticles behave like a strongly coupled Landau-Fermi liquid. It is assumed [103, 104] that pseudogap opens in the hot quasiparticle spectrum and superconductivity occurs when the cold quasiparticles become gapped, independent of the hot quasiparticles. It appears that the pseudogap and crossover temperature $T^*$ unrelated to $T_c$. When only the cold quasiparticles participate in the SC transition, the superfluid density $n_s$ is considerably less than the total number of quasiparticles. In the NAFL model, many unusual properties of the high-$T_c$ cuprates have been argued to be explained by a strong interaction between quasiparticles and overdamped spin fluctuations peaked at $\vec{Q} = (\pi, \pi)$. In particular, the anomalous transport properties of these materials above $T^*$ have been explained within the NAFL model [107]. However, it still remains unsettled how to explain their observed unusual normal-state properties below $T^*$ and SC properties below $T_c$ within the MFL and NAFL models. Note that, for understanding the puzzling normal and SC-state properties of high-$T_c$ cuprates, a more pertinent theory is required.

## 5.9.    BCS-like $s$-, $p$- and $d$-wave Pairing Mechanisms

The pairing mechanism of charge carriers and the nature of the wave function of the Cooper pairs that carry the supercurrent in high-$T_c$ cuprates were a subject of intense debate for many years after discovery of these superconductors [108, 109, 110]. One of the main difficulties in understanding the mechanism of high-$T_c$ superconductivity is related to the symmetry of the pairing state. Many researchers believe that identifying the pairing state symmetry should be the important step towards an understanding of high-$T_c$ superconductivity and knowing it may rule out many contending and unrealistic theoretical models. Some authors argue that in certain situations strong electron correlation in the cuprates may favor non-s-wave pairing (with the non-zero angular momentum $l$ and spin $S$) as in superfluid $^3$He (triplet $p$-wave pairing $l = 1$, $S = 1$) and some heavy fermion superconductors, and favor unconventional pair states such as $d$-wave ($B_{1g}$) pairing (see Ref. [111]). On the other hand, others believe that the pairing state in high-$T_c$ cuprates should reflect the three-dimensional crystal lattice symmetry and correspond to the $s$-wave symmetry [112, 113, 114, 115]. So far, the controversy between $s$-wave or $d$-wave pairing is not resolved [108, 109]. If some experiments seem to provide the evidence for a $d_{x^2-y^2}$-wave symmetry [11, 116, 117], many other experiments support s-wave symmetry [112, 113, 118, 119, 120, 121]. Theoretically, the origin of the energy gap or pseudogap in the high-$T_c$ cuprates is ascribed either to $s$-wave or to $d$-wave pairing symmetry. In particular, in the RVB model the gap equation (5.13) has the different solutions [10, 66, 69, 122]:

$$\Delta(\vec{k}) = \Delta_s \qquad \text{simple s-wave,} \tag{5.15}$$

$$\Delta(\vec{k}) = \Delta_s(\cos k_x + \cos k_y) \quad \text{extended s-wave,} \tag{5.16}$$

$$\Delta(\vec{k}) = \Delta_d(\cos k_x - \cos k_y) \quad \text{pure d-wave,} \tag{5.17}$$

$$\Delta(\vec{k}) = \Delta_{sd}(\cos k_x + i \cos k_y) \quad \text{mixed} \quad (s + id)\text{-wave} \tag{5.18}$$

Baskaran and other authors have argued (see Ref. [69]) that the extended s-wave and the mixed $(s + id)$-wave RVB solutions are irrelevant ones. There are also other theoretical models suggesting the possibility of the d-wave [69, 70, 90, 91, 101, 104, 105] and even p-wave [123, 124] pairing states in the high-$T_c$ cuprates. The pairing potential $V(\vec{k}, \vec{k}')$ can be chosen in the simple separable form

$$V(\vec{k}, \vec{k}') = -g \cdot \eta(\varphi)\eta(\varphi'), \tag{5.19}$$

where $g$ is the coupling constant, $\eta(\varphi)$ is the angular part of the interaction potential, $\varphi$ is the polar angle which determine the direction of the quasiparticle momentum $\vec{k}$ in the $a - b$ plane.

The gap function $\Delta(\vec{k})$ is determined by the gap equation

$$\Delta(\vec{k}) = \Delta\eta(\varphi) = \Delta \cdot \begin{cases} 1 & \text{s-wave pairing,} \\ \sin\varphi & \text{p-wave pairing,} \\ \cos 2\varphi, & \text{d-wave pairing,} \end{cases} \tag{5.20}$$

Theoretical studies indicate [123] that the s-wave pairing is always favored with respect to d- and p-wave pairing. In addition, the layered high-$T_c$ cuprates are the anisotropic three-dimensional electronic systems in which the order parameter will not be of a d-wave symmetry [114] and the d-wave pairing state appears to contradict the c-axis tunneling experiments and the twist junction experiments (see Ref. [109]). Many other experiments [112, 113, 118, 125, 126, 127] rule out also the existence of the d-wave pairing state in the cuprates. Some authors argue [111, 117] that in the high-$T_c$ cuprates the half-integer flux quanta $h/4e$ is observed only for the corner junctions and associated with the d-wave pairing symmetry and $\pi$ phase shift. However, such claims are controversial and not convincing. Since the half-integer flux-quantum effect in the cuprates should be manifested not only in the three-junction ring located at the tricrystal meeting point but also in other areas of the sample [28, 54] and the observed flux of much lower magnitude (i.e., lowest allowed flux state) is located all over and not just at the corners (see Ref. [108]). Finally, identifying the pairing state symmetry does not necessarily determine a specific mechanism of unconventional high-$T_c$ superconductivity and the nature of the SC state in the novel class of superconductors. It was argued [28, 86, 87] that the BCS-like s-,p-, and d-wave pairing of carriers is only necessary but not a sufficient for the occurrence of novel superconductivity in these materials. Note that the existence of gapless excitations (which are often attributed to the nodes of the presumed $d$-wave pairing gap) in high-$T_c$ cuprates may be associated with the gapless excitation spectrum of a superfluid three-dimensional Bose-liquid of Cooper pairs, whereas the presence of the half-integer flux-quantum effect in the grain boundaries of the cuprates is rather associated with the existence of the energy gap in the excitation spectrum of a superfluid two-dimensional Bose-liquid of such composite bosons [27, 28, 54].

# References

[1] J. G. Bednorz and K. A. Müller, *Z. Phys.* B64, 189 (1986).

[2] M. K. Wu, J. R. Ashburn, C. J. Torng, P. H. Hor, R. L. Meng, L. Gao, Z. J. Huang, Y. Q. Wang, and C. W. Chu, *Phys. Rev. Lett.* 58, 908 (1987).

[3] D. Mihailovic, C. M. Foster, K. Voss, and A. J. Heeger, *Phys. Rev.* B42, 7989 (1990).

[4] S. Sugai, *Physica* C185-189, 76 (1991).

[5] M. A. Kastner, R. J. Birgenau, G. Shirane, and Y. Endoh, *Rev. Mod. Phys.* 70, 897 (1998).

[6] A. Lanzara, P. V. Bogdanov, X. J. Zhou, S. A. Kellar, D. L. Feng, E. D. Lu, T. Yoshida, H. Elsaki, A. Fujimori, K. Kishio, J. Shimoyama, T. Noda, S. Uchida, Z. Hussain, and Z. X. Shen, *Nature (London)* 412, 510 (2001).

[7] R. A. Ogg, *Phys. Rev.* 69, 243 (1946).

[8] M. R. Schafroth, *Phys. Rev.* 100, 463 (1955).

[9] J. Bardeen, L. Cooper, and J. R. Schrieffer, *Phys. Rev.* 108, 1175 (1957).

[10] B. K. Chakraverty, M. Avignon and D. Feinberg, *J. Less-Common Metals* 150, 11 (1989).

[11] R. Micnas, J. Ranninger and S. Robaszkiewicz, *Rev. Mod. Phys.* 62, 113 (1990).

[12] L. Landau, *Phys. Z. Sowjetunion* 3, 644 (1933).

[13] J. Appel, in: *Polarons*, ed., Yu. A. Firsov (Nauka, Moscow, 1975).

[14] Ch. B. Lushchik and A. Ch. Lushchik, *Decay of Electronic Excitations with Defect Formation in Solids* (Nauka, Moscow, 1989).

[15] P. W. Anderson, *Phys. Rev. Lett.* 34, 953 (1975).

[16] B. K. Chakraverty, *J. Physique Lett.* 40, L99 (1979); *J. Physique* 42, 1351 (1981).

[17] A. S. Alexandrov and J. Ranninger, *Phys. Rev.* B23, 1796 (1981); *Phys. Rev.* B24, 1164 (1981).

[18]  M. F. Bishop and A. W. Overhauser, *Phys. Rev.* B23, 3627 (1981).

[19]  L. J. DeJongh, *Physica* C152, 171 (1988).

[20]  V. I. Vinetsky, N. I. Kashirina, and E. A. Pashitsky, *Ukrainian J. Phys.* 37, 76 (1992).

[21]  A. S. Alexandrov, *Mod. Phys. Lett.* B2, 1285 (1988).

[22]  D. Emin and M. S. Hillery, *Phys. Rev.* B39, 6575 (1989).

[23]  B. K. Chakraverty, D. D. Sharma, and C. N. R. Rao, *Physica* C156, 413 (1988).

[24]  A. S. Alexandrov, cond-mat/0301541.

[25]  A. S. Alexandrov, *Physica* C282-287, 269 (1997).

[26]  A. S. Alexandrov, V.N. Zavaritsky and S. Dzhumanov, *Phys. Rev.* B69, 052505 (2004).

[27]  S. Dzhumanov, P. J. Baymatov, A. A. Baratov, and N. I. Rahmatov, *Physica* C235-240, 2339 (1994).

[28]  S. Dzhumanov and P. K. Khabibullayev, *Pramana J. Phys.* 45, 385 (1995).

[29]  D. Emin, *Phys. Rev. Lett.* 72, 1052 (1994).

[30]  D. Emin, in: *Polarons and Bipolarons in High-$T_c$ Superconductors and Related Materials*, eds., E. S. H. Salje, A. S. Alexandrov and W. Y. Liang (Cambridge University Press, Cambridge, 1995) p. 80.

[31]  M. Luban, in: *Quantum Fluids*, eds., N. Wiser and D. J. Amit (Gordon and Breach, Science Publishers, Inc. New York, 1970) p. 117.

[32]  W. A. Little, *Phys. Rev.* 134A, 1416 (1964).

[33]  V. L. Ginzburg, *Phys. Lett.* 13, 101 (1964).

[34]  V. Z. Kresin and S. A. Wolf, *Fundamentals of Superconductivity* (Plenum Press, New York, 1990).

[35]  M. L. Cohen, *Physica Scripta* T31, 276 (1990); *Int. J. Mod. Phys.* B5, 1495 (1991).

[36]  D. Allender, J. Bray, and J. Bardeen, *Phys. Rev.* B7, 1020 (1973).

[37]  S. S. Jha, *Phase Transitions* 19, 3 (1989).

[38]  V. L. Ginzburg and D. A. Kirzhnits, *High Temperature Superconductivity* (Consultant Bureau, New York, 1982).

[39]  V. L. Ginzburg, *Usp. Fiz. Nauk* 175, 187 (2005).

[40]  V. Z. Kresin and H. Morawitz, *Physica* C162-164, 1471 (1989).

[41] J. C. Phillips, *Physics of High-$T_c$ Superconductors* (Academic Press Inc., Boston, 1989).

[42] M. Wienstein, *Mod. Phys. Lett.* B1, 327 (1987).

[43] J. R. Schrieffer, X. G. Wen, and S. C. Zhang, *Phys. Rev.* B39, 11663 (1988).

[44] J. B. Goodenough and J. Zhou, *Phys. Rev.* B42, 4276 (1990).

[45] A. S. Davydov, *High Temperature Superconductivity* (Naukova Dumka, Kiev, 1990).

[46] T. Matsuzaki, M. Ido, N. Momono, R. M. Dipasupil, T. Nagata, A. Sakai, and M. Oda, *J. Phys. Chem. Solids.* 62, 29 (2001).

[47] A. J. Leggett, in: *Modern Trends in the Theory of Condensed Matter* (Springer-Verlag, Berlin, 1980) p. 13.

[48] P. Nozieres and S. Schmitt-Rink, *J. Low Temp. Phys.* 59, 195 (1985).

[49] K. Nasu, *Phys. Rev.* B37, 5075 (1988).

[50] J. E. Hirsch, *Physica* C161, 185 (1989).

[51] A. S. Alexandrov, *Phys. Rev.* B46, 14932 (1992-II).

[52] Y. J. Uemura, *Physica* C282-287, 194 (1997).

[53] F. Pistolesi and G. C. Strinati, *Physica* C235-240, 2359 (1994).

[54] S. Dzhumanov, *Int. J. Mod. Phys.* B12, 2151 (1998).

[55] Q. Chen, I. Kosztin, and K. Levin, *Phys. Rev. Lett.* 85, 2801 (2000).

[56] V. B. Geshkenbein, L. B. Ioffe, and A. I. Larkin, *Phys. Rev.* B55, 3173 (1997).

[57] J. Ranninger and S. Robaszkiewicz, *Physica* B135, 468 (1985).

[58] R. Friedberg and T. D. Lee, *Phys. Lett.* A138, 423 (1989).

[59] J. Ranninger and J. M. Robin, *Physica* C253, 279 (1995).

[60] W. R. Czart and S. Robaszkiewicz, *Int. J. Mod. Phys.* B15, 3125 (2001).

[61] P. W. Anderson, *Science* 235, 1196 (1987).

[62] P. W. Anderson, *Mater. Res. Bull.* 8, 153 (1973).

[63] G. Baskaran, Z. Zou, and P. W. Anderson, *Solid State Commun.* 63, 973 (1987).

[64] S. A. Kivelson, D. S. Rokhsar, and J. P. Sethna, *Phys. Rev.* B35, 8865 (1987).

[65] G. Kotliar and J. Liu, *Phys. Rev.* B38, 5142 (1988).

[66] Yu. A. Izyumov, N. M. Plakida, and Yu. N. Skryabin, *Usp. Fiz. Nauk.* 159, 621 (1989).

[67] H. Fukuyama, *Prog. Theor. Phys. Suppl.* 108, 287 (1992); *J. Phys. Chem. Solids.* 62, 3 (2001).

[68] P. W. Anderson, *The Theory of Superconductivity in the High $T_c$ Cuprates* (Princeton University Press, Princeton, 1997).

[69] G. Baskaran, in: *More is Different-Fifty Years of Condensed Matter Physics*, eds., N. P. Ong and R. N. Bhatt (Princeton University Press, Princeton, 2001), Ch. 8.

[70] P. A. Lee, N. Nagaosa, and X.-G. Wen, *Rev. Mod. Phys.* 78, 17 (2006).

[71] E. Dagotto, *Rev. Mod. Phys.* 66, 763 (1994).

[72] P. W. Anderson, G. Baskaran, Z. Zou, and T. Hsu, *Phys. Rev. Lett.* 58, 2790 (1987).

[73] X.-G. Wen and R. Kan, *Phys. Rev.* B37, 595 (1988).

[74] J. M. Wheatley, T. C. Hsu, and P. W. Anderson, *Phys. Rev.* B37, 5897 (1988); *Nature* 333, 121 (1988).

[75] M. J. Rice and Y. R. Wang, *Phys. Rev.* B37, 5893 (1988).

[76] Y. R. Wang and M. J. Rice, *Phys. Rev.* B38, 7163 (1988).

[77] K. A. Moler, J. R. Kirtley, D. G. Hinks, T. W. Li, and M. Ku, *Science* 279, 1193 (1998).

[78] P. A. Lee, *Physica* C317-318, 194 (1999).

[79] L. P. Gor'kov, *Physica* C162-164, 12 (1989).

[80] M. Randeria, cond-mat/9710223.

[81] G.-M. Zhao, H. Keller, and K. Conder, *J. Phys.: Condens. Matter* 13, R569 (2001).

[82] G.V.M. Williams, J. L. Tallon, and J. W. Loram, *Phys. Rev.* B58, 15053 (1998).

[83] J. C. Wynn, D. A. Bonn, B. W. Gardner, Y.-J. Lin, R. Liang, W. N. Hardy, J. R. Kirtley, and K. A. Moler, *Phys. Rev. Lett.* 87, 197002 (2001).

[84] K. Kawabata, S. Tsukui, Y. Shono, O. Michikami, H. Sasakura, K. Yoshiara, Y. Kakehi, and T. Yotsuya, *Phys. Rev.* B58, 2458 (1998).

[85] S. Doniach and M. Inui, *Phys. Rev.* B41, 6668 (1990).

[86] S. Dzhumanov and P. K. Khabibllayev, *Izv. Akad. Nauk Uzb. SSR, Ser. Fiz. Math. Nauk* 1, 47 (1990).

[87] S. Dzhumanov, *Physica* C253-240, 2269 (1994).

[88] V. J. Emery and S. A. Kivelson, *Nature (London)* 374, 434 (1995).

[89] B. Janko, J. Maly, and K. Levin, *Phys. Rev.* B56, R11407 (1997-II).

[90] Q. Chen, I. Kosztin, B. Janko, and K. Levin, *Phys. Rev. Lett.* 81, 4708 (1998).

[91] J. R. Engelbrecht, A. Nazarenko, M. Randeria, and E. Dagotto, *Phys. Rev.* B57, 13406 (1998).

[92] L. B. Ioffe and A. J. Millis, *Science* 285, 1241 (1999); *Phys. Rev.* B61, 9077 (2000).

[93] V. J. Emery, S. A. Kivelson, and O. Zachar, *Phys. Rev.* B56, 6120 (1997-II).

[94] L. P. Kadanoff and P. C. Martin, *Phys. Rev.* 124, 670 (1961).

[95] B. R. Patton, *Phys. Rev. Lett.* 27, 1273 (1971).

[96] J. Corson, R. Mallozzi, J. Orenstein, J. N. Eckstein, and I. Bozovic, *Nature* 398, 221 (1999).

[97] K. Gorny, O. M. Vyaselev, J. A. Martindale, V. A. Nandor, C. H. Pennington, P. C. Hammel, W. L. Hults, J. L. Smith, P. L. Kuhns, A. P. Reyes, and W. G. Moulton, *Phys. Rev. Lett.* 82, 177 (1999).

[98] J. L. Tallon, J. W. Loram, J. R. Copper, C. Panagopoulos, and C. Bernhard, *Phys. Rev.* B68, 180501 (2003).

[99] C. M. Varma, P. B. Littlewood, S. Schmitt-Rink, E. Abrahams, and A. E. Ruckenstein, *Phys. Rev. Lett.* 63, 1996 (1989).

[100] C. M. Varma, *Phys. Rev.* B55, 14554 (1997-I); *Phys. Rev. Lett.* 83, 3538 (1999).

[101] C. M. Varma, Z. Nussinov, and W. van Saarloos, *Phys. Rep.* 361, 267 (2002).

[102] D. Pines, *Z. Phys.* B103, 129 (1997).

[103] A. B. Chubukov, D. Pines, and B. P. Stojkovic, *J. Phys.: Condens. Matter.* 8, 10017 (1996).

[104] J. Schmalian, D. Pines, and B. Stojkovic, *Phys. Rev.* B60, 667 (1999).

[105] S. Chakravarty, R. B. Laughlin, D. K. Morr, and C. Nayak, *Phys. Rev.* B64, 094503 (2001).

[106] J. E. Sonier, J. H. Brewer, R. F. Kiefl, R. I. Miller, G. D. Morris, C.E. Stronach, J. S. Gardner, S. R. Dunsiger, D. A. Bonn, W. N. Hardy, R. Liang, and R. H. Heffner, *Science* 292, 1692 (2001).

[107] B. P. Stojkovic and D. Pines, *Phys. Rev.* B55, 8576 (1997-I).

[108] B. G. Levi, *Phys. Today*, January 19, (1996).

[109] J. F. Annett and J. P. Wallington, *Physica* C341-348, 1621 (2000).

[110]  H.-T. Kim, B.-J. Kim, and K.-Y. Kang, *Physica* C460-462, 943 (2007).

[111]  C. C. Tsuei and J. R. Kirtley, *Physica* C282-287, 4 (1997); *Rev. Mod Phys.* 72, 969 (2000).

[112]  A.G . Sun, D. A. Gajewski, M. B. Maple, and R. C. Dynes, *Phys. Rev. Lett.* 72, 2267 (1994).

[113]  P. Chaudhari and S. Y. Lin, *Phys. Rev. Lett.* 72, 1084 (1994).

[114]  W. Atkinson, J. P. Carbotte, and C. O'Donovan, *Tr. J. Phys.* 20, 670 (1996).

[115]  S. Komiya, Y. Ando, X. F. Sun, and A. N. Lavrov, *Phys. Rev.* B65, 214535 (2002).

[116]  W. N. Hardy, D. A. Bonn, D. C. Morgan, R. Liang, and K. Zhang, *Phys. Rev. Lett.* 70, 3999 (1993).

[117]  D. J. Van Harlingen, D. A. Wollman, D. M. Ginsberg, and A. J. Leggett, *Physica* C235-240, 122 (1994).

[118]  J. Buan, A. M. Goldman, C. C. Huang, O. T. Valls, T. Jacobs, N. Israeloff, S. Sridhar, B. P. Stojkivoc, J.-Z. Liu, R. Shelton, C. R. Shin, and H. D. Yang, *Tr. J. Phys.* 20, 655 (1996).

[119]  W. A. Atkinson and J. P. Carbotte, *Phys. Rev.* B51, 16371 (1995).

[120]  R. A. Klemm and S. H. Liu, *Phys. Rev. Lett.* 74, 2343 (1995).

[121]  R. A. Klemm, *Abstr. 5th Int. Conf. on New Theories, Discoveries, and Applications of Superconductors and Related Materials*, June 11-16, 2004, Hilton-Chongqing, China, p. 13; see also references therein.

[122]  X. Dai, Z.-B. Su, and Lu Yu, *Phys. Rev.* 56, 5583 (1997-I).

[123]  A. Romano, C. Noce, R. Citro, M. Marinaro, and R. Micnas, *Physica* C235-240, 2175 (1994).

[124]  I. O. Kulik, *Tr. J. Phys.* 20, 627 (1996).

[125]  A. Sacuto, R. Combescot, N. Bontemps, P. Monod, V. Viallet, and D. Colson, *Europhys. Lett.* 39, 207 (1997).

[126]  R. S. Gonnelli, G.A. Ummarino, C. Bravi and V.A. Stepanov, *Nuovo Cimento.* 19D, 1207 (1997).

[127]  Y. Ando, S. Ono, X. F. Sun, J. Takeya, F. F. Balakirev, J. B. Betts, and G. S. Boebinger, *Phys. Rev. Lett.* 92, 247004 (2004).

# Chapter 6

# Theory of the Electronic Structure of Undoped and Doped Cuprates

## 6.1. Introduction

The parent (undoped) cuprates have a layered perovskite-type crystal structure and their basic structural element is represented by the one or more $CuO_2$ planes (layers) per unit cell, which are separated by other so-called charge reservoirs layers. They are subdivided into single-layer compounds (e.g., $La_{2-x}Sr_xCuO_4$ (LSCO) and $Bi_2Sr_2CuO_{6+\delta}$), bilayer compounds (e.g., $YBa_2Cu_3O_{7-\delta}$ (YBCO) and $Bi_2Si_2CaCu_2O_{8+\delta}$ (Bi-2212)) and three-layer compounds (e.g., $Bi_2Sr_2Ca_2Cu_3O_{10+\delta}$ and $Tl_2Sr_2Ca_2Cu_3O_{10+\delta}$) [1, 2, 3]. In undoped cuprates, each copper ion $Cu^{2+}$ is surrounded by six or five oxygen ions $O^{2-}$ which form an octahedron (in La compounds) or incomplete octahedron (in Y or Bi compounds) elongated along the $c$-axis perpendicular to the $CuO_2$ layer. The $Cu^{2+}$ ion has nine electrons in the $d$ orbitals, so that its electron configuration is $3d^9$ with a single hole in the higher-lying $3d_{x^2-y^2}$ orbitals. In the cubic crystal field, the five-fold degenerate $d$ level of the $Cu^{2+}$ ion splits into the two doubly and triply degenerate $e_g$ and $t_{2g}$ levels. Further the splitting of these degenerate $e_g$ and $t_{2g}$ levels occurs under the tetragonal crystal field (Fig. 6.1).

Since the Jahn-Teller distortion [4, 5] led to the elongation of the octahedron along the $c$-axis, which is accompanied by the splitting of the degenerate $e_g$ levels into the lower level, $d_{3z^2-r^2}$ and the upper one, $d_{x^2-y^2}$. According to the field theory of ligands [4, 6], the copper $Cu$ $d_{xy}$, $d_{xz}$, $d_{yz}$ orbitals form non-bonding (NB) bonds and the oxygen $O$ $p_{x\pi}$, $p_{y\pi}$, $p_{z\pi}$ orbitals noninteracting with the $Cu$ $d_{x^2-y^2}$ and $d_{3z^2-r^2}$ states form $\pi$ bonds due to the direct overlapping of the $p_\pi$ orbitals, while the $Cu$ $d_{x^2-y^2}$ and $d_{3z^2-r^2}$ orbitals form bonding $\sigma$ and antibonding $\sigma^*$ bonds with the oxygen p orbitals (Fig. 6.2). The low-lying $t_{2g}$ and $d_{3z^2-r^2}$ orbitals are fully occupied, while the $d_{x^2-y^2}$ orbital remains half-filled. In an alongated octahedron configuration, the distance $Cu - O$ along the $c$-axis is larger than the distance $Cu - O$ in the $CuO_2$ planes. Therefore, it is believed that the $Cu - O$ bond along the $c$-axis is much weaker than the in-plane $Cu - O$ bond and the undoped cuprates have a quasi-two-dimensional 2D electronic structure [2, 3, 5].

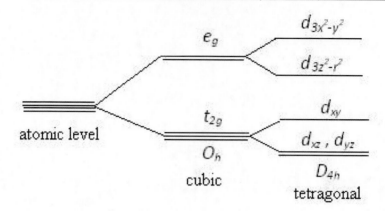

Figure 6.1. Crystal-field splitting of 3d states under cubic ($O_h$) and tetragonal ($D_{4h}$) symmetries [1].

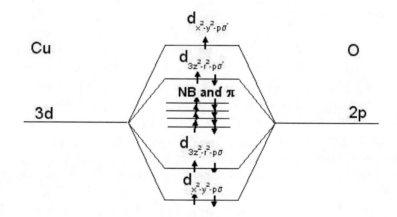

Figure 6.2. Schematic energy level diagram for the undoped copper oxide.

## 6.2. One-Electron Band Theory

The above qualitative picture (Fig. 6.2) was confirmed by band structure calculations [7, 8, 9, 10, 11]. These band structure calculations are based on the density functional theory and effective one-electron schemes, which use delocalized Bloch states and derive an electronic band structure assuming the local density approximation (LDA) to treat correlation effects. Such calculations give practically one picture of the electronic band structure of the undoped cuprates [12] and show that the important electronic states are dominated by the copper Cu $3d$ and oxygen O $2p$ orbitals, with strong hybridization between them. The results of the one-electron band structure calculations performed by using the LDA (see Refs.[1, 13]) is presented in Fig. 6.3. All 17 bands between the Fermi energy $E_F$ and -8 eV correspond to mixtures of copper 3d and oxygen 2p orbitals. The total width of the valence band of $La_2CuO_4$ is about 9.0 eV [1] and the Fermi level $E_F$ lies about 2.0 eV below the top. Only two of the 17 bands so-called bonding (B) and antibonding (AB) bands have a

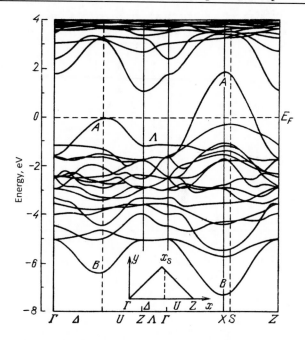

Figure 6.3. One-electron band structure of the parent compound $La_2CuO_4$, calculated by Matheiss within the LDA scheme [7, 8, 9].

large dispersion. These energy bands arise from strong $pd\sigma$ hybridization between the Cu $3d_{x^2-y^2}$ orbital and O $2p\sigma$ orbitals that are directed along the short Cu−O bonds in the $CuO_2$ plane. Both the B band that is full and the half-filled AB band have a strong 2D character. The 15 intermediate bands correspond to more weakly bonding states including $pd\sigma$ bonds along the $c$-axis and NB $dp_\pi$ bonds. The widths of AB and B bands are wide enough (several eV). The 2D band structure calculations; including three orbitals ($Cu3d_{x^2-y^2}$ and $2p_x$, $2p_y$), give results analogous to this one-electron band picture and show the presence of one AB (or $\sigma^*$) band at the Fermi level, and of NB-$\pi$ and B (or $\sigma$) bands [3, 12] (Fig. 6.4). The one-electronic band structures of other undoped cuprates also reveal a similar feature [10, 13]. In particular, the LDA band structures for $YBa_2Cu_3O_{7-\delta}$ (YBCO) show [9, 10] wide bands. The valence band is found to primarily consist of 36 bands originating from the Cu $3d$ and O $2p$ orbitals [10]. The total width of the valence band of YBCO is about 8.5 eV and the Fermi level $E_F$ lies about 2.0 eV below the top of this band.

As is well known, several experiments [3, 12, 13] (e.g., photoemission, $X$-ray absorption and positron spectroscopies) provide important information about the electronic states, and comparison with electronic band structure calculations indicates that, while many features can be interpreted in terms of existing calculations, correlation effects are important for a more detailed understanding.

One serious problem is that the one-electron band-structure calculations predict metallic behavior of the undoped cuprates in the case of a half-filled AB band, which, on the contrary, are antiferromagnetic (AF) insulators with charge transfer ($CT$) gap $E_g \simeq 2.0$ eV [14]. Moreover, experimentally observed photoelectron spectrum approximately is shifted

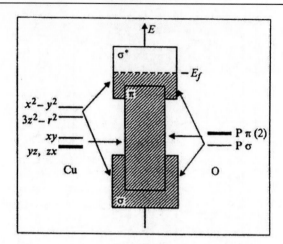

Figure 6.4. Schematic diagram of the one-electron energy bands originating from the Cu
3d- and O 2p-orbitals in the CuO$_2$ plane of La$_2$CuO$_4$ in terms of the crystal-field theory
and the LDA scheme [7, 12].

down by 1-2 eV in comparison with the predictions of the band structure calculations for
the cuprates [12]. These contradictions reflect the failure of the one-electron band picture
and indicate that the undoped cuprates may belong to the CT-type Mott-Hubbard insulators [1, 3, 12]. Since the disadvantage lies in the fact that correlation effects included in
LDA band-structure calculations might not be sufficient to describe these highly correlated
systems.

## 6.3.    Strong Electron Correlations in the Undoped Cuprates

The parent undoped cuprates with an odd number of electrons per unit cell should be metals. Since, according to the one-electron band theory, the valence band (i.e., AB or $\sigma^*$
band) of these compounds as shown in Fig. 6.4 is half-filled and must be metallic. However, experimental results indicate (see Refs. [2, 3, 12, 14]) that these undoped cuprates are
antiferromagnetic (AF) insulators [1, 3, 13]. The reason of the failure of the one-electron
band theory to predict the observed insulating and AF ground state of the undoped cuprates
lies in the strong Coulomb repulsion $U_d$ between two holes at the same Cu-site, which is
much larger than the bandwidth $W$. If the Cu$^{2+}$ $d^9$ state is represented by energy level $\varepsilon_d$
occupied by a single hole, the second hole may appear on the same Cu-site (i.e., in $d^8$ state)
only at energy level $\varepsilon_d + U_d$. Many years ago, Mott [15] and Hubbard [16] have argued that
strong Coulomb repulsion between electrons at the same lattice site could be origin of the
insulating behavior of transition-metal oxides with a partially filled d-electron band. Similarly, in the case of the undoped cuprates, two holes sitting on the same Cu-site would feel a
large Coulomb repulsion, which would split the half-filled AB (or $\sigma^*$) band with mainly Cu
$d_{x^2-y^2}$ character into the so-called upper and lower Hubbard bands. Therefore, the parent
undoped cuprates should be insulating due to strong hole-hole repulsion or correlation effect. An account of this correlation effect within the framework of the single-band Hubbard

model led to the Hamiltonian [17, 18]

$$H = \sum_{i\sigma} \varepsilon_{di} a_{i\sigma}^+ a_{i\sigma} + \sum_{ij\sigma} t_{ij} a_{i\sigma}^+ a_{j\sigma} + U_d \sum_{i\sigma} n_{i\sigma} n_{i,-\sigma}, \qquad (6.1)$$

where $a_{i\sigma}^+ (a_{i\sigma})$ is the creation (annihilation) operator of a hole at the $i$-th Cu site with spin $\sigma$, $n_{i\sigma} = a_{i\sigma}^+ a_{i\sigma}$ is the number operator, $t_{ij}$ is the nearest-neighbor hopping integral expressible by $W/2z$, $z$ is the coordination number (in particular, $z = 4$ and 6 for a square lattice and a simple cubic lattice, respectively) or the number of $Cu^{2+}$ ions which are nearest neighbors of each copper ion. In the Hubbard model, the important parameter is the electron correlation strength $U_d$. Depending on the parameters $W$ and $U_d$, the structure of the half-filled $d_{x^2-y^2}$ band is shown in Fig. 6.5. Hubbard demonstrated [16] that application of the Hamiltonian (6.1) on an array of one-electron atoms yields two split bands which broaden with increasing the parameter $W/U_d$ and at some critical value $(W/U_d)_c = 1.1547$ they begin to overlap (Fig. 6.5). As can be seen from Fig. 6.5b, at $W/U_d > 1.155$ the correlation

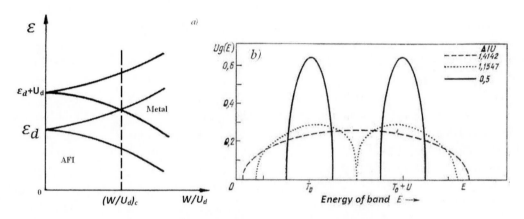

Figure 6.5. (a) Splitting of the half-filled $d_{x^2-y^2}$ band in the undoped cuprates due to the strong electron correlation (on-site Coulomb repulsion) in term of the single-band Hubbard model [16] where $\varepsilon$ is the electron energy, $\varepsilon_d$ is the energy of the $d_{x^2-y^2}$ hole at the $Cu$ site, $U_d$ denotes the on-site Coulomb repulsion energy, $W$ is the width of the $d_{x^2-y^2}$ band. (b) Two Hubbard bands as a function of the parameter $W/U_d$ [17] where $T_0 = \varepsilon_d$, $\Delta = W$, $U = U_d$ and $g(E)$ is the density of states. For one hole carrier per $Cu$ site, on the left of $(W/U_d)_c$ the system is an antiferromagnetic insulator (AFI) and on the right of it a metal.

effect is not important and the simple one-electron band picture is restored. However, various experiments (see Refs. [19, 20]) indicate that the electron correlation in the undoped cuprates is strong enough to produce a Mott insulator at half-filling. According to these experiments, at the Cu-site, there is a strong intra-atomic Coulomb repulsion $U_d \simeq 6 - 10$ eV, which produces the Hubbard splitting the half-filled $d_{x^2-y^2}$ band, and a material should be a Mott insulator.

## 6.4. One- and Three-Band Hubbard Models and High-Energy Electronic Structure of the Undoped Cuprates

As mentioned earlier, in the one-electron band picture (Fig. 6.4) the strong Coulomb repulsion between holes in the same Cu $d_{x^2-y^2}$ orbital is not taken into account. This strong correlation effect is usually considered within the one- and three-band Hubbard models. The simplest model is the single-band Hubbard model given by [17]

$$H = \sum_{ij\sigma} t_{ij} a_{i\sigma}^+ a_{i\sigma} + U_d \sum_i n_{i\uparrow} n_{i\downarrow}, \tag{6.2}$$

where $ij$ are nearest-neighbor copper sites in the square lattice, $n_{i\uparrow}(n_{i\downarrow})$ is the occupation number for holes with spin $\sigma = \uparrow \downarrow$ on site $i$.

Then by taking the nearest-neighbor hopping integral $t = t_{ij}$ to be $\sim 0.25 - 0.40$ eV [12] in the cuprates, the values of $W$ are roughly estimated to be $W = 8t \simeq 2.0 - 3.2$ eV, which is much smaller than $U_d$. Then the values of the parameter $W/U_d$ are expected to be small, i.e., $W/U_d \simeq 0.2 - 0.3$. It follows that for the undoped cuprates the one-electron band picture breaks down and the half-filled AB (or $\sigma^*$) band splits into the two Hubbard bands which are called the upper Hubbard band (UHB) and the lower Hubbard band (LHB), so that these compounds are AF insulators. Many authors follow an approach which is based on the one-band Hubbard model (6.2) (see Refs. [1, 2, 3, 5, 14, 20]) and they believe that the single-band description is valid because the charge excitations in these materials can be described only through the isolated $d_{x^2-y^2}$ band. Therefore, the single-band Hubbard model was choosen as the starting point for the description of the cuprates. This description led to the Mott-Hubbard picture and the energy gap in the excitation spectrum of the cuprates is determined by $U_d$ (Fig. 6.5). However, the simplified one-band Hubbard model where the oxygen atoms are not considered and the interactions are restricted to the on-site Coulombic term, is not very appropriate starting point even for the description of the undoped cuprates [2, 20]. Moreover, experimentally the energy gap of about 1.5-2.0 eV is observed in the parent undoped cuprates and interpreted as the charge-transfer (CT) excitations [19, 20, 21]. For these reasons given, the three-band Hubbard model [22, 23] can be a good approximation for a more complete description of the high energy electronic structure of the undoped cuprates. Since in the cuprates, the oxygen O $2p$ level becomes close to the copper Cu $3d_{x^2-y^2}$ level and the charge excitation gap of the Mott-Hubbard insulator cannot be accounted for solely with $3d_{x^2-y^2}$ electrons, but $2p$-electron degrees of freedom have also to be considered [20]. In the three-band Hubbard model (called $d - p$ model), Cu $3d_{x^2-y^2}$ and O $2p$ orbitals, as well as strong hybridization between these orbitals are explicitly considered. In general, the $d - p$ model is believed to be more suitable for the full description of the electronic structure of the transition-metal oxides [20]. The Hamiltonian of the $d - p$ model can be written as [12, 13]

$$H = \varepsilon_d \sum_{i\sigma} d_{i\sigma}^+ d_{i\sigma} + \varepsilon_p \sum_{j\sigma} p_{j\sigma}^+ p_{j\sigma} + t_{pd} \sum_{\langle ij \rangle \sigma} d_{i\sigma}^+ p_{j\sigma} +$$
$$+ U_d \sum_i n_{di\uparrow} n_{di\downarrow} + U_p \sum_j n_{pj\uparrow} n_{pj\downarrow} + V_{pd} \sum_{ij} n_{di} n_{pj}, \tag{6.3}$$

where $\varepsilon_p$ and $\varepsilon_d$ are the energies of the electron or hole in the oxygen O $2p$ and transition-metal (M) atom $3d$ orbitals, respectively, $t_{pd}$ is the hopping matrix element between nearest-neighbor M $3d$ and O $2p$ orbitals, $U_d$ and $U_p$ are the energies of the Coulomb repulsion between two carriers on copper sites and oxygen sites, $V_{pd}$ is the nearest-neighbor Coulomb repulsion between M and O sites, $d_{i\sigma}^+$ ($d_{i\sigma}$) is the creation (annihilation) operator of the carrier at the $i$-th M site with spin $\sigma$, $p_{j\sigma}^+$ ($p_{j\sigma}$) is the creation (annihilation) operator of the carrier at the j-th O site with spin $\sigma$, $n_{di} = d_{i\sigma}^+ d_{i\sigma}$ and $n_{pj} = p_{j\sigma}^+ p_{j\sigma}$ are the number operators corresponding to the M $3d_{x^2-y^2}$ and O $2p$ orbitals, $\langle ij \rangle$ denotes the summation over all nearest-neighbor sites. The limit case $U_d = U_p = V_{pd} = 0$ corresponds to the one-

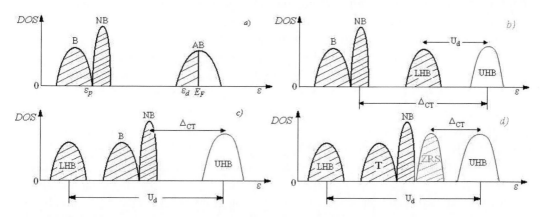

Figure 6.6. Schematic band structures of the 3d transition-metal oxides predicted by the different theoretical models. (a) the band structure (density of states (DOS) as a function of energy $\varepsilon$) for the half-filled correlated metal predicted by the one-electron band theory. (b) and (c) the band structures for a Mott-Hubbard insulator ($W < U_d < \Delta_{CT}$) and a charge-transfer (CT) insulator ($U_d > W$ and $U_d > \Delta_{CT}$) predicted by the three-band Hubbard model. (d) the band structure for a CT-type insulator with the Zhang-Rice singlet-triplet splitting predicted by the t-J model. B, NB and AB denote bonding, non-bonding and antibonding bands, respectively. $\varepsilon_p$ and $\varepsilon_d$ are the energy levels for oxygen and copper atoms, respectively. $E_F$ is the Fermi energy of the undoped cuprates. LHB (UHB) is the lower (upper) Hubbard band. ZRS and T denote Zhang-Rice singlet and triplet, respectively. $U_d$ and $\Delta_{CT}$ are on-site Coulomb repulsion and CT gap, respectively.

electron band-structure calculations which indicate that the upper AB or $\sigma^*$ band (Figs. 6.4 and 6.6a) is two-fold degenerate, and therefore, half-filled (i.e., metallic). This degeneracy of the half-filled metallic band is lifted by the strong on-site Coulombic repulsion $U_d$. As a consequence, the conduction band splits into the lower filled and upper empty Hubbard bands. According to the modern Zaanen-Sawatzky-Allen (ZSA) classification scheme [24], the final band structure of the transition-metal oxides depends on the quantities of the intra-atomic Coulomb repulsion $U_d$, the width of the $d$-band $W$ and the CT gap $\Delta_{CT} = \varepsilon_d - \varepsilon_p$ (Fig. 6.6). The electronic band structure of the transition-metal oxides corresponds to a Mott-Hubbard-type insulator for $\Delta_{CT} > U_d > W$ (Fig. 6.6b). In this case, the oxygen $2p$ band lies much lower than LHB and the charge excitation gap in the Mott-Hubbard insulating phase is mainly determined by the energy parameter $U_d$. However, for the cases

$U_d > W$ and $U_d > \Delta_{CT}$, it is believed that the electronic band structure of the transition-metal oxides (e.g., undoped cuprates) corresponds to the another kind of insulator, which is called a CT-type insulator according to the ZSA classification scheme. In the CT insulators, the LHB lies below the oxygen $2p$ band (Fig. 6.6c) and the minimum CT gap is formed between the O $2p$ band and the UHB. The photoemission, electron-energy-loss spectroscopy, angle-resolved photoemission spectroscopy (ARPES) and other experiments have confirmed this band picture and revealed (see Refs. [2, 12, 19, 20, 25, 26]) that the values of the parameters in Hamiltonian (6.3) are $U_d = 6 - 10$ eV, $U_p \simeq U_d/2 \simeq 3 - 5$ eV, $t_{pd} \simeq 1.0 - 1.5$ eV, $\Delta_{CT} \simeq 1.5 - 3.0$ eV, $V_{pd} \simeq 1.0 - 1.5$ eV for the undoped cuprates. It follows that the parent undoped cuprates are typical CT insulators with the long-range AF order. Since each hole per Cu site in the $Cu^{2+}$ ($3d^9$) configuration produces a localized spin on each Cu site and the $Cu^{2+}$ spins in the undoped cuprates are ordered antiferromagnetically with the Neel temperatures $T_N \simeq 300 - 500K$ [1, 21]. In the three-band Hubbard model, upon doping the new hole added to the unit cell will mainly occupy oxygen orbitals. Actually, by hole doping, development of states at the Fermi level is observed and these states have mainly oxygen $2p$ character [19]. Nevertheless, Zhang and Rice have argued [27] that the three-band Hubbard model can be reduced to an effective so-called one-band t-J model. According to this t-J model, the doped hole originally located at the oxygen (or $O^-$ state) can be combined with the Cu hole to form spin triplet or singlet state (which is known as the Zhang-Rice singlet (ZRS)). As a consequence, the $O^-$ hole is replaced by a spin singlet state centered at the copper ion. The ZRS band represents a band split off from the O $2p$ band (the NB band) and plays the role of the LHB, while the original LHB is lower in energy than ZRS, NB, and triplet (T) bands (Fig. 6.6d). Thus, the three-band Hubbard model simplifies into the one-band t-J Hamiltonian presented in chapter 5 (see sec. 5.6), which is commonly used in studying the essential physics of the half-filled AF insulator [2, 3]. In the one-band t-J model, the charge gap is determined by the interband excitation from the ZRS band to the UHB. Although the reduction of the three-band Hubbard model to the one-band t-J model is still controversial, this effective one-band scheme is widely used to study the electronic band structure of the undoped cuprates and supports the early Anderson's argument [28] that the basic physics of the cuprates would be captured by the one-band Hubbard model. However, for doped cuprates far away from the Mott insulator, the validity of the t-J model is more difficult to justify [2, 20]. Further, the one- and three-band Hubbard models describing the insulating state (or high energy electronic structure) of the parent undoped cuprates seem to be inadequate for studying the low-energy electronic structure of the doped cuprates in which the doped carriers can be delocalized just like in doped semiconductors (e.g., Si and Ge). Therefore, the adequate description of the low-energy electronic structure of doped cuprates requires a more pertinent and realistic theoretical approach.

## 6.5.  Electron-Defect-Phonon and Defect (Impurity)-Assisted Self-Trapping of Carriers in the Lightly Doped Cuprates

As mentioned earlier (sec.6.4), various experiments indicate that the electronic structure of the parent cuprate compounds is well described by the three-band Hubbard model and the oxygen valence band lies within the Mott-Hubbard gap. These CT insulators can be doped with carriers (holes or electrons) by substituting impurity atoms for host lattice atoms or by varying oxygen content. Upon hole doping, the oxygen valence band of the cuprates is occupied first by free holes having the effective mass $m^*$, which interact with acoustic and optical phonons, as well as with defects (dopants or impurities). The hole carriers are assumed to be within both a three-dimensional (3D) and a two-dimensional (2D) deformable medium, the last one being $CuO_2$ layers [21]. In reality, however, no systems can be purely 2D, and therefore, the layered cuprate compounds may be approximated as a 3D deformable medium. There is also convincing experimental evidence that the consideration of cuprates as 3D systems may appear to be more appropriate (see Refs. [29, 30, 31]). Indeed, the experimental results presented in Ref. [30] confirm that the hole-doped system $La_{2-x}Sr_xCuO_4$ (LSCO) becomes less two-dimensional in the strongly localized state (i.e., the strong localization causes the system to become a 3D insulator). In polar materials, the hole carriers interacting both with lattice vibrations (i.e., acoustic and optical phonons) and with lattice defects (e.g., dopants or impurities), can easily be self-trapped near the defects and in a defect-free deformable lattice. Therefore, possible origins for carrier localization in real systems are both extrinsic and intrinsic. So far, there are no detail quantitative studies of the extrinsic and intrinsic self-trapping of carriers in lightly doped cuprates. The low-energy electronic structure of the doped cuprates in the doping region, from an insulator to a metal, can be well described by the theory of self-trapping and pairing of carriers in real space [32, 34, 35, 36]. For better understanding of the situation, the formation possibility of extrinsic self-trapped states and of intrinsic ones in the CT gap of the cuprates need to be thoroughly examined and compared with existing experimental results confirming the existence of such localized in-gap states. In this section, we study the extrinsic self-trapping (i.e., defect (impurity)-assisted self trapping [37]) of carriers in the continuum model and adiabatic approximation taking into account both the short- and long-range carrier-defect-phonon interactions, as well as the Coulomb interaction between the pairing carriers in hole-doped cuprates. The doped hole carriers in these systems are initially delocalized just like in doped semiconductors such as in p-type Si and Ge. In 3D systems, there is potential barrier that must be overcome to initiate self-trapping [32, 34]. In the presence of a defect, the self-trapping of a carrier may occur more easily. Actually, the layered cuprates are the anisotropic 3D systems [29, 31, 38]. Therefore, the formation of a new state bound to the defect potential and to the lattice distortion potential resulting from the presence of a carrier becomes possible in three-dimensions. The self-trapping of a carrier near the defect, which is similar to the self-trapping in perfect lattice, can be studied with the use of a continuum model as developed by Toyozawa and Dzhumanov et al. [37]. In this case, the ground-state energy of the carrier in 3D polar materials is calculated variationally in the adiabatic approximation, taking into account the short- and long-range carrier-phonon, carrier-defect and defect-phonon interactions. In this model, the hole carrier(s) and the defect interact with the elastic dilation $\Delta(r)$ of the medium through their respective deformation potentials $E_d$ and $E_{dD}$, and with the field of electrostatic potential $\phi(r)$ of an ionic displacement polarization through their respective charges $e$ and $Ze$, in addition to the Coulomb interaction between carriers (in two-carrier system) and the carrier-defect interaction consisting of short-range part $V_0\delta(r)$ and long-range part $-Ze^2/\varepsilon_\infty r$ (where $\varepsilon_\infty$ is the high frequency dielectric constant). Therefore, the total energies of the single carrier and two carriers coupled to the defect potential and to the acoustic and optical phonon fields depend on $\Delta(r)$

and $\phi(r)$, as well as on the one-particle $\psi(r)$ and two-particle $\Psi(r_1, r_2)$ wave functions [37] (where $r_1$ and $r_2$ are the position vectors of the carriers). In particular, the functional of the total energy of a single carrier coupled to the defect potential and phonon fields is given by

$$E_1\{\psi, \Delta, \phi\} = \int \Psi(r) \left[ -\frac{\hbar^2}{2m^*} \nabla^2 + V_0 \delta(r) - \frac{Ze}{\varepsilon_\infty r} \right] \Psi(r) d^3 r$$
$$+ \int [E_d \Psi^2(r) + E_{dD} \delta(r)] \Delta(r) d^3(r) + \int [-e\Psi^2(r) + Ze\delta(r)] \phi(r) d^3 r$$
$$+ \frac{K}{2} \int \Delta^2(r) d^3 r + \frac{\tilde{\varepsilon}}{8\pi} \int (\nabla \phi(r))^2 d^3 r, \tag{6.4}$$

where $\tilde{\varepsilon} = \varepsilon_\infty(1 - \eta)$, $\eta = \varepsilon_\infty/\varepsilon_0$, $E_d$ and $E_{dD}$ are the deformation potentials of a carrier and a defect, respectively, $K$ is an elastic constant, $Z$ is the charge state of a defect, $V_0$ is the short-range defect potential, $\varepsilon_\infty$ and $\varepsilon_0$ are the high frequency and static dielectric constants, respectively. By minimizing the functional (6.4) sequentially with respect to $\Delta$ and $\phi$, one obtains the functional

$$E_1\{\psi(\vec{r})\} = \frac{\hbar^2}{2m^*} \int (\nabla \psi(\vec{r}))^2 d^3 \vec{r} - \frac{e^2}{2\tilde{\varepsilon}} \int \frac{\psi^2(\vec{r})\psi^2(\vec{r}')}{|\vec{r} - \vec{r}'|} d^3 \vec{r} d^3 \vec{r}'$$
$$- \frac{E_d^2}{2K} \int \psi^4(\vec{r}) d^3 \vec{r} - \frac{Ze^2}{\varepsilon_0} \int \frac{\psi^2(\vec{r})}{\vec{r}} d^3 \vec{r}$$
$$+ \left( V_0 - \frac{E_d E_{dD}}{K} \right) \int \psi^2(\vec{r}) \delta(\vec{r}) d^3 \vec{r} \tag{6.5}$$

The functional of the total energy of two carriers (with wave function $\Psi(\vec{r}_1, \vec{r}_2)$) interacting with each other and with acoustic and optical phonons, $E_2\{\Psi, \Delta, \phi\}$, is given by simply doubling the terms with $\psi^2(r)$ in Eq. (6.4) and adding the Coulomb repulsion energy

$$U = \int \int \Psi(\vec{r}_1, \vec{r}_2) \frac{e^2}{\varepsilon_\infty |\vec{r}_1 - \vec{r}_2|} \Psi(\vec{r}_1, \vec{r}_2) d^3 \vec{r}_1 d^3 \vec{r}_2 \tag{6.6}$$

After minimizing total energy of the two carriers $E_2\{\Psi, \Delta, \phi\}$ with respect to $\Delta$ and $\phi$ at fixed $\Psi(r_1, r_2)$, we obtain the following functional

$$E_2\{\Psi(\vec{r}_1, \vec{r}_2)\} = \frac{\hbar^2}{2m^*} \int \left[ |\nabla_1 \Psi(\vec{r}_1, \vec{r}_2)|^2 + |\nabla_2 \Psi(\vec{r}_1, \vec{r}_2)|^2 \right] d^3 \vec{r}_1 d^3 \vec{r}_2$$
$$+ \frac{e^2}{\varepsilon_\infty} \int \frac{\Psi^2(\vec{r}_1, \vec{r}_2)}{|\vec{r}_1 - \vec{r}_2|} d^3 \vec{r}_1 d^3 \vec{r}_2$$
$$- \frac{2e^2}{\tilde{\varepsilon}} \int \frac{\Psi^2(\vec{r}_1, \vec{r}_2) \Psi^2(\vec{r}_3, \vec{r}_4)}{|\vec{r}_1 - \vec{r}_3|} d^3 \vec{r}_1 d^3 \vec{r}_2 d^3 \vec{r}_3 d^3 \vec{r}_4$$
$$- \frac{2E_d^2}{K} \int \Psi^2(\vec{r}_1, \vec{r}_2) \Psi^2(\vec{r}_2, \vec{r}_3) d^3 \vec{r}_1 d^3 \vec{r}_2 d^3 \vec{r}_3$$
$$- \frac{2Ze^2}{\varepsilon_0} \int \frac{\Psi^2(\vec{r}_1, \vec{r}_2)}{\vec{r}_1} d^3 \vec{r}_1 d^3 \vec{r}_2$$
$$+ 2 \left( V_0 - \frac{E_d E_{dD}}{K} \right) \int \Psi^2(\vec{r}_1, \vec{r}_2) \delta(\vec{r}_1) d^3 \vec{r}_1 d^3 \vec{r}_2, \tag{6.7}$$

The total energy of the two carriers $E_2\{\Psi(\vec{r}_1, \vec{r}_2)\}$ can be calculated without and with intercarrier correlation. If we ignore this correlation effect, the wave function $\Psi(\vec{r}_1, \vec{r}_2)$ is approximated by a simple product $\psi(\vec{r}_1), \psi(\vec{r}_2)$. However, this wave function is rough approximation. Therefore, we use more correct wave function $\Psi(\vec{r}_1, \vec{r}_2)$ taking into account the correlation between the pairing carriers. In order to minimize the functionals (6.5) and (6.7) with respect to $\psi(r)$ and $\Psi(r_1, r_2)$ we can take the trial wave functions as

$$\psi(r) = N_1 \exp[-(\sigma \vec{r})] \tag{6.8}$$

and

$$\Psi(r_1, r_2) = N_2[1 + \gamma(\sigma r_{12})] \exp[-\sigma(r_1 + r_2)], \tag{6.9}$$

where $N_1 = \sigma^{3/2}/\sqrt{\pi}$ and $N_2 = \sigma^3/\pi\sqrt{C_1(\gamma)}$ are the normalization factors, $\sigma = \beta/a_0$, $C_1(\gamma) = 1 + \frac{35}{8}\gamma + 6\gamma^2$ is the correlation coefficient, $\beta$ and $\gamma$ are the variational parameters, characterizing the localization degree of carriers and the correlation in their motions, respectively, $r_{12} = |r_1 - r_2|$ is the distance between the carriers, $a_0$ is the lattice constant. Substituting equations (6.8) and (6.9) into equations (6.5) and (6.7), and performing the integrations in equations (6.5) and (6.7), we obtain the following functionals

$$E_1(\beta) = A\left[\beta^2 - g_s(1+b_s)\beta^3 - g_l\left(1 - \eta + \frac{16}{5}Z\eta\right)\beta\right] \tag{6.10}$$

and

$$E_2(\beta, \gamma) = 2A\frac{C_2(\gamma)}{C_1(\gamma)}\left\{\beta^2 - \frac{8}{5}g_l\right.$$
$$\times\left[2(1-\eta)\frac{C_4(\gamma)}{C_1(\gamma)C_2(\gamma)} + Z\eta\frac{C_5(\gamma)}{C_2(\gamma)} - \frac{C_3(\gamma)}{C_2(\gamma)}\right]\beta$$
$$\left. -16g_s\left[\frac{C_6(\gamma)}{C_1(\gamma)C_2(\gamma)} + \frac{b_s}{16}\frac{C_7(\gamma)}{C_2(\gamma)}\right]\beta^3\right\} \tag{6.11}$$

where $A = \hbar^2/2m^*a_0^2$, $g_s = E_d^2/16\pi Ka_0^3 A$ and $g_l = 5e^2/16\varepsilon_\infty a_0 A$ are the dimensionless short-range and long-range carrier-phonon coupling parameters, $b_s = 16\left[E_{dD}/E_d - KV_0/E_d^2\right]$ is the short-range carrier-defect-phonon coupling parameter, and the correlation coefficients are analytical functions of the variational parameter $\gamma$:

$$C_2(\gamma) = 1 + \frac{25}{8}\gamma + 4\gamma^2, \quad C_3(\gamma) = \frac{5}{8} + 2\gamma + \frac{35}{16}\gamma^2,$$

$$C_4(\gamma) = \frac{5}{8} + \frac{1087}{216}\gamma + \frac{38237}{2304}\gamma^2 + \frac{67639}{2592}\gamma^3 + \frac{4293}{256}\gamma^4,$$

$$C_5(\gamma) = 2 + \frac{15}{2}\gamma + 9\gamma^2,$$

$$C_6(\gamma) = \frac{1}{8} + \frac{185}{216}\gamma + \frac{4199}{1728}\gamma^2 + \frac{8591}{2592}\gamma^3 + \frac{477}{256}\gamma^4,$$

$$C_7(\gamma) = 1 + 3\gamma + 3\gamma^2.$$

Minimization of the functionals (6.10) and (6.11) over the variational parameters $\beta$ and $\gamma$ would give the ground state energies $E_1^{min}(\beta)$ and $E_2^{min}(\beta,\gamma)$ of single and pair self-trapped carriers. As a function of $\beta$ and $\gamma$, these functionals have also the maxima $E_1^{max}(\beta)$ and $E_2^{max}(\beta,\gamma)$. The other parameters $A$, $g_s$, $g_l$, $b_s$, and $Z$ entering into Eqs. (6.10) and (6.11) play different roles in the formation of self-trapped states and determine the nature of the localized states of carriers in doped polar materials. The values of the parameters $A$, $g_s$, and $g_l$ can be obtained by using the experimental values of the parameters $a_0$, $m^*$, $K$, $\varepsilon_\infty$, $\varepsilon_0$, and the Fermi energy $E_F$ of the undoped cuprates. The parameters $b_s$ and $Z$ characterize the formation of the extrinsic (i.e., hydrogenic and non-hydrogenic) self-trapped states of carriers, whereas the parameters $g_s$ and $g_l$ characterizing the strengths of the short-and long-range carrier-phonon interactions are responsible for the formation of the intrinsic self-trapped states.

Using the equations (6.10) and (6.11), we calculate the energies of the different localized in-gap states in the CT gap of the cuprates. In order to determine the nature of these in-gap states and the quasi-free to localized state transition, we distinguish different physical situations in these systems. One can make an interesting analysis of real systems on the basis of the sign and magnitude of $b_s$. In hole-doped cuprates, the situations might be quite different for different types of dopants. In particular, the signs of the deformation potential constants $E_d$ and $E_{dD}$ for holes and small-radius defects are always positive, while $E_{dD}$ for large-radius defects is negative [37]. However, no informations are available for the magnitudes of the parameters $E_{dD}$ and $V_0$ at present. Therefore, the parameter $b_s$ in Eqs. (6.10) and (6.11) can be considered as the free parameter.

### 6.5.1.  Formation of the Shallow Hydrogen-like Defects States

We will first discuss the possibility for the formation of shallow hydrogen-like impurity states in hole-doped cuprates. If the carrier-phonon interactions near the dopants are weak, the simple hydrogen-like impurity centers can be formed in these systems. Such a situation is realized in $La_{2-x}Sr_xCuO_4$ (LSCO) or $La_{2-x}Ba_xCuO_4$ (LBCO), where the radius of $Sr^{2+}$ ions is larger than that of $La^{3+}$ ions [39], so that for $Sr^{2+}$ ion $Z = 1$, $E_{dD} < 0$ or $b_s < 0$. In this case, the short-range part of the impurity potential in Eq. (6.5) is repulsive. Therefore, one can treat it like a hard core. The hole-lattice interactions near the large-radius dopants in LSCO and LBCO are suppressed by this repulsive defect potential and hole carriers are localized at a distance from the dopants (i.e., hole-carriers are loosely bound to dopants by long-range Coulomb attraction). From these considerations, it follows that the hole-lattice interaction near the large-radius dopants is weak and the localized impurity state may have hydrogen-like character described by a rigid lattice model [40]. Therefore, we can consider the hydrogen-like impurity centers having the Bohr radius $a_H$ and the ionization energy $E_I^H$ in lightly doped LSCO and LBCO. A similar argument can be made for other cuprates, such as $La_2CuO_{4+\delta}$, $YBa_2Cu_3O_{7-\delta}$ (YBCO), and $Bi_2Sr_2CaCu_2O_{8+\delta}$ (Bi-2212). In these systems the doping centers are excess oxygen atoms which capture the electrons from the oxygen conduction band and form the acceptor centers, i.e., $O^-$ ions. One can assume that such extra $O^-$ ions just as $Sr^{2+}$ ions may have negative $E_{dD}$.

Thus, at $b_s < 0$ the simple hydrogen-like model for the description of the acceptor centers and shallow impurity states in the hole-doped cuprates is well justified. Then at

$b_s < 0$ and $Z = 1$, the ionization energy $E_I$ and the Bohr radius of the localized hydrogen-like impurity states are given by

$$E_I = 13.575 \left(\frac{Z}{\varepsilon_0}\right)^2 \frac{m^*}{m_e} eV, \qquad (6.12)$$

and

$$a_H \simeq 0.529 \frac{\varepsilon_0}{Z}(m_e/m_*)\text{Å}, \qquad (6.13)$$

where $m_e$ is the free electron mass.

By taking $m^* = m_e$ [21] $\varepsilon_0 \simeq 25$ [35], we obtain $E_I \simeq 0.022$ eV which is close to the binding energy of the Sr acceptor $E_I = 19 \pm 2$ meV observed in LSCO [21]. One can assume that the oxygen acceptor in YBCO has some effective charge $Z = Z^* \simeq 1.5$. Using $m^* \simeq m_e$ and $\varepsilon_0 \simeq 30$, one obtains $a_H \simeq 10.5\text{Å}$ and $E_I \simeq 0.034$ eV is in reasonable agreement with experimental values $a_H \simeq 8 \pm 2\text{Å}$ and $E_I \simeq 0.035$ eV (for the oxygen acceptor in the lightly doped cuprates) [21].

### 6.5.2.    Formation of the Non-hydrogen-like Localized Defect States

Another interesting question is how small-radius dopants in cuprates affect the carrier-phonon system, especially near such defects. The signs of $E_d$ and $E_{dD}$, as mentioned before, are positive for holes and small-radius dopant (or impurities). For example, such small-radius dopants in $La_{2-x}Ba_{x-y}M_yCuO_4$ (where, $M = Ca^{2+}$ and $Sr^{2+}$) and $La_{2-x-y}Nd_ySr_xCuO_4$ are $Ca^{2+}$ or $Sr^{2+}$ and $Nd^{3+}$ ions, respectively. These cations having sufficiently large positive deformation potential $E_{dD}$ (which would satisfy the condition $b_s > 0$) may play an important role in the formation of the deep non-hydrogenic impurity states in the CT gap of the lightly doped cuprates. Since at $b_s > 0$ the carrier-phonon interactions near the dopants are strong enough and the formation of large polarons bound to the dopants becomes possible. If the carrier-phonon interactions in the vicinity of small-radius dopants (impurities) are strong enough to overcome the Coulomb repulsion between two carriers at the same impurity center, a bound state of two large polarons can be formed near the small-radius impurity. Such a bound state of two large polarons can be considered as the extrinsic bipolaron. We consider now the possibility of formation of localized in-gap states at single and pair self-trapping of carriers near the small-radius dopants (with $E_{dD} > 0$ or $b_s > 0$) in La-based cuprates. In this case, both the short and long range parts of the defect potential in equations (6.5) and (6.7) is attractive, so that the substitution of small-radius cations (e.g., $Ca^{2+}$ and $Nd^{3+}$ ions) for $La^{3+}$ ions in $La_2CuO_4$ and for $Sr^{2+}$ ions in LSCO led to the combined defect- and phonon-assisted self-trapping of hole carriers with the formation of the localized single-carrier and two-carrier impurity states, which are extrinsic polaronic and bipolaronic (so-called U pairing) states.

### 6.5.3.    Basic Parameters of Extrinsic Large Polarons and Bipolarons

At $Z \neq 0$ and $b_s > 0$, the minima of $E_1(\beta)$ and $E_2(\beta,\gamma)$ correspond to the ground-state energies of the extrinsic large polaron and bipolaron, respectively; measured with respect to the top of the oxygen valence band. The binding energies of such extrinsic large polaron and bipolaron (or negative $U$ center) are defined as $E_{pl} = |E_1^{min}(\beta)|$ and $E_{bU} = |E_2^{min}(\beta,\gamma) - 2E_1^{min}(\beta)|$, respectively. In 3D systems there is generally a potential barrier between the large- and small-radius self-trapped states. The two states of the extrinsic large polaron are separated by a potential barrier, with activation energy $E_1^A = E_1^{max}(\beta) - E_1^{min}(\beta)$ needed for the transition from the large-radius localized state to the small-radius one. The potential barrier $E_2^A = E_2^{max}(\beta,\gamma) - E_2^{min}(\beta)$ exists between the large and small-radius extrinsic bipolaronic states.

We now calculate the basic parameters of the extrinsic large (bi)polarons in La-based cuprates. At low temperature the La-based cuprates is orthorhombic with the lattice parameter $a_0 \simeq 5.4 \text{Å}$. According to the spectroscopy data, the Fermi energy of the undoped cuprates is about $E_F \simeq 7$ eV [41]. To determine the value of the short-range carrier-phonon coupling constant $g_s$, we can estimate the deformation potential $E_d$ as $E_d = (2/3)E_F$ [42]. For the cuprates, typical values of other parameters are $m^* = m_e$ [21] ($m_e$ is the free electron mass), $\varepsilon_\infty = 3 - 5$ [35, 44], $K = 1.4 \times 10^{12} dyn/cm^2$ [43], and $Z = 1$. The calculated values of $E_{pl}$, $E_{bU}$, $E_1^A$, and $E_2^A$, for $b_s = 1$ and different values of $\varepsilon_\infty$ and $\eta$ are presented in Table 6.1.

**Table 6.1. Calculated parameters of the extrinsic large polarons and bipolarons (with correlation between the pairing carriers) in 3D cuprates at $Z = 1$, $b_s = 1$, and different values of $\varepsilon_\infty$ and $\eta$**

| $\eta$ | $\varepsilon_\infty = 3.5$ | | | | $\varepsilon_\infty = 4.5$ | | | |
|---|---|---|---|---|---|---|---|---|
| | $E_{pl}$,eV | $E_{bU}$,eV | $E_1^A$,eV | $E_2^A$,eV | $E_{pl}$,eV | $E_{bU}$,eV | $E_1^A$,eV | $E_2^A$,eV |
| 0.00 | 0.1135 | 0.0610 | 5.3373 | 5.8611 | 0.0679 | 0.0354 | 5.9807 | 6.7958 |
| 0.02 | 0.1240 | 0.0525 | 5.2128 | 5.7649 | 0.0741 | 0.0303 | 5.8801 | 6.7090 |
| 0.04 | 0.1349 | 0.0434 | 5.0893 | 5.6693 | 0.0806 | 0.0247 | 5.7800 | 6.6224 |
| 0.06 | 0.1464 | 0.0336 | 4.9668 | 5.5743 | 0.0874 | 0.0188 | 5.6804 | 6.5359 |
| 0.08 | 0.1584 | 0.0231 | 4.8453 | 5.4799 | 0.0945 | 0.0125 | 5.5815 | 6.4495 |
| 0.10 | 0.1709 | 0.0120 | 4.7248 | 5.3861 | 0.1019 | 0.0058 | 5.4831 | 6.3633 |
| 0.12 | 0.1839 | 0.0001 | 4.6053 | 5.2929 | 0.1096 | – | 5.3854 | 6.2773 |

We see from the Table 6.5.3 that the potential barriers separating the large - and small-radius extrinsic (bi)polaronic states are rather high. Such high potential barriers prevent the formation of small extrinsic (bi)polarons in 3D cuprates. We have determined the stability region of the extrinsic large bipolaron in cuprates and found that such bipolarons exist, as long as $\eta$ is less than the critical value $\eta_c = 0.127$ and the ratio $E_{bU}/2E_{pl}$ reaches up to 0.287 (at $\varepsilon_\infty = 3$ and $\eta \to 0$) (Fig. 6.7).

## 6.5.4. Formation of Large Polarons and Bipolarons

In order to calculate the total energies of the single carrier and two carriers interacting with the acoustic and optical phonons, we assume $Z = 0$, $V_0 = 0$, and $E_{dD} = 0$ in Eq. (6.5) and (6.7). Then, we obtain the following functionals for the total energies $E_p\{\psi(r)\}$ and

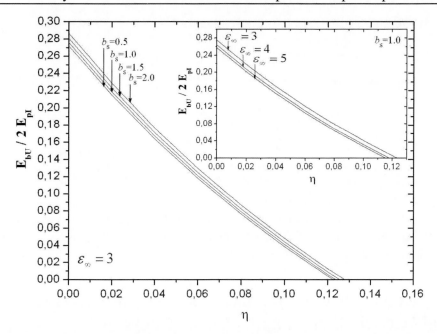

Figure 6.7. Ratio of the binding energy of the extrinsic large bipolaron (negative $U$ center) to twice the extrinsic large polaron binding energy as a function of $\eta$ for different values of $b_s$ ($b_s = 0.5, 1.0, 1.5, 2.0$) in 3D cuprates. The inset shows the dependence of the ratio of the binding energy of the extrinsic large bipolaron to twice that of the extrinsic large polaron on $\eta$ for different values of $\varepsilon_\infty$ ($\varepsilon_\infty = 3, 4, 5$) in 3D cuprates.

$E_B\{\Psi(\vec{r}_1, \vec{r}_2)\}$ of the coupled carrier-phonon and two-carrier-phonon systems to describe the formation of the polaronic and bipolaronic states in the CT gap of the lightly doped cuprates [36, 45]

$$E_p\{\psi(\vec{r})\} = \frac{\hbar^2}{2m^*}\int (\nabla\psi(r))^2 d^3r - \frac{e^2}{2\tilde{\varepsilon}}\int \frac{\psi^2(r)\psi^2(r')}{|r-r'|}d^3r d^3r'$$

$$-\frac{E_d^2}{2K}\int \psi^4(r)d^3r \qquad (6.14)$$

and

$$E_B\{\Psi(\vec{r}_1,\vec{r}_2)\} = \frac{\hbar^2}{2m^*}\int \left[|\nabla_1\Psi(r_1,r_2)|^2 + |\nabla_2\Psi(r_1,r_2)|^2\right]d^3r_1 d^3r_2$$

$$+\frac{e^2}{\varepsilon_\infty}\int \frac{\Psi^2(r_1,r_2)}{|r_1-r_2|}d^3r_1 d^3r_2$$

$$-\frac{2e^2}{\tilde{\varepsilon}}\int \frac{\Psi^2(r_1,r_2)\Psi^2(r_3,r_4)}{|r_1-r_3|}d^3r_1 d^3r_2 d^3r_3 d^3r_4$$

$$-\frac{2E_d^2}{K}\int \Psi^2(r_1,r_2)\Psi^2(r_2,r_3)d^3r_1 d^3r_2 d^3r_3 \qquad (6.15)$$

Using the wave functions (6.8) and (6.9), we obtain

$$E_p(\beta) = A \left[ \beta^2 - g_s \beta^3 - g_l (1-\eta) \beta \right] \tag{6.16}$$

and

$$\begin{aligned} E_B(\beta, \gamma) = 2A \frac{C_2(\gamma)}{C_1(\gamma)} \bigg\{ &\beta^2 - 16 g_s \frac{C_6(\gamma)}{C_1(\gamma) C_2(\gamma)} \beta^3 \\ &- \frac{8}{5} g_l \left[ 2(1-\eta) \frac{C_4(\gamma)}{C_1(\gamma) C_2(\gamma)} - \frac{C_3(\gamma)}{C_2(\gamma)} \beta \right] \bigg\} \end{aligned} \tag{6.17}$$

By minimizing the functionals (6.16) and (6.17) with respect to the variational parameters $\beta$ and $\gamma$, we obtain the lowest electronic or hole states which represents a discrete (bi)polaronic states in the CT gap of the lightly doped cuprates. The pairing of large polarons in these systems is assumed to occur in real-space [36].

## 6.6. Strong Electron-Phonon Interactions and Self-Trapping of Carriers in the Lightly Doped Cuprates

The next important situation is that the hole carriers are liberated from the hydrogen-like impurity centers at the certain doping level (at which Mott transition occurs) and are self-trapped in a defect-free deformable lattice with the formation of intrinsic large polarons and bipolarons. In this section, we discuss the possibility for the formation of such intrinsic polarons and bipolarons in the lightly doped cuprates. In the strong coupling limit, the ground-state energies of self-trapping carriers in a 3D polar lattice are calculated variationally in the continuum model and adiabatic approximation taking into account the short- and long-range carrier-phonon interactions, as well as the Coulomb repulsion between two pairing carriers.

### 6.6.1. Basic Parameters of Large Polarons and Bipolarons

Using the values of the parameters entering into Eqs. (6.16) and (6.17), we have also calculated the ground state energies of the intrinsic large polarons and bipolarons, the binding energies $E_p$ and $E_{bB}$ of such (bi)polarons, the heights of the potential barriers $E_p^A$ ($E_B^A$) separating large and small radius (bi)polaronic states. Here, we distinguish the real (i.e., acousto-optic) and optical (bi)polarons in polar cuprates. Using equations (6.16) and (6.17), we obtain the values of $E_p = |E_p^{min}(\beta)|$, $E_{bB} = |E_B^{min}(\beta, \gamma) - 2E_p^{min}(\beta)|$, $E_p^A = E_p^{max}(\beta) - E_p^{min}(\beta)$ and $E_B^A = E_B^{max}(\beta, \gamma) - E_B^{min}(\beta, \gamma)$ at different values of $\varepsilon_\infty$ and $\eta$. The results obtained for large (bi)polarons are summarized in Table 6.2. The large- and small-radius (bi)polaronic states are separated by very high potential barriers (Table 6.2). It follows that the relevant charge carriers in 3D cuprates are large intrinsic and extrinsic polarons or bipolarons. While the small polarons and bipolarons may be formed in the $CuO_2$ layers of the cuprates, where the self-trapping of carriers may occur more easily due to the absence of the potential barrier between the large- and small-radius self-trapped states in 2D systems [46]. However, such 2D (bi)polarons with very large binding energies and effective masses tend to be localized rather than mobile and their transition from the insulating state to the metallic one does not

**Table 6.2. Calculated parameters of the real large polarons and bipolarons (with correlation between the pairing carriers) in 3D cuprates at different values of $\varepsilon_\infty$ and $\eta$**

| $\eta$ | $\varepsilon_\infty = 3.5$ | | | | $\varepsilon_\infty = 4.5$ | | | |
|---|---|---|---|---|---|---|---|---|
| | $E_p,$ eV | $E_{bB},$eV | $E_p^A,$ eV | $E_B^A,$ eV | $E_p,$ eV | $E_{bB},$eV | $E_p^A,$ eV | $E_B^A,$ eV |
| 0.00 | 0.1107 | 0.0583 | 27.275 | 19.989 | 0.0666 | 0.0343 | 28.656 | 21.744 |
| 0.02 | 0.1063 | 0.0484 | 27.398 | 20.269 | 0.0640 | 0.0284 | 28.753 | 21.980 |
| 0.04 | 0.1019 | 0.0389 | 27.521 | 20.551 | 0.0614 | 0.0228 | 28.851 | 22.217 |
| 0.06 | 0.0977 | 0.0299 | 27.645 | 20.834 | 0.0588 | 0.0175 | 28.949 | 22.453 |
| 0.08 | 0.0935 | 0.0215 | 27.769 | 21.118 | 0.0563 | 0.0125 | 29.046 | 22.690 |
| 0.10 | 0.0895 | 0.0136 | 27.893 | 21.404 | 0.0539 | 0.0078 | 29.144 | 22.928 |
| 0.12 | 0.0855 | 0.0061 | 28.017 | 21.691 | 0.0515 | 0.0003 | 29.242 | 23.166 |
| 0.14 | 0.0816 | – | 28.142 | 21.980 | 0.0491 | – | 29.341 | 23.404 |

occur at any doping levels (see Ref. [47]). We have obtained the conditions for the 3D large bipolaron stability and estimated the values of $E_{bB}/2E_p$. Figure 6.8 shows the variation of the ratio $E_{bB}/2E_p$ with $\eta$ for $\varepsilon_\infty = 3$, 4 and 5 for real large bipolarons in cuprates. One can see that in 3D cuprates, the intrinsic large bipolarons can exist at $\eta = \eta_c \leq 0.138$ and the ratio $E_{bB}/2E_p$ reaches up to 0.27 (at $\varepsilon_\infty = 3$ and $\eta \to 0$). While the inset of figure 6.8 shows the variation of the ratio $E_{bB}/2E_p$ (calculated from equations (6.10) and (6.11) at $g_s = 0$ and $Z = 0$) with $\eta$ for large optical bipolaron. Of course, besides the ratio $\eta = \varepsilon_\infty/\varepsilon_0$, the values of the Fröhlich electron-phonon coupling constant $\alpha$ are very important for the formation of large optical bipolarons. Since the long-range coupling of carriers with optical phonons is rather stronger than their short-range coupling with acoustic phonons. Therefore, the long-range Fröhlich-type electron-phonon interaction in polar materials have been studied extensively [48, 49], although the short-range deformation potential type interaction is also important and led to new effects. The dimentionless Fröhlich coupling constant is defined as

$$\alpha = \frac{e^2(1-\eta)}{2\varepsilon_\infty \hbar\omega_{LO}}\left[\frac{2m^*\omega_{LO}}{\hbar}\right]^{1/2}, \tag{6.18}$$

where $\hbar\omega_{LO}$ is the longitudinal-optical (LO) phonon frequency.

In polar materials, the formation of optical bipolarons is favored by larger values of $\alpha$ and by smaller values of $\eta$ [49, 50], i.e., the optical (Fröhlich or Pekar) bipolarons exist only if $\alpha$ is greater than a critical value $\alpha_c$ and when $\eta < \eta_c$. Such 3D bipolarons can exist above rather high critical values $\alpha_c$, e.g., $\alpha_c = 7.3$ as found by Adamowski [51] and $\alpha_c = 6.8$ found by Verbist, Peeters, and Devreese [52]. Further, the value of $\alpha_c$ corresponding to the onset of the strong coupling regime is found to be $\alpha_c = 5.8$ [53], below which the formation of large optical bipolaron in 3D systems is unlikely. At a given value of $\eta$, the value of $\alpha_c$ depends on $m^*$, $\varepsilon_\infty$, and $\omega_{LO}$. The values of $\hbar\omega_{LO}$ in high-$T_c$ cuprates range from 0.03

to 0.05 eV [21, 54]. Then the values of $\alpha$ corresponding to these high-$T_c$ materials with $m^* = m_e$, $\varepsilon_\infty = 3$, and $\eta = 0.02 - 0.10$, are equal to $\alpha = 4.96 - 6.95$. So, the conditions for the formation of large optical bipolarons are more favorable in the cuprates with $\varepsilon_\infty = 3$, $\eta = 0.02 - 0.06$, and $\hbar\omega_{LO} = 0.03 - 0.04$ eV, at which conditions $\alpha > \alpha_c \simeq 5.8$ [53] and $\alpha > \alpha_c = 6.8$ [52] are well satisfied.

We note here that the largest values of $\eta_c = 0.079 - 0.14$ and $E_{bB}/2E_p = 0.22 - 0.25$ as found in the literature [55, 56, 57] (see also [49])were obtained for the optical bipolaron and do not correspond to specific substances. While the critical values of $\eta$ below which the optical bipolarons can exist in cuprates were small enough ($\eta_c = 0.040 - 0.055$), as estimated in [49]. Our results are quite impressive in the sense that both the real and the optical bipolaron in 3D cuprates, can indeed exist for relatively large values of $\eta$ (figure 6.8) and the large bipolarons are formed with the binding energies reaching up to 27% (at $\eta \to 0$) of twice the large polaron energy. The distinctive feature of the cuprates is their very large ratio of static to high frequency dielectric constants. This situation is favorable for carriers attracted to polarization well created by the other ones or to Coulomb centers (dopants) to form 3D intrinsic or extrinsic large bipolarons. At $\varepsilon_0 > 30$ such bipolarons (pair states) can be formed in lightly doped cuprates and they become unstable in underdoped regime. As can be seen from Tables 6.5.3 and 6.6.1, the binding energies of extrinsic and intrinsic large (bi)polarons and the ratios $E_{bU}/2E_{pI}$ and $E_{bB}/2E_p$ depend on several parameters. In particular, $E_{pI}$, $E_p$, $E_{bU}$, and $E_{bB}$ would increase rapidly with decreasing $\varepsilon_\infty$ from 5 to 3, while the ratios $E_{bU}/2E_{pI}$ and $E_{bB}/2E_p$ increase more slowly as $\varepsilon_\infty$ is decreased. Interestingly, $E_{pI}$ is an increasing function of $\eta$ (Table 6.5.3), while $E_p$ is a decreasing function of $\eta$ (Table 6.6.1). Furthermore, we find that both $E_{bU}$ and $E_{bB}$ are decreased with increasing $\eta$. We also find that the ratio $E_{bU}/2E_{pI}$ increases appreciably with $b_s$ as shown in figure 6.7. The calculated values of the radii of extrinsic large (bi)polarons $R_I$ ($R_{BI}$) (at $Z = 1$ and $b_s = 1$) and intrinsic large (bi)polarons, $R_p$ ($R_B$) (at $Z = 0$ and $b_s = 0$) for different values of $\varepsilon_\infty$ and $\eta$ are given Table 6.6.1.

**Table 6.3. Calculated values of the radii of intrinsic and extrinsic large (bi)polarons $R_p$, $R_I$, $R_B$ and $R_{BI}$ in 3D cuprates at different values of $\varepsilon_\infty$ and $\eta$**

| $\eta$ | $\varepsilon_\infty = 3.5$ | | | | $\varepsilon_\infty = 4.5$ | | | |
|---|---|---|---|---|---|---|---|---|
| | $R_p$, A | $R_B$, A | $R_I$, A | $R_{BI}$, A | $R_p$, A | $R_B$, A | $R_I$, A | $R_{BI}$, A |
| 0.00 | 8.6096 | 13.045 | 8.2839 | 12.403 | 11.158 | 17.066 | 10.841 | 16.457 |
| 0.02 | 8.7917 | 13.577 | 7.9061 | 12.084 | 11.392 | 17.746 | 10.357 | 16.052 |
| 0.04 | 8.9813 | 14.146 | 7.5586 | 11.777 | 11.636 | 18.475 | 9.9111 | 15.662 |
| 0.06 | 9.1791 | 14.756 | 7.2378 | 11.482 | 11.890 | 19.256 | 9.5001 | 15.288 |
| 0.08 | 9.3854 | 15.413 | 6.9409 | 11.199 | 12.155 | 20.098 | 9.1197 | 14.928 |
| 0.10 | 9.6009 | 16.121 | 6.6652 | 10.926 | 12.432 | 21.005 | 8.7665 | 14.581 |
| 0.12 | 9.8261 | 16.887 | 6.4084 | 10.662 | 12.722 | 21.986 | 8.4379 | 14.248 |
| 0.14 | 10.062 | 17.718 | 6.1688 | 10.408 | 13.025 | 23.051 | 8.1312 | 13.926 |

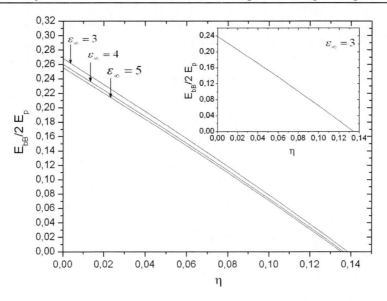

Figure 6.8. Ratio of the binding energy of the real large bipolaron to twice that of the real large polaron as a function of $\eta$ for different values of $\varepsilon_\infty$ ($\varepsilon_\infty = 3, 4, 5$) in 3D cuprates. The inset illustrates the ratio of the binding energy of the optical large bipolaron to twice that of the optical large polaron on $\eta$ for different values of $\varepsilon_\infty$ ($\varepsilon_\infty = 3, 4, 5$) in 3D cuprates.

## 6.7. Experimental Verifications of Extrinsic and Intrinsic Large Polarons and Bipolarons in the Insulating Phase of High-$T_c$ Cuprates

We now make some remarks about the characteristic (i.e., binding) energies of large bipolarons in the cuprates. The binding energies of extrinsic and intrinsic bipolarons strongly depend on $\varepsilon_\infty$, $\varepsilon_0$, and $\eta$. The values of $\varepsilon_\infty$ and $\varepsilon_0$ observed in high-$T_c$ cuprates are 3 - 5 [21, 35, 44] and 33 - 105 [21, 58], respectively, so that the values of $\eta$ range from 0.028 to 0.15. Using the values of $\varepsilon_\infty = 3$ and $\eta \simeq 0.03$, we find $E_{bU} \simeq 0.07$ eV and $E_{bB} \simeq 0.061$ eV. If we take other experimental values of $\varepsilon_\infty = 4$ and $\varepsilon_0 \simeq 50$ for the cuprates (see Refs. [49, 50]), then we obtain $E_{bU} \simeq 0.017$ eV and $E_{bB} \simeq 0.016$ eV at $\eta = 0.08$. Further, at $\varepsilon_\infty = 5$ and $\eta = 0.08$ we find $E_{bU} \simeq 0.0097$ eV and $E_{bB} \simeq 0.0102$ eV. Thus, the extrinsic and intrinsic bipolarons can be found experimentally in high-$T_c$ cuprates in the energy ranges ~0.01-0.07 eV and ~0.01-0.06 eV, respectively. The binding energies of large polarons and bipolarons are manifested in the excitation spectra of the hole-doped cuprates as the temperature-independent low-energy gaps or pseudogaps, which are different from the high-energy CT gaps ($\Delta_{CT} \simeq 1.5 - 2.0 eV$ [20, 25]) of the cuprates.

It is of interest to compare our results with experimental data on localized in-gap states (or bands) and energy gaps (which are responsible for the existing of insulating phase and are precursors to the pseudogaps observed in the metallic state) in hole-doped cuprates. The extrinsic and intrinsic (bi)polaronic states, as well as hydrogenic impurity states emerge in the CT gap of the cuprates. In the experiments, these localized states are displayed as the in-gap states. One can see that the value of $E_{pI} \simeq 0.13$ eV obtained at $\varepsilon_{\infty} = 4$ and $\eta = 0.1$ (Table 6.1) is consistent with experimental data for lightly doped $La_2CuO_{4+\delta}$ [21]. The in-gap impurity band observed in this system at 0.13 eV might be associated with the extrinsic large polarons. While the values of $E_p \simeq 0.096 - 0.105$ eV (Table 6.2) obtained at $\varepsilon_{\infty} = 3.5$ and $\eta = 0.04 - 0.06$ agree reasonably well with the large pseudogap value $\sim$ 0.1 eV observed in LSCO [59]. One of the important experimental observations is that in LSCO; the flatband [60], which is $\sim 0.12$ eV below the Fermi energy for $x = 0.05$, moves upwards monotonically with increasing $x$, but the flatband is lowered as $x$ decreases and loses its intensity in the insulating phase. Apparently, the flatband observed by ARPES in the lightly doped LSCO ($x = 0.05$) is the energy band of large polarons since the effective mass of carriers obtained from analysis of the ARPES spectra is about $2.1m_e$ [60]. The values of $R_p$ (Table 6.3) are also in good agreement with the experimental values of the radii of polarons which vary from 6 to 10 $A$ in cuprates [21].

The temperature-independent pseudogaps seen in the optical conductivity of under-doped LSCO at 500-600 $cm^{-1}$ (0.060-0.072 eV) [61, 62] and in the Raman spectra of underdoped YBCO at 500 $cm^{-1}$ [63, 64] are associated with the formation of large ex-trinsic and intrinsic bipolarons. The magnitudes of these pseudogaps are very close to the previously mentioned binding energies $E_{bU} \simeq 0.07$ eV and $E_{bB} \simeq 0.06$ eV of large bipo-larons. Another pseudogap observed in YBCO at 0.05 eV [65, 66] can be also interpreted as the pairing bipolaronic gap $E_{bB} = 0.05$ eV (at $\varepsilon_{\infty} = 3$ and $\eta = 0.05$). Further, the values of the binding energies $E_{bB} \simeq 0.01 - 0.04$ eV of large bipolarons obtained at $\varepsilon_{\infty} = 3 - 5$ and $\eta = 0.06 - 0.08$ (which are typical for LSCO and YBCO [50]) are consistent with the energies of the absorption peaks in the far-infrared transmission spectra observed in YBCO at 0.013-0.039 eV [67]. It seems that the temperature-independent gap-like feature seen in the optical conductivity of underdoped YBCO and Bi-2212 (see Ref. [62]) at 700-750 $cm^{-1}$ (0.085-0.090 eV) is likely associated with the excitation of carriers from the polaronic bound state to the unbound quasi-free states. Other experimental observations indicate the existence of localized in-gap states and the well-defined semiconducting gap in the lightly doped LSCO ($x = 0.02$) [68], where the observed energy gap has the value 0.04 eV and is almost temperature independent up to 160 K. The value of this small energy gap is close to those of the binding energies of intrinsic large bipolarons presented in Table 6.2 for $\varepsilon_{\infty} = 3.5$ and $\eta = 0.04$.

For the case $b_s < 0$, as mentioned already, the hydrogen-like impurity centers can be formed in LSCO and other cuprates. Using the values of $\varepsilon_0 = 25$ and $m^* = m_e$ [21], we obtain $a_H = 13.225\text{Å}$ and $E_l \simeq 0.022$ eV, which is also close to the observed values of the binding energy $0.019 \pm 0.002$ eV of the Sr acceptor in LSCO [21].

## 6.8.   Low-Energy Electronic Structure of the Doped Cuprates

As mentioned before, the insulating behavior of the undoped cuprates is characterized by the high energy CT gap $\Delta_{CT} \simeq 1.5 - 2.0$ eV. Experimental studies revealed a complicated character of the electronic structure of doped cuprates in which the new insulating gap $E_g$ is nearly ten times smaller than the CT gap $\Delta_{CT}$ [3, 20, 21, 59, 60]. Since the electronic structure of the cuprates are changed dramatically with doping and spectral weight of the CT excitations is transferred to low-energy excitations [20, 25]. Such an evolution of the electronic structure of the doped cuprates is believed to be caused by the carrier-dopant-phonon and carrier-phonon interactions, and the formation of in-gap states and low-energy gaps in the excitation spectrum of these materials [36, 69, 70]. The energy gap (or threshold energy) $|E_1^{min}(\beta)|$ or $|E_p^{min}(\beta)|$ exist for the excitation of a carrier from the polaronic state of its self-trapping potential well to a free-carrier state of the oxygen valence band. While the formation energy $|E_2^{min}(\beta,\gamma)|$ or $|E_B^{min}(\beta,\gamma)|$ of a large bipolaron is the second threshold energy for the excitation of self-trapped carriers from the bipolaronic states. The another energy gap $E_{bB}$ is expected to appear as the small or lowest-energy gap for the excitation of self-trapped carriers from their bound bipolaronic state to the polaronic state. These low-energy gaps are almost independent of doping in the lightly doped regime. Such gap-like features were observed in the underdoped cuprates in which the low-energy gaps experimentally observed at $0.04 - 0.06$ eV [62, 68] and $0.08 \div 0.15$ eV [3, 62, 71] may be associated with the binding (or dissociation) energies $E_{bB}$ and $|E_1^{min}(\beta)|$ or $|E_p(\beta)|$ of large bipolarons and polarons, respectively. From this observation, the doped cuprates have the low-energy electronic structure (with the insulating gaps $E_g \simeq 0.1 \div 0.2$ eV), which is quite different from the high-energy electronic structure (with the insulating gaps $\Delta_{CT} \simeq 1.5 - 2.0$ eV [20, 25]) of the undoped cuprates. In the next sections, we shall discuss the distinctive feature of the new electronic structure of the doped cuprates.

## 6.8.1. Specific Charge Ordering and Formation of Different Superlattices and In-Gap Impurity Bands

In doped cuprates, the spatial variation in the density of dopants or charge carriers and the ordering of defect centers (impurities with trapped charge carriers) are expected to be very important in the formation of in- or mid-gap defect (impurity) bands and these realities should be taken into account in the description of the doped cuprates. There is experimental evidence for the existence of charge carriers (free holes or hole polarons) bound to defects and microscopic charge inhomogeneities in hole-doped cuprates [21, 72, 73, 74]. The existence of nanoscale electronic charge inhomogeneities in LSCO and Bi2212 has been directly observed by scanning tunneling spectroscopy (STS) as the spatial variation of energy gaps and local density of states [72, 73]. In addition, in NMR/NQR experiments electronic charge inhomogeneities have also been detected in the underdoped LSCO system [75]. Possible explanation of the origin of the charge inhomogeneity, such as the dopant-driven electron disorder and the electronic phase separation have been proposed (see, e.g., Ref. [74]). Other proposal is based on the existence of quite different dopant-driven charge orderings and the formation of distinctly different impurity bands in the CT gap of the doped cuprates [76, 77]. This theoretical model highlights the importance of the dopant-driven electronic charge inhomogeneity and specific charge ordering for underdoped cuprates and their possible connection to the variations of the low-energy electronic states and insulating energy gaps in these materials. The electronic charge inhomogeneity is thought to be a typical aspect of the heavily underdoped high-$T_c$ cuprates. Actually, the hole-doped cuprates are inhomogeneous systems (where the dopants and charge carriers are distributed inhomogeneously) and the underdoped cuprates are more inhomogeneous than overdoped ones [73, 78, 79]. The dopant-driven and carrier-driven inhomogeneities may produce regions with different doping levels or with spatially varying local density of charge carriers. The doped cuprates have a rich phase diagram and their metallic and superconducting states are quite different from those of conventional metals and superconductors [14, 20, 80, 81]. The insulating state of these materials is also substantially different from that of undoped cuprates [80, 82]. Instead of strong electron correlations (i.e., on-site Coulomb interactions), which play a dominating role only in undoped cuprates and drive these systems into a CT-type Mott insulating state [24], the carrier-defect-phonon and carrier-phonon interactions and the electronic inhomogeneities play an important role in doped cuprates and are responsible for the carrier localization and pairing and the charge segregation, which may manifest itself via local phase separation and stripe formation (i.e., the charge carriers form metallic stripes, "rivers of charge carriers" [80], separated by insulating stripes). In particular, in doped high-$T_c$ cuprates the inhomogeneous spatial distribution of charge carriers led to their segregation into carrier-rich and carrier-poor regions. Whereas the short- and long-range carrier-defect-phonon and carrier-phonon attractive interactions may dominate and give rise to charge aggregation in carrier-rich metallic regions together with charge depletion in spatially separated carrier-poor regions with no mobile carriers. In high-$T_c$ cuprates, the local inhomogeneity and the competitions between the kinetic energy, these attractive interactions and the long-range Coulomb interaction produce nanoscale self-organized structures called stripes. Further, the anisotropy of the dielectric constants ($\varepsilon_\infty$ and $\varepsilon_0$) and the smallness of $\eta$ in the cuprates favor such phase separation into alternating carrier-rich and carrier-poor regions. As the doping level increases towards underdoped regime, specific charge ordering in the form of a 3D network of dynamic (metallic) and static (insulating) stripes takes place in these regions, where distinctly different superlattices and energy bands of dopants and self-trapped carriers (intrinsic large polarons) are formed at their inhomogeneous spatial distribution. In particular, the hydrogenic impurity centers (impurities with loosely bound quasi-free carriers or large polarons) and extrinsic large polarons (or impurities with tightly bound large polarons) are assumed to form the superlattices with the lattice constant $a_I$ and coordination number $z$. The charge ordering in carrier-poor and carrier-rich domains results in the formation of simple cubic, body-centered cubic and face-centered cubic superlattices with coordination numbers $z = 6$, 8, and 12, respectively, and the formation of different impurity bands in the CT gap of the cuprates. In the tight-binding approximation the widths of the impurity bands can be determined from the relation

$$W_I = 2zJ, \tag{6.19}$$

where $J$ is the hopping integral between nearest-neighbor impurity centers.

For the case of the hydrogenic impurity centers, the hopping integral in equation (6.19) may be approximated as [40]

$$J = \frac{e^2\lambda}{\varepsilon_0} \exp\left[-\lambda R\right], \tag{6.20}$$

where $\lambda$ is the reciprocal radius of an impurity state, $R$ is the distance between the impurity centers. For increasing $R$, the impurity band is continuously narrowed, finally ending in the discrete levels of individual impurity centers ($R \gg 1/\lambda$). In this case, carriers are localized to the dopant sites or confined to the potential wells at impurity sites and the system is converted into an insulator. Therefore, conduction takes place in a narrow impurity band by hopping of carriers from one to another impurity site. When the number of impurity states increases, their overlap increases, thus increasing $W_I$ and the charge transport in

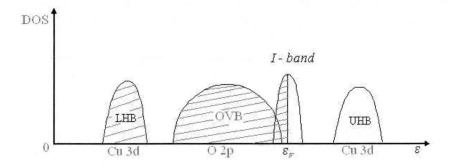

Figure 6.9. Schematic band structure (density of states (DOS) as a function of energy $\varepsilon$) of the underdoped cuprates. LHB: lower Hubbard band. UHB: upper Hubbard band. OVB: oxygen valence band. I: impurity (defect) band. $\varepsilon_F$ is the Fermi energy of the impurity band.

sufficiently broadened impurity bands becomes band-like (i.e., metal-like). Determination of the critical carrier concentration at which such a transition from the hopping-like to the metal-like charge transport occurs in cuprates is a very intricate problem, which is at present not completely solved.

At low doping level the Fermi level is pinned near the center of the CT gap of lightly doped cuprates. Because of the formation of in-gap impurity band, the position of the Fermi level (or chemical potential) shifts to the top of the oxygen valence band (OVB) (Fig. 6.9) just like Fermi level in the $p$-type semiconductors shifts to the top of their valence band. Early experimental results show [26] that this indeed happens in the underdoped cuprates and there is a continuous increase of unoccupied density of states at the Fermi level which is pinned close to the top of the OVB.

## 6.8.2.    Formation of the In-Gap Polaronic and Bipolaronic Bands

As mentioned earlier, the self-trapping of carriers in a defect-free lattice led to the formation of the large-radius polaronic and bipolaronic states in the CT gap of the lightly doped cuprates. We believe that the localized 3D large bipolarons can exist only in these materials (see section 6.9) Therefore, theoretical understanding of the possible forms of charge ordering and the formation of different in-gap polaronic bands is very important for a more complete description of the inhomogeneous low-energy electronic structure of underdoped cuprates. In reality, the inhomogeneous spatial distribution of large polarons leading to their segregation into the carrier-poor and carrier-rich domains may play crucial role in the unusual electronic properties of doped high-$T_c$ cuprates. We believe that the intrinsic large polarons like impurity centers form different superlattices and the widths of the polaronic bands just as the widths of the impurity bands are determined from a relation just like equation (6.19) [48]. There is a serious problem in describing the formation of the new in-gap bands, the existence of the different low-energy gaps and the shift of the Fermi energy with increasing doping [83]. Some experiments are indicative of the shift of the Fermi level to the top of the OVB in the lightly doped cuprates [26], while other experiments indicate that the shift of the Fermi level to the top of the OVB occurs in the optimally doped cuprates [3, 20]. We argue that the theory of in-gap polaronic bands describes these experimental observations and the gap inhomogeneity (or gap distribution) in the underdoped cuprates naturally. For example, the Fermi energy moves into the polaronic band when doping level exceeds some critical value $x_B$ at which large bipolarons dissociate into two large polarons. Therefore, depending on the values of $\varepsilon_\infty$ an $\varepsilon_0$ (or $\eta$) the Fermi energy shifts to the top of the OVB at different doping levels in accordance with the experimental observations [3, 20, 26]. At higher doping levels the Fermi energy moves into the polaronic band and is located in this narrow polaronic band (Fig. 6.10). The gap inhomogeneity observed in the

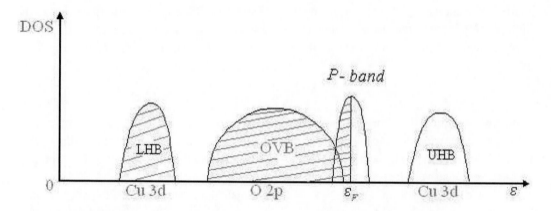

Figure 6.10. Schematic band structure (DOS as a function of energy $\varepsilon$) of the underdoped cuprates. P: polaronic band. $\varepsilon_F$ is the Fermi energy of the polaronic band.

underdoped cuprates is then explained by the formation of the distinctly different energy gaps between OVB and in-gap polaronic energy bands.

## 6.9.  Metal-Insulator Transitions in Crystalline and Non-Crystalline Solids

The mechanisms of carrier localization and metal-insulator transitions (MITs) in undoped and doped materials have been central problems of the solid state physics for many decades [15, 16, 17, 18, 20, 84]. According to the one-electron band theory, crystalline solids are metals with a partially filled valence band or insulators with a completely filled valence band. Such a classification of solids into metals and insulators was originally proposed by Wilson [85]. According to the Wilson's band theory of non-interacting electrons, MITs in crystalline solids can occur when two band will overlap due to the change in volume (under pressure) or temperature of the materials (Fig. 6.11). This one-electron band theory has been very successful in describing many crystalline materials. But it was inadequate for transition metal oxides with a partially filled $d$-electron band, which are insulators [17, 20]. Since in conventional simplified band theory, the most important features of many-body systems, such as strong Coulomb repulsion between electrons (i.e., electron-electron correlation), disorder in atomic and electronic subsystems and electron-lattice interaction were

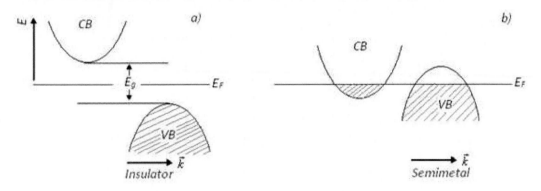

Figure 6.11. Schematic illustration of a Wilson-type insulator-to-metal transition. (a) Insulator with the energy gap $E_g$ between the conduction band (CB) and the valence band (VB). (b) Semimetal with the overlapping CB and VB. $E$ and $\vec{k}$ are the energy and wave vector, respectively. $E_F$ denotes the Fermi energy.

ignored. Further, Mott [15] and Anderson [86] suggested the ideas of the localization of electrons and MITs due to the strong electron-electron correlation and structural disorder, respectively. These correlation- and disorder-induced MITs called Mott and Anderson transitions were discussed as the basic mechanism of the carrier localization in crystalline and non-crystalline solids [16, 17, 18, 20, 84]. Mott considered a half-filled $d$-electron band (with bandwidth $W$ and on-site Coulomb repulsion $U_d$ between electrons) or a perfect crystal lattice of one-electron hydrogen-like atoms with the lattice constant $a$. According to Mott, the electrons of the half-filled valence band are delocalized at small $a$ (or large $W$) satisfying the condition $W/U_d > 1$ (see Fig. 6.5b) and characterized by metal-like conductivity. When $a$ is increased, the band is continuously narrowed. The electrons of this narrow band are localized at their respective atoms and the crystalline material is converted into an AF insulator due to the splitting of the half-filled band into UHB and LHB at $W/U_d < 1$ (see Fig. 6.5). The Mott criterion for the MIT in crystalline solids is defined as [15, 17, 87]

$$n_c^{1/3} a_H = 0.25, \qquad (6.21)$$

where $a_H$ is the Bohr radius of hydrogen-like atoms, $n_c$ is the critical concentration of these atoms initiating the MIT of the system. This model of a perfect crystal structure is not relevant to real crystalline solids in which there is a certain degree of disorder (e.g., vacancies, impurities, displaced atoms, and deformed chemical bonds). Therefore, Anderson considered the possibility of the localization of non-interacting electrons due to disorder. Anderson used a crystalline array of potential wells with a random potential $V$, varying between the limits $\pm(1/2)V_0$ (Fig. 6.12). In the tight-binding approximation the Hamiltonian of the Anderson model in the Wannier representation is given by [17, 18]

$$H = \sum_i \varepsilon_i a_i^+ a_i + \sum_{ij} J_{ij} a_i^+ a_j, \qquad (6.22)$$

where $a_i^+(a_i)$ is the creation (annihilation) operator of an electron at site $i$, $n = a_i^+ a_i$ is the number operator, $J_{ij}$ is the hopping integral between sites $i$ and $j$, $\varepsilon_i$ is the energy of an electron at site $i$.

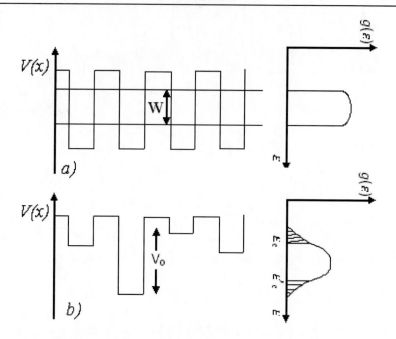

Figure 6.12. (a) Potential wells of a perfect crystal lattice. (b) Potential wells of the Anderson lattice with a random potential $(\pm V_0/2)$. Density of states $g(\varepsilon)$ as a function of the energy $\varepsilon$ is also shown. The energies $\varepsilon_c$ and $\varepsilon_c'$ separate the localized states (shaded) from that of delocalized ones.

The disorder led to smearing the band edges with the formation of the band tails. According to Anderson, the criterion for electron localization is defined as [84, 87]

$$V_0/W > A_0 \qquad (1.4 \leq A_0 \leq 2.7) \qquad (6.23)$$

If $V_0/W < A_0$, as first pointed out by Mott [84], the states in the tails of a band are localized, and the energies $\varepsilon_c$ and $\varepsilon_c'$ (called the mobility edges) separate the localized and extended states. The value of $A_0$ obtained originally by Anderson is about 5, but subsequent calculations (see Refs. [84, 87]) predict different values for $A_0$, which are much less than 5. Although carrier localization and MITs driven by electron correlation and disorder have been already studied for more than five decades, many questions, particularly concerning quantitative aspects, are still open. The questions concerning the applicability of the Mott and Anderson MITs to doped cuprates are still not settled [84, 88].

## 6.10.  Possible Mechanisms of Metal - Insulator Transitions and Stripe Formation in Doped Cuprates

In this section, we discuss the different mechanisms that cause carrier localization in hole-doped cuprates. The question now arises how, under certain conditions, a system with $n$ carriers in cuprates may undergo a phase transition from a delocalized into a localized state. In inhomogeneous hole-doped cuprates, the strong carrier-carrier interactions, structural disorder, carrier-defect-phonon and carrier-phonon interactions may play an important role in carrier localization and MITs. We first examine the condition for the existence of the localized bipolaronic states in cuprates. At very low doping, the separate levels of extrinsic and intrinsic large bipolarons are formed in the CT gap of the cuprates. As the doping increases towards underdoped region, the binding energies of such large bipolarons start to decrease gradually and become zero at some doping levels. In particular, the binding energy of the intrinsic large bipolaron is now defined as

$$\Delta_b = E_{bB} - 2\varepsilon_F, \tag{6.24}$$

where $\varepsilon_F$ is the Fermi energy of large polarons.

Actually, large bipolarons can exist in cuprates in carrier-poor domains at $\eta < \eta_c$ and remain localized. At a certain doping level $n = n_c$ or $x = x_c = n_c/n_a$ (where $n_a = 1/V_a$ is the density of the host lattice atoms, $V_a$ is the volume per $CuO_2$ unit in cuprates), $\Delta_b = 0$ and the large bipolaron will dissociate into two large polarons. Therefore, the critical carrier concentration $n_c$ determined from the equation (6.24) is

$$n_c = \frac{(m_p E_{bB})^{3/2}}{3\pi^2 \hbar^3} \tag{6.25}$$

For the LSCO system we can evaluate $n_c$ using the parameter values $m_p = 2.1 m_e$, $\varepsilon_\infty = 3.5 - 4.5$, $\eta = 0.04 - 0.08$, $E_{bB} \approx 0.01 - 0.10$ eV (Table 6.2). Then, we obtain $n_c \simeq (0.0514 - 1.6238) \times 10^{20} cm^{-3}$. Taking into account that the value of $V_a$ in the orthorhombic LSCO is $190 \mathring{A}^3$, we find the doping levels $x_c = 0.001 - 0.031$ at which large bipolarons dissociate into large polarons. This means that such localized 3D bipolarons can exist only in the lightly doped LSCO. At $x > x_c$ the energy bands of extrinsic and intrinsic large polarons may exist, thus permitting charge transport by means of intra-band conduction. In case of narrow polaronic bands, charge transport becomes hopping-like and is caused by intra-band hopping processes [87]. One can assume that if the bandwidth of the extrinsic large polarons exceeds some critical value, their intra-band conduction becomes metal-like. We attempt to find the conditions under which such a insulator-to-metal transition occurs in doped materials.

The conditions for carrier localization or delocalization can be obtained by using the uncertainty principle: $\Delta p \Delta x \geq \hbar/2$, where $\Delta p$ and $\Delta x$ are the uncertainties in the momentum and coordinate of a carrier, respectively. This uncertainty relation can be written as

$$\Delta x \cdot \Delta E \simeq \frac{\hbar^2 (\Delta k)^2}{2m^*} \frac{1}{2\Delta k}, \tag{6.26}$$

where $\Delta E$ and $\Delta k$ are the uncertainties in the energy and wave vector of the carrier. The expression $\hbar^2 (\Delta k)^2/2m^*$ in equation (6.26) represents the uncertainty in the kinetic energy of quasi-free carriers. By taking into account that in the impurity band the uncertainties in the energy of carriers is of order $W_I/2$ and the uncertainty in their wave vector is about $1/a_I$, the relation (6.26) can be rewritten in the form (cf. [89])

$$\Delta x \cdot \Delta E \cong \frac{W_I a_I}{4} \tag{6.27}$$

On the other hand, the uncertainty in the energy $\Delta E$ of carriers at the hydrogen-like impurity centers is of the order of the repulsive Hubbard energy $U$, whereas $\Delta x$ would be of the order of $a_H$. In this case, the condition for carrier localization can be written in the form

$$U/W_I > \frac{0.25a_I}{a_H}, \tag{6.28}$$

which is useful in determining the quantitative criteria for the Mott MITs. From equation (6.28), it follows that the Mott MIT is governed by the ratios $U/W_I$ and $a_I/a_H$. When the impurity centers are distributed randomly the disorder-induced spatial localization of carriers can drive the Anderson-type MIT in the cuprates. Since, a random potential $V_0$ leads to the uncertainties in the energy $\Delta E \sim V_0/2$ and coordinate $\Delta x \sim a_H$ of carriers, the condition for Anderson localization can be written as

$$\frac{V_0}{W_I} > \frac{0.5a_I}{a_H}, \tag{6.29}$$

In addition to the Mott and Anderson scenarios, there are other possible mechanisms that cause carrier localization. We believe that the strong carrier-defect-phonon and carrier-phonon interactions can initiate MITs in cuprates. If the uncertainty in the energy of large polarons bound to impurities is of order $E_{pI}$ and the uncertainty in the coordinate $\Delta x$ of these carriers is the order of the radius of the impurity centers $R_I$, the condition for carrier localization or a new type of MIT can be written as

$$\frac{E_{pI}}{W_I} > \frac{0.25a_I}{R_I}, \tag{6.30}$$

from which it follows that the MIT is governed by the ratios $E_{pI}/W_I$ and $a_I/R_I$.

Similarly, the MIT may be also driven by varying the Fermi energy $\varepsilon_F$ and the lattice constant $a_p$ of intrinsic large polarons. The condition for such a MIT can be written as

$$\frac{E_p}{\varepsilon_F} \geq \frac{0.5a_p}{R_p}. \tag{6.31}$$

Next, we examine the possibility of the Mott, Anderson, and new MITs and stripe formation in doped cuprates.

### 6.10.1.    The Mott-Type Metal-Insulator Transitions

We now discuss the applicability of the Mott MITs to doped cuprates. One can assume that in these materials the doped carriers bound to the large-radius dopants or impurities (with $E_{dD} < 0$) form the hydrogenic impurity centers. As the concentration of dopants increases, a narrow energy band of hydrogen-like impurities with the bandwidth $W_I$ is formed in the CT gap of the cuprates. When the Coulomb repulsive energy $U$ of two carriers on the same hydrogenic impurity center is larger than $W_I$, the impurity band splits into lower and upper Hubbard impurity bands, which are separated by the Mott gap $U$. The value of $U$ can be evaluated taking into account the screening due to the presence of two carriers in the 1s orbital of the hydrogen-like impurity center. Such a screening effect leads to the decreasing of the charge $Z$ of the impurity. As a consequence, the impurity has any effective charge

$Z^*$. Then the Hamiltonian for the case of two-carrier hydrogenic impurity center is given by [76]

$$H = -\frac{\hbar^2}{2m_1^*}\nabla_1 - \frac{\hbar^2}{2m_2^*}\nabla_2 - \frac{Z^*e^2}{\varepsilon_0}\left(\frac{1}{r_1} + \frac{1}{r_2}\right) + \frac{e^2}{\varepsilon_0 r_{12}}, \qquad (6.32)$$

where $m_1^*$ and $m_2^*$ are the effective masses of carriers, $r_{12} = |r_1 - r_2|$ is the distance between two carriers which have the coordinates $r_1$ and $r_2$. The ground-state energy of the system is a functional of the effective charge $Z^*$ and is given by

$$E(Z^*) = \int\int \Psi^*(r_1, r_2) H \Psi(r_1, r_2) d^3r_1 d^3r_2, \qquad (6.33)$$

where $\Psi(r_1, r_2)$ is the two-electron wave function.

We choose the wave function $\Psi$ in the form

$$\Psi(r_1, r_2) = \psi_{1s}(r_1)\psi_{1s}(r_2) = \frac{1}{\pi}\left(\frac{Z^*}{a_H}\right)^3 \exp\left[-\frac{Z^*(r_1 + r_2)}{a_H}\right], \qquad (6.34)$$

where $a_H = \hbar^2\varepsilon_0/m^*e^2$, $m^* = m_1^* = m_2^*$.

Substituting Eq. (6.34) into Eq. (6.33) and performing the minimization of $E(Z^*)$ with respect to $Z^*$, we obtain $Z^* = Z - 5/16$.

The Mott gap is then given by

$$U = \int\int \psi_{1s}^2(r_1)\frac{e^2}{\varepsilon_0 r_{12}}\psi_{1s}^2(r_2)d^3r_1 d^3r_2 \simeq \frac{5}{4}\left(Z - \frac{5}{16}\right)E_I^H, \qquad (6.35)$$

where $E_I^H = e^2/2\varepsilon_0 a_H$ is the ionization energy of the impurity center. Knowing the Hubbard energy $U$ and the bandwidth $W_I$, one can find the criterion for the Mott MIT from the condition (6.28). For the case of hydrogen-like impurity centers $Z = 1$, the value of $U$ is equal to $(55/64)E_I^H$ [76], whereas the bandwidth $W_I$ is given by [40]

$$W_I \simeq 2z\frac{e^2}{\varepsilon_0 a_H}\exp[-\lambda R], \qquad (6.36)$$

where $\lambda = a_H^{-1}$.

For $a_I = 4a_H$, we obtain from the relation (6.28) the familiar localization picture described by the Mott criterion $W_I/U \simeq 1$. If we assume $a_I \simeq 3.4783a_H$, we find $W_I/U \simeq 1.15$, which is known as the Hubbard criterion for the MIT.

As described before, the large-radius dopants or impurities with $E_{dD} < 0$ or $b_s < 0$ may form the hydrogenic acceptor centers in La-based cuprates and the Hubbard model based on the strong on-center Coulomb repulsion $U$ is applicable for these systems. Then, the Mott MIT point is determined from the condition

$$\frac{W_I}{U} = \frac{64z}{55}\exp\left[-\frac{R}{a_H}\right] = \frac{4a_H}{a_I}. \qquad (6.37)$$

If the impurity centers form simple cubic, body-centered cubic and face-centered cubic superlattices with $a_I = R$ (for $z = 6$), $a_I = 2R/\sqrt{3}$ (for $z = 8$) and $a_I = \sqrt{2}R$ (for $z = 12$), the appropriate densities of carriers per unit cells of such superlattices are $n = 1/a_I^3$, $n = 2/a_I^3$ and $n = 4/a_I^3$, respectively. It follows that the distance between nearest-neighbor impurity centers are equal to $R = 1/n^{1/3}$ (for $z = 6$), $R = \sqrt{3}/(4n)^{1/3}$ (for $z = 8$) and $R = 2^{1/6}/n^{1/3}$ (for $z = 12$). Thus, equation (6.37) can be written as

$$\frac{64z}{55n^{1/3}a_H} \exp\left[-\frac{1}{n^{1/3}a_H}\right] = 1 \quad \text{for} \quad z = 6, \tag{6.38}$$

$$\frac{64\sqrt[3]{2}z}{55n^{1/3}a_H} \exp\left[\frac{\sqrt{3}}{\sqrt[3]{4}n^{1/3}a_H}\right] = 1 \quad \text{for} \quad z = 8, \tag{6.39}$$

$$\frac{64\sqrt[3]{4}z}{55n^{1/3}a_H} \exp\left[\frac{2^{1/6}}{n^{1/3}a_H}\right] = 1 \quad \text{for} \quad z = 12, \tag{6.40}$$

from which we obtain the following criteria for the Mott MITs: $n_c^{1/3}a_H \simeq 0.3265$ (for $z = 6$), $n_c^{1/3}a_H \simeq 0.2968$ (for $z = 8$), $n_c^{1/3}a_H \simeq 0.2504$ (for $z = 12$).

If we take $m^* = m_e$ and $\varepsilon_0 = 30$, we find $a_H = 15.87A$ in LSCO, so that the Mott MITs would occur at the hole concentrations $x_c = n_c/n_a \simeq 0.00075 - 0.00166$. These values of $x_c$ are much smaller than the value of $x_c \simeq 0.02$ at which the destruction of the AF order is observed in LSCO [21]. However, the large-radius dopant and large polaron may form the hydrogenic impurity center in LSCO. When $b_s < 0$ (or $E_{dD} < 0$), the defect and the self-trapped hole repel each other at short distance but attract each other at long distance. Therefore, the hydrogenic state of a large polaron in LSCO has an effective Bohr radius $a_H = 0.529\varepsilon_0(m_e/m_p)\text{Å}$. If we take $m_p = 2.1m_e$ and $\varepsilon_0 = 28$, we find $a_H \simeq 7.06\text{Å}$. In this case, the Mott transitions would occur at $x_c = 0.0141$ (for $z = 8$) and $x_c \simeq 0.0188$ (for $z = 6$). These values of $x_c$ are close to the experimental values $x \simeq 0.018 - 0.02$ at which the AF order is destroyed in LSCO [21, 90].

### 6.10.2. The Anderson-Type Metal-Insulator Transitions

In inhomogeneous hole-doped cuprates the randomness in dopant distribution affects on the depths of the potential wells of impurities. When the impurities are uniformly distributed, the volume $\Omega_0 = (4\pi/3)a_H^3$ contains one impurity atom. However, in disorder system the volume $\Omega_0$ may contain two or more impurities at the random spatial distribution of dopants and the energy of a carrier in the field of $l$ impurities is equal to $lE_I$ [91]. One can expect that the depth of the potential well for the carrier varies from 0 to $lE_I$ and $V_0/2 \simeq lE_I/2$. The case $l = 2$ is assumed to be more probable. Therefore, we can take $V_0 = 2E_I^H$ and write the condition (6.29) in the form

$$z\exp\left[-\frac{R}{a_H}\right] = \frac{a_H}{a_I} \tag{6.41}$$

By taking into account that dopants form different superlattices with the site disorder (i.e., with random on-site energies), we obtain the following criteria for the Anderson-type MITs:

$$\frac{z}{n^{1/3}a_H} \exp\left[-\frac{1}{n^{1/3}a_H}\right] = 1 \quad \text{for} \quad z = 6, \tag{6.42}$$

$$\frac{\sqrt[3]{2}\,z}{n^{1/3}a_H}\exp\left[-\frac{\sqrt{3}}{\sqrt[3]{4}\,n^{1/3}a_H}\right]=1 \quad \text{for} \quad z=8, \tag{6.43}$$

$$\frac{\sqrt[3]{4}\,z}{n^{1/3}a_H}\exp\left[-\frac{2^{1/6}}{n^{1/3}a_H}\right]=1 \quad \text{for} \quad z=12. \tag{6.44}$$

¿From equations (6.42), (6.43), and (6.44), we find $n^{1/3}a_H \simeq 0.3530$, $n^{1/3}a_H \simeq 0.3148$, and $n^{1/3}a_H \simeq 0.2618$, respectively. If we assume $a_H = 7-8\text{Å}$ [21], we find $x_c \simeq 0.0116 - 0.0173$ (for $z=8$), and $x_c \simeq 0.0163 - 0.0243$ (for $z=6$) at which the transition from the metallic to the insulating behavior were observed in lightly doped cuprates (see Ref. [92]).

### 6.10.3.  The New Metal-Insulator Transitions

There are also other mechanisms that cause carrier localization or MIT in doped cuprates in which the strong carrier-defect-phonon and carrier-phonon interactions are responsible for the formation of the localized extrinsic and intrinsic large polarons. In the lightly doped regime, the states at the Fermi energy $\varepsilon_F$ of such polarons are localized. As the doping is increased, the localized hole carriers start to delocalize and the transition of the system from the insulating phase to the metallic one occurs. The width of the energy band of extrinsic large polarons or impurities with tightly bound large polarons can be defined as (see Ref. [40])

$$W_I = 2z\lambda^3 v_0 D_0 \exp[-\lambda R] \tag{6.45}$$

where $\lambda \sim 1/R_I$, $v_0$ is the volume in which the potential energy of the well is nonzero and $D_0$ is the depth of the impurity potential well.

If $v_0$ would be of the order of $R_I^3$, the quantity $\lambda^3 v_0$ may be replaced by unity. The $D_0$ is of the order of $E_{pI}$. Thus, we obtain the following criteria for the new MITs from the relation (6.30):

$$\frac{0.5z}{n^{1/3}R_I}\exp\left[-\frac{1}{n^{1/3}R_I}\right]=1 \quad \text{for} \quad z=6,$$

$$\frac{0.5\sqrt[3]{2}\,z}{n^{1/3}R_I}\exp\left[-\frac{\sqrt{3}}{\sqrt[3]{4}\,n^{1/3}R_I}\right]=1 \quad \text{for} \quad z=8,$$

$$\frac{0.5\sqrt[3]{4}\,z}{n^{1/3}R_I}\exp\left[-\frac{2^{1/6}}{n^{1/3}R_I}\right]=1 \quad \text{for} \quad z=12,$$

from which it follows that $n^{1/3}R_I \simeq 0.651$ (for $z=6$), $n^{1/3}R_I \simeq 0.453$ (for $z=8$), $n^{1/3}R_I \simeq 0.3354$ (for $z=12$).

We are now able to evaluate $n_c$ in La-based cuprates using these values of $n_c^{1/3}R_I$. For $\varepsilon_\infty = 4.5$, and $\eta = 0.04-0.12$ the value of $R_I$ (Table 6.3) is found to vary between 8.44 and 9.91 Å. In these cases, the MITs and stripe formation occur at $x_c \simeq 0.0539 - 0.0872$ (for $z=6$) and $x_c = 0.0182 - 0.0294$ (for $z=8$) in La- based cuprates with small-radius dopants. When $\varepsilon_\infty = 3.5$, $\eta = 0.04 - 0.12$ and $R_I \simeq (6.41 - 7.56)\text{Å}$ (Table 6.3), the MITs and stripe formation occur in these systems at $x_c \simeq 0.1213 - 0.1990$ (for $z = 6$) and $x_c \simeq 0.0409 - 0.0671$ (for $z = 8$). For $\varepsilon_\infty < 3.5$ and $z = 6$, the metal-insulator boundary of La-based cuprates containing small-radius dopants lies in the deeply overdoped region ($x_c > 0.2$). Further, the double substitution of smaller cations for host lattice ions and dopants

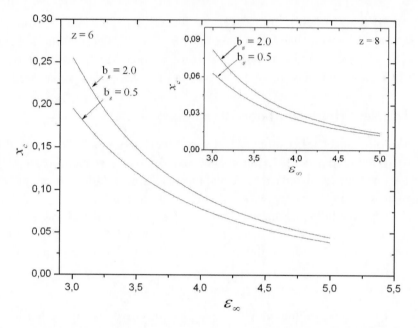

Figure 6.13. Variation of the critical carrier concentration $x_c$ corresponding to the MIT in 3D cuprates as a function of $\varepsilon_\infty$ and $b_s$ for $z = 6$ (main figure) and $z = 8$ (inset).

may also favor the MITs and stripe formation occurring in a wide range of doping of La-based cuprates. When the doping increases, there is a significant probability of at least two neighboring $La^{2+}$ ions replaced by large-radius $Sr^{2+}$ ion (with $Z = 1$, $V_0^{Sr} > 0$ and $E_{dD}^{Sr} < 0$) and by small-radius $Nd^{3+}$ ion (with $Z = 0$, $V_0^{Nd} > 0$ and $E_{dD}^{Nd} > 0$) in $La_{2-x-y}Nd_ySr_xCuO_4$ (where $y >> x$). The attractive potentials of these two-dopant centers may be stronger than those of more separated dopants. For $La_{2-x-y}Nd_ySr_xCuO_4$ with such two-dopant centers, we should replace $V_0$ and $E_{dD}$ by $V_0^{Sr} + V_0^{Nd}$ and $E_{dD}^{Sr} + E_{dD}^{Nd}$ in equation (6.5) or in the expression for $b_s$. At $E_{dD}^{Sr} + E_{dD}^{Nd} > 0$ (i.e., $b_s > 0$) the short-range part of the two-dopant potential is attractive and the hole carriers are self-trapped near the two neighboring dopants with the formation of the extrinsic large polarons. The two-dopant-driven charge inhomogeneity and ordering lead to formation of the superlattices of such extrinsic large polarons. In order to illustrate the effects of anisotropy of $\varepsilon_\infty$, $\eta$ and the short-range defect potential on $x_c$, we show in figure 6.13 the results of our calculations for La-based cuprates with two-dopant centers for which $Z = 1$ and $b_s > 0$. Figure 6.7 shows that the anisotropy of $\varepsilon_\infty$ and the size effect of small-radius dopants are the main driving forces for the new MITs and stripe formation in a wide range of doping in La-based cuprates containing two types of dopants.

As mentioned earlier, the size of dopants is a key parameter in cuprates containing large-radius dopants and the self-trapping of hole carriers in these systems becomes possible far away from the dopants with the formation of intrinsic large polarons. Such polarons in LSCO, LBCO, YBCO, and Bi-2212 may form different superlattices and polaronic bands. By increasing carrier concentrations the polaronic bands broaden, thereby causing delocalization of large polarons and transition from the insulating state to the metallic one at the critical doping level $n = n_c$ determined from the relation (6.31). This type of MIT is governed by the ratios $E_p/\varepsilon_F$ and $a_p/R_p$. Using the relation (6.31), we obtain the following criteria for such MITs: $n_c^{1/3} = 4m_p E_p R_p/\hbar^2 (3\pi^2)^{2/3}$ for $z = 6$, $(2n_c)^{1/3} = 4m_p E_p R_p/\hbar^2 (3\pi^2)^{2/3}$ for $z = 8$, $(4n_c)^{1/3} = 4m_p E_p R_p/\hbar^2 (3\pi^2)^{2/3}$ for $z = 12$. The effective masses of carriers in hole-doped cuprates deduced from the optical conductivity spectra (see Ref. [21]) and ARPES [60] at different doping levels are slightly different and equal to 2.0 - 2.1 times the free electron mass. Therefore, we can evaluate $n_c$ by taking $m_p = 2.1m_e$ for LSCO and LBCO. For $\varepsilon_\infty = 4$ and $\eta = 0.08 - 0.12$, the calculated values of $E_p$ and $R_p$ are 0.0683-0.0714 eV and 10.770-11.274 Å, respectively (Tables 6.2 and 6.3). Using this criteria for the MITs, we find $x_c \simeq 0.058 - 0.066$ (for $z = 8$) and $x_c \simeq 0.115 - 0.131$ (for $z = 6$), which are well consistent with existing experimental data on MITs in LSCO and LBCO [26, 93, 94, 95].

## 6.11.   The Agreement of the Theory with the Experiment

According to the spectroscopic data [3, 12, 19, 20], the undoped cuprates are CT-type Mott insulators with long-range AF order and the three-band Hubbard model (or d-p model) is more appropriate for description of the high-energy electronic structure of these materials. Good agreement of this d-p model with the experimental data was obtained with the following parameter set [1, 2, 12, 19, 20]: $\Delta_{CT} \simeq 1 - 3$ eV, $U_d \simeq 4.5 - 10$ eV, $t_{pd} \simeq 1.0 - 1.5$ eV, $U_p \simeq 1.0 - 4.0$ eV, and $V_{pd} \simeq 1.0 - 1.5$ eV. But the doped cuprates with the new and very complex low-energy electronic structure, which is quite different from their high-energy electronic structure, remain mysterious both for the one-electron band model and for the one- and three-band Hubbard models [2, 3, 20]. Whereas, the above developed alternative approaches that incorporate carrier-defect-phonon interactions near the dopants (impurities) and carrier-phonon interactions in a defect-free region may properly describe the low-energy electronic structure of the lightly doped cuprates. The phenomena of self-trapping and pairing of hole carriers at their interaction with dopants (impurities), acoustic and optical lattice vibrations in 3D lightly doped cuprates are well described quantitatively within the continuum model of ionic crystal and adiabatic approximation. There are three distinctly different scenarios for carrier localization in these systems: (i) self-trapping and pairing of hole carriers near the small-radius dopants; (ii) self-trapping of hole carriers away from the large-radius dopants; and (iii) self-trapping and pairing of hole carriers in a defect-free deformable lattice. These possible mechanisms of carrier localization lead to the formation of the extrinsic (bi)polaronic states, the hydrogenic impurity states, and the intrinsic (bi)polaronic states in the CT gap of the cuprates. The energies of the extrinsic self-trapped states of carriers in these materials calculated variationally within the continuum model and adiabatic approximation are about $0.022 - 0.034$ eV (for hydrogenic impurity states) and $0.08 - 0.24$ eV (for non-hydrogenic impurity states) and different values of $\varepsilon_\infty = 3.0 - 4.5$,

$\eta = 0.04 - 0.14$), which are in reasonable agreement with experimental values of the ionization energies of the acceptor centers $0.021 - 0.035$ eV [21] and with the observed optical gaps $0.08 - 027$ eV [3, 59, 60, 96]. The values of the binding energies of large polarons ($E_p \simeq 0.087 - 0.14$ eV) and bipolarons ($E_{bB} \simeq 0.037 - 0.06$ eV) calculated at $\varepsilon_\infty = 3 - 4$ and $\eta = 0.02 - 0.06$ are close to experimentally observed values of energy gaps $0.04 - 0.06$ eV [62, 68], and $0.08 - 0.15$ eV [3, 59, 60, 71] in the lightly doped cuprates. The observed inhomogeneous low-energy electronic structure in the underdoped cuprates would be explained by the formation of the different superlattices and in-gap energy bands of impurities and large polarons at their inhomogeneous spatial distribution. It seems more likely that the distinctly different in-gap bands observed in the underdoped regime around 0.1 eV [3, 75, 97] and $0.2 - 0.3$ eV [3, 98] are associated with the different polaronic energy bands. The newly derived criteria for the Mott and Anderson MITs are satisfied in the lightly doped cuprates and predict that the Mott- and Anderson-like MITs occur at low critical doping levels $x_c \simeq 0.02 - 0.025$, which correspond to the observed onset of the MIT in these materials [92]. While the new MITs may take place in lightly doped, underdoped, optimally doped and even overdoped cuprates. The predictions of the theory of new MITs in doped cuprates in which such MITs take place at doping levels $x_c \simeq 0.05 - 0.08$ are in good agreement with the experimental values of $x_c \simeq 0.05 - 0.08$ at which the MITs are most commonly observed in underdoped cuprates [20, 26, 99].

# References

[1] Yu. A. Izyumov, N. M. Plakida, and Yu. N. Skryabin, *Usp. Fiz. Nauk* 159, 621 (1989).

[2] E. Dagotto, *Rev. Mod. Phys.* 66, 763 (1994).

[3] A. Damascelli, Z. Hussain, and Z.-X. Shen, *Rev. Mod. Phys.* 75, 473 (2003).

[4] I. B. Bersuker, *The Jann-Teller Effect and Vibronic Interactions in Modern Chemistry* (Nauka, Moscow, 1987).

[5] P. W. Anderson, *The Theory of Superconductivity in the High-$T_c$ Cuprates* (Princeton University Press, Princeton, 1997).

[6] Ch. Ballhausen, *Introduction to the Field Theory of Ligands* (Mir, Moscow, 1964).

[7] L. F. Mattheiss, *Phys. Rev. Lett.* 58, 1028 (1987).

[8] A. Freeman, J. Yu, and C. L. Fu, *Phys. Rev.* B36, 7111 (1987).

[9] W. E. Pickett, *Rev. Mod. Phys.* 61, 433 (1989).

[10] R. Pankaluoto and K. Kaski, *Phys. Scripta.* T33, 227(1990).

[11] P. Horsh and W. Stephan, *Electronic Properties of High-$T_c$ Superconductors*(Springer, Berlin, 1993) v. 113, p. 351.

[12] P. V. Abramov and S. G. Ovchinnikov, *Fiz. Tverd. Tela* 42, 770 (2000).

[13] B. K. Chakraverty, M. Avignon and D. Feinberg, *J. Less-Common Metals* 150, 11 (1989).

[14] P. A. Lee, N. Nagaosa, and X.-G. Wen, *Rev. Mod. Phys.* 78, 17 (2006).

[15] N. F. Mott, *Proc. Phys. Soc. London* A62, 416 (1949).

[16] J. Hubbard, *Proc. Roy. Soc. London* A277, 237 (1964); *Proc. Roy. Soc. London* 281, 401 (1964).

[17] O. Madelung, *Solid State Physics. Localized States* (Nauka, Moscow, 1985).

[18] H. Böttger and V. V. Bryksin, *Hopping Conduction in Solids* (Akademie-Verlag, Berlin, 1985).

[19]  M. Tachiki and H. Matsumoto, *J. Mag. Mag. Mater.* 90-91, 597 (1990).

[20]  M. Imada, A. Fujimory, and Y. Tokura, *Rev. Mod. Phys.* 70, 1039 (1998).

[21]  M. Kastner, R. Birgeneau, G. Shirane, and Y. Endoh, *Rev. Mod. Phys.* 70, 897 (1998).

[22]  V. J. Emery, *Phys. Rev. Lett.* 58, 2794 (1987).

[23]  C. M. Varma, S. Schmitt-Rink, and E. Abrahams, *Solid State Commun.* 62, 681 (1987).

[24]  J. Zaanen, G. A. Sawatzky, and J. W. Allen, *Phys. Rev. Lett.* 55, 418 (1985).

[25]  S. Uchida, *Physica* C185-189, 28 (1991).

[26]  J. Fink, N. Nücker, M. Alexander, H. Romberg, M. Knupfer, M. Merkel, P. Adelmann, R. Claessen, G. Mante, T. Buslaps, S. Harm, R. Manzke, and M. Skibowski, *Physica* C185-189, 45 (1991).

[27]  F. C. Zhang and T. Rice, *Phys. Rev.* 37, 3759 (1988).

[28]  P. W. Anderson, *Science* 235, 1196 (1987).

[29]  A. N. Lavrov and V. F. Gandmakher, *Phys. Usp.* 41, 223 (1998).

[30]  S. Komiya, Y. Ando, X. F. Sun, and A. N. Lavrov, *Phys. Rev.* B65, 214535 (2002).

[31]  H. E. Hussey and J.R. Copper, in: *IRC Research Review. High Temperature Superconductivity*, ed., W. Y. Liang (Cambridge University Press, Cambridge, 1998) p. 52.

[32]  Y. Toyozawa, *Technical Report ISSP, Ser. A*, No. 648 (1974).

[33]  A. S. Davydov, *Solid State Theory* (Nauka, Moscow, 1976).

[34]  D. Emin and T. Holstein, *Phys. Rev. Lett.* 36, 323 (1976).

[35]  D. Emin and M.S . Hillery, *Phys. Rev.* B39, 6575 (1989).

[36]  S. Dzhumanov, A. A. Baratov, and S. Abboudy, *Phys. Rev.* B54, 13121 (1996-I).

[37]  Y. Toyozawa, *Physica* B116, 7 (1983); S. Dzhumanov, P.J. Baimatov, O.K. Ganiev, Z.S. Khudayberdiev, and B.V. Turimov, *J. Phys. Chem. Solids.* 73, 484 (2012).

[38]  H. Shibata and T. Yamada, *Phys. Rev.* B56, R14275 (1997-II).

[39]  J. T. Markert, Y. Dalichaouch, and M. B. Maple, in: *Physical Properties of High Temperature Superconductors I*, ed., D. M. Ginsberg (Mir, Moscow, 1990) p. 265.

[40]  N. F. Mott and E. A. Devis, *Electronic Proceses in Non-Crystaline Materials* (Mir, Moscow,1974).

[41]  J. P. Lu and Q. Si, *Phys. Rev.* B42, 950 (1990).

[42]  Ch. Kittel, *Quantum Theory of Solids* (Nauka, Moscow, 1967).

[43]  R. C. Baetzold, *Phys. Rev.* B42, 56 (1990).

[44]  M. Weger and L. Burlachkov, *Physica* C235-240, 2387 (1994).

[45]  E. Dushanov and S. Dzhumanov, *Int. J. Mod. Phys.* B19, 1061 (2005).

[46]  Y. Toyozawa and Y. Shinozuka, *J. Phys. Soc. Jpn.* 48, 472 (1980).

[47]  A. S. Alexandrov, *Physica* C282-287, 269 (1997).

[48]  J. Appel, in: *Polarons*, ed., Ya. A. Firsov (Nauka, Moscow, 1975) p. 11.

[49]  G. Verbist, F. M. Peeters and J. T. Devreese, *Phys. Scripta* T39, 66 (1991).

[50]  J. T. Devreese and A. S. Alexandrov, *Rep. Prog. Phys.* 72, 066501 (2009).

[51]  J. Adamowskii, *Phys. Rev.* B39, 3649 (1989).

[52]  G. Verbist, F. M. Peeters, and J. T. Devreese, *Phys. Rev.* B43, 2712 (1991).

[53]  P. J. Baimatov, D. Ch. Khuzhakulov, and Kh. T. Sharipov, *Fiz. Tverd. Tela* 39, 284 (1997).

[54]  Ch. Thomsen and M. Cardona, in: *Physical Properties of High Temperature Super-conductors I*, ed., D. M. Ginsberg (Mir, Moscow, 1990) p. 411.

[55]  S. G. Suprun and B. Ya. Moizhes, *Fiz. Tverd. Tela* 24, 1571 (1982).

[56]  H. Hiramoto and Y. Toyozava, *J. Phys. Soc. Jpn.* 54, 245 (1985).

[57]  V. L. Vinetskii, O. Meredov, and V. A. Yanchuk, *Teor. Eksp. Kim.* 25, 641 (1989).

[58]  S. V. Varyukhin and A. A. Zakharov, *Physica* C185-189, 975 (1991).

[59]  A. Ino, T. Mizokawa, K. Kobayashi, A. Fujimori, T. Sasagawa, T. Kimura, K. Kishio, K. Tamasaku, H. Eisaki, and S. Uchida, *Phys. Rev. Lett.* 81, 2124 (1998).

[60]  A. Ino, C. Kim, M. Nakamura, T. Yoshida, T. Mizokawa, A. Fujimori, Z.-X. Shen, T. Kakeshita, H. Eisaki, and S. Uchida, *Phys. Rev.* B65, 094504 (2002).

[61]  S. Uchida, K. Tamasaki, and S. Tajima, *Phys. Rev.* B53, 14558 (1996).

[62]  T. Timusk and B. Statt, *Rep. Prog. Phys.* 62, 61 (1999).

[63]  F. Slakey, M. V. Klein, J. P. Rice, and D. Ginsberg, *Phys. Rev.* B42, 2643 (1990).

[64]  G. Ruani and P. Ricci, *Phys. Rev.* B55, 93 (1997).

[65]  P. Bourges, H. F. Fong, L. P. Regnault, J. Bossy, C. Vetier, D. L. Milius, I. A. Aksay, and B. Keimer, *Phys. Rev.* B56, R11439 (1997).

[66]  D. Mihailovic, T. Mertelj, and K. A. Müller, *Phys. Rev.* B57, 6116 (1997-II).

[67]  T. H. H. Vuong, D. C. Tsui, and V. G. Goldman, *Solid State Commun.* 63, 525 (1987).

[68] T. Ekino, S. Hashimoto, H. Fujii, J. Hori, F. Nakamura, and T. Fujita, *Physica* C357-360, 158 (2001).

[69] S. Dzhumanov, *Solid State Commun.* 115, 155 (2000).

[70] S. Dzhumanov, *Preprint* IC/IR/2001/17 (Trieste, Italy).

[71] M. Suzuki, K. Anagawa, M. Lmouchter, and T. Watanabe, *Physica* C362, 164 (2001).

[72] S. H. Pan, J. P. O'Neal, R. L. Badzey, C. Chamon, H. Ding, J. R. Engelbrecht, Z. Wang, H. Eisaki, S. Uchida, A. K. Gupta, K.-W. Ng, E. W. Hudson, K. M. Lang, and J. C. Davis, *Nature* 413, 282 (2001).

[73] K. K. Gomes, A. Pasupathy, A. Pushp, S. Ono, Y. Ando, and A. Yozdani, *Physica* C460-462, 212 (2007).

[74] T. Kato, T. Noguchi, R. Saito, T. Machida, and H. Sakata, *Physica* C460-462, 880 (2007).

[75] S. Strässle, J. Roos, M. Mali, K. Conder, E. Pomjakushina, and H. Keller, *Physica* C460-462, 890 (2007).

[76] S. Dzhumanov, U. T. Kurbanov, and A. Kurmantayev, *Int. J. Mod. Phys.* B21 (2007).

[77] S. Dzhumanov, U. T. Kurbanov, and Z. S. Khudayberdiev, *Physica* C460-462, 1037(2007).

[78] A. Matsuda, T. Fujii, and T. Watanabe, *Physica* C388-389, 207 (2003).

[79] K. McElroy, D.-H. Lee, J. E. Hoffman, K. M. Lang, J. Lee, E. W. Hudson, H. Eisaki, S. Uchida, and J. C. Davis, *Phys. Rev. Lett.* 94, 197005 (2005).

[80] J. Zaanen, cond-mat/0103255.

[81] S. Dzhumanov, *Int. J. Mod. Phys.* B12, 2151 (1998).

[82] S. Chakravarty, R. B. Laughlin, D. K. Morr, and C. Nayak, *Phys. Rev.* B63, 094503 (2001).

[83] H. Fukuyama, *Physica* C185-189, XXV (1991).

[84] N. F. Mott, *Metal-Insulator Transitions and edn* (Taylor and Francis, London, 1990).

[85] A. H. Wilson, *Proc. Roy. Soc. London* A133, 458 (1931); *Proc. Roy. Soc. London* A134, 277 (1931).

[86] P. W. Anderson, *Phys. Rev.* 109, 1492 (1958).

[87] F. Walz, *J. Phys.: Condens. Matter.* 14, R285 (2002).

[88] P. Quemerais, *Mod. Phys. Lett.* B9, 1665 (1995).

[89] B. K. Ridley, *Quantum Processes in Semiconductors* (Mir, Moscow, 1986).

[90] K. Ishida, H. Aya, Y. Tokunaga, H. Kotegawa, Y. Kitaoka, M. Fujita, and K. Yamada, *Phys. Rev. Lett.* 92, 257001 (2004).

[91] B. I. Shklowskii and A. L. Efros, *Electronic Properties of Doped Semiconductors* (Nauka, Moscow, 1979).

[92] N. V. Anshukova, A. I. Golovashkin, L. I. Ivanova, and A. P. Rusakov, *Zh. Eksp. Teor. Fiz.* 123, 1188 (2003).

[93] S. Ono, Y. Ando, T. Murayama, F. F. Balakirev, J. B. Betts, and G. S. Boebinger, *Physica* C357-360, 138 (2001).

[94] Sh. Sakita, F. Nakamura, T. Suzuki, and T. Fujita, *J. Phys. Soc. Jpn.* 68, 2755 (1999).

[95] B. Nachumi, Y. Fudamoto, A. Keren, K. M. Kojima, M. Larkin, G. M. Luke, J. Merrin, O. Tchernyshyov, Y. J. Uemura, N. Ichikawa, M. Goto, H. Takagi, S. Uchida, M. K. Crawford, E. M. McCarron, D. E. MacLaughlin, and R.H. Heffner, *Phys. Rev.* B58, 8760 (1998-I).

[96] T. Ekino, S. Hashimoto, and H. Fujii, *J. Phys. Chem. Solids* 62, 149 (2001).

[97] A. Fujimory, A. Ino, T. Yoshida, T. Mizokawa, M. Nakamura, C. Kim, Z.-X. Shen, K. Kishio, T. Kakeshita, H. Eisaki, and S. Uchida, *J. Phys. Chem. Solids* 62, 19 (2001).

[98] S. Maekawa and T. Tohyama, *Rep. Prog. Phys.* 64, 383 (2001).

[99] Z. Konstantinovic, Z. Z. Li and H. Raffy, *Physica* C351, 163 (2001).

# Chapter 7

# Theory of the Pseudogap Phenomena, Quantum Criticality and Stripe Formation in Doped High-$T_c$ Cuprates

## 7.1.  Introduction

The pseudogap phenomena in high-$T_c$ cuprates and other superconductors mean the suppression of spectral weight or density of states (DOS) at the Fermi level above $T_c$ without the emergence of any superconducting (SC) order. The existence of a normal-state (pseudo)gap in both spin and charge excitations has been observed in many experiments on underdoped, optimally doped and even overdoped high-$T_c$ cuprates [1, 2, 3, 4, 5] (see also chapter 4). Various experiments have also provided evidence for the presence of the so-called small and large pseudogaps (PGs) [4, 6]. The PG phenomena are the most intriguing features of high-$T_c$ cuprates and remain a major unsolved problem. The well-known one-electron band theory, usual Fermi-liquid and BCS pairing theories have been successful enough in describing the metallic and SC properties of conventional superconductors but have proven inadequate for the description of PG phenomena and other electronic processes in high-$T_c$ cuprates. The breakdown of these theories occurs in a wide region of the phase diagram of high-$T_c$ cuprates. In the hole-doped cuprates, competitions between different ground states led to different quantum phase transitions at zero temperatures (i.e., at quantum critical points (QCP)) in a substantial region of their phase diagram [2, 7, 8, 9, 10]. The high-$T_c$ superconductivity, the PG formation and the formation of the static (insulating) and dynamic (metallic) stripes occur also in these region of the phase diagram of the hole-doped cuprates. Many experiments point to the existence of the distinctly different QCPs which lie hidden under the SC dome of the phase diagram and play an important role in the exotic properties of the hole-doped cuprates. It is believed that the stripe formation is closely related to the peculiar QCP and is responsible for the suppression of superconductivity in the underdoped cuprates. While the PG phenomenon is related to the existence of the another QCP somewhat above optical doping, where the breakdown of the one-electron band theory, usual Fermi liquid and BCS pairing theories occurs. So far, our understanding of the PG phenomena, the quantum criticality and the stripe formation is still far from satisfactory. The high-$T_c$ cuprates are polar materials, where the formation of large (bi)polarons becomes possible at the strong electron-phonon interactions. Therefore, the relevant charge carriers in these materials might be large (bi)polarons and Cooper-like polaron pairs, and the unconventional electron-phonon interactions should be responsible for the PG formation, the quantum criticality and the stripe formation in high-$T_c$ cuprates. In this chapter, we deal with theory of PG phenomena, quantum criticality, and stripe formation in doped high-$T_c$ cuprates.

## 7.2. Formation of a Large Temperature-Independent Non-Pairing Pseudogap and Its Doping Dependence

As mentioned in Chapter 6, the parent undoped cuprates are charge-transfer (CT) Mott-Hubbard insulators with CT gap $\Delta_{CT} \simeq 1.5 - 2.0$ and the lightly doped cuprates behave like conventional doped semiconductors [11, 12]. Therefore, the strong electron correlations (on-site Coulomb interactions) exist in undoped cuprates or behind the phase diagram [4] and drive these systems into the Mott insulating state [13]. In contrast, the doped carriers in CT insulators are delocalized just as in semiconductors (e.g., Si and Ge) as established experimentally [11, 12]. The doped cuprates are more analogous to the three-dimensional (3D) doped semiconductors [12, 14] than the two-dimensional (2D) systems that are like CT Mott-Habbard insulators. As the doping level increases towards the underdoped region, the importance of electron correlations diminishes [11, 13, 14], and other interactions (such as the electron-phonon and long-range Coulomb interactions) really play an important role in the metallic state of high-$T_c$ cuprates. Actually, the strong electron correlations or Coulomb interactions of the lattice scale disappear in the doped cuprates due to metallic screening [13].

A large ionicity of the high-$T_c$ cuprates $\eta = \varepsilon_\infty/\varepsilon_0 << 1$ (where $\varepsilon_\infty$ and $\varepsilon_0$ are the high-frequency and static dielectric constants, respectively) and the unconventional electron-phonon interactions should play a key role in the PG formation. The doped cuprates are inhomogeneous systems, where the formation of large polarons and bipolarons is possible in the domains with $\eta > \eta_c$ and $\eta < \eta_c$, respectively; (where $\eta_c$ is the critical value of $\eta$ below which the bipolaron is stable). At low doping levels and $\eta > \eta_c$, a narrow energy band of self-trapped carriers (large polarons) is formed in the CT gap of the cuprates, whereas the quasi-free hole (electron) states of the valence (or conduction) band becomes the excited states. In the lightly doped regime, the polaronic Fermi level $\varepsilon_F$ lies inside the CT gap and the threshold energy for photoexcitation of a carrier from the polaronic state to a free carrier state is given by

$$\Delta\varepsilon_F = \varepsilon_F^f - \varepsilon_F, \tag{7.1}$$

where $\varepsilon_F^f = \hbar^2(3\pi^2 n_f)^{2/3}/2m^*$ is the Fermi energy of free carriers in the valence (or conduction) band, $\varepsilon_F = \hbar^2(3\pi^2 n_p)^{2/3}/2m_p$ is the Fermi energy of large polarons, $m^*$ is the effective mass of a free carrier, $m_p$ is the mass of a large polaron, $n_f$ is the concentration of free carriers, $n_p$ is the concentration of polaronic carriers, $n_f = n_p$ (at $\eta > \eta_c$). One can assume that the polaronic effect weakens with increasing doping and disappears in the overdoped region. This means that the value of $m_p$ decreases with increasing doping and becomes equal to $m^*$ in the overdoped regime. The excitation energy $\Delta\varepsilon_F$ of large polarons is manifested in the single-particle spectrum of the lightly doped cuprates as the polaronic PG. Since the strong carrier-phonon interactions result in lowering the electronic energy (i.e., the Fermi level or chemical potential is shifted) by the value $\Delta\varepsilon_F$ or polaronic shift of the electronic states with opening polaronic PG at the Fermi level of free carriers. So, a large Fermi surface transforms into a small polaronic one. As the doping is increased towards the underdoped region, the in-gap polaronic band broadens due to the interaction of large polarons and merges with the valence (or conduction) band at more higher doping levels. In the underdoped regime the polaronic Fermi level $\varepsilon_F$ of hole carriers lies above the top of the valence band and the single-particle spectrum of the underdoped cuprates has the temperature-independent polaronic PG (i.e., reduction of DOS at the Fermi level $\varepsilon_F^f$) determined from the Eq. (7.1). With increasing doping level the Coulomb repulsion between polarons increases in the metallic state and the binding energy $E_p$ of large polarons (see chapter 6) decreases, so that the dissociation of large polarons occurs at some critical doping level $x = x_p$. At $x < x_p$, the threshold energy for the thermal excitation of a carrier from the polaronic state to a free-carrier state or for the thermal dissociation of a large polaron can be approximately defined as [8]

$$\Delta_p = E_p - E_c, \tag{7.2}$$

where $E_c = e^2/\varepsilon_0 a_p$ is the Coulomb interaction energy between two large polarons, $a_p = (3/4\pi n_p)^{1/3}$ is the mean distance between these polarons. On the one hand, the energy required for the excitation of a carrier from the polaronic state to a free-carrier state is equal to $\varepsilon_F^f - \varepsilon_F$. However, on the other hand, the energy required for such a excitation is given by $E_p - \varepsilon_c$. Therefore, depending on the excitation ways, the doping-dependent non-pairing polaronic PG should be determined either from Eq. (7.1) or from Eq. (7.2). Clearly, both $\Delta\varepsilon_F$ and $\Delta_p$ decrease with increasing doping and their energy scales are in general slightly different. To evaluate the energy scales of the PGs, $\Delta\varepsilon_F$ and $\Delta_p$ in the hole-doped cuprates $La_{2-x}Sr_xCuO_4$ (LSCO), we write the doping level in the dimensionless form $x = n_p/n_a$ (where $n_a = 1/V_a$ is the density of the host lattice atoms, $V_a \simeq 190\text{Å}^3$ is the volume per $CuO_2$ unit in the orthorhombic LSCO) and choose the parameters as $x = 0.06$, $m^* = m_e$ [11] (where $m^*$ is the free electron mass), $m_p = 2m_e$ (for underdoped case)[11], $\varepsilon_0 = 30$ [11] and $E_p \simeq 0.12eV$. We then obtain $\Delta\varepsilon_F \simeq 0.085eV$ and $\Delta_p \approx 0.07eV$, which agree reasonably well with the temperature-independent large PGs observed experimentally in the hole-doped cuprates [15, 16]. In particular, the large PGs $\Delta_p \simeq 0.084eV$ [17] and $\Delta_p \simeq 0.07eV$ [16] are observed in LSCO and $YBa_2Cu_3O_{7-\delta}$ (YBCO), respectively. According to the expression (7.2), the large polaronic PG decreases with an increase of $x$ and disappears at $x = x_p$ (see section 7.6.3) in accordance with experimental observations [2, 18, 19]. The origin of the large PG ($\Delta_p \simeq 0.1eV$) observed in all underdoped cuprates [1, 2] is most likely associated with the formation of the non-pairing polaronic PG. In Fig. 7.1, we compare the calculated doping dependence of the polaronic PG crossover temperature $T_p \simeq \Delta_p/k_B$ to the PG temperature $T_{PG}$ values (which behave like the doping dependence of an energy gap $E_g$) measured on LSCO [2]. As can be seen in Fig. 7.1, there is fair agreement between the calculated curve $T_p(x)$ and the experimental data for $T_{PG} \simeq E_g/k_B$ [2].

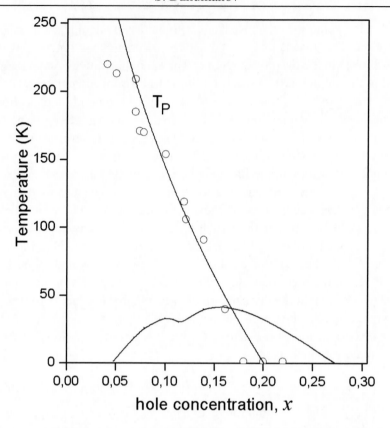

Figure 7.1. Doping dependence of $T_p$ (solid line) calculated using the relation (7.2) at $\varepsilon_0 = 39.5$, $n_a = 1.3 \times 10^{22} cm^{-3}$ and $E_p = 0.06$ eV. For comparison the experimental points (open circles) corresponding to the opening of the PG in LSCO have been taken from [2].

## 7.3. Formation of a Small Temperature-Independent Pairing Pseudogap and Its Doping Dependence

We believe that the precursor pairing of carriers in real space and the formation of large bipolarons in doped inhomogeneous cuprates can occur in the domains with $\eta < \eta_c$. Also, the strong anisotropy of the dielectric constants $\varepsilon_\infty$ and $\varepsilon_0$ of these materials favors the bipolaron formation. When the separate energy levels of large polarons (at $\eta > \eta_c$) and bipolarons (at $\eta < \eta_c$) are formed in the CT gap of the lightly doped cuprates, their binding energies are equal to $E_p$ and $E_{bB}$, respectively. When the concentration of large polarons is increased, their bandwidth becomes nonzero and each large polaron have the kinetic energy $\varepsilon_F$. In doped cuprates, two large polarons repel each other via the Coulomb potential and, in most cases, do not form a bound state (i.e., bipolaronic state). However, in some domains, the attractive interaction of the carrier-phonon coupling can be strong enough to overcome the Coulomb repulsion between two large polarons and create a stable large bipolaron (hole or electron pair above $T_c$). In the presence of many polarons, the energy of the pair of large polarons without their phonon-mediated attractive interaction can be written as

$$\varepsilon_p = 2(E_p + \varepsilon_F) \tag{7.3}$$

The ground-state energy of a large bipolaron or pair of large polarons at their phonon-mediated attractive interaction is equal to $E_B$ (see chapter 6). Then the binding energy of the large bipolaron in the presence of many polarons is given by

$$\Delta_{bB} = |E_B - \varepsilon_p| = E_{bB} - 2\varepsilon_F, \tag{7.4}$$

where $E_{bB} = |E_B - 2E_p|$. The binding energy of the large bipolaron $\Delta_{bB}$ is manifested in the excitation spectrum of the underdoped cuprates as the temperature-independent pairing PG. The formation of large bipolarons becomes possible only at $\eta < \eta_c$ and in the strong carrier-phonon coupling regime. Therefore, the mass of the strong-coupling large polarons $m_p$ is expected to be much greater than $m_e$. Finally, we can show that the pairing PG $\Delta_{bB}$ decreases with the increasing $x$ and disappears at some critical doping, which is determined from the relation

$$x_c = (m_p E_{bB})^{3/2} / 3\pi^2 \hbar^3 n_a \tag{7.5}$$

The real-space pairing of large polarons is different from their k-space pairing which is characteristic of Cooper pairs. The energy levels of the large bipolarons lie above the top of the polaronic band in the p-type cuprates or below the bottom of the polaronic band in the n-type cuprates. In contrast, the energy levels of the polaron Cooper pairs lie inside the polaronic band.

## 7.4. Precursor BCS-Like Pairing of Large Polarons and Formation of a Small Temperature- and Doping-Dependent Pairing Pseudogap

The theory of ordinary metals is based on the Migdal adiabatic approximation $\hbar\omega/E_F \ll 1$ [20], where $\omega$ is the characteristic phonon frequency, $E_F$ is the Fermi energy. Later, Eliashberg extended the Migdal theory to describe the BCS pairing state at intermediate and strong electron-phonon coupling regimes [21]. The Migdal-Eliashberg theory based on the perturbation expansion in powers of $\lambda_{ph}\hbar\omega/E_F$ (where $\lambda_{ph}$ is the dimensionless electron-phonon coupling constant) is asymptotically correct in ordinary metals. Because the assumption of the small adiabatic ratio $\hbar\omega/E_F \lesssim 10^{-2}$ is justified in conventional superconductors. However, the low Fermi energy $\varepsilon_F$, high-$T_c$, and the high-frequency phonons are the characteristics of the cuprates. Therefore, the validity of Migdal-Eliashberg theory breaks down in the high-$T_c$ cuprates [22, 23, 24] where the adiabatic ratio $\hbar\omega/\varepsilon_F$ is no longer small. Indeed, the Fermi energies $\varepsilon_F$ in doped high-$T_c$ cuprates at $m_p \simeq 2m_e$ and $n_p \simeq (0.5 \div 2.0) \times 10^{21} cm^{-3}$ are about 0.1-0.3 eV (cf. [23, 25]) and the values of the characteristic phonon energy $\hbar\omega$ range from 0.05 to 0.08 eV [3, 11, 26]. In particular, the Fermi energy, $\varepsilon_F$, in underdoped La- and Y- based cuprates is about 0.04 eV [27] and less or about 0.4 eV in heavily over-doped cuprates [28]. As seen, the ratio $\hbar\omega/\varepsilon_F$ is not small even in overdoped cuprates and the application of the Eliashberg equations to high-$T_c$ cuprate superconductors is problematic.

It is believed that the non-SC lightly doped cuprates and high-$T_c$ cuprates fall in strong and intermediate electron-phonon coupling regimes, respectively; where the polaronic effects seem to be important and the standard BCS pairing theory describing the formation of Cooper pairs at the SC transition temperature $T_c$ does not work. In the strong electron-phonon coupling regime the static (or static lattice deformation)-mediated precursor pairing of self-trapped carriers (large polarons) occurs in real-space and leads to the formation of large bipolarons in the lightly doped cuprates. While, the combined static and dynamic phonon-mediated Cooper pairing of large polarons is expected in the intermediate BCS-like coupling regime and the formation of incoherent (non-SC) Cooper-like polaron pairs becomes possible in the normal state of underdoped, optimally doped and even overdoped cuprates [29]. In this case, the unconventional electron-phonon interactions (i.e., the combined and more effective BCS-and Fröhlich-type attractive interactions) are believed to be responsible for the pairing correlation at a characteristic temperature $T^* > T_c$ in these materials. In the weak-coupling limit, however, the conventional dynamic phonon-mediated Cooper pairing of quasi-free carriers occurs at $T^* = T_c$ in ordinary metals and heavily over-doped cuprates due to the absence of the polaronic effects.

We now consider two different regimes of the BCS-like pairing model by considering the real situations in cuprates and distinguish the cases of small Fermi surface (with $\varepsilon_F < 0.1$ eV) and large Fermi surface (with $\varepsilon_F > 0.1$ eV). The large Fermi surfaces (with $0.1 < \varepsilon_F < 0.4$ eV) in high-$T_c$ cuprates are not so large as in ordinary metals in which $E_F \simeq 5 - 10$ eV$>> \varepsilon_F$. We believe that underdoped, optimally doped, and moderately overdoped cuprates are unusual metals and have a well-defined and large Fermi surface as follows from angle-resolved photoemission spectroscopy (ARPES) data [1, 23, 30]. In these systems, the new situation arises when the polaronic effects exist and the attractive interaction mechanism (e.g., due to exchange of static and dynamic phonons) between the carriers operating in the energy range $\{-(E_p + \hbar\omega_{LO}), (E_p + \hbar\omega_{LO})\}$ is more effective than in the simple BCS picture, where $\omega_{LO}$ is the longitudinal-optical (LO) phonon frequency. The energy $\varepsilon(\vec{k})$ of polarons is $\hbar^2 k^2 / 2m_p$ and measured from the polaronic Fermi energy $\varepsilon_F$, where $\vec{k}$ and $m_p$ are the wave vector and effective mass of polarons, respectively. It was argued [29, 31, 32] that the extension of the BCS theory to the intermediate coupling regime describes the precursor (non-SC) pairing of carriers above $T_c$ naturally. In this case, the formation of incoherent Cooper pairs and the opening of a gap at the Fermi surface occurs at $T^* > T_c$ or even $T^* >> T_c$. Such a normal-state gap appearing in the temperature range $T_c < T < T^*$ is called as the pairing PG (which coexists with SC gap below $T_c$ [29, 31].

Here, we note that the symmetry of the PG is still one of the most controversial issues in the physics of high-$T_c$ cuprates. Although some experimental observations advocate in favor of a d-wave symmetry [33], many other experiments [34, 35, 36] closely trace a s-wave pairing gap and are incompatible with a d-wave pairing symmetry. In particular, a d-wave pairing state is incompatible with the c-axis tunneling and twist junction experiments [37], the Andreev-Saint-James reflections [38], Josephson junction experiments [34], the ARPES results [36], and the other experiments. The scanning tunneling microscopy studies of vortices in high-$T_c$ cuprates (as discussed in Ref. [39]) have also revealed a very different low-energy electronic structure from that predicted by the d-wave BCS models, whereas the

$c$-axis bicrystal twist Josephson junction and natural cross-whisker junction experiments provide strong evidence for a $s$-wave order parameter in the cuprates [40]. Müller has argued [41] that a $s$-wave pairing state may, in fact, exist in the bulk. Therefore, we take the view that for high-$T_c$ cuprates, the $s$-wave pairing state is favored in the bulk and the $s$-wave PG could originate from unconventional electron-phonon interactions and carry the physics of novel BCS-like precursor pairing effects above $T_c$.

Applying the modified BCS formalism [29, 31] to the interacting Fermi-gas of large polarons, we can write the mean-field Hamiltonian of this system with the pair interaction in the form

$$H_{MF} = \sum_{k\sigma} \varepsilon(\vec{k}) a_{\vec{k}\sigma}^+ a_{\vec{k}\sigma} + \sum_{\vec{k}\vec{k}'} V_p(\vec{k}, \vec{k}') a_{\vec{k}\uparrow}^+ a_{-\vec{k}\downarrow}^+ a_{-\vec{k}'\downarrow} a_{\vec{k}'\uparrow} \tag{7.6}$$

where $a_{\vec{k}\sigma}^+ (a_{\vec{k}\sigma})$ is the creation (annihilation) operator for a polaron that has momentum $\vec{k}$ and spin projection $\sigma(=\uparrow or \downarrow)$, $V_p(\vec{k}, \vec{k}')$ is the pair interaction potential (which has both an attractive and a repulsive part) between large polarons. The Hamiltonian (7.6) is diagonalized by using the standard Bogolubov transformation of Fermi operators (see Eq. (3.56) in chapter 3). We then obtain the ground state energy of polaron Cooper pairs and the excited state of these pairs is separated from their ground state by the BCS-like energy gap $\Delta(\vec{k})$ which at finite temperature is given by

$$\Delta(\vec{k}, T) = -\sum_{\vec{k}'} V_p(\vec{k}, \vec{k}') \frac{\Delta(\vec{k}', T)}{E(\vec{k}', T)} \tanh \frac{E(\vec{k}', T)}{2k_B T}, \tag{7.7}$$

where $E(\vec{k}, T) = \sqrt{\varepsilon^2(\vec{k}) + \Delta^2(\vec{k}, T)}$ is the single-particle excitation energy. Further, we use the Bogoliubov-like model potential [42] which may be chosen as

$$V_p(\vec{k}, \vec{k}') = \begin{cases} V_c - V_{ph} & \text{for } |\varepsilon(\vec{k})|, |\varepsilon(\vec{k}')| \leq \varepsilon_A = E_p + \hbar\omega_{LO}, \\ V_c & \text{for } \varepsilon_A \leq |\varepsilon(\vec{k})|, |\varepsilon(\vec{k}')| < \varepsilon_c, \\ 0 & \text{otherwise,} \end{cases} \tag{7.8}$$

where $V_{ph}$ is the dynamic and static phonon-mediated attractive interaction potential between two polarons, $V_c$ is the repulsive Coulomb interaction potential between these carriers, $\varepsilon_c$ is the cutoff energy for the Coulomb interaction.

For the model potential (7.8), $\Delta(\vec{k}, T)$ will be given by

$$\Delta(\vec{k}, T) = \begin{cases} \Delta_1(T) & \text{for } |\varepsilon(\vec{k})|, |\varepsilon(\vec{k}')| \leq \varepsilon_A = E_p + \hbar\omega_{LO}, \\ \Delta_2(T) & \text{for } \varepsilon_A \leq |\varepsilon(\vec{k})|, |\varepsilon(\vec{k}')| < \varepsilon_c, \\ 0 & \text{otherwise.} \end{cases} \tag{7.9}$$

Then the equation (7.7) (after replacing the sum over $\vec{k}$ by an integral over $\varepsilon$) is reduced to the two equations

$$\Delta_1(T) = -D_p(\varepsilon_F)(V_c - V_{ph})\Delta_1(T)I_1 - D_p(\varepsilon_F)V_c\Delta_2(T)I_2 \tag{7.10}$$

$$\Delta_2(T) = -D_p(\varepsilon_F)V_c[\Delta_1(T)I_1 + \Delta_2(T)I_2], \tag{7.11}$$

where

$$I_1 = \int\limits_0^{\varepsilon_A} \frac{d\varepsilon}{\sqrt{\varepsilon^2 + \Delta_1^2(T)}} \tanh \frac{\sqrt{\varepsilon^2 + \Delta_1^2(T)}}{2k_BT}$$

$$I_2 = \int\limits_{\varepsilon_A}^{\varepsilon_c} \frac{d\varepsilon}{\sqrt{\varepsilon^2 + \Delta_2^2(T)}} \tanh \frac{\sqrt{\varepsilon^2 + \Delta_2^2(T)}}{2k_BT},$$

$D_p(\varepsilon_F)$ is the DOS at the Fermi polaronic level.

¿From Eqs. (7.10) and (7.11) we obtain

$$1 = \lambda_1^* I_1, \tag{7.12}$$

where $\lambda_1^* = D_p(\varepsilon_F)\tilde{V}_p$ is the BCS-like coupling constant, $\tilde{V}_p = V_{ph} - \tilde{V}_c$ is the effective polaron-polaron interaction potential, $\tilde{V}_c = V_c/[1 + D_p(\varepsilon_F)V_cI_2]$ is the screened Coulomb interaction between two polarons.

At $\varepsilon_c = \varepsilon_F > \varepsilon_A >> k_BT^*$, the integral $I_2$ becomes equal to $ln[\varepsilon_c/\varepsilon_F]$. Using Eq. (7.12), we obtain the BCS-like equation for the determination of the normal state gap or pairing PG, $\Delta_{PG}(T) = \Delta_1(T) = \Delta_{BCS}$ and mean-field pairing temperature $T^*$

$$\frac{1}{\lambda_1^*} = \int\limits_0^{\varepsilon_A} \frac{d\varepsilon}{\sqrt{\varepsilon^2 + \Delta_{PG}^2(T)}} \tanh \frac{\sqrt{\varepsilon^2 + \Delta_{PG}^2(T)}}{2k_BT} \tag{7.13}$$

from which we can find the temperature-dependent PG, $\Delta_{PG}(T)$, and the PG formation temperature $T^*$ in the intermediate BCS-like coupling regime $\lambda_1^* = \tilde{V}_pD_p(\varepsilon_F) < 1$, where $\tilde{V}_p = V_{ph} - V_c/[1 + V_cD_p(\varepsilon_F)ln(\varepsilon_c/\varepsilon_A)]$ is the effective pairing interaction potential between two large polarons.

At $T = 0$, solving Eq. (7.13) for $\Delta_{PG}(0)$, we have

$$\Delta_{PG}(0) = \frac{\varepsilon_A}{\sinh[1/\lambda_1^*]} \tag{7.14}$$

The numerical solution of Eq. (7.13) determines the temperature-dependence of the BCS-like PG, $\Delta_{PG}(T)$, which is shown in Fig. 7.2.

Using the value of $\varepsilon_A = 0.12eV$ and the BCS-like coupling constants $\lambda_1^* = 0.6$ and $\lambda_1^* = 0.45$ for underdoped and nearly optimally doped cuprates, we find $\Delta_{PG}(0) \simeq 44meV$ and $\Delta_{PG}(0) \simeq 25meV$, which are consistent with the leading edge gaps 42 meV and 25 meV observed in the normal state of $Bi_2Sr_2CaCu_2O_{8+\delta}$ (Bi-2212) [1]. One can assume that the normal-state gap $\Delta = 28meV$ observed in the underdoped samples of $YBa_2Cu_3O_{6.6}$ [1] is also BCS-like pairing PG corresponding to the values of the parameters $\varepsilon_A = 0.1eV$ and $\lambda_1^* \simeq 0.5$.

Evidently, as $T \to T^*$, the BCS-like gap $\Delta_{PG}(T)$ tends to zero. Therefore, the equation (7.13) can be written as

$$\frac{1}{\lambda_1^*} = \int\limits_0^{\varepsilon_A} \frac{d\varepsilon}{\varepsilon} \tanh \frac{\varepsilon}{2k_BT^*}, \tag{7.15}$$

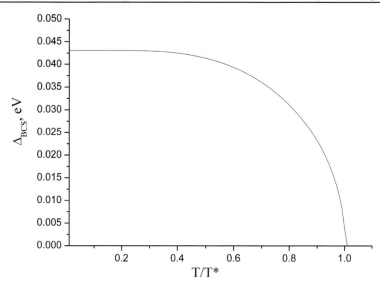

Figure 7.2. Temperature dependence of the BCS-like pairing PG, $\Delta_{PG}$ calculated using the Eq. (7.13) at $\varepsilon_A = 0.11 eV$ and $\lambda_1^* = 0.6$.

At $\varepsilon_A = E_p + \hbar\omega_{LO} >> k_B T^*$, we obtain from Eq. (7.15) a new and more general expression for the mean-field pairing temperature $T^*$ [43]:

$$k_B T^* \simeq 1.134(E_p + \hbar\omega_{LO}) \exp\left[-\frac{1}{\lambda_1^*}\right]. \tag{7.16}$$

This relation is one of the key results of the new BCS-like pairing theory. The usual BCS picture as the particular case is recovered in the weak electron-phonon coupling regime (i.e., in the absence of polaronic effects, $E_p = 0$), and the prefactor in Eq. (7.16) is replaced by Debye energy $\hbar\omega_D$. In this case, the Cooper pairing of carriers and the SC phase transition occur at the same temperature and the BCS gap serves as the SC order parameter.

The SC transition in cuprates is still treated by many researchers as a BCS transition. We believe that polaronic effects control the essential physics of high-$T_c$ cuprates. Therefore, the BCS-like transition at the mean-field temperature $T^*$ might be non-SC transition taking place in the normal state of underdoped, optimally doped, and overdoped cuprates; where the polaronic effects play a crucial role in the precursor Cooper pairing at $T^*(> T_c)$. The separation between the two temperatures $T^*$ (the onset of the BCS-like transition) and $T_c$ (the $\lambda$-like SC transition) occurs in high-$T_c$ cuprates due to the polaronic effects. In these unconventional superconductors the Cooper-pair formation and the condensation of pre-formed Cooper pairs into a superfluid Bose-liquid state would occur at different mean-field temperatures [29, 31]. In polar high-$T_c$ materials (in which the polaronic effects are rather strong), the mean-field temperature $T^*$ determined from the BCS-like equation (7.16) is not a mean-field $T_c$. Indeed, the $\lambda$-like anomaly of the electronic specific heat $C_e$ at $T_c$ and the BCS-like anomaly of $C_e$ at $T^*$ observed in high-$T_c$ cuprates in a wide range of doping [6] are indicative of the BCS-like and non-BCS-like mean-field transitions at $T^*$ and $T_c$, respectively. If we take the ratio of the binding energy of polaron Cooper pairs $2\Delta_{PG}(0)$ to the mean-field temperature $T^*$, we find

$$2\Delta_{PG}(0)/k_B T^* \simeq 3.52 \qquad (7.17)$$

To determine the doping dependences of $\Delta_{PG}$ and $T^*$, we can approximate the polaronic DOS in a simple form [31]

$$D_p(\varepsilon_F) = \begin{cases} 1/\varepsilon_F & \text{for} \quad \varepsilon < \varepsilon_F \\ 0 & \text{otherwise} \end{cases} \qquad (7.18)$$

Using this approximation we obtain from Eqs. (7.14) and (7.16)

$$\Delta_{PG}(x) = \frac{\varepsilon_A}{\sinh(\frac{1}{\lambda_1^*})} = \frac{\varepsilon_A}{\sinh[\hbar^2(3\pi n_a x)^{2/3}/2m_p \tilde{V}_p]}, \qquad (7.19)$$

and

$$k_B T^*(x) \simeq 1.134\varepsilon_A \exp[-1/\lambda_1^*] \simeq 1.134\varepsilon_A \exp\left[-\frac{\hbar^2(3\pi^2 n_a x)^{2/3}}{2m_p \tilde{V}_p}\right] \qquad (7.20)$$

from which it follows that the BCS-like pairing PG and the PG formation temperature are increased with decreasing doping $x$. Such doping dependences of the PG and the characteristic temperature $T^*$ were observed experimentally in high-$T_c$ cuprates [1, 5, 44, 45]. Now, we calculate the PG temperature $T^*(x)$ for given values of $\varepsilon_A = 0.12$ eV, $m_p = 2m_e$ and $\tilde{V}_p = 0.11$ eV in LSCO. The experimental values of $T^*$ for LSCO are shown in Fig. 7.3, where they compared with the calculated doping dependence of $T^*$. As seen in Fig. 7.3, the theoretical curve $T^*(x)$ agrees reasonably with experimental data for $T^*(x)$. The BCS-like pairing PG, $\Delta_{PG}$ exhibits a very similar doping dependence (solid curve in Fig. 7.4); it increases with decreasing $x$ in the underdoped region. The agreement between the calculated $\Delta_{PG}(x)$ and experimental points for the energy gap $\Delta^*(x)$ in Bi-2212 [47] (as shown Fig. 7.4) is also good.

We now shall study the precursor Cooper pairing for the deeply underdoped cuprates. The situation is different for such a underdoped system, which we assume to have a small Fermi surface. In this case, the polaronic effect is strong enough and the condition $\varepsilon_F < E_p + \hbar\omega_{LO}$ is satisfied. Therefore, $E_p + \hbar\omega_{LO}$ in Eq. (7.13) would be replaced by $\varepsilon_F$. We can then determine the characteristic PG temperature $T^*$ from the equation

$$\frac{1}{\lambda_2^*} = \int_0^{\varepsilon_F} \frac{d\varepsilon}{\varepsilon} \tanh\frac{\varepsilon}{2k_B T^*} = \int_0^1 \frac{dy}{y} \tanh y + \int_1^{y^*} \frac{dy}{y} \tanh y, \qquad (7.21)$$

where $y^* = \varepsilon_F/2k_B T^*$.

In order to evaluate the second integral in (7.16), it may be written in the form

$$\int_1^{y^*} \frac{dy}{y} \tanh y = C_1 + \int_1^{y^*} \frac{dy}{y} = C_1 + \ln y^* \qquad (7.22)$$

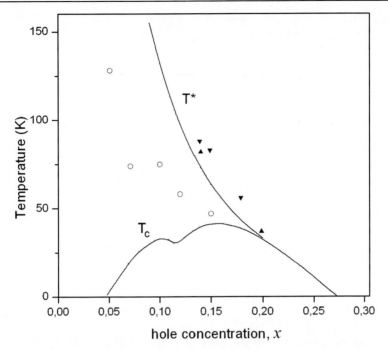

Figure 7.3. Doping dependence of the PG temperature $T^*$ (solid line) calculated using the relation (7.20) (with $\varepsilon_A = 0.105$ eV, $n_a = 5.3 \times 10^{21} cm^{-3}$, $V_p = 0.068$ eV and $m_p = 2m_e$). The experimental points for $T^*$ have been taken from ARPES (open circles) and tunneling (full triangles) data for LSCO [46].

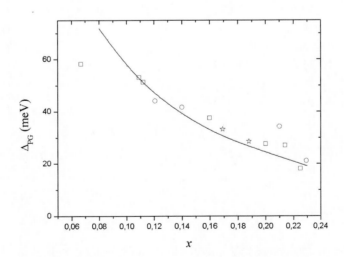

Figure 7.4. Doping dependence of $\Delta_{PG}(x)$ (solid line) calculated using the relation (7.19) (with $\varepsilon_A = 0.11$ eV, $n_a = 1 \times 10^{22} cm^{-3}$, $V_p = 0.13 eV$ and $m_p = 2m_e$) and compared to the experimental values of the energy gap $\Delta^*(x)$ in Bi-2212 [47] (open circles, open squares, and stars).

from which $C_1$ is determined for a given value of $y^*$.

Then, Eq. (7.21) can be rewritten as

$$\frac{1}{\lambda_2^*} = C_2 + \ln y^* = \ln\left(C\frac{\varepsilon_F}{k_B T^*}\right) \qquad (7.23)$$

where

$$C_2 = C_1 + \int_0^1 \frac{dy}{y}\tanh y = C_1 + 0.909675,$$

$$C \simeq 0.5\exp[C_1 + 0.909675].$$

Thus, the PG formation temperature $T^*$ can be determined from the relation

$$k_B T^* \simeq C\varepsilon_F \exp\left[-\frac{1}{\lambda_2^*}\right], \qquad (7.24)$$

where $\lambda_2^* = (V_{ph} - V_c)N_p(\varepsilon_F)$.

**Table 7.1. Calculated values of the prefactor $C$ and effective BCS-like coupling constant $\lambda_2^*$ in Eq.(7.23) at different values of $\varepsilon_F/k_B T^*$**

| $\varepsilon_F/k_B T^*$ | $C$ | $\lambda_2^*$ | $\varepsilon_F/k_B T^*$ | $C$ | $\lambda_2^*$ |
|---|---|---|---|---|---|
| 3.00 | 1.16303 | 0.80022 | 7.00 | 1.13413 | 0.48268 |
| 3.50 | 1.14952 | 0.71833 | 7.50 | 1.13401 | 0.46714 |
| 4.00 | 1.14238 | 0.65815 | 8.00 | 1.13395 | 0.45348 |
| 4.50 | 1.13855 | 0.61206 | 8.50 | 1.13391 | 0.44135 |
| 5.00 | 1.13646 | 0.57558 | 9.00 | 1.13389 | 0.43050 |
| 5.50 | 1.13532 | 0.54595 | 9.50 | 1.13388 | 0.42071 |
| 6.00 | 1.13468 | 0.52134 | 10.00 | 1.13387 | 0.41182 |
| 6.50 | 1.13433 | 0.50054 | | | |

The values of $\lambda_2^*$ and $C$ calculated using Eqs. (7.22) and (7.23) for different values of $\varepsilon_F/k_B T^*$ are given in table 7.1.

## 7.5.  Stripe Formation in the Underdoped Cuprates

There is experimental evidence that charge and spin inhomogeneities are present in underdoped high-$T_c$ cuprates, where charge-ordering takes place with the formation of the dynamic (metallic) and static (insulating) stripes (see [3, 48, 49, 50, 51, 52, 53]. It is believed that the essential physics of the cuprates in the underdoped regime is governed by competitions between different ground states. The stripes may be considered as a particular form of nanoscale phase separation and the high-$T_c$ cuprates exhibit such stripe phases which continuously connect the insulating and metallic or SC phases. The static spin and charge stripe ordering was directly observed by neutron scattering [49] in Nd-doped LSCO having $x = 0.12$, $La_{1.48}Nd_{0.4}Sr_{0.12}CuO_4$. Such a stripe ordering in LSCO was also observed by muon [54] and neutron-scattering [55] measurements at $x = 1/8$. To study the doping evolution of the electronic properties of high-$T_c$ cuprates over the full doping range the most suitable and simplest typical cuprate system is LSCO. The hole concentration in LSCO can be controlled and determined by the Sr content $x$, from the undoped insulating state ($x = 0$) to the heavily observed metallic one ($x > 0.25$). In this system, there is a strong tendency towards structural distortion in the $CuO_2$ plane and associated ordering of doped hole carriers in a stripe form [48, 49, 52, 56] especially near the magic doping $x = 1/8$. There is also similar tendency for the stripe ordering in other high-$T_c$ cuprates [10, 52], such as YBCO and Bi2212. Neutron-scattering experiments show (see Ref. [52]) that the dynamic stripes exist in a wide range of doping in LSCO, YBCO, and Bi2212. In the underdoped cuprates the superconductivity is markedly suppressed when the dynamic stripes become static at $x = 1/8$ and are pinned by the local structural distortions [51, 52]. Therefore, in these systems the suppression of $T_c$ and the onset of the insulating behavior at $x = 1/8$ are regarded as the 1/8 effect or anomaly [52, 57]. The reduction of $T_c$ due to the existence of the static stripes is particularly large in $La_{1.6-x}Nd_{0.4}Sr_xCuO_4$ at $x = 1/8$ [4, 58]. At fixed Nd concentration, the pinning effect is reduced with increasing Sr content, and leads to metallic and SC behavior. Although considerable progress was made during the last two decades in experimental studying the dynamic and static stripes in the cuprates (see [49, 51, 52, 54, 55, 56, 57]), the origin of these stripes and their relation to the high-$T_c$ superconductivity are not fully understood and should be explained theoretically within a more realistic model.

### 7.5.1. The Charge Segregation and Ordering Due to Inhomogeneous Spatial Distribution of Charge Carriers

As discussed in chapter chaptr6, the underdoped high-$T_c$ cuprates are inhomogeneous or disordered systems, where the doped carriers (holes and electrons) are distributed inhomogeneously and the charge inhomogeneity, segregation and ordering produce regions with different local carrier densities or with different doping levels. In these anisotropic 3D polar materials the charge carriers interact both with lattice vibrations and with lattice defects (e.g., dopants and impurities) and they are self-trapped in a defect-free regions and near the defects with the formation of the intrinsic and extrinsic large polarons [53]. When the impurity centers and intrinsic large polarons are distributed randomly and ordered differently with the formation of different superlattices, the narrow impurity bands and polaronic bands are formed in the CT gap of the cuprates. Such localized in-gap states develop into metallic states at some critical carrier concentrations. We believe that the MITs in inhomogeneous La-based and other cuprates are accompanied by the formation of a 3D self-organized network of the carrier-poor and carrier-rich regions in the form of static and dynamic stripes, and would occur at different critical carrier concentrations depending on the ionic size of dopants, the anisotropy of dielectric constants and the type of the ordering of extrinsic and intrinsic large polarons [53].

### 7.5.2. Formation of the Static and Dynamic Stripes Due to the Competing Carrier Localization and Delocalization

In the underdoped cuprates, the charge inhomogeneities and the strong carrier-phonon and carrier-defect-phonon interactions are expected to be responsible for the coexistence of large (bi)polarons and Cooper-like pairs of large polarons and for the striped phase separation [8, 53]. The carrier-poor, moderately well distorted regions of the crystal lattice alternate with the carrier-rich, slightly distorted regions of the lattice just as the alternation of spin and charge stripes discussed in [48, 50]. The variation of $\eta = \varepsilon_\infty/\varepsilon_0$ in a wide range leads to the formation of large polarons and bipolarons in the domains with $\eta > \eta_c$ and $\eta < \eta_c$, respectively. In the carrier-poor regions, these charge carriers are localized and the system still remains insulated. In some carrier-poor domains (with $\eta < \eta_c$), the localized large bipolarons would dissociate into two large polarons at $x > x_c$ and the possible ordering of these polarons results in the formation of dynamic (metallic) stripes at $x = x_{MIT}$ (where $x_{MIT}$ is the critical polaron concentration at which the MIT occurs). When the condition $\eta > \eta_c$ is satisfied in other carrier-poor and carrier-rich regions, the charge carriers in these regions are large polarons and they can form different superlattices and polaronic bands. The large polarons have different binding energies in the segregated domains due to the anisotropy of $\varepsilon_\infty$ and $\eta$, and they metallize at different doping levels. Further, the mechanisms for the MITs at different doping levels are also different. Therefore, the coexistence of static and dynamic stripes in cuprates is expected in a wide range of doping. In carrier-poor domains the pairing of large polarons in real-space is accompanied by charge aggregation or confinement (bipolaron formation) and local lattice distortions, which would stabilize the static stripe order and cause strong localization of the charge carriers. The expression in Eq.(6.25) allows to determine the doping level $x = x_c$ below which the large bipolarons exist. If we take $\varepsilon_\infty = 3$, $\eta = 0.04$, $m_p \simeq 3.5m_e$, $E_{bB} \simeq 0.06eV$ and $n_a \simeq 5.3 \cdot 10^{21} cm^{-3}$ (for the orthorhombic LSCO), the large bipolarons exist at $x \leq 0.03$. As the doping is increased towards the underdoped region the large bipolarons dissociate into the mobile large polarons and the static stripes may become dynamic ones. If the large-radius dopant and large polaron form the hydrogen-like impurity center in LSCO, the Bohr radius of such an impurity center is about 6.35Å at $\varepsilon_0 = 30$ and $m_p = 2.5m_e$. Using the criteria for the Mott MITs (see chapter 6), we find $x_{MIT} \simeq 0.0193$ (for $z = 8$) and $x_{MIT} \simeq 0.0256$ (for $z = 6$). Similarly, the Anderson-type MITs would occur at $x_{MIT} \simeq 0.023$ (for $z = 8$) and $x_{MIT} \simeq 0.0324$ (for $z = 6$). Indeed, the coexistence of the metallic and insulating stripes (i.e., the formation of a 3D self-organized network of carrier-poor and carrier-rich stripes) and the transition from metallic to the insulating behavior were observed in lightly doped cuprates ( $x \simeq 0.02 - 0.03$) [59]. Whereas, in $La_{2-x-y}Nd_ySr_xCuO_4$ and $La_{2-x-y}Eu_ySr_xCuO_4$ with small-radius dopants $Nd^{3+}$ and $Eu^{3+}$, the static stripe phases are observed in a wide range of carrier concentration and not restricted to a narrow range around $x = 1/8$ in which superconductivity is suppressed [60, 61]. Other experimental studies on $La_{2-x}Ba_{x-y}M_yCuO_4$ (where M = Sr, Ca) show that the 1/8 anomaly is reduced by substituting smaller divalent cations instead of large $Ba^{2+}$ [61]. Double doping experiments on $La_{2-x-y}Ba_xTh_yCuO_4$ indicate that superconductivity is suppressed when the hole concentration $p = x - y$ (not the individual or total dopant concentrations $x$, $y$, and $x + y$) is 1/8 [62]. In this system, $Th^{4+}$ ions compensate the negative effective charge of Ba-sites, so that the concentration of intrinsic large polarons is now given by $p = x - y$. This means that the superlattice and stripe formation accompanied by the suppression of superconductivity in $La_{2-x-y}Ba_xTh_yCuO_4$ are associated with the ordering of these polarons.

As discussed in chapter 6, the new MITs take place at $x_{MIT} \simeq 0.041 - 0.067$ (for $z = 8$) and $x_{MIT} \simeq 0.12 - 0.20$ (for $z = 6$) in La-based cuprates with small-radius dopants. Clearly, these MITs are accompanied by the stripe formation. These results are also in agreement with experiments [59, 63], which indicate that the metallic and insulating phases coexist for $0.05 < x < 0.13$. In LSCO and LBCO the average value of $\varepsilon_\infty$ is equal to 4 and the formation of simple cubic superlattices ($z = 6$) of large polarons is more likely. Under these circumstances the stripe order corresponds to the $1/8$ doping of LSCO and LBCO. We expect the same stripe order in other cuprates. In particular, for YBCO the relevant parameters are $\varepsilon_\infty = 3$, $\eta = 0.10$, $m_p = 2.1m_e$, $E_p \simeq 0.12eV$ and $R_p \simeq 8.18Å$. Then the critical carrier concentration determined from the relation $n_c^{1/3} = 4m_pE_pR_p/\hbar^2(3\pi^2)^{2/3}$ [53] (for $z = 6$) is equal to $1.427 \times 10^{21}cm^{-3}$. By taking into account that the value of $V_a$ in YBCO is $90Å^3$, we find the doping level $x_c = 0.128$, which is also close to the doping level $x = 1/8$ at which the MIT is accompanied by the stripe formation. Thus, one can assume that $x = 1/8$ is particular (or "magic") doping level for hole-doped cuprates in which the fraction of insulating phase becomes larger than that of metallic phase at $x \simeq 1/8$. If we take into account a possible anisotropy of $\varepsilon_\infty = 3.5 - 4.5$ [64] and $\eta = 0.08 - 0.14$ in inhomogeneous hole-doped cuprates with large-radius dopants, the MITs and stripe formation may also occur in a wide hole concentration range from $x \sim 0.02$ (lightly doped region) to $x \sim 0.19$ (overdoped region). In particular, taking the values of $E_p \simeq 0.0816 - 0.0935$ eV and $R_p = 9.3854 - 10.0618Å$ (for $\varepsilon_\infty = 3.5$ and $\eta = 0.08 - 0.14$) from tables 6.2 and 6.3, we obtain $x_c \simeq 0.1596 - 0.1948$ (for $z = 6$), $x_c \simeq 0.0798 - 0.0974$ (for $z = 8$) and $x_c \simeq 0.0399 - 0.0484$ (for $z = 12$).

We now discuss the MITs, stripe formation and suppression of superconductivity (so-called $1/8$ anomaly) in high-$T_c$ cuprates associated with the ordering of intrinsic large polarons. We have already demonstrated in chapter 6 that such MITs in the cuprates would occur at $x_{MIT} \simeq 0.06 - 0.07$ (for $z = 8$) and $x_{MIT} \simeq 0.12 - 0.13$ (for $z = 6$), which are in fair agreement with the experimental data on MITs and stripe formation in LSCO and LBCO [57, 61, 65, 66]. As mentioned previously, the experimental results provide evidence for the existence of metallic stripes in LSCO at $x \approx 0.02 - 0.05$ [59, 67]. While the ARPES experiments on LSCO [63] provide evidence for the coexistence of the metallic and insulating phases both in the underdoped region ($x = 0.05 - 0.13$) and in the overdoped region ($x \lesssim 0.19$). Our results are therefore in agreement with the experimental situation; they demonstrate that in LSCO and LBCO, the first insulating stripes appear at $x < 0.19$, while the first metallic stripes are already formed at $x > 0.02$. Hence, it follows that for $0.02 \lesssim x \lesssim 0.05$ and $x \lesssim 0.19$, the metallic and insulating stripes coexist in these systems on local scale. Thus, one can expect the coexistence of such metallic and insulating phases on a global scale in underdoped ($x \simeq 0.05 - 0.13$) and optimally doped ($x \simeq 0.15 - 0.16$) cuprates, and the suppression of superconductivity at $x = 1/8$ due to the preponderance of insulating phase over metallic one. At high doping levels ($x > 0.19$), only the metallic phase exist in LSCO and LBCO as reported also for LSCO in ARPES studies [68]. However, depending on the values of $\varepsilon_\infty$ and $\eta$ (e.g., for $\varepsilon_\infty < 3.5$ or $\eta < 0.06$ and $\varepsilon_\infty \sim 3.5$) and the types of charge ordering, the MITs and stripe formation may occur within these systems in the deeply overdoped region ($x > 0.2$).

## 7.6.    Quantum Critically and Possible Quantum Critical Points

An important issue in the phenomenology of the high-$T_c$ cuprates is the quantum criticality, which occurs as a function of doping $x$, at a particular doping point in the phase diagram where a quantum phase transition takes place at zero temperature. The existence of such a QCP hidden below the SC dome of the phase diagram of the cuprates slightly above optimal doping has been predicted theoretically [7, 8, 10] and suggested experimentally [2]. Moreover, there is also substantial evidence that the quantum criticality or QCP takes place near the $x = 1/8$ [9] and at optimal doping ($x = 0.15 - 0.16$) [69]. Note that the QCP hidden below the SC dome would probably exist in heavy fermion superconductors [70]. The high-$T_c$ cuprates are complicated materials where the ubiquitous competitions between different ground states govern the essential physics in a wide range of doping and are responsible for the quantum phase transitions that take place at different doping levels or QCPs. There are many indications that various QCPs control the anomalous behaviors of these complicated systems. Apparently, the MITs and stripe formation in the underdoped and optimally doped cuprates are governed by a particular QCP. While the PG behavior of the cuprates is controlled by another QCP somewhat above optimal doping, where the break-down of the traditional band theory, usual Fermi-liquid and BCS pairing theories occurs. The quantum criticality and the physical nature of the possible QCPs in doped high-$T_c$ cuprates have been intensively studied over the past two decades. However, our understanding of the QCPs and their governing role in different fundamental phenomena in these systems is still far from satisfactory and very incomplete. In particular, most of the theoretical approaches are based on different electronic models (i.e., electron correlations or antiferromagnetic (AF) spin fluctuations, which play a dominate role only in the undoped cuprates and diminish with increasing doping) and ignore effects arising from the electron-phonon interactions. In these theories the exact positions and the nature of the QCPs, which is probably more important, remain unknown. In the next sections, we shall further explore the quantum criticality and the properties of the distinctly different QCPs in these materials within a more realistic and pertinent theoretical approaches by taking into account the strong electron-phonon interactions.

### 7.6.1.    Metal-insulator Crossover Quantum Critical Point

One of the possible QCPs is the MIT point located at $x = x_{MIT}$. The presented theory of the MITs allows us to determine the positions of the metal-insulator crossover, which can signify the quantum phase transitions taking place at zero temperature and different doping levels. When the large polarons form the different superlattices with the coordination numbers $z = 6$, 8, and 12 at their inhomogeneous spatial distribution, the values of $x_{MIT}$ corresponding to the metal-insulator crossover points or QCPs are determined by the criteria for the MITs, which are presented in chapter 6. Then the possible positions of the metal-insulator crossover QCPs in cuprates correspond to the different doping levels $x_{QCP} (= x_{MIT}) \simeq 0.02 - 0.20$ (see Fig. 7.5) depending on the values of the parameters $\varepsilon_\infty$, $\varepsilon_0$, $m_p$, $R_1$, $R_p$ and $E_p$ (see chapter 6).

## 7.6.2.  Stripe Quantum Critical Point

As mentioned earlier, the new MITs in underdoped and optimally doped high-$T_c$ cuprates are responsible for the coexistence of the static and dynamic stripes on a global scale. It follows that the metal-insulator crossover ending near the optimal doping corresponds to the onset of the insulating behavior of the cuprates. Therefore, the metal-insulator crossover taking place around the $x = 1/8$ doping corresponds to the stripe instability or so-called stripe QCP. It seems that the number $x = 1/8$ is the particular doping level for the underdoped cuprates in which the insulating domains become larger than the metallic ones. One can expect that the preponderance of carrier-poor regions over carrier-rich regions at $x = 1/8$ has a stabilizing effect on the static stripes and causes the pinning of the chemical potential $\mu$ inside the CT gap of the cuprates. This would explain the pinning effect of the Fermi level $\varepsilon_F$ inside the CT gap of these systems for $x \lesssim 1/8$ and its shift downwards significant only for $x \gtrsim 0.15$, which has been observed in hole-doped cuprates [3, 56]. Clearly, the metal-insulator crossover taking place near the stripe QCP, $x_{QCP} = 1/8$ (Fig. 7.5), which corresponds to the formation of static stripes on a global scale is also accompanied by a marked suppression of superconductivity in underdoped cuprates.

## 7.6.3.  Pseudogap Quantum Critical Point

As described in sections 7.2 - 7.4, two distinctly different pseudogaps (PGs) may exist in the underdoped cuprates. In these high-$T_c$ materials, the polaronic and BCS-like PGs appear at the characteristic temperatures $T_p$ and $T^*$, respectively. The polaronic PG, $\Delta_p$, is temperature-independent and characterized by the energy scale of order $k_B T_p$. While the BCS-like pairing PG, $2\Delta_{PG}$, is characterized by energy of order $3.52\ k_B T^*$. The PG, $\Delta_p$ decreases with increasing doping level and disappears at some critical carrier concentrations $x_p$. The characteristic PG temperature $T_p$ also decreases with increasing doping $x$ and approaches zero at the QCP, $x_p$. As shown in section 7.5.2, the dissociation of large bipolarons occurs at low doping levels $x < 0.05$. While the dissociation of large polarons occurs at a higher doping level, $x = x_p >> 0.05$. At $\Delta_p = 0$, we can find the position of the polaronic PG-QCP from Eq. (7.2). By taking $E_p \approx 0.095 eV$, $\varepsilon_0 \simeq 25$, and $n_a \simeq 1/V_a \simeq 5.3 \times 10^{21} cm^{-3}$ (at $V_a = 190 Å^3$) for LSCO, we find $x_{QCP} = x_p \simeq 0.2$ in accordance with experimental results [2, 18]. Many experimental studies [6, 18, 46, 56, 72] provide direct evidence for the presence of a finite PG in the overdoped LSCO (with $x = 0.20 - 0.22$). In particular, transport measurements on overdoped LSCO have shown that the characteristic PG temperature is much greater than $T_c$ for $x \leq 0.22$ [73] and becomes equal to $T_c$ well into the overdoped region. These experimental results indicate that the large PG observed in LSCO remains even at a higher doping level $x > 0.22$. Such a PG-like feature in LSCO is likely to be polaronic PG, which vanishes at $x_{QCP} = x_p = 0.20 - 0.24$ [71, 73, 74]. Indeed, using Eq. (7.2) and the value of $E_p \simeq 0.10 eV$, we obtain $x_{QCP} = x_p = 0.24$, so that in LSCO the polaronic PG temperature $T_p \to 0$ for $x \to 0.20 - 0.24$. The large PG was also observed in YBCO [2, 18] in which this PG determined by using different experimental techniques vanishes at $x_{QCP} = 0.19$ and the PG temperature tends to zero as $x \to 0.19$. If we take $E_p \simeq 0.096 eV$, $\varepsilon_0 = 30$, and $n_a \approx 10^{22} cm^{-3}$ for YBCO, we find $x_{QCP} = x_p = 0.19$ in accordance with these experimental results. The QCP hidden below SC dome in the phase diagram of the high-$T_c$ cuprates and located around $x_p = 0.20$ separates two types of

Fermi liquids [8] (i.e., usual Landau Fermi-liquid and polaronic Fermi-liquid). As shown in section 7.4, the BCS-like pairing PG, $\Delta_{PG}$ also decreases with increasing $x$ but this PG does not vanish under the SC dome. In Fig. 7.5, we summarize characteristic PG temperatures as a function of doping to demonstrate that there are two types of PG crossover temperatures above $T_c$ and different QCPs hidden under the SC dome of the $T - x$ phase diagram of Bi-2212. The $T - x$ phase diagram presented in Fig. 7.5 is generic for all high-$T_c$ cuprates, but the crossover temperatures $T_p(x)$ and $T^*(x)$ above $T_c$ may be very close or far-away depending on the type of the cuprates. The values of $x_p$ in various high-$T_c$ cuprates may be also different.

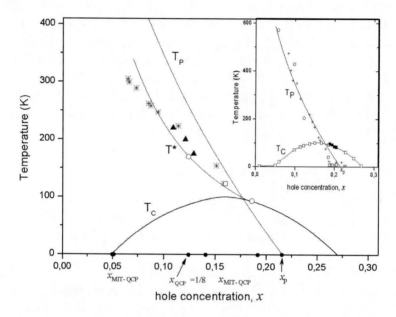

Figure 7.5. Main panel. Temperature-doping (T-$x$) phase diagram for the cuprates according to the polaronic PG-QCP and BCS-like PG scenarios in Bi-2212. The solid line $T_p(x)$ calculated by using expression (7.2) at $E_p = 0.131\ eV$, $\varepsilon_0 = 25$ and $n_a = 1.3 \times 10^{22} cm^{-3}$ is the polaronic PG formation temperature or polaronic metal↔normal metal crossover line ending at $T = 0$ and at $x_p$. The other solid line $T^*(x)$ calculated by using expression (7.20) at $m_p = 2m_e$, $\varepsilon_A = 0.095$ eV, $V_p = 0.125 eV$ $n_a = 1.3 \times 10^{22} cm^{-3}$ is the BCS-like phase transition line (or BCS-like PG crossover temperature) and merges with the SC critical line $T_c(x)$ in the overdoped region. The experimental points for $T^*$ in Bi-2212 have been taken from [74] (open circles), [75] (open square), [76] (black triangles), [77] (black stars) and are also shown for comparison. The presence of other QCPs in the (T-$x$) phase diagram of the cuprates are shown by $x_{MIT} < 1/8$, $x_{QCP} \approx 1/8$, and $x_{MIT} > 1/8$. Inset: calculated doping dependence of the polaronic PG temperature (solid line which is the same crossover line $T_p(x)$ as in the main panel) compared with the experimental data for the temperature of PG opening in Bi-2212 [2] (crosses and open circles).

# 7.7. Pseudogap and Stripe Effects on the Normal State Properties of High-$T_c$ Cuprates

The PGs, especially BCS-like pairing PG, and stripe formation affect the physical properties of the underdoped and optimally doped cuprates in the normal state and result in the appearance of their unusual or anomalous behavior around the characteristic crossover temperatures. Because the PG phenomena and stripe formation have strong effects on the electronic states of these materials and manifest themselves both in doping dependencies and in temperature dependencies of various physical quantities such as the normal-state gaps, thermodynamic quantities (e.g., specific heat and entropy), resistivity and magnetic susceptibility and other anomalies. In this section, we discuss the main effects of the PGs and the static and dynamic stripes on the normal state properties of the underdoped and optimally doped cuprates.

## 7.7.1.  Optical Properties

After the discovery of high-$T_c$ cuprate superconductors, tunneling and photoemission (in particular, ARPES) spectroscopies have been developed as two complementary and powerful techniques for investigating the excitation spectra and low-energy electronic structure of these novel materials. ARPES technique measures the electronic DOS below the Fermi level and provides information on the excitation energy $\Delta$ with respect to the Fermi energy. This technique provides evidence for the existence of a Fermi surface in doped high-$T_c$ cuprates, which are unconventional superconductors. ARPES results on underdoped, optimally doped, and overdoped cuprates show [1, 30] that these high-$T_c$ materials have well-defined and very different Fermi surface. Among spectroscopic probes, tunneling spectroscopy has been the most powerful tool used to measure the electronic DOS both below and above the Fermi level. There are different experimental techniques that have used to investigate tunneling spectra. The important quantities that need to be measured are the current-voltage characteristics $I - V$ and tunneling conductance $dI/dV$ as a function of the voltage at different temperatures and doping levels. For the cuprates, the situation is complicated by the presence of polaronic effects, electronic inhomogeneity and multi-gap structures [4, 23, 53, 78, 79, 80]. The tunneling spectra (differential conductance-voltage characteristics $dI/dV - V$) of high-$T_c$ cuprates provide a direct information about the electronic states (or gap-like structure) and the gap or PG inhomogeneity in these materials.

Scanning tunneling microscopy and spectroscopy (STM and STS) [81] and angle-resolved photoemission spectroscopy (ARPES) [3, 30] have made significant progress in the studies of the low-energy electronic structure of high-$T_c$ cuprates and other materials. In fact, the shapes of the tunneling and ARPES spectra of high-$T_c$ cuprate superconductors are very similar. The STM and STS techniques are very sensitive to the quasiparticle DOS and to the electronic (or gap) inhomogeneities that are intrinsic to the cuprates and have an affect on their tunneling spectra [81, 82, 83, 84, 85]. Tunneling measurements on cuprate superconductors have revealed a rich variety of tunneling spectra of high-$T_c$ cuprate superconductor (HTSC)-insulator (I)-normal metal (N) (called SIN) junctions. These tunneling spectra show many unusual features such as nearly U- and V-shaped subgap features [81, 85], asymmetric conductance peaks [86, 87, 88], dip-hump structures systematically observed outside the conductance peak on the negative bias side [81, 82, 86, 87, 88], suppression of the peak on the negative bias side with increasing temperature and its vanishing somewhat below $T_c$ or near $T_c$, leaving the hump feature (i.e., linearly increasing conductance) and the second peak (on the positive bias side) [81, 86, 88], shoulders inside the conductance peaks [83, 84]. Similar peak-dip-hump feature and its persistence above $T_c$ were also observed in ARPES spectra [3, 89].

The unusual features of the tunneling spectra of high-$T_c$ cuprates are neither expected within the simple $s$-wave BCS model nor within the $d$- wave BCS model. For example, the tunneling spectra showing a low-bias and more flatter; U-shaped BCS-like feature is difficult to reproduce in the $d$-wave model. While the origin of the other type of tunneling spectra showing a more V-shaped feature in high-$T_c$ cuprates still remains unclear. Such unusual tunneling spectra might be expected not only within the $d$-wave gap model (which fails to reproduce quantitatively the conductance peak height and shape [81, 84, 90]), but also within the $s$-wave multi-gap model proposed in Ref. [91]. The origins of the peak-dip-hump feature and the asymmetry of the conductance peaks have also been the subject of controversy. These features of the tunneling spectra have been attributed either to extrinsic (band-structure) effects (i.e., the van Hove singularities (VHS's) and bilayer splitting) [92, 93]; or, to intrinsic effects such as particle-hole asymmetry [94]; and strong coupling effects (which originate from the coupling to a collective electronic mode [95]; or, to a phonon mode [96]) and effects of energy-dependent gap function [97]. According to Refs. [94, 96, 98] the existence of VHS's in high-$T_c$ cuprates is somewhat questionable. Although several theoretical models were successful in reproducing some tunneling spectra with the peak-dip-hump-like features and asymmetric or nearly symmetric peaks observed in cuprates and fits the experimental data are reasonably good, the question of the spectral line shape is still undecided and the other well- established experimental SIN tunneling spectra that showed distinctly different peak-dip-hump features [81, 86, 88] (e.g., the presence of shallow dip-like feature at negative bias and its absence at positive bias, high-bias conductances, which are nearly flat, linearly increasing at a negative bias or decreasing at a positive bias, temperature- and doping-dependent peaks, dip-hump features and asymmetry of the conductance peaks) characteristic of high- $T_c$ cuprates were not explained yet. The quantitative fits of the experimental spectra of $Ba_2Sr_2CaCu_2O_{8+\delta}$ (Bi-2212) to a BCS $d$-wave gap and a $T$-independent gap functions [81] have been inadequate in reproducing the asymmetry (which is opposite to that of the observed tunneling spectra) and the temperature-dependent conductance curves. Further, STM and STS studies have shown that the energy gap in both SC and PG states of Bi-2212 is widely inhomogeneous and the gap distribution (i.e., inhomogeneity) has a strong effect on the tunneling spectra [82, 83, 84]. Therefore, it is necessary for any theoretical model to explain not only the asymmetry and peak-dip-hump features in SIN tunneling spectra but also their systematic evolution with temperature and doping, a flat (i.e., U-shaped) and more V-shaped subgap conductances, the systematic presence of dip-hump-like feature at a negative bias, the gap-inhomogeneity-induced shoulders inside the conductance peaks that are observed recently by STM in tunneling spectra of Bi-2212 [83, 84].

Here, we propose a simple and generic model for quasiparticle tunneling based on the different mechanisms for tunneling of charge carriers across the SIN junction at negative and positive biases and the multi-gap (i.e., gap inhomogeneity) picture. The proposed model reproduces the well-established experimental SIN tunneling spectra of high-$T_c$ cuprates and their more U- and V-shaped features, asymmetry, peak-dip-hump structure, and shoulder-like features inside the conductance peaks. We will focus on the Bi-2212 system (which has been well studied experimentally) and show that the main experimental features of the tunneling spectra and their temperature and doping dependences can be easily produced by using a BCS ($s$-wave) DOS at positive bias voltages ($V > 0$) and the combined BCS ($s$-wave) DOS and quasi-free-state DOS (originating from the dissociation of large polarons) at negative bias voltages ($V < 0$) and taking into account the distribution of BCS and polaronic gap values.

## Modeling Unconventional SIN Tunneling

The charge carriers in doped high-$T_c$ cuprates are assumed to be within both a 3D and a 2D polarizable medium, the last one being $CuO_2$ layers. In reality, however, no systems can be purely 2D, and therefore, the doped cuprates (in which the doped carriers are delocalized just as in semiconductors as established experimentally [11, 12]) may be approximated as a 3D medium. Various experiments suggest that the consideration of high-$T_c$ cuprates as 3D systems may appear to be more appropriate (see Refs. [11, 12, 14, 99, 100]). The role of the interlayer coupling or 3D interactions in the cuprates cannot be ignored. Therefore, the band structure effects such as the logarithmic singularities (the 2D VHS's) in the DOS near the Fermi level are likely present at isolated areas on the surface and weak or absent in the layered 3D high-$T_c$ cuprates. Further, there is ample reason to believe that the electron-phonon interaction in cuprates is strong enough and the relevant charge carriers in these systems are large polarons [11, 31, 53, 80]. Therefore, the precursor Cooper pairing of large polarons may occur above $T_c$ with opening the BCS-type gap $\Delta$ in their excitation spectrum [31]. As argued in Ref. [8], the binding energies of large polarons $\Delta_p$ and Cooper-like large polaron pairs $\Delta$ are manifested as the two distinct energy scales in high-$T_c$ cuprates, one a temperature-independent polaronic PG and the other a BCS-like gap.

We consider the model which describes two specific mechanisms for quasi-particle tunneling across the SIN junction at $V < 0$ and $V > 0$, and explains the asymmetry of the tunneling current when taken into account the different tunneling DOS existing in these cases. The first mechanism describes the $S \rightarrow N$ tunneling processes associated with the dissociation of Cooper-like polaron pairs and large polarons at $V < 0$. In this case, the Cooper pair dissociates into an electron in a normal metal and a polaron in a polaron band of the HTSC. This $S \rightarrow N$ tunneling is allowed only at $|eV| > \Delta$. The dissociation of large polaron occurs at $|eV| > \Delta_p$ and the carrier released from the polaron potential well can tunnel from the quasi-free state into the free states of the normal metal. Such a $S \rightarrow N$ transition gives an additional contribution to the tunneling current. The other mechanism describes the electron tunneling from the normal metal to the BCS-like quasi-particle states in HTSC at $V > 0$, while the quasi-free states that appear only at the polaron dissociation are absent. Therefore, if the tunneling matrix element $M$ is considered to be constant, the tunneling current across SIN junction at $V > 0$ is proportional to the $|M|^2$ [101] and the BCS quasiparticle DOS of HTSC given by

$$D_{BCS}(E,\Delta) = \begin{cases} D_p(\varepsilon_F)\dfrac{|E|}{\sqrt{E^2-\Delta^2}} & \text{for } |E| > \Delta, \\ 0 & \text{for } |E| < \Delta, \end{cases} \qquad (7.25)$$

where the polaronic DOS, $D_p(\varepsilon_F)$, can be approximated in a simple form as in Eq. (7.18). Note that the $s$-wave BCS quasiparticle DOS, $D_{BCS}(E,\Delta)$ is insensitive to the band structure effects (i.e., VHS's).

In the $V < 0$ case, the total current is the sum of two different tunneling currents, which are proportional to the $|M|^2$; the BCS quasiparticle DOS $D_{BCS}(E,\Delta)$ and the quasi-free state DOS. This current flows from HTSC to normal metal at the dissociation of Cooper pairs and large polarons. In HTSC, the quasi-free carriers that appear at the dissociation of large polarons have the effective mass $m^*$ and energy $E = \Delta_p + \hbar^2 k^2/2m^*$. Then the quasi-free state DOS is defined as

$$D_f(E,\Delta_p) = \begin{cases} D(\varepsilon_F^f)\sqrt{(|E| - \Delta_p)/\varepsilon_F^f} & \text{for } |E| > \Delta_p, \\ 0 & \text{for } |E| < \Delta_p, \end{cases} \tag{7.26}$$

where $D(\varepsilon_F^f)$ is the DOS at the Fermi energy of quasi-free carriers and approximated as $D(\varepsilon_F^f) = 1/\varepsilon_F^f$. For the normal metal, the DOS at the Fermi energy $E_F$ is independent of energy $E$, i.e., $D(E) \simeq D(0)$. Thus, at $V > 0$ the tunneling current from the normal metal to HTSC is

$$I_{N \to S}(V) = C|M|^2 D(0) D_p(\varepsilon_F) \int_{-\infty}^{+\infty} \frac{|E + eV|}{\sqrt{(E + eV)^2 - \Delta^2}} [f(E) - f(E + eV)]\, dE$$

$$= \frac{G(\varepsilon_F)}{e} \int_{-\infty}^{+\infty} \frac{|\varepsilon|}{\sqrt{\varepsilon^2 - \Delta^2}} [f(\varepsilon - eV) - f(\varepsilon)]\, d\varepsilon, \tag{7.27}$$

where $G(\varepsilon_F) = eC|M|^2 D(0) D_p(\varepsilon_F)$ is the doping-dependent conductance factor, $C$ is a constant, $f(\varepsilon)$ is the Fermi function, $\varepsilon = E + eV$. The differential conductance, $dI_{N \to S}/dV$ is then given by

$$dI_{N \to S}/dV = G(\varepsilon_F)[A_1(\Delta_T, a_V) + A_2(\Delta_T, a_V)], \tag{7.28}$$

where

$$A_1(\Delta_T, a_V) = \int_{\Delta_T}^{+\infty} \frac{y \exp[-y - a_V]\, dy}{\sqrt{y^2 - \Delta_T^2}(\exp[-y - a_V] + 1)^2},$$

$$A_2(\Delta_T, a_V) = \int_{\Delta_T}^{+\infty} \frac{y \exp[y - a_V]\, dy}{\sqrt{y^2 - \Delta_T^2}(\exp[y - a_V] + 1)^2},$$

$y = \varepsilon/k_B T$, $\Delta_T = \Delta/k_B T$, $a_V = eV/k_B T$.

For negative bias voltages of $V < 0$, two different tunneling processes or currents (with two independent conductance factors) contribute to the total current. Therefore, the result-

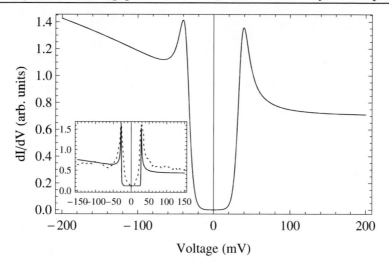

Figure 7.6. Main panel: SIN tunneling conductance for T=40 K calculated using the one-gap model with single *s*-wave BCS gap $\Delta$=35 meV and single polaronic gap $\Delta_p$=40 meV, exhibiting U-shaped feature at a low-bias. Inset: comparison of the model ($\Delta$=28 meV and $\Delta_p$=22 meV, solid line) with optimally doped Bi-2212 ($T_c$=92 K) tunneling data at 4.8 K (dashed line) [90].

ing tunneling current and differential conductance are given by

$$I_{S\to N} = \frac{G(\varepsilon_F)}{e} \int\limits_{-\infty}^{+\infty} \frac{|\varepsilon|d\varepsilon}{\sqrt{\varepsilon^2 - \Delta^2}} [f(\varepsilon) - f(\varepsilon + eV)]$$

$$+ \frac{G(0)}{e} \int\limits_{-\infty}^{+\infty} \sqrt{|\varepsilon| - \Delta_p} [f(\varepsilon) - f(\varepsilon + eV)] d\varepsilon, \tag{7.29}$$

and

$$\frac{dI_{S\to N}}{dV} = G(\varepsilon_F) \left[ A_1(\Delta_T, -a_V) + A_2(\Delta_T, -a_V) \right.$$

$$\left. + G(0)\sqrt{k_B T} B_1(\Delta_p^*, a_V) + B_2(\Delta_p^*, a_V) \right], \tag{7.30}$$

where $\varepsilon = E - eV$, $\Delta_p^* = \Delta_p/k_B T$,

$$B_1(\Delta_p^*, a_V) = \int\limits_{\Delta_p^*}^{\infty} \sqrt{|y| - \Delta_p^*} \frac{\exp[y + a_V] dy}{(\exp[y + a_V] + 1)^2},$$

$$B_2(\Delta_p^*, a_V) = \int\limits_{\Delta_p^*}^{\infty} \sqrt{|y| - \Delta_p^*} \frac{\exp[-y + a_V] dy}{(\exp[-y + a_V] + 1)^2},$$

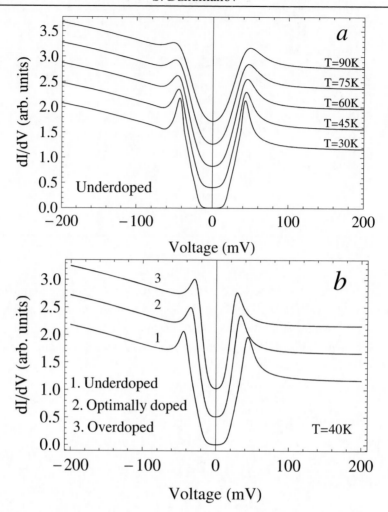

Figure 7.7. Tunneling conductance as a function of temperature (a) and doping (b), calculated using the three-gap model. In (a) the gap values are: $\Delta=40$, 30, and 22 meV, $\Delta_p=65$,
47, and 31 meV. In (b) $T=40$ K and set of gap values: $\Delta=40$, 30, and 24 meV, $\Delta_p=52$, 38,
and 28 meV for curve 1; $\Delta=30$, 24, and 18 meV, $\Delta_p=33$, 28, and 22 meV for curve 2; and
$\Delta=25$, 20, and 16 meV, $\Delta_p=21$, 17, and 14 meV for curve 3.

$$G(0) = eC|M|^2 D(0) D(\varepsilon_F^f)/\sqrt{\varepsilon_F^f}.$$

The parameters $G(\varepsilon_F)$ and $G(0)$ are adjusted to the experimental data. The SIN tunneling conductance curve calculated at $T=30$ K for the single-gap case (concerning both
the polaronic gap $\Delta_p$ and the $s$-wave BCS-type gap $\Delta$) is shown in Fig. 7.6 (main panel).
In this simple model, the absence of gap distribution would lead to the $U$-shaped spectral
behavior at low bias and a more flatter subgap conductance would be expected for homogeneous high-$T_c$ cuprates. As can be seen in Fig. 7.6 (main panel), there are dip-hump feature
and asymmetric peaks (with the higher peak in the negative bias voltage), which arise from

the simple superposition of the tunneling conductances associated with the BCS DOS and quasi-free state DOS. The experimental gap in the tunneling spectra of high-$T_c$ cuprates measured as half the energy separating the conductance peaks represents the BCS gap $\Delta$, while the dip-like feature at energy$\sim 2\Delta$ is indicative of the presence of polaronic gap $\Delta_p$ in their excitation spectrum. The proposed simple model is compared with the well-known tunneling spectra measured at $T \simeq 4.8K$ in Bi-2212 [90], as shown in the inset of Fig. 7.6.

The normal state $(T > T_c)$ of high-$T_c$ cuprates is characterized by two crossover phenomena such as the transition from quasi-free state to polaronic one at $T_p(x)$ and the BCS-like transition at $T^*(x)$. The magnitudes of the temperature-independent polaronic PG and temperature-dependent BCS-like gap (or PG) are proportional to the crossover temperatures $T_p(x)$ and $T^*(x)$, respectively. With increasing doping, $T_p$ and $T^*$ would decrease, while $T_c$ first increases nearly as $\sim x^{2/3}$ (for a 3D Bose gas of polaron Cooper pairs) and goes through a maximum at optimal doping $x = x_0$ and then decreases at $x > x_0$ [8]. In the underdoped region of the $T - x$ phase diagram of high-$T_c$ cuprates, the crossover temperatures $T_p(x)$ are higher than $T^*(x)$, where $\Delta_p > \Delta$. As the doping level increases towards overdoped region, the curve $T_p(x)$ first crossing the lower $T^*(x)$ curves and then the $T_c(x)$ dome at $x > x_0$ and ending in the polaronic PG-QCP, $x_p$, characterizes the transition between ordinary and polaronic metals [8]. It follows that the magnitude of $T_p \sim \Delta_p$ becomes smaller than $T^* \sim \Delta$ with overdoping. Thus, the position of the quasiparticle peak (at $E = \Delta$) or BCS-like tunneling gap in high-$T_c$ cuprates is not the energy scale of the SC order parameter [29, 31], as was also argued in Refs. [97, 102]

**Multi-gap Model**

As mentioned in section 7.5, the electronic inhomogeneity and charge ordering play an important role in doped high-$T_c$ cuprates and are responsible for charge segregation and phase separation in the form of alternating metallic and insulating regions or so-called stripes [13, 48, 50]. One can expect that the electronic inhomogeneity in HTSC may produce different metallic regions with various doping levels and with a distribution of gap amplitudes ($\Delta$ and $\Delta_p$) and variation in the local DOS. Recent STM and STS experimental data on Bi-2212 and other high-$T_c$ systems corroborate this conclusion and indicate that the gap inhomogeneities commonly exist in these materials regardless of doping level [81, 82, 83, 84, 103]. Therefore, in order to reproduce the main features of the tunneling spectra of high-$T_c$ cuprates, we have to consider the multi-gap case and the multi-channel tunneling processes, which contribute to the total tunneling current. In this case, the Fermi energy, BCS-like gap, polaronic gap, and local DOS in various metallic regions (or stripes) will be different and denoted by $\varepsilon_{Fi}$, $\Delta(i)$, $\Delta_p(i)$, $D_{BCS}(E, \Delta(i))$, and $D_f(E, \Delta_p(i))$, respectively $(i = 1, 2, \ldots)$. At positive bias voltages $V > 0$, the tunneling of electrons from the normal metal into these metallic regions of HTSC with different BCS DOS takes place and the resulting conductance is

$$\frac{dI_{N \to S}}{dV} = \sum_i G_i(\varepsilon_{Fi})[A_{1i}(\Delta_T(i), a_V) + A_{2i}(\Delta_T(i), a_V)]. \tag{7.31}$$

In the case $V < 0$, all the possible contributions to the $S \to N$ tunneling current come from various metallic regions of HTSC at the dissociation of distinctly different Cooper-like polaron pairs and large polarons. Therefore, the total current is the sum of tunneling currents flowing from these metallic regions of HTSC with different local DOS ($D_{BCS}(E, \Delta(i))$ and $D_f(E, \Delta_p(i))$) to the normal metal. The $i-th$ component of this $S \rightarrow N$ tunneling current is given by Eq. (7.30) and the resulting conductance is

$$\frac{dI_{S \rightarrow N}}{dV} = \sum_i G_i(\varepsilon_{Fi})[A_{1i}(\Delta_T(i), -a_V) + A_{2i}(\Delta_T(i), -a_V)$$

$$+ a_{Fi}(T)[B_{1i}(\Delta_p^*(i), a_V) + B_{2i}(\Delta_p^*(i), a_V)]]. \tag{7.32}$$

In such a multi-gap model, the tunneling spectra exhibit a more V-shaped behavior at low bias, the peak-dip-hump feature at negative bias and the asymmetry of the conductance peaks. In particular, the existence of two or more distinctly different $s$-wave BCS gaps in the excitation spectrum of inhomogeneous HTCS is manifested as the $V$-shaped subgap feature in their tunneling spectra due to the superposition of different BCS-like tunneling conductances. During increasing temperature, the dip and peak on the negative bias side gradually disappear (see Fig. 7.7a), leaving the hump feature and the second conductance peak (on the positive bias side), as observed in tunneling experiments [81]. Figure 7.7b shows that the conductance peaks become more asymmetric with decreasing doping and the conductance peaks, dip- and hump-like features all move to higher binding energies with underdoping, as seen in experiments [86, 88].

### Comparison of Theoretical Tunneling Spectra with the Experimental SIN Tunneling Data

The parameters entering into Eqs. (7.31) and (7.32) can be varied to fit experimental data. The comparison of the theoretical results with the different experimental data on under-doped, slightly underdoped and overdoped Bi-2212 is presented in Fig. 7.8. We obtained the best fits to the experimental spectra by taking only two or three terms in Eqs. (7.31) and (7.32). In this way, we succeeded in fitting almost all of experimental conductance curves by taking different gap values. The V-shaped subgap feature, the asymmetric peaks, and the dip-hump features, their temperature dependencies observed in tunneling spectra of under-doped Bi-2212 (left inset in Fig.7.8), slightly underdoped Bi-2212 (right inset in Fig.7.8) and overdoped Bi-2212 (main panel in Fig.7.8) are well reproduced,

The high energy part of the tunneling spectra on the negative bias side show a broad line-width which grows linearly in energy and the peak-dip separation decreases with over-doping. As can be seen from Fig. 7.8, the agreement of the theory with the well-known experimental results of Renner et al. [86] and Matsuda et al. [88] is quite good, though the experimental conductance peaks in some tunneling spectra of overdoped Bi-2212 [see Fig.7.8 (main panel)] are slightly higher than those calculated. Some slight difference be-tween the calculated and measured conductance peaks can be due to several reasons such as, for example, the quality of the sample surface and tip-sample contact [81], the experimental resolution of the peaks, the local variation of the temperature. Although great progress has been made in making remarkably clean tunneling experiments, the existing experimental SIN tunneling spectra disagree with each other. In particular, the opposite asymmetries and doping dependences of the conductance peaks observed in the SIN tunneling experi-ments on underdoped and overdoped Bi2212 [87] and the sharp dips seen in some STM and STS tunneling measurements on both bias sides [85, 97, 104] have not been found in other

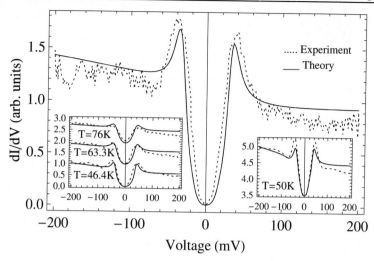

Figure 7.8. Main panel: SIN tunneling spectrum measured on overdoped Bi-2212 at 43.1 K [86] fitted by using two-gap model, with $\Delta$=31 and 18 meV; $\Delta_p$= 22 and 15 meV. Left inset: fits of SIN tunneling spectra measured on underdoped Bi-2212 [86] by using three-gap model, with $\Delta_p$=44, 28, and 20 meV and the set of gap values $\Delta$=38, 26, and 17 meV for 46.4 K, $\Delta$=37, 25, and 16 meV for 63.3 K and $\Delta$=36, 24, and 15 meV for 76 K. Right inset: fit of SIN tunneling spectrum measured on slightly underdoped Bi-2212 at 50 K [88] by using three gap model, with $\Delta$=36, 24, and 15 meV; $\Delta_p$= 73, 56, and 39 meV.

SIN tunneling experiments [81, 86, 88, 90]. Considering the possible errors in experiment and theory, the multi-gap model suggests that, even in the cases of overdoped Bi-2212 (at 43.1K) [86] and slightly underdoped Bi-2212 (at 50K) [88]; there exists reasonable agreement between the calculated and the measured conductance peaks (Fig.7.8), and the main aspects of the problem are successfully modeled. We believe that the multi-gap model with the combined BCS DOS and quasi-free-state DOS, give an adequate description of the PG phenomena observed in tunneling spectroscopy and ARPES measurements. To demonstrate this, other experimental data also fitted remarkably by using the multi-gap model. We see that the proposed multi-gap model reproduces other tunneling spectra (with varying local gap value, ranging from 20 to 70 meV) and shoulders inside the conductance peaks observed in Bi-2212 [83, 84]. In particular, this model reproduces rather well one of the experimental spectra of inhomogeneous Bi-2212 [83] by taking six terms in Eqs. (7.31) and (7.32), as shown in Fig. 7.9 (main panel). Further, the theoretical conductance curve in the inset of Fig.7.9 as calculated by using the multi-gap model exhibits kink-like features or shoulders inside the conductance peaks and is similar to that seen in inhomogeneous Bi-2212 (see Fig. 1(c) of Ref. [84]). The pronounced V-shaped and shoulder-like features in tunneling spectra of these high-$T_c$ cuprates result from the superposition of different $s$-wave contributions of the BCS-like quasiparticle spectral weight originating from various metallic regions with the gap amplitudes $\Delta(i)$. In the numerical calculations the specific BCS-gap values are chosen taking into account the approximate positions of the conductance peaks, the V-shaped, and shoulder-like features inside the conductance peaks observed in tunnel-

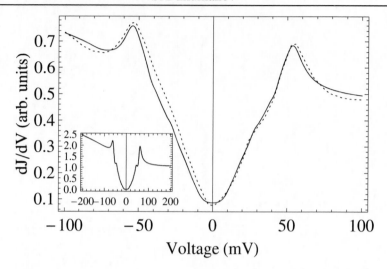

Figure 7.9. Comparison of the tunneling conductance data on inhomogeneous Bi-2212 (dashed line) [83] with the tunneling conductance calculated at 30 K (main panel) using the multi-gap model ($\Delta$=52, 45, 36, 27, 19, and 12 meV; $\Delta_p$= 78, 65, 47, 34, 23, and 15 meV). Inset represents the conductance curve with pronounced shoulder-like feature, calculated at 30 K using the multi-gap model ($\Delta$=59, 43, 34, 25, and 16 meV; $\Delta_p$= 64, 52, 44, 28, and 18 meV).

ing spectra of Bi-2212 at different doping levels and temperatures. Further, the specific polaronic gap values are chosen taking into account their possible link to the electronic phase diagram of high-$T_c$ cuprates as a function of temperature $T$ and doping $x$ (Fig.7.5). Thus, the values of the BCS-like gaps $\Delta(i)$ and polaronic PGs $\Delta_p(i)$ are chosen taking into account the situations in underdoped, optimally doped, and overdoped Bi-2212; and, the temperature dependences of $\Delta(i)$ according to the BCS-like gap equation. (We first put the value of the temperature and the approximate value of $\Delta$ taken from one of the experimental tunneling spectra into the equation (7.13). Then, find the value of the BCS-like coupling constant $\lambda_1^*$ and determine the value of $\Delta$ in other tunneling spectra measured at the given temperature).

We now discuss the relation between the BCS-like tunneling gap and the SC order parameter. This issue is still controversial and many different ideas have been proposed (see, e.g., Refs. [1, 2, 4]). One idea is that the PG results from SC fluctuations above $T_c$ and is related to the SC order parameter [105]. The other idea is that the Cooper-like pairing of carriers in high-$T_c$ cuprates is necessary but not a sufficient condition for the occurrence of superconductivity and the BCS-like gap might be different from the SC order parameter appearing below $T_c$ [29, 31] (cf. Refs. [97, 102]). In this view, the precursor (non-SC) Cooper pairing of carriers in the normal state of high-$T_c$ cuprates might be caused by the polaronic effects and the PG region ($T_c < T < T^*$) behaves as an unusual metal. The unusually large reduced-gap values $2\Delta/k_B T_c \simeq 7 - 22$ observed in Bi-2212 [81] compared to the BCS value 3.52 give evidence that the BCS gap determined by tunneling and ARPES measurements does not close at $T_c$. While the peak suppression on the negative bias side near $T_c$ observed in Bi-2212 is due to a spectral superposition of the tunneling conductances associated with the BCS DOS and quasi-free state DOS (originating from the polaron dissociation (or transition from polaronic metal state to ordinary metal one)). The persistence of the conductance peak on the positive bias side well above $T_c$ is evidence for the opening of a non-SC BCS gap at $T^*$ (for which the ratio $2\Delta/k_B T^*$ remains constant and close to the value 3.52 [8, 29, 31]). The pre-formed Cooper pairs condense into a coherent or superfluid (SF) Bose-liquid state at $T_c$ below which the SC order parameter appears [29, 31] (cf. Ref. [105]) and the BCS pairing gap persists as the non-SC gap both below $T_c$ and above $T_c$. According to Landau criterion for superfluidity, the Bose-Einstein condensation of an ideal Bose gas of such Cooper pairs in cuprates exists without coherence (i.e., without superconductivity). Actually, measurements of the specific heat in high-$T_c$ cuprates have indicated [6, 106] that the SC transition at $T_c$ in these materials is very similar to the $\lambda$-transition of $^4He$ since the specific heat jump at $T_c$ in the cuprates is clearly different from the step-like BCS anomaly usually seen in conventional superconductors. Hence, if the appearance of SC order parameter at $T_c$ in high-$T_c$ cuprates is associated with the condensation of preformed Cooper pairs into a SF Bose-liquid state (that is like the SF state of $^4$He) described by the boson mean-field theory [29, 31], the tunneling spectroscopy and ARPES techniques, which are sensitive to the excitation gaps at $\varepsilon_F$, meet with difficulties in providing direct information about such a novel SC order parameter (cf. Ref. [5]). Since a SF Bose-liquid's condensate and excitations are unlike those of a BCS-type Fermi-liquid described by the fermion (or BCS) mean-field theory. It seems that the non-BCS (or $\lambda$-like) SC transition and non-SC (precursor) BCS-like phase transition and the SC order parameter in high-$T_c$ cuprates are distinguishable by the thermodynamic methods (see, e.g., Refs. [6, 107]), whereas the methods of critical magnetic field [108] and current [109] measurements are better suited for the identification of the SC order parameter as the energy needed for destruction of a SF Bose-condensate.

### 7.7.2.  Thermal Properties

The most important normal state properties of high-$T_c$ cuprates superconductors closely related to the mechanism of superconductivity are their thermal properties, which are substantially different from those of conventional superconductors (see, e.g., Refs. [2, 6, 23, 100, 107, 110]). The existing experimental data give evidence that the thermal properties, especially specific heat properties of these high-$T_c$ materials are unusual in many respects, both in the SC state and in the normal state. One of the earliest experimental indications of normal state anomalies in the high-$T_c$ cuprates came from the specific heat measurements [106, 111, 112]. In particular, measurements of the specific heat in LSCO and YBCO showed a clear $\lambda$-like anomaly at $T_c$ [6, 106], a BCS-type step anomaly somewhat above $T_c$ or even well above $T_c$ [6, 106] and a linear term at low temperatures [23, 111]. The linear term appears in the low-temperature specific heat of the cuprate superconductors in contrast to the exponentially vanishing specific heat value expected for conventional superconductors. It seems more likely that this specific heat anomaly is not intrinsic property of the SC state in the cuprates, but due to the presence of some impurity phases [113]. In addition to a clear $\lambda$-like anomaly at $T_c$, the other unexpected feature is the presence of jump-like anomalies above $T_c$ in the specific heat spectrum of high-$T_c$ cuprates. The existence of the specific heat anomaly in high-$T_c$ cuprates above $T_c$ is believed to be a key to understanding their unconventional superconductivity. Although the existence of the BCS-like (i.e., step-like) jump in the electronic specific heat $C_e(T)$ and incoherent Cooper pairs above $T_c$ in unconventional cuprate superconductors was predicted long ago [29, 31], many researchers still thought that the BCS-type jump in $C_e(T)$ takes place just at $T_c$ without such a specific heat jump related to the precursor Cooper pairing at $T = T^* > T_c$. Therefore, understanding a new $\lambda$-like SC transition in the cuprate superconductors at $T_c$ is one thing, and determining whether there is a BCS-like transition above $T_c$ is quite another. So far, the question of whether the electronic specific heat anomaly at $T > T_c$ is related to the BCS-like transition or not is unresolved and there is no quantitative analysis of such specific heat anomalies in the PG state of high-$T_c$ cuprates. Also, the contributions of incoherent Cooper pairs and un-paired polaronic carriers to $C_e(T)$ and their effects on the electronic specific heat anomalies above $T_c$ in the cuprates have not been studied. Some theoretical analysis of $C_e(T)$ in the PG state of the underdoped cuprates was performed within a SC (or pair) fluctuation model [114], but this model is justified only in a narrow region near $T_c$. In this section, we discuss the BCS-like phase transition at a characteristic temperature $T^*(> T_c)$ and the electronic specific heat anomalies in the PG normal state of underdoped and optimally doped high-$T_c$ cuprates by considering the inhomogeneous spatial distribution of charge carriers and a multi-component carrier picture. Here the theoretical results obtained by Dzhumanov, Karimboev et al. and reported in Int. conf. of young scientists and specialists "Current issues on the peaceful use of atomic energy" (June 6-8, 2012, Almaty, Kazakhstan) will be presented.

### 7.7.3.   Electronic Specific Heat above $T^*$

As discussed in Section 6.8, charge carriers are spatially inhomogeneous in underdoped and optimally doped cuprates and such inhomogeneities in the charge carrier distribution might be responsible for the formation of the intrinsic and extrinsic large polarons in the defect-free regions and near the defects (impurities). Now, let us assume that in the metallic state of high-$T_c$ cuprates the precursor BCS-like pairing of large polarons would occur in the defect-free regions below $T^*$, whereas the large polarons localized near the impurities may remain unpaired. Above $T^*$, the contributions to $C_e(T)$ come from these two types of large polarons and the normal-state electronic specific heat is given by

$$C_e(T) = (\gamma_{en} + \gamma_{e2})T, \qquad (7.33)$$

where $\gamma_{ei} = (\pi^2/3)k_B^2 g(\varepsilon_{Fi})$, $g(\varepsilon_{Fi}) = 3N_i/2\varepsilon_{Fi} = 3Nf_i/2\varepsilon_{Fi}$ is the density of states at the polaronic Fermi level $\varepsilon_{Fi}$ (i=1,2), $N_i$ is the number of the $i$-th type of large polarons, $N = N_1 + N_2$ is the total number of polaronic carriers in the system, $f_i = N_i/N$ is the fraction of the $i$-th type of large polaronic carriers. For doped cuprates, the coefficient of the linear term in $C_e(T)$ is defined as

$$\gamma_e = \gamma_{e1} + \gamma_{e2} = (\pi^2/2)k_B^2 x N_A(f_1/\varepsilon_{F1} + f_2/\varepsilon_{F2}), \qquad (7.34)$$

where the number of the $CuO_2$ formula unit (or the host lattice atoms) per unit molar volume is equal to the Avogadro number $N_A = 6.02 \times 10^{23} mole^{-1}$, $x = N/N_A$ is the dimensionless carrier concentration or doping level, $k_B N_A = 8.314 J/moleK$. Let us estimate the values of $\gamma_e$ for LSCO and YBCO. Using the values of the Fermi energy and fraction of carriers in the polaronic band ($\varepsilon_{F1} \simeq 0.15$ eV, $f_1 = 0.6$) and impurity band ($\varepsilon_{F2} = 0.06$ eV, $f_2 = 0.4$), we obtain $\gamma_e \simeq 5.67 mJ/moleK^2$ at $x = 0.1$ for LSCO. The experimental value of $\gamma_e$ lies in the range $(4.9 - 7.3) mJ/moleK^2$ [100]. For $YBa_2Cu_3O_{7-\delta}$, the doping level can be determined from the relation [115]

$$x(\delta) = \begin{cases} (1-\delta)^3 & \text{for } 0 \leq 1-\delta \leq 0.5, \\ (0.5-\delta)^3 + 0.125 & \text{for } 0.5 < 1-\delta \leq 1 \end{cases} \tag{7.35}$$

from which if follows that $x(\delta = 0.115) \simeq 0.182$. By taking $\varepsilon_{F1} = 0.20 eV$, $\varepsilon_{F2} = 0.1 eV$, $f_1 = 0.6$, and $f_2 = 0.4$ for YBCO, we find $\gamma_e \simeq 4.65 mJ/moleK^2$. This value of $\gamma_e$ is well consistent with the experimental data $\gamma_e \simeq 4.3 - 4.9 mJ/moleK^2$ [116]

### 7.7.4. Electronic Specific Heat below $T^*$

Below $T^*$, three contributions to $C_e(T)$ come from: (i) the Bogoliubov-like quasiparticles appearing at the dissociation (excitation) of Cooper pairs in the polaronic band; (ii) the unpaired polarons in the impurity band; and (iii) the ideal Bose-gas of incoherent Cooper pairs. The contribution to $C_e(T)$ coming from the Bogoliubov-like quasiparticles is determined from the relation.

$$C_{e1}(T) = \frac{g(\varepsilon_{F1})}{k_B T^2} \int\limits_0^{E_p + \hbar\omega_{LO}} f(E)(1-f(E)) \left[ E^2(\xi) - \frac{T}{2}\frac{d\Delta^2(T)}{dT} \right] d\xi,$$

where $g(\varepsilon_{F1}) = 3N_A x f_1/2\varepsilon_{F1}$, $f(E) = \left[e^{E/k_B T} + 1\right]^{-1}$, $E(\xi) = \sqrt{\xi^2 + \Delta^2(T)}$, $\Delta(T)$ is the BCS-like normal-state energy gap (or PG).

The energy of an ideal Bose-gas below the Bose-Einstein condensation (BEC) temperature $T_{BEC}$ is given by [117]

$$U = 0.77 N_c k_B T (T/T_{BEC})^{3/2}, \tag{7.36}$$

where $N_c$ is the number of Bose particles. The specific heat of such a Bose-gas of incoherent Cooper pairs is determined from the relation

$$C_{e3}(T) = \frac{dU}{dT} = 1.925 k_B N_c (T/T_{BEC})^{3/2}. \tag{7.37}$$

Then the total electronic specific heat below $T^*$ is given by

$$C_e(T) = C_{e1}(T) + C_{e2}(T) + C_{e3}(T), \tag{7.38}$$

where $C_{e2}(T) = (\pi^2/3)k_B^2 g(\varepsilon_{F2})T$, $g(\varepsilon_{F2}) = 3N_A x f_2/2\varepsilon_{F2}$.

The BCS-like pairing PG, $\Delta(T)$ and PG temperature, $T^*$ are determined from the equation (7.13). Such a normal-state PG somewhat below $T^*$ is determined by the formula

$$\Delta(T) \simeq 3.06 k_B T^* \sqrt{1 - T/T^*} \tag{7.39}$$

which is better approximation in the temperature range $0.7 < T^* \leq T^*$. The number of incoherent Cooper pairs $N_c$ and their BEC temperature are determined from the relations

$$N_c = \frac{1}{4} g(\varepsilon_{F1}) \int\limits_{-(E_p + \hbar\omega_{LO})}^{E_p + \hbar\omega_{LO}} \left[1 - \frac{\xi}{E}\right] \frac{e^{E/k_B T}}{e^{E/k_B T} + 1} d\xi, \tag{7.40}$$

and

$$T_{BEC} = \frac{3.31 \hbar^2 N_c^{2/3}}{k_B m_c}, \tag{7.41}$$

where $m_c = 2m_p$ is the mass of Cooper-like polaron pairs, $\varepsilon_{F1} > E_p + \hbar\omega_{LO} \gtrsim 0.1 eV$, $m_p \simeq 2m_e$.

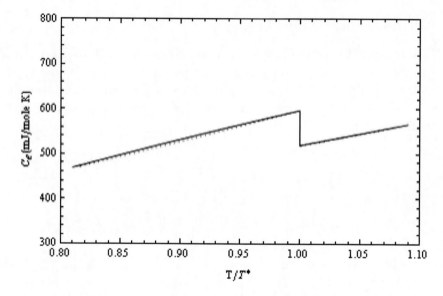

Figure 7.10. Electronic specific heat of LSCO with doping level $x = 0.104$ (solid line) calculated as a function of the reduced temperature $T/T^*$ near $T^* = 98K$ using the fitting parameters $\varepsilon_{F1} \simeq 0.1607$ eV, $\varepsilon_{F2} \simeq 0.0424$ eV, $f_1 = 0.53$, $f_2 = 0.47$ and the corresponding experimental data for LSCO with doping level $x = 0.10$ (dotted line) [6].

Numerical calculations of $N_c$ and $T_{BEC}$ show that just below $T^*$ the value of $T_{BEC}$ is very close to $T^*$ (i.e., $T_{BEC} \geq T^*$), but somewhat below $T^*$, $T_{BEC} >> T^*$. Theoretical results obtained for $C_e(T \leq T^*)$ and $C_e(T \leq T^*)/T$, which are compared with the experimental data of the electronic specific heat reported by Oda's group for LSCO, are presented in Figs. 7.10 and 7.11 for the temperature range $0.8T^* < T \leq T^*$. As seen in Fig.7.10, the jump in $C_e(T)$ near $T^*$ is similar, in shape, to the step-like BCS anomaly of $C_e(T)$, which is observed in high-$T_c$ cuprates above $T_c$ [6, 106]. The specific heat jump at $T > T_c$ discovered in [106] was attributed to some cause other than the BCS-like transition. However, we argue that Inderhees et al. [106] found a BCS-type specific heat jump at $T^*(= 93K) > T_c(= 89K)$ for the overdoped YBCO. Dunlap et al. also reported the existence of a phase transition in

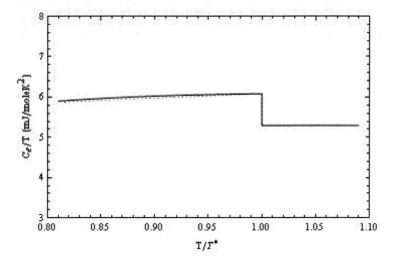

Figure 7.11. Temperature dependence of $C_e/T$ for LSCO with doping level $x = 0.104$ (solid line) calculated using the same fitting parameters as in Fig. 7.10 and compared with experimental data for LSCO with doping level $x = 0.10$ (dotted line) [6].

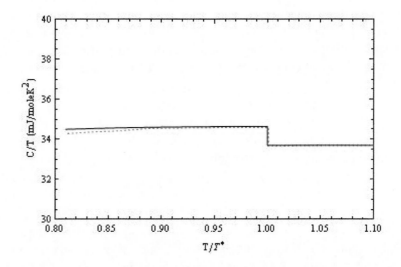

Figure 7.12. The electronic specific heat coefficient $(C_e/T)$ of $YBa_2Cu_3O_{7-\delta}$ with doping level $x = 0.14$ calculated as a function of the reduced temperature $T/T^*$ near $T^* = 145K$ using the fitting parameters, $\varepsilon_{F1} = 0.116eV$, $\varepsilon_{F2} = 0.0107eV$, $f_1 = 0.3$ and $f_2 = 0.7$ and compared with experimental data for $YBa_2Cu_3O_{6.73}$ (dotted line) [112].

LSCO at $T^* \approx 80K$, which is probably associated with a BCS-transition at the PG formation temperature. While Loram's group argued [112] that there is no such phase transition at the PG temperature in high-$T_c$ cuprates. But, they have found that $\gamma_e$ is insensitive to $T$ above $T^*$ and decreases rapidly below $T_c$ just like in BCS theory. In reality, the step-like BCS jump in $C_e(T)$ becomes practically unobservable with increasing $f_2$ and decreasing $\varepsilon_{F2}$

(Fig.7.12). Also, it is well known that the specific heat of the system at high temperature $(T = T^*)$ is dominated by the phonon contribution and one cannot accurately isolate the electronic part from the total specific heat. Therefore, it is difficult to observe this predicted BCS-like jump at $T^*$ in the electronic specific spectrum of high-$T_c$ cuprates due to sample inhomogeneity and the presence of impurities (cf. Ref. [110]).

### 7.7.5.    Unconventional Isotope Effects on the Pseudogap Formation Temperature

It is well known that charge carriers (electrons or holes) can change their mass in solids due to the interactions with lattice vibrations and themselves. Under certain conditions, the multi-carrier system might be metallic with dressed charge carriers rather than free electrons or holes. However, there is an important difference between the dressed carriers in ordinary metals and ionic solids. In ordinary metals the effective mass of electrons is independent of the ionic mass $M$. In contrast, the charge carriers in polar high-$T_c$ materials are self-trapped and form large polarons (as argued by Emin and Hillery [64] and in Refs. [31, 53]), so their effective mass will depend on $M$. Therefore, it is necessary for any theory to explain not only the formation of the PG, but also other anomalies, such as the various unexpected isotope effects observed in high-$T_c$ cuprates [118, 119]. Various experiments [118, 119, 120, 121, 122, 123, 124, 125, 126] revealing peculiar isotope effects on $T_c$, $T^*$ and other physical quantities in cuprates have shown that the electron-phonon interactions play a major role in these materials. In particular, some experiments showed that the oxygen and copper isotope effects on $T^*$ in Y- and La- based cuprates are absent or very small [120, 124, 126] and sizable [121, 124]. While other experiments revealed the presence of large negative oxygen and copper isotope effects on $T^*$ in Ho-based cuprates [122, 123]. The origin of the anomalous oxygen isotope effect on $T^*$ in cuprates has especially been the subject of controversy [120, 121, 122, 123, 126]. Although several theoretical attempts have been made to explain the oxygen isotope effect on $T^*$ in high-$T_c$ cuprates [127, 128, 129, 130], there is no correct quantitative theory, which could explain all the observed experimental data and give an answer to the puzzling question why such an isotope effect is sizable or very large negative in some cuprates and absent or vanishingly small in others. Also, there is no explanation for the observed copper isotope effect on $T^*$ in cuprate superconductors. In the doped cuprates, many factors can effect the value of the isotope-effect exponent $\alpha$. An important factor is the unconventional electron-phonon interaction that causes the polaronic effect which manifest itself in an isotope dependence of various quantities in cuprates [80, 131]. Further, the different doping levels (or Fermi surfaces) and effective dielectric constants are the other factors which characterize the different samples of high-$T_c$ cuprates and effect the isotope dependence of the PG temperature $T^*$ above $T_c$. For better understanding of the PG phenomena and high-$T_c$ superconductivity, the precursor Cooper pairing of polarons and the oxygen-and-cooper-isotope effects on the PG in cuprates need to be thoroughly examined and compared with the existing experimental data [118, 119, 120, 121, 122, 123, 124, 126] confirming the presence of polaronic effects and incoherent Cooper-like polaron pairs above $T_c$. In this section, we discuss the isotope effects on the PG in cuprates within the two new BCS-based approaches extended to the intermediate BCS-like coupling regime [43], which allow to describe the precursor

Cooper pairing of large polarons and formation of a new PG state above $T_c$ in the cuprates with small and large Fermi surfaces (see section 7.4). We show that the new BCS-like approaches describe the unconventional electron-phonon interactions (i.e., the combined and more effective BCS- and Fröhlich-type interactions), the pairing correlations in the metallic state of high-$T_c$ cuprate superconductors and the novel isotope effects on $T^*$ in these materials. In so doing, we demonstrate that the polaronic effects may change significantly the simple BCS picture and are responsible for various unexpected isotope effects on $T^*$ in high-$T_c$ cuprates with small and large Fermi surfaces. The optical vibrations of the lattice with two atoms in the primitive cell are associated with the vibrations of the sublattices of these atoms (e.g., oxygen and copper atoms in the cuprates) and the frequency of the optical vibrations $\omega_{LO}$ depends on the masses $M$ and $M'$ of two different atoms. In the large polaron theory, $m_p$, $E_p$ and $\varepsilon_F = \hbar^2(3\pi^2 n)^{2/3}/2m_p$ (where $n$ is the concentration of large polarons) depend on the Fröhlich-type electron-phonon coupling constant $\alpha_F$ which in turn depends on the masses $M(= M_O$ or $M_{Cu})$ and $M'(= M_{Cu}$ or $M_O)$ of the oxygen O and copper Cu atoms in cuprates:

$$\alpha_F = \frac{e^2}{2\hbar\omega_{LO}} \left[ \frac{1}{\varepsilon_\infty} - \frac{1}{\varepsilon_0} \right] \left( \frac{2m\omega_{LO}}{\hbar} \right)^{1/2} \tag{7.42}$$

where $\omega_{LO} \simeq \left( 2\beta \left( \frac{1}{M} + \frac{1}{M'} \right) \right)^{1/2}$, $\beta$ is a force constant of the lattice, $m$ is the effective mass of a carrier in a rigid lattice (i.e., in the absence of the electron-phonon interaction).

In the intermediate Fröhlich-type electron-phonon coupling regime the mass and binding energy of a large polaron are given by [132]

$$m_p = m(1 + \alpha_F/6) \tag{7.43}$$

and

$$E_p = \alpha_F \hbar\omega_{LO}. \tag{7.44}$$

First, we calculate the PG formation temperature $T^*$ and its isotope shift in high-$T_c$ cuprates with large Fermi surfaces. From Eq.(7.16), the exponent of the isotope effect on $T^*$ is defined as

$$\alpha_{T^*} = -\frac{d\ln T^*}{d\ln M}. \tag{7.45}$$

Using Eqs.(7.18), (7.43), and (7.44), we find that Eqs.(7.16) and (7.45), become

$$k_B T^* = 1.134A\mu^{-1/4} \left( 1 + a\mu^{-1/4} \right) \exp\left[ -1/\lambda^*(\mu) \right] \tag{7.46}$$

and

$$\alpha_{T^*} = \frac{1}{4(1 + M/M')} \left\{ 1 + \frac{a\mu^{-1/4}}{1 + a\mu^{-1/4}} - \frac{1}{(\lambda^*(\mu))^2} \left( \lambda_{ph} b\mu^{1/4} \right. \right.$$
$$- \frac{\lambda_c b\mu^{1/4}}{U_c(\mu)} + \frac{\lambda_c^2(1 + b\mu^{1/4})}{U_c^2(\mu)} \left[ b\mu^{1/4}\ln B_c(\mu) + (1 + b\mu^{1/4}) \right.$$
$$\left. \left. \left. \times \left( 1 + \frac{a\mu^{-1/4}}{1 + a\mu^{-1/4}} \right) \right] \right) \right\} \tag{7.47}$$

where $\lambda_1^*(\mu) = \lambda_{ph}(1 + b\mu^{1/4}) - \lambda_c(1 + b\mu^{1/4})/U_c(\mu)$, $U_c(\mu) = 1 + \lambda_c(1 + b\mu^{1/4})\ln B_c(\mu)$, $\lambda_{ph} = [2m/\hbar^2(3\pi^2 n)^{2/3}]V_{ph}$, $\lambda_c = [2m/\hbar^2(3\pi^2 n)^{2/3}]V_c$, $B_c(\mu) = \varepsilon_F/A\mu^{-1/4}(1 + a\mu^{-1/4})$, $A = \frac{e^2}{\tilde{\varepsilon}}\sqrt{\frac{m}{2\hbar}}(2\beta)^{1/4}$, $a = \hbar\tilde{\varepsilon}\sqrt{\frac{2\hbar}{m}}(2\beta)^{1/4}/e^2$, $b = 1/6a$, $\tilde{\varepsilon} = \varepsilon_\infty/(1 - \varepsilon_\infty/\varepsilon_0)$ is the effective dielectric constant, $\mu = MM'/(M + M')$ is the reduced mass of ions.

Note that the expression for $\alpha_{T^*}$, Eq.(7.47) contains not only the electron-phonon coupling constant $\lambda_{ph}$ and Coulomb parameter $\lambda_c$, but also the effective BCS-like coupling constant $\lambda_1^*(\mu)$, carrier concentration $n$ and parameters ($\tilde{\varepsilon}$, $\beta$, $M$, $M'$ and $\mu$) of the cuprates. By Eqs.(7.46) and (7.47), one can explain the anomalous features of both the oxygen isotope effect (evaluating Eq.(7.47) at $M = M_O$ and $M' = M_{Cu}$) and the copper isotope effect (evaluating Eq.(7.47) at $M = M_{Cu}$ and $M' = M_O$) in cuprates discussed later. These equations allow us to calculate the PG formation temperatures $T^*$ and the exponents $\alpha_{T^*}^O$ and $\alpha_{T^*}^{Cu}$ of the oxygen and copper isotope effects on $T^*$. In our numerical calculations, we take $m \simeq m_e$ [11], $\varepsilon_\infty = 3 - 5$ [11, 64, 133], $\varepsilon_0 = 22 - 30$ [11, 64, 133] and $\hbar\omega_{LO} = 0.043 - 0.08 eV$ [3, 11, 26], typical values for the cuprates. Then the values of $\tilde{\varepsilon}$ and $\alpha_F$ are $\tilde{\varepsilon} \simeq 3.33 - 6.47$ and $\alpha_F = 2.02 - 5.33$ (which correspond to the intermediate electron-phonon coupling regime). Notice that when discussing the experimental data for isotope effects on $T^*$ in cuprates we have taken the fact that the physical situations (doping levels $n$, dielectric constants $\varepsilon_\infty$ and $\varepsilon_0$, $\lambda_{ph}$, $\lambda_c$ and $T^*$) in various experiments are rather different. Since the phonon energy (or frequency $\omega_{LO}$) fixes $\beta$, the free parameters $\tilde{\varepsilon}$, $n$, $\lambda_{ph}$, and $\lambda_c$ can be examined for specific input parameters $T^*$ and $\alpha_{T^*}$. In our theory, the parameter $n$ enters into the expressions for $\lambda_{ph}$ and $\lambda_c$, so that we have really three adjustable parameters. The magnitude of $\beta$ is kept at the value estimated for the oxygen and copper unsubstituted compound using the value of $\hbar\omega_{LO} = 0.05 eV$. The $\ln B_c(\mu)$ entering into the expressions for $T^*$ and $\alpha_{T^*}$ will be small, so that the Coulomb pseudopotential $\tilde{V}_c$ is of the order of bare Coulomb potential $V_c$. The results of numerical calculations of $T^*$ and $\alpha_{T^*}$ according to Eqs. (7.46) and (7.47) at different values of $\tilde{\varepsilon}$, $n$, $\lambda_{ph}$ and $\lambda_c$ are shown in Figs. 7.13-7.15.

These obtained results provide a consistent picture of the existence of crossover temperature $T^*$ above $T_c$ and various isotope effects on $T^*$ in cuprates. They explain why the small positive (see Fig. 7.13) and very large negative (see Figs. 7.14 and 7.15) oxygen isotope effects and the large negative and near-absent copper isotope effects on $T^*$ are observed in various experiments. The obtained $T^*$ is plotted in the insets of Figs. 13 - 15 as a function of $\tilde{\varepsilon}$ and $n$ for different values of $\lambda_{ph}$ and $\lambda_c$. The value of $\lambda_1^*(\mu)$ varies from 0.3 to 0.5 and $T^*$ increases with decreasing $n$ (see inset of Fig. 7.14). We have verified that $T^*$ decreases with increasing $\tilde{\varepsilon}$ for $\lambda_{ph} < 0.35$ and $\lambda_c < 0.1$ (Fig. 7.13).

In contrast, $T^*$ increase with increasing $\tilde{\varepsilon}$ for $\lambda_{ph} > 0.4$ and $\lambda_c > 0.25$ (Fig. 7.14). The existing experimental data on $T^*$ and $\alpha_{T^*}$ for $YBa_2Cu_4O_8$, $HoBa_2Cu_4O_8$ and $La_{1.96-x}Sr_xHo_{0.04}CuO_4$ could be fitted with an excellent agreement using Eqs. (7.46) and (7.47), and adjusting the parameters $\tilde{\varepsilon}$, $n$, $\lambda_{ph}$ and $\lambda_c$ for each cuprate superconductor. One can assume that in $YBa_2Cu_4O_8$ and $HoBa_2Cu_4O_8$ the optimally doped level corresponds to the value $n \gtrsim 0.9 \times 10^{21} cm^{-3}$. Provided $n = 0.92 \times 10^{21} cm^{-3}$, $\tilde{\varepsilon} = 4.827 - 5.030$, $\lambda_{ph} \simeq 0.297$ and $\lambda_c \simeq 0.077$, one can see that $T^* = 150 - 161 K$ and $\alpha_{T^*}^O$ is very small (i.e., $\alpha_{T^*}^O = (0.0055 - 0.0096) < 0.01$) (cf. [134]), which are consistent with the experimental data of Refs. [120, 126] for $YBa_2Cu_4O_8$. Further, using other sets of parameters $n = 0.94 \times 10^{21} cm^{-3}$, $\tilde{\varepsilon} = 5.904 - 6.119$, $\lambda_{ph} = 0.311 - 0.313$ and $\lambda_c = 0.067 - 0.070$, we

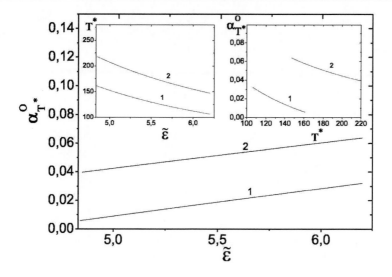

Figure 7.13. Variation of $\alpha^O_{T*}$ as a function of $\tilde{\varepsilon}$ for two sets of parameters:(1) $\lambda_{ph} = 0.297$, $\lambda_c = 0.077$, $n = 0.92 \times 10^{21} cm^{-3}$ and (2) $\lambda_{ph} = 0.313$, $\lambda_c = 0.067$, $n = 0.94 \times 10^{21} cm^{-3}$. The insets show the dependences $T^*(\tilde{\varepsilon})$ and $\alpha^O_{T*}(T^*)$ for the same values of $\lambda_{ph}$, $\lambda_c$, $n$.

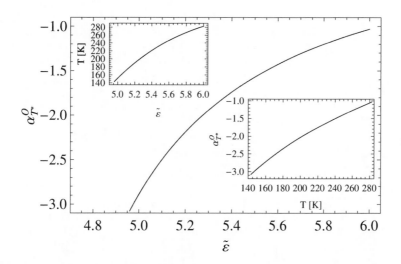

Figure 7.14. The dependence of $\alpha^O_{T*}$ on $\tilde{\varepsilon}$ for $\lambda_{ph} = 0.975$, $\lambda_c = 0.820$ and $n = 0.88 \times 10^{21} cm^{-3}$. The insets show the dependences $T^*(\tilde{\varepsilon})$ and $\alpha^O_{T*}(T^*)$ for the same values of $\lambda_{ph}$, $\lambda_c$, $n$.

obtain $T^* \approx 150K$ and $\alpha^O_{T*} \simeq 0.052 - 0.062$, which are in good agreement with the measured values: $T^* = 150K$ and $\alpha^O_{T*} = 0.052 - 0.061$ for $YBa_2Cu_4O_8$ (with $T_c = 81K$) [121]. Figure 7.13 illustrates the predicted behaviors of $\alpha^O_{T*}$ and $T^*$ as a function of $\tilde{\varepsilon}$ for $\lambda_{ph} < 0.4$ and $\lambda_c < 0.1$. We see that $\alpha^O_{T*}$ decreases slowly with decreasing $\tilde{\varepsilon}$. Relatively strong electron-phonon and Coulomb interactions (i.e., $\lambda_{ph} > 0.5$ and $\lambda_c > 0.5$) change the picture signif-

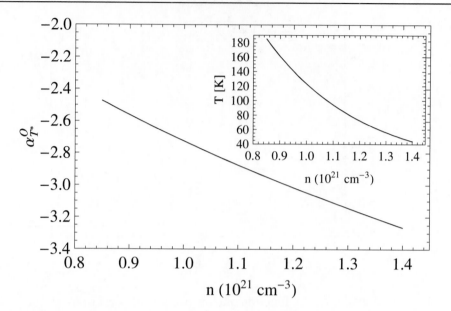

Figure 7.15. The doping dependence of $\alpha_{T^*}^O$ (main panel) and $T^*$ (inset) for $\lambda_{ph} = 0.975$, $\lambda_c = 0.820$ and $\tilde{\varepsilon} = 5.092$.

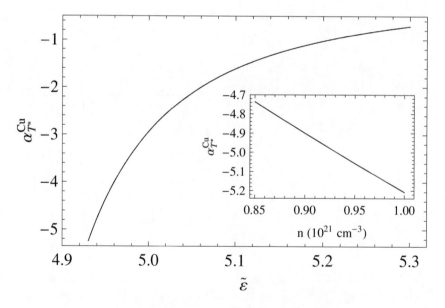

Figure 7.16. The dependence of $\alpha_{T^*}^{Cu}$ on $\tilde{\varepsilon}$ for $\hbar\omega_{LO} = 0.05eV$, $n = 0.9 \times 10^{21}cm^{-3}$, $\lambda_{ph} = 2.196$ and $\lambda_c = 2.064$. The inset shows the dependence of $\alpha_{T^*}^{Cu}$ on $n$ for $\tilde{\varepsilon} = 4.9371$, $\lambda_{ph} = 2.196$ and $\lambda_c = 2.064$.

icantly and cause $\alpha_{T^*}^O$ to decrease rapidly with decreasing $\tilde{\varepsilon}$. In this case, the value of $\alpha_{T^*}^O$ is negative and becomes very large negative with decreasing $\tilde{\varepsilon}$ or $T^*$. The pictures shown in Figs. 14 and 15 are likely realized in some cuprates (which exhibit a large negative isotope exponent $\alpha_{T^*}^O$) and explain another important puzzle of the cuprates [122]: the huge oxygen-isotope effect on $T^*$ observed in HoBa$_2$Cu$_4$O$_8$, whose characteristic PG temperature $T^*$ increases significantly upon replacing $^{16}$O by $^{18}$O. Indeed, with fitting parameters, $n = 0.88 \times 10^{21} cm^{-3}$, $\tilde{\varepsilon} = 5.092$, $\lambda_{ph} = 0.975$ and $\lambda_c = 0.82$, one can explain the observed experimental data of Ref. [122]. In this case, we obtain $T^*(^{16}O) \simeq 170K$, $T^*(^{18}O) \simeq 220K$, $\Delta T_O^* = T^*(^{18}O) - T^*(^{16}O) \simeq 50K$, and $\alpha_{T^*}^O \simeq -2.53$, which are in remarkably good agreement with the experimental data $T^*(^{16}O) \simeq 170K$, $T^*(^{18}O) \simeq 220K$, $\Delta T_O^* \simeq 50K$, and $\alpha_{T^*}^O \simeq -2.2 \pm 0.6$ [122]. These, predicted behaviors of $T^*$ and $\alpha_{T^*}^O$ could be checked experimentally in other slightly underdoped and optimally doped cuprates. We have also performed similar calculations for the copper isotope effect on $T^*$ in slightly underdoped HoBa$_2$Cu$_4$O$_8$ (where the electron-phonon and Coulomb interactions seem to be much stronger than in YBa$_2$Cu$_4$O$_8$), and for the oxygen and copper isotope effects on $T^*$ in optimally doped La$_{1.81}$Ho$_{0.04}$Sr$_{0.15}$CuO$_4$. Figure 16 shows the predicted behaviors of $\alpha_{T^*}^{Cu}$ as a function of $\tilde{\varepsilon}$ and $n$ for $\lambda_{ph} = 2.196$ and $\lambda_c = 2.064$. In order to obtain the values of $T^* \simeq 160$ and $\simeq 185K$ observed accordingly in copper unsubstituted and substituted HoBa$_2$Cu$_4$O$_8$, we took $n = 0.9 \times 10^{21} cm^{-3}$, $\tilde{\varepsilon} = 4.9342$, $\lambda_{ph} = 2.199$, $\lambda_c = 2.064$. Then we found $T^*(^{63}Cu) \simeq 160K$, $T^*(^{65}Cu) \simeq 184.8K$, $\Delta T_{Cu}^* = T^*(^{65}Cu) - T^*(^{63}Cu) \approx 25K$ and $\alpha_{T^*}^{Cu} \simeq -4.9$ in accordance with experimental findings $T^*(^{63}Cu) \approx 160K$, $T^*(^{65}Cu) \approx 185K$ and $\alpha_{T^*}^{Cu} \simeq -4.9$ [123]. In the orthorhombic La$_{2-x}$Sr$_x$CuO$_4$ the optimally doped level ($x \simeq 0.15$) corresponds to the value $n = 0.8 \times 10^{21} cm^{-3}$. By taking $\tilde{\varepsilon} = 5.274$, $\lambda_{ph} = 0.645$ and $\lambda_c = 0.474$ for La$_{1.81}$Ho$_{0.04}$Sr$_{0.15}$CuO$_4$, we obtained $T^*(^{16}O) = T^*(^{63}Cu) \simeq 60K$, $T^*(^{18}O) \simeq 69.7K$, $\Delta T_O^* \simeq 9.7K$, $T^*(^{65}Cu) \simeq 60.6K$; $\Delta T_{Cu}^* \simeq 0.6K$, which agree well with the experimental data of Ref. [124]. Further, using other fitting parameters $n = 0.62 \times 10^{21} cm^{-3}$, $\tilde{\varepsilon} = 6.188$, $\lambda_{ph} = 0.883$, $\lambda_c = 0.683$ and $n = 1 \times 10^{21} cm^{-3}$, $\tilde{\varepsilon} = 4.637$, $\lambda_{ph} = 0.484$, $\lambda_c = 0.332$ for moderately underdoped and overdoped systems La$_{1.96-x}$Sr$_x$Ho$_{0.04}$CuO$_4$ (with $x = 0.11$ and $x = 0.20$), we found $T^*(^{16}O) \simeq 80K$, $T^*(^{18}O) \simeq 100K$, $\Delta T_O^* \simeq 20K$ and $T^*(^{16}O) \simeq 50K$, $T^*(^{18}O) \simeq 55K$, $\Delta T_O^* \simeq 5K$ for these La-based compounds with $x = 0.11$ and $x = 0.20$, respectively. These results are in quantitative agreement with the experimental results reported in Ref. [135] for La$_{1.96-x}$Sr$_x$Ho$_{0.04}$CuO$_4$, in which upon oxygen substitution ($^{18}O$ vs. $^{16}O$), $T^*$ is shifted upwards by 20 and 5 K for $x = 0.11$ and $x = 0.20$, respectively.

We now calculate the PG formation temperature $T^*$ and its isotope shift in high-$T_c$ cuprates with small Fermi surfaces (i.e., in the deeply underdoped cuprates). We assume that these systems have a small Fermi surface ($\varepsilon_F < 0.1eV$). In this case the condition $\varepsilon_F < E_p + \hbar\omega_{LO}$ is satisfied, and the PG formation temperature is determined from the relation (7.24) (see section 7.4). Using Eqs. (7.24) and (7.45), we obtain

$$\alpha_{T^*} = \frac{b\mu^{\frac{1}{4}}}{4(1 + \frac{M}{M'})(1 + b\mu^{1/4})} \left[1 - \frac{1}{\lambda_2^*(\mu)}\right], \qquad (7.48)$$

where $\lambda_2^*(\mu) = (\lambda_{ph} - \lambda_c)(1 + b\mu^{1/4})$. From Eq.(7.48) we see that $\alpha_{T^*}$ is negative (at $\lambda_2^*(\mu) < 1$) and depends on the ratio $M/M'$ and coupling constant $\lambda_2^*(\mu)$ as well as on other parameters characterizing the cuprates, doping level, electron-phonon and Coulomb interactions. The dependencies $\alpha_{T^*}(\tilde{\varepsilon})$ and $T^*(\tilde{\varepsilon})$ for $n = 0.5 \times 10^{21} cm^{-3}$ and $\lambda_{ph} - \lambda_c = 0.3$ will be as presented in Fig. 7.17: $\alpha_{T^*}^O$ is negative but sizable, and $\alpha_{T^*}^{Cu}$ is also negative but its absolute value nearly four times smaller than that of $\alpha_{T^*}^O$ (see inset of Fig. 7.17).

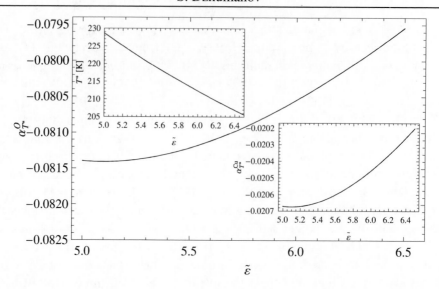

Figure 7.17. Variation of $\alpha_{T^*}^O$ (main panel) and $\alpha_{T^*}^{Cu}$ (lower inset) and $T^*$ (upper inset) as a function of $\tilde{\varepsilon}$ for $\lambda_{ph} - \lambda_c = 0.3$ and $n = 0.5 \times 10^{21} cm^{-3}$.

## 7.8. Pseudogap Phenomena in Other Systems

Depending on the strength of the attractive interaction between two fermions, the physical contents of the SC (or SF) states of superconductors, liquid $^3$He and nuclear matter could be distinguishably altered. When the pairing interaction is weak, the formation of loosely correlated Cooper pairs and their superfluid condensation occur simultaneously at $T_c$. In this case the BCS gap serves as a SC gap and the superconductors are called conventional or BCS superconductors (e.g., ordinary metals and heavily doped cuprates become such superconductors at low temperatures). When the pairing interaction becomes sufficiently strong, the precursor Cooper pairing of carriers would occur at a higher temperature $T^*$ than the $T_c$ not only in high-$T_c$ cuprates but also in other superconductors such as organic and heavy-fermion superconductors. Such preformed Cooper pairs may behave like composite bosons and condense into a SF Bose-liquid state at $T_c$. Actually, as a consequence of precursor Cooper pairing, the organic and heavy-fermion superconductors and the low-density nuclear matter exhibit PG phenomena above the critical temperature $T_c$ of SF transition and have an exotic normal state that is different from the normal state of conventional BCS superconductors [29, 31, 105, 136, 137, 138, 139]. In these systems, the BCS-like energy gap opening above $T_c$ is no longer SC gap and persists below $T_c$.

### 7.8.1. Pseudogap State in Organic Superconductors

The representatives of an important class of unconventional superconductors are organic solids. In comparison to covalently bonded semiconductors, organic compounds are characterized by weak intermolecular van der Waals bonds and, hence, narrower electronic bandwidths, stronger electron-lattice interaction, and more pronounced polaron formation. The ground state of charge carriers in organic solids is self-trapped one (called polaronic state) with appreciable lattice distortion when the carrier-phonon interaction is strong enough [140, 141]. Therefore, the concept of a self-trapped carrier (such a carrier is surrounded by a polaron cloud) in organic superconductors may also play an important role in the theory of PG phenomena in these materials. The self-trapping of carriers leads to a renormalization (narrowing) of the conduction band and the polaron motion is band-like, so that the pairing of self-trapped carriers may be considered in the momentum ($k$) space as in BCS-like theory presented in section 7.4. Note, that a pure BCS pairing is possible only in free states of carriers, whereas in their self-trapped (polaronic) states the combined phonon- and polaron-mediated pairing is always realized as in the case of the combined electron- and phonon-mediated pairing discussed in Ref. [142]. The polaronic effects in organic super-conductors change the attractive interaction mechanism between the carriers into the static- and dynamic-phonon mediated pairing mechanism which is more effective than in the usual BCS picture. In this case, the precursor Cooper pairing of polaronic carriers and opening of a PG, $\Delta_{PG}$, at the Fermi surface occur at a mean-field temperature $T^* > T_c$.

To calculate the mean-field pairing temperature $T^*$, we use the generalized BCS formalism and the BCS-like gap equation (7.13). For the Bogoliubov-like model potential (7.8), the BCS-like gap equation at finite temperature $T$ reduces to

$$\frac{1}{\lambda^*} = \int\limits_{0}^{E_b + \hbar\omega_D} \frac{d\varepsilon}{\sqrt{\varepsilon^2 + \Delta^2(T)}} \tanh\left[\frac{\sqrt{\varepsilon^2 + \Delta^2(T)}}{2k_B T}\right], \qquad (7.49)$$

where $\lambda^* = D(\varepsilon_F)\tilde{V}_p$ is the BCS-like coupling constant, $D(\varepsilon_F)$ is the density of states at the polaronic Fermi level, $\tilde{V}_p = V_{ph} - \tilde{V}_c$ is the effective pairing interaction potential, $\tilde{V}_c = V_c/[1 + D(\varepsilon_F)V_c \ln(W_p/(E_b + \hbar\omega_D))]$ is the screened Coulomb interaction between two polaronic carriers, $V_{ph}$ is the attractive electron-phonon interaction potential (which has both dynamic and static phonon-mediated attractive parts), $V_c$ is the Coulomb interaction potential, $W_p$ is the width of the polaron band, $E_b$ is the polaron binding energy, $\hbar\omega_D$ is the Debye energy for dynamic phonons in the lattice, $\Delta(T) = \Delta_{PG}(T)$ is the BCS-like PG.

Since the BCS-like gap $\Delta$ goes to zero continuously as $T$ approaches $T^*$ from below, the PG formation temperature corresponding to $\Delta(T^*) = 0$ is determined from the equation

$$\frac{1}{\lambda^*} = \int\limits_{0}^{E_b + \hbar\omega_D} \frac{d\varepsilon}{\varepsilon} \tanh\left[\frac{\varepsilon}{2k_B T}\right], \qquad (7.50)$$

At $W_p > E_b + \hbar\omega_D >> k_B T^*$ this equation gives

$$k_B T^* = 1.134(E_b + \hbar\omega_D)\exp(-1/\lambda^*) \qquad (7.51)$$

When the polaron bandwidth $W_p < E_b + \hbar\omega_D$, the cut-off energy for the attractive electron-phonon interaction is replaced by $W_p$, i.e., the prefactor $E_b + \hbar\omega_D$ in Eq. (7.51) is replaced by $W_p$. The BCS-like equation (7.51) for $T^*$ is well applicable at $\lambda^* \leq 0.55$ (see Table 7.1). For organic materials the Debye temperature $\Theta_D$ is about 100 K [143] and the value of the polaron binding energy $E_b$ varies from 0.03 to 0.06 eV [140, 144]. The band structure calculations yielded the values of $W_p$ between 0.1 and 0.3 eV [141]. At $E_b = 0.05eV$, $\hbar\omega_D \simeq 0.009$ eV and $\lambda^* = 0.4$, we find from (7.51) that in organic superconductors the BCS-like pairing PG opens well above $T_c$, namely, at $T^* \simeq 64K >> T_c \simeq 10 - 12K$ (for BEDT-TTF system superconductors [145]). If we use the values of the parameters $E_b = 0.036$ eV, $\lambda^* = 0.361 - 0.365$ and $E_b = 0.04$ eV, $\lambda^* = 0.380 - 0.392$, we obtain $T^* \simeq 37 - 38$ and $T^* \simeq 46 - 50K$, which are in good agreement with the values of $T^* = 37 - 38K$ and $T^* = 46 - 50K$ observed in organic superconductors $k - (ET)_2Cu[N(CN)_2]Br$ and $k - (ET)_2Cu[N(NCS)_2]$, respectively [146].

### 7.8.2. Possible Pseudogap States in Heavy-fermion Systems and Liquid $^3$He

Another important class of unconventional superconductors is comprised of intermetallic compounds containing Ce, U, Yb, or Np ions known as heavy-fermion systems. The common feature of these compounds is that they contain $f$ electrons having localized orbitals and characterized by the narrow $f$ electron bands, so that the effective masses of charge carriers are very large $m^* \simeq 50 - 200m_e$ [138]. The $f$ electrons become partly itinerant as a nearly localized $f$-band is formed and they become completely delocalized due to their strong hybridization with the conduction electrons [138]. The strong interaction of the conduction electrons with nearly localized $f$ electrons leads to an enhanced density of states at the Fermi level. The exchange interactions take place between the magnetic moments of $f$ electrons and the spins of the conduction electrons, to cause a new bound (paired) state of charge carriers in heavy-fermion compounds. It is interesting that the properties of heavy-fermion superconductors are similar to those of liquid $^3He$. While much emphasis has been placed on the question of unconventional versus conventional Cooper pairing, little progress has yet been made toward an understanding of the possible ground states of these systems both above $T_c$ and below $T_c$. Magnetic interactions are surely the most important part of the pairing interaction both in heavy-fermion systems and in liquid $^3$He. These interactions are likely to produce Cooper pairs above $T_c$ in spin-triplet states with an odd orbital angular momentum $l$ and might be relevant for describing the possible PG states in heavy-fermion systems. Magnetic couplings are also thought to arise in liquid $^3$He and play an important role in the formation of the triplet p-wave pairing states below a SF transition temperature $T_c$ [147, 148, 149]. Although the role of unconventional Cooper pairing in either the formation of the superfluid state or the formation of the PG-like state in $^3$He is not established, it is likely to be a central importance, as is certainly the case for heavy-fermion systems and possibly also for high-$T_c$ cuprates. The theories developed to explain the PG behavior of high-$T_c$ cuprates may be also applicable to heavy-fermion superconductors which exhibit a similar behavior in many regards [150, 151]. The electronic structure of heavy-fermion systems can be described by the nearly localized narrow $f$-band that cause the heavy-fermion behavior and the itinerant hybridized $f$-band [152] which is a relatively broad to support superconductivity. In the presence of strong hybridization of the $f$ electrons with electrons on neighboring non-$f$-electron atoms, a competition can exist between localized $f$ electrons (which support magnetism) and itinerant hybridized $f$ bands in which the charge carriers having relatively smaller effective masses $m^* \simeq 10 - 30m_e$ [138, 153] take part in unconventional Cooper pairing. The Cooper pairs in heavy-fermion superconductors are assumed to be in a spin triplet state with the spin $S = 1$ and orbital angular momentum $l = 1$, just like the Cooper pairs in liquid $^3$He. Two possible forms of spin-triplet p-wave pairing in $^3$He have been studied by Anderson and Model [154], and Balian and Werthamer [155]. Anderson and Morel considered an equal spin pairing (EPS) ground state (later named the Anderson-Brinkman-Morel (ABM) state) with parallel spins ($S_z = \pm 1$) and predicted an anisotropic energy gap that has nodes (i.e., zero-points) on the Fermi surface. Whereas Balian and Werthamer studied the non-ESP ground state containing all three spin substates, $S_z = 0, \pm 1$ and showed that such a p-wave pairing state (later called the Balian-Werthamer (BW) state) would have an isotropic energy gap (just like $s$-wave BCS gap) and be energetically favorable. Many authors claim that the A and B phases of superfluid $^3$He are described by the ABM and BW states, respectively. However, the Anderson-Morel and Balian-Werthamer models could not account for the existence of the first-order transition between A and B phases of superfluid $^3$He. These models predict only the second-order BCS transition at a mean-field pairing temperature $T_{MF} = T^*$ which might be different from the SF transition temperature $T_c$. We believe that the SF phase transition in $^3He$ is more similar to the $\lambda$-transition (see, e.g., Fig. 1.9a presented in Ref. [149]) than to the step-like BCS one; and the nature of the SF phases of $^3$He is still not understood. It seems likely that the ABM and BM states are possible precursor pairing (or PG-like) states and these state may exist both below $T_c$ and above $T_c$.

The mean-field pairing temperature $T^*$ for $^3$He and heavy-fermion superconductors is determined from the BCS-like gap equation (7.7) which holds for either spin singlet or spin triplet pairing. In this equation, the expansion of the effective pair interaction function $V(\vec{k}, \vec{k}')$ in terms of Legendre polynomials $P_l(\hat{\vec{k}}, \hat{\vec{k}'})$ with different $l$ contains the radial part of the p-wave attractive interaction potential $V_l(\vec{k}, \vec{k})$ which is responsible for the highest mean-field pairing temperature. In the case of the spin-triplet ($S = 1$) Cooper pairing, the pair interaction potential can be written as [148]

$$V(\vec{k}, \vec{k}') = \sum_{l=0}^{\infty}(2l+1)V_l(\vec{k}, \vec{k}')P_l(\hat{\vec{k}}, \hat{\vec{k}'}) \tag{7.52}$$

where $\hat{\vec{k}} = \vec{k}/k_F$, $k_F$ is the Fermi wave vector.

Further, the interaction potential $V_l(\vec{k}, \vec{k}')$ is assumed to be constant within a thin layer near the Fermi surface and zero elsewhere:

$$V_l(\vec{k}, \vec{k}') = \begin{cases} -V_l, & \text{for } |\varepsilon(\vec{k})|, |\varepsilon(\vec{k}')| \leq \varepsilon_A, \\ 0 & \text{otherwise} \end{cases} \tag{7.53}$$

For the model interaction of Eq. (7.53), the gap function $\Delta(\vec{k})$ is independent of $\vec{k}$. Substituting Eq. (7.53) into Eq. (7.7) and using the angular average over $\hat{\vec{k}}$ [156], the BCS-like gap equation may be written as

$$1 = V_l \sum_{\vec{k}'} \frac{1}{2E(\vec{k}')} \tanh \frac{E(\vec{k})}{2k_B T}, \tag{7.54}$$

where $E(\vec{k}) = \sqrt{\varepsilon^2(\vec{k}) + \Delta^2(\vec{k})}$. The summation in Eq. (7.54) over momenta can be replaced by an integral over energies $\varepsilon$ within the thin energy layer near the Fermi surface by introducing the DOS $D(\varepsilon_F)$. Then the gap equation (7.54) reduces to

$$1 = V_l D(\varepsilon_F) \int_0^{\varepsilon_A} \frac{\tanh(E/2k_B T)}{E} d\varepsilon \tag{7.55}$$

At a mean-field pairing temperature $T^*$, $\Delta(T^*) = 0$, so that for $\varepsilon_A \gg k_B T^*$, Eq. (7.55) yields a relation between the temperature $T^*$, the cutoff energy $\varepsilon_A$ and the pair interaction constant $V_l$:

$$k_B T^* = 1.134\varepsilon_A \exp\left(-1/\lambda_l^*\right) \qquad (7.56)$$

where $\lambda_l^* = V_l D(\varepsilon_F)$ is the BCS-like coupling constant.

One can assume that for $^3$He, the Fermi temperature $T_F$ is of order 1K and the coupling constant $\lambda_l^*$ varies between 0.2 and 0.3 [148, 149]. By taking $\varepsilon_A \simeq 0.15 k_B T_F$ and $\lambda_l^* = 0.25$, we find $T^* \simeq 3.06 \cdot 10^{-3}$K. Experimental results show [149] that the heat capacity of liquid $^3$He decreases linearly with temperature between 4 and 300 mK. It follows that the formation of PG-like state in $^3$He is expected below 4 mK.

In heavy-fermion systems, the energy $J$ of the exchange interaction is likely larger than the Fermi energy $\varepsilon_F$ of these systems. Therefore, the cutoff energy $\varepsilon_A$ in Eq. (7.56) can be replaced by $\varepsilon_F$. If we take $m^* \simeq 30m_e$ and the carrier concentration $n_f \simeq 10^{22} cm^{-3}$, we obtain $\varepsilon_F = \hbar^2 (3\pi^2 n_f)^{2/3}/2m^* \simeq 0.06$ eV. Then from Eq. (7.56), we obtain the following values of $T^* \simeq 40$ K and 49 K for $\lambda_l^* \simeq 0.335$ and 0.360 respectively, which are close to the PG temperatures $T \simeq 40$ K and 50 K observed in heavy-fermion superconductors UPd$_2$A$_3$ [138] and YbAl$_3$ [153].

### 7.8.3.  Pseudogap State in Nuclear Matter

The protons and neutrons, usually called nucleons, in nuclei just like electrons in metals may be considered as a degenerate Fermi-gas [156, 157]. Therefore, the properties of an attractive Fermi-gas play key roles not only in condensed matter physics but also in nuclear matter physics. In particular, pairing correlations are universal properties of attractive fermions and play an important role in nuclear and neutron-star physics. The importance of Cooper-like pairing in nuclear structure has been realized already in the early stages of nuclear physics and the study of the pairing correlations in nuclei has been initiated in the works of Migdal [158], Solovev [159], Ginzburg and Kirzhnits [160], and Bohr [161], which have been triggered by the BCS theory. It is believed that the presence of the residual interactions between the nucleons makes their Cooper-like pairing possible in nuclei, The nucleons near the Fermi surface might be paired in the singlet $^1S_0$ state in such a way as charge carriers are paired in a superconducting material. In general, there are remarkable similarities between pairing correlations in nuclei and pairing correlations in superconductors. The nuclear matter can be divided into two parts, one (inter part) corresponding to the high-density nuclear matter and the other one (outer part) corresponding to the low-density nuclear matter. The low-and high-density regions of nuclear matter are rather similar to the underdoped and overdoped cuprate superconductors. It was argued [31, 162, 163] that the low-density nuclear matter can be in a PG state, which plays a crucial role in a variety of nuclear many body problems, from finite nuclei to neutron stars. Actually, as a consequence of precursor Cooper pairing, the low density nuclear matter just like underdoped cuprates exhibits PG phenomena above the SF transition temperature $T_c$. Therefore, the PG phase of nuclei and high-$T_c$ cuprates is in many ways similar. Depending on the strength of the attractive interaction between two nucleons, the physical contents of their pairing state could be distinguishably altered. In high-density region of nuclear matter this pairing interaction is weak enough. In this case, Cooper like pairing and superfluidity of loosely correlated Cooper pairs of nucleons may occur semultaneously at $T_c$ and the BCS gap serves as the SF gap. When the pairing interaction become more stronger in the intermediate- and low-density regions of nuclear matter, the tightly bound two-fermion Cooper pairs could form, which may behave like composite bosons. In this situation, the superfluidity of such bosons is due to their condensation into a SF Bose-liquid state at $T_c$, which is different from the non-SF BEC state, and the BCS-type gap opens at $T^* > T_c$ and becomes PG in the excitation spectrum of nuclear matter. For a degenerate Fermi-gas of nucleons, the BCS-like gap equation can be written in the form

$$\Delta(\vec{k}) = -\sum_{\vec{k}'} V_N(\vec{k},\vec{k}') \frac{\Delta(\vec{k}')}{2E(\vec{k}')} \tanh\left(\frac{E(\vec{k}')}{2k_B T}\right), \tag{7.57}$$

where $E(\vec{k}) = \sqrt{\xi^2(\vec{k}) + \Delta^2(\vec{k})}$, $\xi(\vec{k})$ is the energy of nucleons measured relative to their Fermi energy $\varepsilon_F$, $V_N(\vec{k},\vec{k}')$ is the nucleon-nucleon interaction potential.

Equation (7.57) can be solved self-consistently in order to determine the pairing PG and the mean-field pairing temperature $T^*$ for the intermediate-density regions of nuclear matter using the model interaction potential

$$V_N(\vec{k},\vec{k}') = \begin{cases} -V_N & \text{for } |\xi(\vec{k})|, |\xi(\vec{k}')| \le \varepsilon_c, \\ 0 & \text{otherwise}, \end{cases} \tag{7.58}$$

which is assumed to be constant within the energy layer (with the thickness $2\varepsilon_c$) near the Fermi surface, where $\varepsilon_c$ is the cut-off energy for $V_N(\vec{k},\vec{k}')$. At $T = 0$, Eq. (7.57) may then be written as

$$1 = \frac{V_N D_N(\varepsilon_F)}{2} \int_{-\varepsilon_c}^{\varepsilon_c} \frac{d\xi}{\sqrt{\xi^2 + \Delta^2(0)}}, \tag{7.59}$$

where $D_N(\varepsilon_F)$ is the DOS at the Fermi level.

¿From Eq. (7.59), we obtain

$$\Delta(0) = \frac{\varepsilon_c}{\sinh[1/V_N D_N(\varepsilon_F)]} \tag{7.60}$$

At the mean-field pairing temperature $T^*$, $\Delta(T^*) = 0$, so that Eq. (7.59) becomes

$$1 = V_N D_N(\varepsilon_F) \int_0^{\varepsilon_c} \frac{d\xi}{\xi} \tanh\frac{\xi}{2k_B T^*} \tag{7.61}$$

For $\varepsilon_c \ge 4k_B T^*$, this equation yields (see table 7.1)

$$k_B T^* \simeq 1.14\varepsilon_c \exp[-1/\lambda_N^*], \tag{7.62}$$

where $\lambda_N^* = V_N D_N(\varepsilon_F)$.

This equation can be used to evaluate the PG formation temperature for nuclear matter in the intermediate BCS-like coupling regime (i.e., $\lambda_N^* < 0.7$).

One can assume that in low-density regions of nuclear matter, all nucleons take part in Cooper pairing. In this case, the cut-off energy $\varepsilon_c$ in Eqs. (7.60) and (7.62) should by replaced by $\varepsilon_F$. If the nuclear matter is close to the high-density limit, the PG formation temperature $T^*$ is somewhat higher than $T_c$. Whereas the PG formation temperature will be much higher than $T_c$ in the intermediate-and low-density regions of nuclear matter, where the PG persists both below $T_c$ and above $T_c$. We now evaluate the magnitudes of the pairing PG and the PG formation temperature in nuclear matter. By taking typical nuclear density $n_0 \simeq 0.16 fm^{-3}$ [164], we find $\varepsilon_F \simeq 58.8$ MeV. Further, if we use the values of $\varepsilon_c = 0.4\varepsilon_F$ and $\lambda_N^* = 0.37$, we obtain $\Delta(0) \simeq 3.18$ MeV and $k_B T^* \simeq 1.8$ MeV. This result is in close agreement on the $^1S_0$ pairing gap value $\Delta(0) \sim 3$ MeV obtained by other authors (see Ref.[164]).

# References

[1] T. Timusk and B. Statt, *Rep. Prog. Phys.* 62, 61 (1999).

[2] J. L. Tallon and J. W. Loram, *Physica* C349, 53 (2001).

[3] A. Damascelli, Z. Hussain, and Z.-X. Shen, *Rev. Mod. Phys.* 75, 473 (2003).

[4] P. A. Lee, N. Nagaosa, and X.-G. Wen, *Rev. Mod. Phys.* 78, 17 (2006).

[5] S. Hüfner, M. A. Hossain, A. Damascelli, and G. A. Sawatzky, *Rep. Prog. Phys.* 71, 062501 (2008).

[6] T. Matsuzaki, M. Ido, N. Momono, R. M. Dipasupil, T. Nagata, A. Sakai, and M. Oda, *J. Phys. Chem. Solids* 62, 29 (2001); T. Matsuzaki, N. Momono, M. Oda, and M. Ido, *J. Phys. Soc. Jpn.* 73, 2232 (2004).

[7] C. M. Varma, *Phys. Rev.* B55, 14554 (1997-I); C. M. Varma, *Phys. Rev. Lett.* 83, 3538 (1999).

[8] S. Dzhumanov, *Solid State Commun.* 115, 155 (2000).

[9] C. Castellani, C. Di Castro, and M. Grilli, *J. Phys. Chem. Solids* 59, 1694 (1998).

[10] S. Chakravarty, R. B. Laughlin, D. K. Morr, and C. Nayak, *Phys. Rev.* B63, 094503 (2001).

[11] M. A. Kastner, R. J. Birgeneau, G. Shirane, and Y. Endoh, *Rev. Mod. Phys.* 70, 897 (1998).

[12] J. Phillips, *Int. J. Mod. Phys.* B13, 3419 (1999).

[13] J. Zaanen, cond.-mat/0103255.

[14] A. N. Lavrov and V. F. Gantmakher, *Phys. USP.* 41, 223 (1998).

[15] Ch. Renner, B. Revaz, J.-Y. Genoud, K. Kadowaki, and O. Fischer, *Phys. Rev. Lett.* 80, 149 (1998).

[16] D. Mihailovic, V. V. Kabanov, K. Zagar, and J. Demsar, *Phys. Rev.* B60, R6995 (1999).

[17] X. K. Chen, J. C. Irwin, M. Okuya, T. Kimura, and K. Kishio, *Phys. Rev.* B59, 9642 (1999-II).

[18] J. E. Sonier, J. H. Brewer, R. F. Kiefl, R. I. Miller, G. D. Morris, C. E. Stronach, J. S. Gardner, S. R. Dunsiger, D. A. Bonn, W. N. Hardy, R. Liang, and R. H. Heffner, *Science* 292, 1692 (2001).

[19] S. H. Naqib and J. R. Cooper, *Physica* C460-462, 750 (2007); R. S. Islam, J. R. Cooper, J. W. Loram, and S. H. Naqib, *Physica* C460-462, 753 (2007).

[20] A. B. Migdal, *Zh. Eksp. Teor. Fiz.* 34, 1438 (1958).

[21] G. M. Eliashberg, *Zh. Eksp. Teor. Fiz.* 38, 966 (1960); 39, 1437 (1960).

[22] J. Ranninger, *Z. Phys. B: Condens. Matter* 84, 167 (1991).

[23] V. Z. Kresin, H. Morawitz, and S. A. Wolf, *Mechanisms of Conventional and High $T_c$ Superconductivity* (Oxford University Press, New-York-Oxford, 1993).

[24] A. S. Alexandrov, *Europhys. Lett.* 56, 92 (2001); A. S. Alexandrov and A. M. Bratkovsky, *Phys. Rev. Lett.* 105, 226408 (2010).

[25] J. Ashkenazi and C. G. Kuper, *Physica* C162-164, 767 (1989).

[26] R. E. Cohen, W. E. Pickett, and H. Krakauer, *Phys. Rev. Lett.* 62, 831 (1989); M. Reedyk and T. Timusk, *Phys. Rev. Lett.* 69, 2705 (1992).

[27] N. Doiron-Leyraud, C. Proust, D. LeBoeuf, J. Levallois, J.-B. Bonnemaison, R. Liang, D. A. Bonn, W. N. Hardy, and L. Taillefer, *Nature* 447, 565 (2007); E. A. Yelland, J. Singleton, C. H. Mielke, N. Harrison, F. F. Balakirev, B. Dabrowski, and J. R. Cooper, *Phys. Rev. Lett.* 100, 047003 (2008).

[28] B. Vignolle, A. Carrington, J. R. Cooper, M. M. J. French, A. P. Mackenzie, C. Jaudet, D. Vignolles, C. Proust, and N. E. Hussey, *Nature* 455, 952 (2008); A. F. Bangura, P. M. C. Rourke, T. M. Benseman, M. Matusiak, J. R.Cooper, N. E. Hussey, and A. Carrington, arXiv: 1005.0573.

[29] S. Dzhumanov, *Physica* C235-240, 2269 (1994); S. Dzhumanov and P. K. Khabibullaev, *Pramana J. Phys.* 45, 385 (1995).

[30] M. Eschrig, *Adv. Phys.* 55, 47 (2006).

[31] S. Dzhumanov, A. A. Baratov, and S. Abboudy, *Phys. Rev.* B54, 13121 (1996-II); S. Dzhumanov, *Int. J. Mod. Phys.* B12, 2995 (1998).

[32] A. S. Alexandrov, V. N. Zavaritskiy, and S. Dzhumanov, *Phys. Rev.* B69, 052505 (2004).

[33] D. A. Wollman, D. J. Van Harlingen, J. Giapintzakis, and D. M. Ginsberg, *Phys. Rev. Lett.* 74, 797 (1995); C. C. Tsuei and J. R. Kirtley, *Rev. Mod. Phys.* 72, 969 (2000).

[34] A. G. Sun, D. A. Gajewski, M. B. Maple, and R. C. Dynes, *Phys. Rev. Lett.* 72, 2267 (1994); P. Chaudhari and S. Y. Lin, *Phys. Rev. Lett.* 72, 1084 (1994).

[35] A. Bussmann-Holder, H. Keller, A. R. Bishop, A. Simon, and K. A. Müller, *J. Supercond. Nov. Magn.* 21, 353 (2008).

[36] S. Komiya, Y. Ando, X. F. Sun, and A. N. Lavrov, *Phys. Rev.* B65, 214535 (2002).

[37] J. F. Annett and J. P. Wallington, *Physica* C341-348, 1621 (2000).

[38] G. Deutscher, *Rev. Mod. Phys.* 77, 109 (2005).

[39] J. E. Hoffman, E. W. Hudson, K. M. Long, V. Madhavan, H. Eisaki, S. Uchida, and J. C. Davis, *Science* 295, 466 (2002).

[40] Q. Li, Y. N. Tsay, M. Suenaga, R. A. Klemm, G. D. Gu, and N. Koshizuka, *Phys. Rev. Lett.* 83, 4160 (1999); R. A. Klemm, in *Fifth International Conference on New Theories, Discoveries, and Applications of Superconductors and Related Materials*, Abstracts, (Hilton-Chongqing, China, 2004).

[41] K. A. Müller, *J. Supercond.* 17, 3 (2004).

[42] N. N. Bogoliubov, V. V. Tolmachev, and D. V. Shirkov, *A New Method in the Theory of Superconductivity* (Izd. Akad. Nauk USSR, Moscow, 1958).

[43] S. Dzhumanov, *Physica* C460-462, 1131 (2007); S. Dzhumanov, O. K. Ganiev, Sh. S. Djumanov, arXiv:1006.2892.

[44] N. Miyakawa, P. Guptasarma, J. F. Zasadzinski, D. G. Hinks, and K. E. Gray, *Phys. Rev. Lett.* 80, 157 (1998).

[45] T. Nakano, N. Momono, and M. Oda, *J. Phys. Soc. Jpn.* 67, 2622 (1998); R. M. Dipasupil, M. Oda, N. Momono, and M. Ido, *J. Phys. Soc. Jpn.* 71, 1535 (2002).

[46] A. Ino, C. Kim, M. Nakamura, T. Yoshida, T. Mirozawa, A. Fujimori, Z.-X. Shen, T. Kakeshita, H. Eisaki, and S. Uchida, *Phys. Rev.* B65, 094504 (2002).

[47] N.-C. Yeh, C.-T. Chen, G. Hammerl, J. Mannhart, A. Schneider, R. R. Schulz, S. Tajima, K. Yoshida, D. Garrigus, and M. Strasik, *Phys. Rev. Lett.* 87, 087003(4) (2001).

[48] J. Zaanen and O. Gunnarsson, *Phys. Rev.* B40, 7391 (1989); J. Zaanen, *Science* 286, 251 (1999).

[49] J. M. Tranquada, B. J. Sternlieb, J. D. Ake, Y. Nakamura, and S. Uchida, *Nature* 375, 561 (1995).

[50] S. A. Kivelson, E. Fradkin, and V. J. Emery, *Nature* 393, 550 (1998); S. A. Kivelson, I. Bindloos, E. Fradkin, V. Oganesyan, J. Tranquada, A. Kapitulnik, and C. Howard, *Rev. Mod. Phys.* 75, 1201 (2003).

[51] N. L. Saini, A. Lanzara, A. Bianconi, D. Law, A. Menovsky, K. B. Garg, and H. Oyanagi, *J. Phys. Soc. Jpn.* 67, 393 (1998).

[52] Y. Koike, M. Akoshima, M. Aoyama, K. Nishimaki, T. Kawamata, T. Adachi, T. Noji, M. Kato, I. Watanabe, S. Ohira, W. Higemoto, K. Nagamine, H. Kimura, K. Hirota, K. Yamada, and Y. Endoh, *Physica* C357-360, 82 (2001).

[53] S. Dzhumanov, P. J. Baimatov, O.K. Ganiev, Z. S. Khudayberdiev, and B.V. Turimov, *J. Phys. Chem. Solids* 73, 484 (2012).

[54] K. Kumagai, K. Kawano, I. Watanabe, K. Nishiyama, and K. Nagamine, *J. Supercond.* 7, 63 (1994).

[55] T. Suzuki, T. Goto, K. Chiba, T. Shinoda, T. Fukase, H. Kimura, K. Yamada, M. Ohashi, and Y. Yamaguchi, *Phys. Rev.* B57, 3229 (1998).

[56] A. Fujimori, A. Ino, T. Yoshida, T. Mizokawa, M. Nakamura, C. Kim, Z.-X. Shen, K. Kishio, T. Kakeshita, H. Eisaki, and S. Uchida, *J. Phys. Chem. Solids* 62, 15 (2001).

[57] S. Ono, Y. Ando, T. Murayama, F. F. Balakirev, J. B. Betts, and G. S. Boebinger, *Physica* C357-360, 138 (2001).

[58] R. Saito, N. Tsuji, T. Kato, T. Machida, T. Noguchi, and H. Sakata, *Physica* C460-462, 878 (2007).

[59] S. Komiya, Y. Ando, X. F. Sun, and A. N. Lavrov, *Phys. Rev.* B65, 214535 (2002); N. V. Anshukova, A. I. Golovashkin, L. I. Ivanova, and A. P. Rusakov, *Zh. Eksp. Teor. Fiz.* 123, 1188 (2003).

[60] P. M. Singer, A. W. Hunt, A. F. Cederström, and T. Imai, *Phys. Rev.* B60, 15345 (1999-II); M. Hücker, G. D. Gu, J. M. Tranquada, M. V. Zimmermann, H.-H. Klauss, N. J. Curro, M. Braden, and B. Büchner, *Physica* C460-462, 170 (2007).

[61] Sh. Sakita, F. Nakamura, T. Suzuki, and T. Fujita, *J. Phys. Soc. Jpn.* 68, 2755 (1999).

[62] Y. Maeno, N. Kakehi, M. Kato, Y. Tanaka and T. Fujita, *Physica* C185-189, 909 (1991); Y. Maeno, N. Kakehi, M. Kato, and T. Fujita, *Phys. Rev.* B44, 7753 (1991).

[63] A. Ino, C. Kim, M. Nakamura, T. Yoshida, T. Mizokawa, Z.-X. Shen, A. Fujimori, T. Kakeshita, H. Eisaki, and S. Uchida, *Phys. Rev.* B62, 4137 (2000).

[64] D. Emin and M. S. Hillery, *Phys. Rev.* B39, 6575 (1989); Th. Timusk and D. B. Tanner, in: *Physical Properties of High Temperature Superconductors I*, ed., D. M. Ginsberg (Mir, Moscow, 1990) p. 341.

[65] J. Fink, N. Nücker, M. Alexander, H. Romberg, M. Knupfer, M. Merkel, P. Adelmann, R. Claessen, G. Mante, T. Buslaps, S. Harm, R. Manzke, and M. Skibowski, *Physica* C185-189, 45 (1991).

[66] B. Nachumi, Y. Fudamoto, A. Keren, K. M. Kojima, M. Larkin, G. M. Luke, J. Merrin, O. Tchernyshyov, Y. J. Uemura, N. Ichikawa, M. Goto, H. Takagi, S. Uchida, M. K. Crawford, E. M. McCarron, D. E. MacLaughlin, and R. H. Heffner, *Phys. Rev.* B58, 8760 (1998-I).

[67] N. Ichikawa, S. Uchida, J. M. Tranquada, T. Niemöller, P. M. Gehring, S.-H. Lee, and J. R. Schneider, *Phys. Rev. Lett.* 85, 1736 (2000).

[68] A. Ino, C. Kim, T. Mizokawa, Z.-X. Shen, A. Fujimori, M. Takaba, K. Tamasaku, H. Eisaki, and S. Uchida, *J. Phys. Soc. Jpn.* 68, 1496 (1999).

[69] Y. Ando, S. Ono, X. F. Sun, J. Takeya, F. F. Balakirev, J. B. Betts, and G. S. Boebinger, *Phys. Rev. Lett.* 92, 247004 (2004).

[70] N. D. Mathur, F. M. Grosche, S. R. Julian, I. R. Walker, D. M. Freye, R. K. W. Haselwimmer, and G. G. Lonzarich, *Nature* 394, 39 (1998).

[71] J. G. Naeini, X. K. Chen, K. C. Hewitt, J. C. Irwin, T. P. Devereaux, T. Kimura, and K. Kishio, *Phys. Rev.* B57, R11077 (1998-II).

[72] T. Kato, T. Noguchi, R. Saito, T. Machida, and H. Sakata, *Physica* C460-462, 880 (2007).

[73] H. Y. Hwang, B. Batlogg, H. Takagi, H. L. Kao, J. Kwo, R. J. Cava, J. J. Krajewski, and W. F. Jr. Peck, *Phys. Rev. Lett.* 72, 2636 (1994).

[74] H. Ding T. Yokoya, J. C. Campuzano, T. Takahashi, M. Randeria, M. R. Norman, T. Mochiku, K. Kadowaki, and J. Giapintzakis, *Nature* 382, 51 (1996).

[75] K. Ishida, K. Yoshida, T. Mito, Y. Tokunaga, Y. Kitaoka, K. Asayama, Y. Nakayama, J. Shimoyama, and K. Kishio, *Phys. Rev.* B58, R5960-R5963 (1998).

[76] T. Watanabe, T. Fujii, and A. Matsuda, *Phys. Rev. Lett.* 84, 5848 (2000); arXiv: cond-mat/0005434.

[77] A. Kaminski, S. Rosenkraz, H. M. Fretwell, Z. Li, H. Raffy, M. Randeria, M. R. Norman, and J. C. Campuzano, *Phys. Rev. Lett.* 90, 207003 (2003) arXiv:cond-mat/0210531.

[78] D. Mihailovic, T. Mertelj, and K. A. Müller, *Phys. Rev.* B57, 6116 (1998-II).

[79] J. T. Devreese and A. S. Alexandrov, *Rep. Prog. Phys.* 72, 066501 (2009).

[80] V. Z. Kresin and S. A. Wolf, *Rev. Mod. Phys.* 81, 481 (2009).

[81] Ø. Fischer, M. Kugler, I. Maggio-Aprile, and C. Berthod, *Rev. Mod. Phys.* 79, 353 (2007).

[82] A. Matsuda, T. Fujii, and T. Watanabe, *Physica* C388-389, 207 (2003).

[83] K. McElroy, D.-H. Lee, J. E. Hoffman, K. M Lang, E. W. Hudson, H. Eisaki, S. Uchida, J. Lee, and J. C. Davis, cond-mat/0404005; *Phys. Rev. Lett.* 94, 197005 (2005).

[84] A. C. Fang, L. Capriotti, D. J. Scalapino, S.vA. Kivelson, N. Kaneko, M. Greven, and A. Kapitulnik, *Phys. Rev. Lett.* 96, 017007 (2006).

[85] Y. De Wilde, N. Miyakawa, P. Guptasarma, M. Iavarone, L. Ozyuzer, J. F. Zasadzinski, P. Romano, D. G. Hinks, C. Kendziora, G. W. Crabtree, and K.E. Gray, *Phys. Rev. Lett.* 80, 153 (1998).

[86] Ch. Renner, B. Revaz, J. Y. Genoud, K. Kadowaki, and Ø. Fischer, *Phys. Rev. Lett.* 80, 149 (1998).

[87] N. Miyakawa, J. F. Zasadzinski, L. Ozyuzer, P. Guptasarma, D. G. Hinks, C. Kendziora, and K. E. Gray, *Phys. Rev. Lett.* 83, 1018 (1999).

[88] A. Matsuda, S. Sugita, T. Fujii, and T. Watanabe, *J. Phys. Chem. Solids* 62, 65 (2001).

[89] S. Rast, B. H. Frazer, M. Onellion, T. Schmauder, M. Abrecht, O. Touzelet, H. Berger, G. Margaritondo, and D. Pavina, *Europhys. Lett.* 51, 103 (2000).

[90] Ch. Renner and Ø. Fischer, *Physica* C235-240, 53 (1994); Ch. Renner and Ø. Fischer, *Phys. Rev.* B51, 9208 (1995).

[91] S. Dzhumanov, O. K. Ganiev, and Sh. S. Djumanov, arXiv: 1106.1308.

[92] A. J. Fedro and D. D. Koelling, *Phys. Rev.* B47, 14342 (1993); J. Bok and J. Bouvier, *Physica* C274, 1 (1997); B. W. Hoogenboom, C. Berthod, M. Peter, Ø. Fischer, A. A. Kordyuk, *Phys. Rev.* B67, 224502 (2003).

[93] J. Y. T. Wei, C. C. Tsuei, P. J. M. Van Bentum, Q. Xiong, C. W. Chu, and M. K. Wu, *Phys. Rev.* B57, 3650 (1998-II); J. Nieminen, H. Lin, R. S. Markiewicz, and A. Bansil, arXiv: 0805.1675.

[94] J. E. Hirsh, *Phys. Rev.* B59, 11962 (1999); P. W. Anderson, *Fiz. Nizk. Temp.* 32, 381 (2006).

[95] M. Eschrig and M. R. Norman, *Phys. Rev. Lett.* 85, 3261 (2000).

[96] J. F. Zasadzinski, L. Coffey, P. Romano, and Z. Yusof, *Phys. Rev.* B68, 180504 (2003).

[97] T. Cren, D. Roditchev, W. Sacks, and Klein, *Europhys. Lett.* 52, 203 (2000); W. Sacks, T. Cren, D. Roditchev, and B. Doucot, *Phys. Rev.* B74, 174517 (2006).

[98] K. Kouznetsov, and L. Coffey, *Phys. Rev.* B54, 3617 (1996-I); A. S. Alexandrov and J. Beanland, arXiv: 0910.4295.

[99] H. E. Hussey and J. R. Copper, in: *IRC Research Review. High Temperature Superconductivity*, ed., W. Y. Liang (Cambridge Univercity Press, Cambridge, 1998) p. 52; Y. J. Uemura, *Physica* C341-348, 2117 (2000).

[100] B. D. Dunlap, M. V. Nevitt, M. Slaski, T. E. Klippert, Z. Sungaila, A. G. McKale, D. W. Capone, R. B. Poeppel, and B. K. Flandermeyer, *Phys. Rev.* B35, 7210 (1987).

[101] M. Tinkham, *Introduction to Superconductivity*, 2nd ed.(McGraw-Hill, New York, 1996).

[102] G. Deutscher, *Nature* 397, 410 (1999).

[103] T. Kato, T. Noguchi, R. Saito, T. Machida, and H. Sakata, *Physica* C460-462, 880 (2007).

[104] E. W. Hudson, S. H. Pan, A. K. Gupta, K.-W. Ng, and J. C. Davis, *Science* 285, 88 (1999); S. Pan, E. Hudson, A. Gupta, K. Ng, H. Eisaki, S. Uchida, and J. Davis, *Phys. Rev. Lett.* 85, 1536 (2000).

[105] V. J. Emery and S. A. Kivelson, *Nature* 374, 434 (1995); M. R. Norman, H. Ding, M. Renderia, J. C. Campuzano, T. Yokoya, and T. Takeuchi, *Nature* 392, 157 (1998).

[106] S. E.Inderhees, M. B. Salamon, N. Goldfeld, J. P. Rice, B. G. Pazol, D. M. Ginsberg, J. Z. Liu, and G. W. Crabtree, *Phys. Rev. Lett.* 60, 1178 (1988); K. Fossheim, O. M. Nes, T. Legreid, C. N. W. Darlington, D. A. O'Connor, and C. E. Gough, *Int. J. Mod. Phys.* B1, 1171 (1988).

[107] M. A. Izbizky, M. Nunez Regueiro, P. Esquinazi, and C. Fainstein, *Phys. Rev.* B38, 9220 (1988).

[108] H. Adrian, W. Assmus, A. Höhr, J. Kowalewski, H. Spille, and F. Steglich, *Physica* C162-164, 320 (1989); M. Ledvij, D. Davidovic, and L. Dobrosavljevic-Grujic, *Physica* C165-166, 1119 (1990).

[109] G. Oya, M. Aoyama, S. Kishida, and H. Tokutaka, *Physica* C185-189, 2453 (1991); P. Müller, *Physica* C235-240, 289 (1994).

[110] P. C. W. Fung, and W. Y. Kwok, *J. Superconduct.* 4, 67 (1991); Y. Zhang, N. P. Ong, Z. A. Xu, K. Krishana, R. Gagnon, and L. Taillefer, *Phys. Rev. Lett.* 84, 2219, (2000).

[111] R. A. Fisher, J. E. Gorden, and N. E. Phillips, *J. Superconduct.* 1, 231 (1988).

[112] J. W. Loram, K. A. Mirza, J. M. Wade, J. R. Cooper, and W. Y. Liang, *Physica* C235-240, 134 (1994).

[113] A. Junod, *Physica* C153-155, 1078 (1988); T. Sasaki, O. Nakatsu, N. Kobayashi, A. Tokiwa, M. Kikuchi, A. Liu, K. Hiraga, Y. Syono, and Y. Muto, *Physica* C156, 395 (1988).

[114] C. P. Moca and B. Janko, *Phys. Rev.* B65, 052503 (2002).

[115] M. Muroi and R. Street, *Physica* C246, 357 (1995).

[116] A. Junod, D. Sanchez, J.-Y. Genoud, T. Graf, G. Triscone, and J. Muller, *Physica* C185-189, 1399 (1991).

[117] L. D. Landau and E. M. Lifshitz, *Statistical Physics*, Part I (Nauka, Moscow, 1976).

[118] G.-M. Zhao, M. B. Hunt, H. Keller, and K. A. Müller, *Nature* 385, 236 (1997).

[119] G.-M. Zhao, H. Keller, and K. Conder, *J. Phys.: Condens. Matter* 13, R569 (2001).

[120] G. V. M. Williams, J. L. Tallon, J. W. Quilty, H. J. Trodahl, and N. E. Flower, *Phys. Rev. Lett.* 80 377 (1998); G. V. M. Williams, D. J. Pringle, and J. L. Tallon, *Phys. Rev.* B61, R9257 (2000).

[121] F. Raffa, T. Ohno, M. Mali, J. Roos, D. Brinkmann, K. Conder, and M. Eremin, *Phys. Rev. Lett.* 81, 5912 (1998).

[122] D.R. Temprano, J. Mesot, S. Janssen, K. Conder, A. Furrer, H. Mutka, and K. A. Müller, *Phys. Rev. Lett.* 84, 1990 (2000).

[123] D.R. Temprano, J. Mesot, S. Janssen, K. Conder, A. Furrer, A. Sokolov, V. Trounov, S. M. Kazakov, J. Karpinski, and K. A. Müller, *Eur. Phys. J.* B19, 5 (2001).

[124] D.R. Temprano, K. Conder, A. Furrer, H. Mutka, V. Trounov, and K. A. Müller, *Phys. Rev.* B66, 184506 (2002).

[125] G.-H. Gweon, T. Sasagawa, S.Y. Zhou, J. Graf, H. Takagi, D.-H. Lee, and A. Lanzara, *Nature* 430, 187 (2004).

[126] J. L. Tallon, R. S. Islam, J. Storey, G. V. M. Williams, and J. R. Cooper, *Phys. Rev. Lett.* 94, 237002 (2005).

[127] I. Eremin, M. Eremin, S. Varlamov, D. Brinkmann, M. Mali, and J. Roos, *Phys. Rev.* B56, 11305 (1997).

[128] A. Bussmann-Holder, *J. Supercond.* 13, 773 (2000).

[129] S. Andergassen, S. Caprara, C. Di Castro, and M. Grilli, *Phys. Rev. Lett.* 87, 056401 (2001); C. Di Castro, M. Grilli, and S. Caprara, *J. Phys. Chem. Solids* 63, 2219 (2002).

[130] V. V. Kabanov and D. Mihailovic, *J. Supercond.* 13, 959 (2000); D. Mihailovic and V. Kabanov, *Phys. Rev.* B63, 054505 (2002).

[131] R. Khasanov, S. Strässle, K. Conder, E. Pomjakushina, A. Bussmann-Holder, and H. Keller, arXiv: 0710.5053.

[132] J. Appel, in: *Polarons*, ed., Yu. A. Firsov (Nauka, Moscow, 1975).

[133] M. Weger and L. Burlachkov, *Physica* C235-240, 2387 (1994).

[134] R. Zeyher and A. Greco, *Phys. Rev.* B80, 064519 (2009).

[135] A. Furrer, K. Conder, P. Häfliger, and A. Podlesnyak, *Physica* C408-410, 773 (2004).

[136] T. Yujo and K. Yamada, *J. Phys. Soc. Jpn.* 68, 2198 (1999).

[137] A. Ugawa and D. B. Tanner, *Physica* C341-348, 2201 (2000).

[138] M. Dressel, N. Kasper, K. Petukhov, B. Gorshunov, G. Griiner, M. Huth, and H. Adrian, *Phys. Rev. Lett.* 88, 186404 (2002).

[139] P. Bozek, *Nucl. Phys.* A657, 187 (1999); arXiv: nucl-th/9902019; *Phys. Rev.* C62, 054316 (2000); arXiv: nucl-th/0003048.

[140] E. A. Silinsh, M. V. Kurik, and V. Chapek, *Electronic Processes in Organic Molecular Crystals: Localization and Polarization Phenomena* (Riga, Ziinatne, 1988).

[141] K. Hannewald, V. M. Stojanovic, J. M. T. Schellekens, P.A. Bobbert, G. Kresse, and J. Hafner, *Phys. Rev.* B69, 075211 (2004).

[142] M. Singh and K. P. Sinha, *Solid State Commun.* 70, 149 (1989).

[143] M. C. Böhm, *Physica* C169, 152 (1990).

[144] K. D. Meisel, H. Vocks, and P. A. Bobbert, *Phys. Rev.* B71, 205206 (2005).

[145] H. Mori, *Int. J. Mod. Phys.* B8, 1 (1994).

[146] T. Sasaki, N. Yoneyama, A. Matsuyama, and N. Kobayashi, *Phys. Rev.* B65, 060505 (2002).

[147] A. J. Leggett, *Rev. Mod. Phys.* 47, 331 (1975).

[148] D. Vollhardt and P. Wölfle, *The Superfluid Phases of Helium*-3 (London, Taylor and Francis, 1990).

[149] E. R. Dobbs, *Helium Three* (Oxford, Oxford University Press, 2000).

[150] M. B. Maple, *Physica* C341-348, 47 (2000).

[151] R. Joynt and L. Taillefer, *Rev. Mod. Phys.* 74, 235 (2002).

[152] G.P . Meisner, A. L. Giorgi, A. C. Lawson, G. R. Stewart, J. O. Willis, M. S. Wire, and J. L. Smith, *Phys. Rev. Lett.* 53, 1829 (1984).

[153] H. Okamura, T. Michizawa, T. Nanba, and T. Ebihara, J. *Phys. Soc. Jpn.* 73, 2045 (2004).

[154] P. W. Anderson and P. Morel, *Phys. Rev.* 123, 1911 (1961).

[155] R. Balain and N. R. Werthamer, *Phys. Rev.* 131, 1553 (1963).

[156] D. R. Tilley and J. Tilley, *Superfluidity and Superconductivity* (Adam Hilger, Bristol, 1990).

[157] V. L. Ginzburg, *Usp. Fiz. Nauk* 167, 429 (1997).

[158] A. B. Migdal, *Zn. Eksp. Teor. Fiz.* 37, 249 (1959);*Nucl. Phys.* 13, 655 (1959).

[159] V.G. Solovev, *Influence of Superconducting-type Pair Correlations on the Properties of Atomic Nuclei* (Atomizdat, Moscow, 1963).

[160] V. L. Ginzburg and D. A. Kirzhnits, *Zn. Eksp. Teor. Fiz.* 47, 2006 (1964).

[161] A. Bohr, *Int. Symp. on Nuclear Structure* (Dubna, 1968) *Proc. IAEA* (Vienna, 1969) p. 169.

[162] P. Bozek, *Nucl. Phys.* A657, 187 (1999); arXiv: nucl-th/ 9902019.

[163] X.-G. Huang, arXiv: 1002. 0060.

[164] H. Heiselberg and M. Hjorth-Jensen, *Phys. Rep.* 328, 237 (2000).

# Chapter 8

# Theory of Unconventional Superconductivity in the Pseudogap State of High-$T_c$ Cuprates and Other Systems

## 8.1. Introduction

The problem of unconventional superconductivity in the new classes of superconducting (SC) materials (such as high-$T_c$ cuprates and other related high-$T_c$ oxides, organic super-conductors, and heavy-fermion compounds) was the subject of numerous experimental and theoretical research projects for over three decades. After the discovery of the unconventional superconductors, especially high-$T_c$ cuprate superconductors, the astonishing SC properties of these systems have led to a great number of fundamentally new concepts (see chapter 5) and have thereby enlarged our knowledge of the possible SC states in various Fermi systems. As mentioned in chapter 7, there is marked similarity between unconventional superconductors and SF $^4$He. Actually, the SC transition in high-$T_c$ cuprates and other unconventional superconductors closely resembles the λ-like superfluid (SF) transition in $^4$He. The phenomenon of superconductivity can be considered as superfluidity of electron liquids. The superfluidity of $^4$He and electron liquids in superconductors is the first remarkable indication of macroscopic quantum effects in these systems. The phenomena of superfluidity and superconductivity are associated with the coherent (or collective) motion of large number of particles condensed into the same quantum state and with the currents of these condensed particles flowing without any friction. It is believed that the SF behavior of liquid $^4$He and electron liquids in solids is governed by the laws of quantum mechanics (i.e., the laws of quantum statistics [1, 2, 3, 4, 5]) applied to systems of identical particles and by the Landau criterion for superfluidity applied to the excitation spectrum of a given liquid [6]. The $^4$He atom containing even numbers of elementary particles has spin zero and consequently obeys Bose-Einstein statistics. At low temperatures, any number of $^4$He atoms as the Bose particles can occupy the lowest-energy single quantum state and this phenomenon is now called Bose-Einstein condensation (BEC) in the non-interacting particle approximation. F. London in 1938 suggested [1] that the SF transition in liquid $^4$He is associated with the BEC of Bose particles. However, the liquid $^4$He is strongly interacting Bose-liquid and not an ideal Bose gas which undergoes a BEC. Later, a crucial step was made in 1941 when Landau [6] showed that the frictionless flow (i.e., superfluidity) of liquid $^4$He would be possible, if this liquid has the sound-like excitation spectrum satisfying the criterion for superfluidity. On the other hand, the non-interacting electrons (or holes) in solids obey Fermi statistics and they occupy all the single-particle states up to the Fermi energy. Because of the Pauli exclusion principle, two Fermi particles cannot occupy the same quantum state, so that multiple occupation of the lowest-energy single quantum state in a Fermi system is not permissible. Moreover, the excitation spectrum of a non-interacting Fermi system does not satisfy the Landau criterion for superfluidity. The BCS theory overcome this difficulty and was quite successful in explaining the superconductivity in conventional metals [7] in which the interelectron interactions are such that they tend to bind electrons into Cooper pairs and lend to the electron liquids the properties of superfluidity. According to this theory, all Cooper pairs in metals could occupy the same quantum state (by analogy with BEC), though they do not behave like Bose particles [5]. Thus, the SC transition in metals corresponds to the BCS condensation of Cooper pairs. We believe that the Landau criterion for superfluidity should be applied to moving Cooper pairs (i.e., center-of-mass motion of Cooper pairs) and not to the excitation spectrum of BCS (or Bogoliubov) quasiparticles, which are independent fermions and not moving Cooper pairs. The SC transition in unconventional superconductors is still treated by many researchers as a BCS transition, which is, however, quite different from the $\lambda$-like transition observed in these SC materials [8, 9, 10, 11]. It is possible that unconventional superconductors are in the bosonic limit of pre-formed Cooper pairs, so these Cooper pairs in contrast to Cooper pairs in conventional superconductors may be looked upon in a way as composite bosons [12, 13, 14]. According to the Landau criterion, the BEC of an ideal Bose gas with the excitation spectrum $\varepsilon = \hbar^2 k^2 / 2 m_B$ (where $m_B$ is the mass of Bose particles) cannot support the phenomenon of superfluidity. Indeed, the ideal Bose-gas (or BEC) model does not yield an accurate description of the $\lambda$ transition in $^4$He [3] and high-$T_c$ cuprate superconductors in which the attractive forces both between the $^4$He atoms and between the composite bosonic Cooper pairs play an essential role in SF Bose condensation.

For understanding the phenomenon of unconventional superconductivity, numerous theoretical models have been proposed (see Refs. [14, 15, 16, 17, 18, 19, 20, 21, 22, 23] and chapter 7 for a review). Although much theoretical effort has been devoted to examining the problem of unconventional superconductors, not very much is known, especially of the underlying mechanism of novel superconductivity in these systems. Because many of the theories proposed for explaining the high-$T_c$ superconductivity in the cuprates range from BCS pairing to BEC and the main attention in these theories is usually given to one of intermediate (but not SC) states; namely, to explain the BCS-like $s$- $p$-, and $d$- wave pairing of carriers by means of phonon (including van Hove singularity), exciton, plasmon, magnon, and other excitations exchange or to use the concept of the BEC of pre-formed Cooper pairs and other boson-like carriers (e.g., holons and bipolarons). However, the pairing of carriers is only necessary but not a sufficient condition for appearance of superconductivity in unconventional superconductors [12, 13, 14]. Whereas the BEC state of an ideal Bose gas of pre-formed Cooper pairs in high-$T_c$ cuprates and other unconventional superconductors is not at all their SF or SC state. Therefore, many observed unusual SC properties of unconventional superconductors are difficult to be explained consistently on the basis of both the BCS condensation theory of quasi-fermionic Cooper pairs and the BEC theory of pre-formed quasi-bosonic Cooper pairs. In particular, such inexplicable anomalies observed in the high-$T_c$ cuprates, heavy-fermion, and organic superconductors are: (i) non-zero density of states (DOS) inside and in the bottom of the BCS-like gap [24, 25, 26]; (ii) anomalous upward increasing or kink-like change of the lower $H_{c1}$ [27], thermodynamic $H_c$ [28] and upper $H_{c2}$ [29] critical magnetic fields, the critical current $I_c$ [30], sound velocity [15, 31], entropy [31], and SC order parameter [32, 33] near a characteristic temperature $T = T_c^* \simeq (0.30 - 0.95)T_c$ or $T = T_c^* \sim (0.6 \div 0.7)$; (iii) the positive curvature of $H_{c1}(T)$, $H_c(T)$, $H_{c2}(T)$, $I_c(T)$ and SC order parameter near $T = T_c^*$ and its wide-spreading up to $T_c$ [26, 27, 28, 29, 33, 34] as well as extremely high negative slope of these dependences and their root-like behaviors in the vicinity of $T_c$ [35]; (iv) the first-order phase transition [36] and specific heat jump [37, 38] somewhat below $T_c$, sound attenuation maximum at $T = T_c^* \sim 0.7T_c$ [15] and $\lambda$-like transition at $T_c$ [8]; (v) power-law temperature dependences of the London penetration depth varying as $\sim (T/T_c)^n$ (with $n \simeq 1 - 4$) [19, 39, 40, 41, 42]; (vi) half-integer $\hbar/4e$ magnetic flux quantization [43]; (vii) gapless superconductivity [9, 19, 24, 25, 40]; (viii) the existence of the Bose-type species with charge 2e and diamagnetic effect above $T_c$ [44]; (ix) the existence of the vortex-like excitations above the bulk SC transition temperature [45], etc. During the last two decades there has been significant progress in understanding the pseudogapped normal state properties of high-$T_c$ cuprates (see chapter 7). However, there are still many unresolved problems of unconventional superconductivity in these materials and the necessity of a unified Fermi-Bose-liquid (FBL) approach to this phenomenon with going beyond the scope of the standard Fermi-liquid and ideal Bose gas models becomes more and more clear. In this respect, a new approach based on the two-stage FBL model of superfluidity (in liquid $^3$He) and superconductivity (unconventional superconductors) [13, 14, 46, 47] represents one of possible alternative and allows to describe consistently the unusual SC properties of high-$T_c$ cuprates and other unconventional superconductors from a unified position. One can believe that the high-$T_c$ cuprates in the underdoped, optimally doped and moderately overdoped regimes are neither BCS nor BEC superfluids. Because the experimental observations give evidence for the existence of the SF composite bosons (with charge 2e) and composite boson pairs and their SF single particle condensate below $T_c^* < T_c$ and pair Bose condensate below $T_c$ in unconventional superconductors (e.g., in high-$T_c$ cuprates) predicted in [13, 14, 46] starting from the early 1990s. According to the SF Bose-liquid theory [13, 14, 47], two new SC states of boson-like Cooper pairs are formed at their single particle condensation (SPC) at $T_c^*$ and pair condensation (PC) at $T_c$ and are qualitatively different from the usual BCS and BEC states of Cooper pairs. In such a more realistic bosonic picture, the existence of the SC state of pre-formed Cooper pairs depends on two types of excitations; one characterizes the excitation of Fermi components of these Cooper pairs, and the other characterizes the excitation of Cooper pairs themselves. The first of these excitations may be considered within the BCS-like pairing model (see chapter 7) and the second one within the boson mean-field theory (i.e., within a SF Bose-liquid theory) [13, 14, 47]. As mentioned earlier, strong deviations from the BCS (Fermi-liquid) behavior are indicative of a new SC state in high-$T_c$ cuprates, which is a SF Bose-liquid of pre-formed

Cooper pairs. The aim of this chapter is to present a consistent microscopic theory for a novel superconductivity (or superfluidity) as a theory of SF Bose-liquid. It will be shown that, the SPC and PC of attracting composite bosons (pre-formed Cooper pars) and not their formation at the Cooper pairing of fermions, plays a crucial role in the novel superconductivity in high-$T_c$ cuprates and other related SC materials. Of course, there is also much experimental evidence that the heavily overdoped cuprates are similar to the conventional superconductors in which the BCS-type condensation of quasi-fermionic Cooper pairs is responsible for the appearance of superconductivity.

In this chapter, we take the view that the phenomenon of both the conventional and the unconventional superconductivity in solids is the result of two distinct quantum phenomena [12, 13, 14, 47] (cf. Ref.[48]): formation of Cooper pairs and their subsequent condensation into a SF state at the SC transition temperature $T_c$. Further, we argue that the unconventional superconductivity driven by the SPC and PC of pre-formed Cooper pairs (composite bosons) occurs in the pseudogap state of the so-called bosonic superconductors (e.g., the underdoped, optimally doped, and moderately overdoped cuprates are the same), whereas the conventional superconductivity driven by the BCS-type condensation of Cooper pairs would occur in fermionic superconductors, such as the heavily overdoped cuprates and ordinary metals. In conventional BCS-type superconductors, Cooper pairing of electrons and superfluidity of Cooper pairs occur, simultaneously at $T^* = T_c$. However, in unconventional high-$T_c$ cuprates the precursor Cooper pairing of large polarons may occur at a mean-field temperature $T^* > T_c$ and pre-formed Cooper pairs condense into a SF Bose-liquid state at $T_c$ [12, 13, 14]. We describe the basic principles and concepts of unconventional superconductivity in high-$T_c$ cuprates and other systems, as well as conventional superconductivity in the heavily overdoped cuprates. One can hope that the solution of the problems of unconventional superconductivity within the framework of a new SF Bose-liquid approach would be very important step in our understanding of the unusual SC properties of high-$T_c$ cuprates and other related SC materials.

## 8.2.   Bosonization of Cooper Pairs in High-$T_c$ Cuprates

Barden and Schriffer argued [5] that Cooper pairs in conventional superconductors have fermionic character and are not condensed composite bosons due to extremely large ratio of the Fermi energy and SC transition temperature $T_c$ or Debye energy. On the other hand, it is widely believed [12, 13, 14, 48, 49, 50] that Cooper pairs in superconductors are bosons and obey the Bose-Einstein statistics. It seems likely that Cooper pairs in high-$T_c$ cuprates are composite bosons due to the not very large ratio of the Fermi energy and phonon energy or Cooper-pair formation temperature $T^*(> T_c)$. In general, Cooper pairs may have zero $(K = 0)$ and non-zero $(K \neq 0)$ center-of-mass momenta (CMM). According to the BCS-like pairing theory [14, 47] (see chapter 7), below $T^*$ (which is determined from the relation (7.16)) large polarons in the energy layer of width $\varepsilon_A$ around the Fermi surface take part in the Cooper pairing and form Cooper-like polaron pairs. The total number of unpaired polarons (excited Fermi components of Cooper pairs) and Cooper-like polaron pairs is given by

$$n_p = n_p^* + 2n_c = 2 \sum_k \left[ u_k^2 f(k) + v_k^2 (1 - f(k)) \right], \tag{8.1}$$

where $n_p^* = 2\sum_k u_k^2 f(k)$ is the number of unpaired polarons, $n_c = \sum_k v_k^2(1-f(k))$ is the number of Cooper-like polaron pairs, $f(k) = [\exp[E/k_B T]+1]^{-1}$ is the Fermi distribution function of polarons, $E = \sqrt{\xi^2 + \Delta^2}$ is the excitation spectrum of these quasiparticles, $\xi = \varepsilon - \mu$ is the energy of polarons measured from the polaronic Fermi level, $\varepsilon$ is their kinetic energy, $u_k = \frac{1}{2}(1 + \frac{\xi}{E})$, $v_k = \frac{1}{2}(1 - \frac{\xi}{E})$, $\Delta$ is the BCS-like energy gap in the excitation spectrum of polarons.

The layered high-$T_c$ cuprates are anisotropic three-dimensional (3D) systems, so that the equation for determining the number of Cooper pairs in these materials can be written as

$$n_c = \frac{1}{2}\sum_k (1 - \frac{\xi}{E})[1 - f(k)]$$

$$= \frac{\sqrt{2m_{ab}^2 m_c}}{4\pi^2 \hbar^3} \int_{-\varepsilon_A}^{+\varepsilon_A} (1 - \frac{\xi}{E})\frac{e^{E/k_B T}}{e^{E/k_B T} + 1}(\xi+\mu)^{1/2}d\xi, \qquad (8.2)$$

where $m_{ab}$ and $m_c$ are the effective masses of large polarons in the $CuO_2$ layer and along the $c$-axis, respectively, $\mu$ is the chemical potential of these polarons and $\varepsilon_A$ is the cut-off energy for the pair interaction of large polarons. If the coherence length or size of Cooper pairs in cuprates $\zeta(T)$ is much larger than the mean distance $R_c$ between nearest-neighbor Cooper pairs, the bosonization of such Cooper pairs is not realized due to their strong overlapping (as argued by Bardeen and Schriffer [5, 7]). The size of Cooper pairs can be estimated using the uncertainty principle $\zeta = 1/2\Delta k$. The uncertainty in the wave vector $\Delta k$ is estimated using the uncertainty in the energy $\Delta \varepsilon = \hbar v_F \Delta k$, which should be of the order of the binding energy of Cooper pairs $2\Delta(T)$. Then the size of the Cooper-like polaron pairs is estimated as

$$\zeta(T) = \frac{\hbar}{2\Delta(T)}\sqrt{\frac{\varepsilon_F}{2m_p^*}} \qquad (8.3)$$

where $v_F = \sqrt{2\varepsilon_F/m_p^*}$ is the Fermi velocity of large polarons, $\varepsilon_F$ is the Fermi energy, $m_p^* = (m_{ab}^2 m_c)^{1/3}$.

The mean distance between the Cooper pairs is evaluated as

$$R_c = (3/4\pi n_c)^{1/3} \qquad (8.4)$$

It is evident that the heavily overdoped cuprates with $T^* = T_c$ are in the fermionic limit of Cooper pairs and the condition

$$\zeta(T) = \frac{\hbar}{2\Delta(T)}\sqrt{\frac{\varepsilon_F^f}{2m^*}} >> R_c \qquad (8.5)$$

is satisfied in these systems, where $m^*$ and $\varepsilon_F^f$ are the effective mass and Fermi energy of quasi-free carriers. The value of $m^*$ in high-$T_c$ cuprates is about the free electron mass $m_e$ [51]. Then, with the values of $\lambda_1^* \simeq 0.388$ (see Eq. (7.16)), $T^* = T_c = 60K$ (determined from

Eq. (7.16) at $E_p = 0$ and $\varepsilon_A = 0.2\varepsilon_F^f$), $\Delta(T = 0.9T_c) \simeq 0.005eV$, $\varepsilon_F^f \simeq 0.3eV$ and $n_c \simeq 1.02 \times 10^{20}cm^{-3}$ (determined from Eq. (8.2)), one obtains $\zeta(T = 0.9T_c) \simeq 1.07 \times 10^{-6}cm$ and $R_c \simeq 1.328 \times 10^{-7}cm$ for heavily overdoped cuprates, so that $\zeta(T) >> R_c$. We believe that the underdoped, optimally doped and moderately overdoped cuprates are unconventional superconductors with $T^* > T_c$ or even $T^* >> T_c$ and they might be in the bosonic limit of pre-formed Cooper-like polaron pairs. The bosonization of such pre-formed Cooper pairs could be realized due to the absence of their overlapping at $\zeta(T) \lesssim R_c$ or due to the weak overlapping of small-size Cooper pairs with $\zeta(T) \gtrsim R_c$.

To illustrate the point, let us estimate $\zeta(T)$ and $R_c$ in unconventional high-$T_c$ cuprates in which the effective masses of large polarons $m_p^*$ are about $(2 - 3)m_e$ [51]. For underdoped cuprates, we take the following values of parameters: $\lambda_1^* = 0.622$, $T^* \simeq 200K$ (determined from Eq. (7.16) at $\varepsilon_A = 0.76\varepsilon_F$), $\Delta(T = 0.8T^*) \simeq 0.0236\,eV$, $m_{ab} = 2m_e$, $m_c = 2m_{ab}$, $\varepsilon_F \simeq 0.1\,eV$, $n_c \simeq 2.44 \times 10^{20}\,cm^{-3}$ (determined from Eq.(8.2)). Then, we have $\zeta(T = 0.8T^*) \simeq 8.24 \times 10^{-8}\,cm$ and $R_c \simeq 9.93 \times 10^{-8}\,cm$, i.e., the condition for bozonization of pre-formed tightly-bound Cooper pairs with $\zeta(T) \lesssim R_c$ is satisfied. Further, using the values of $\lambda_1^* = 0.58$, $\varepsilon_A = 0.5\varepsilon_F$, $T^* = 140K$, $\Delta(T = 0.8T^*) \simeq 0.0166$ eV, $m_{ab} = 2m_e$, $m_c = 1.8m_{ab}$, $\varepsilon_F \simeq 0.12eV$, $n_c \simeq 2.216 \times 10^{20}cm^{-3}$, we obtain $\zeta(T = 0.8T^*) \simeq 1.30 \times 10^{-7}cm$ and $R_c \simeq 1.03 \times 10^{-7}cm$ for optimally doped cuprates. In this case, the size of pre-formed Cooper pairs $\zeta(T)$ is comparable with the distance between these Cooper pairs $R_c$ in the optimally doped and moderately overdoped cuprates with $\varepsilon_F \gtrsim 0.12\,eV$, where the nearly non-overlapping or weakly-overlapping Cooper-like polaron pairs may behave like composite bosons. Thus, one can argue that weakly-bound Cooper pairs in heavily overdoped cuprates just like in conventional superconductors are quasi-fermions and not bosons, whereas the pre-formed Cooper-like polaron pairs are composite bosons in unconventional high-$T_c$ cuprates. The BEC temperature of an ideal Bose gas of composite bosonic Cooper pairs is then given by

$$T_{BEC} = \frac{3.31\hbar^2 n_c^{2/3}}{k_B M_c^*}, \qquad (8.6)$$

where $M_c^* = (M_{ab}^2 M_c)^{1/3}$, $M_{ab}$ and $M_c$ are the effective masses of Cooper pairs in the $CuO_2$ layer and along the $c$-axis, respectively.

At $m_p^* = 2.52m_e$, $M_c^* = 5.04m_e$, and $n_c = 2.44 \times 10^{20}\,cm^{-3}$, we obtain $T_{BEC} \simeq 227\,K$ which is higher than $T^* \simeq 200\,K$ in underdoped cuprates. By taking $m_p^* = 2.433m_e$, $M_c^* = 4.866m_e$, and $n_c = 2.216 \times 10^{20}\,cm^{-3}$, for optimally doped cuprates; we find $T_{BEC} \simeq 221\,K$, which is much higher than $T^* \simeq 140\,K$.

## 8.3.  Superfluidity of the BCS Condensate of Cooper Pairs in Heavily Overdoped Cuprates

The Landau criterion for superfluidity applied to the excitation spectrum of weakly-bound Cooper pairs allows us to understand the phenomenon of conventional superconductivity, which is associated with the coherent motion of Cooper pairs. This criterion should be applied to the excitation spectrum (energy-momentum relation) $\varepsilon(\vec{K})$ of moving Cooper pairs (with CMM $\vec{K}$). The critical velocity of the SF BCS condensate is often determined from the criterion

$$v_c = \min \frac{E(\vec{k})}{\hbar(\vec{k})} > 0, \tag{8.7}$$

where $E(\vec{k})$ is the excitation spectrum of independent BCS (Bogoliubov) quasiparticles and not moving Cooper pairs. Actually, the energy spectrum $\varepsilon(\vec{K})$ of Cooper pairs should be used to determine the condition of their superconductivity. Therefore, we define the criterion for superfluidity of Cooper pairs as

$$v_c = \min \frac{\varepsilon(\vec{K})}{\hbar(\vec{K})} > 0 \tag{8.8}$$

The criterion (8.8) is satisfied for the system of the moving Cooper pairs with the linear energy-momentum relation

$$\varepsilon(\vec{K}) = \frac{1}{2}\hbar v_F \vec{K} + 0(K^2), \tag{8.9}$$

which is obtained from the solution of the Cooper problem in the weak electron-phonon coupling regime for a special case of the Cooper model interaction [7].

Let us now consider the pairing of two carriers in $k$-space above the filled Fermi sea in heavily overdoped cuprates and the formation of Cooper pairs with zero- and non-zero CMM. The Schtödinger equation for two carriers interacting via the potential $V$ above the filled Fermi sea is written as

$$\left[ -\frac{\hbar^2}{2m^*} \left( \nabla_1^2 + \nabla_2^2 \right) + V(\vec{r}_1 - \vec{r}_2) \right] \Psi(\vec{r}_1, \vec{r}_2) = (\varepsilon + 2\varepsilon_F^f) \Psi(\vec{r}_1, \vec{r}_2), \tag{8.10}$$

where $\Psi(\vec{r}_1, \vec{r}_2)$ is the two-carrier wave function, $\varepsilon$ is the energy defined relative to the Fermi level of quasi-free carriers $(2\varepsilon_F^f)$. Defining the center of mass coordinate $\vec{R} = \frac{1}{2}(\vec{r}_1 + \vec{r}_2)$ and the relative coordinate $\vec{r} = \vec{r}_1 - \vec{r}_2$, one can write the Eq.(8.10) and wave function $\Psi(\vec{r}_1, \vec{r}_2)$ in terms of these coordinates. Then, the wave function $\Psi(R, r)$ is a product of the CMM wave function $\Omega^{-1/2} \exp(i\vec{K}\vec{R})$ and a bound-state wave function $\psi(\vec{r})$ that describe the structure of the Cooper pair, so that

$$\Psi(\vec{R}, \vec{r}) = \frac{1}{\sqrt{\Omega}} \exp(i\vec{K}\vec{R})\psi(\vec{r}), \tag{8.11}$$

where $\Omega$ is the volume of the system.

Therefore, Eq.(8.10) is rewritten as

$$\left[ -\frac{\hbar^2}{m^*}\nabla_r^2 + V(\vec{r}) \right] \psi(\vec{r}) = \left[ \varepsilon + 2\varepsilon_F^f - \frac{\hbar^2 K^2}{4m^*} \right] \psi(\vec{r}). \tag{8.12}$$

When the wave function $\psi(\vec{r})$ is expressed as

$$\psi(\vec{r}) = \sum_{k>k_F} a_k \exp(i\vec{k}\vec{r}), \tag{8.13}$$

the Eq.(8.12) has the form

$$\left[\frac{\hbar^2 K^2}{4m^*} + \frac{\hbar^2 k^2}{m^*} - \varepsilon - 2\varepsilon_F^f\right] a_{\vec{k}} + \sum_{\vec{k}'} a_{\vec{k}'} \langle \vec{k} | V(\vec{k}, \vec{k}') | \vec{k}' \rangle = 0, \tag{8.14}$$

where $V(\vec{k}, \vec{k}') = \int V(\vec{r}) \exp[-i(\vec{k} - \vec{k}')\vec{r}] d^3\vec{r}$. In order to find the solution of Cooper-pair equation (8.14) we choose the Cooper model interaction potential in the form [7]

$$V(k, k') = \begin{cases} -V & \text{if } k_F < |\vec{k} \pm \frac{\vec{K}}{2}|, |\vec{k}' \pm \frac{\vec{K}}{2}| < \sqrt{k_F^2 + k_c^2} \\ 0 & \text{otherwise,} \end{cases} \tag{8.15}$$

where $k_F$ and $k_c$ are the Fermi and characteristic cut off wave vectors defined by $k_F = \sqrt{2m^*\varepsilon_F^f}/\hbar$ and $k_c = \sqrt{2m^*\varepsilon_c}/\hbar$, $\varepsilon_c$ is the characteristic cut off energy for the interaction potential $V(\vec{k}, \vec{k}')$.

For the potential (8.15) the Cooper pair equation becomes [7]

$$\frac{1}{V} = \sum_{\vec{k}}' \frac{1}{\frac{\hbar^2 k^2}{m^*} + \frac{\hbar^2 K^2}{4m^*} - E} = \sum_{\vec{k}}' \frac{1}{2(\varepsilon(\vec{k}) - \varepsilon_F^f) + \varepsilon(\vec{K}) + \Delta_K}, \tag{8.16}$$

where $E = \varepsilon + 2\varepsilon_F^f$, $\varepsilon(\vec{k}) = \hbar^2 k^2/2m^*$, $\varepsilon(\vec{K}) = \hbar^2 K^2/4m^*$, $\Delta_K = -\varepsilon$.

The prime on the summation sign implies the restriction $|\vec{k} \pm \frac{\vec{K}}{2}| > k_F$. The condition in Eq.(8.15) is rewritten as

$$k_F < [k^2 \pm \vec{K}\vec{k}\cos\Theta + K^2/4]^2 < \sqrt{k_F^2 + k_c^2}, \tag{8.17}$$

where $\theta$ is the angle between wave vectors $\vec{k}$ and $\vec{K}$.

Replacing the sum in Eq.(8.16) by an integral and taking into account the condition (8.17), after some algebra we obtain

$$\frac{1}{V} = \frac{\sqrt{2}(m^*)^{3/2}}{(2\pi)^2 \hbar^3} \int_0^{\frac{\pi}{2}} \sin\theta d\theta \int_{\varepsilon_{min}}^{\varepsilon_c} \sqrt{\xi + \varepsilon_F^f} \frac{d\xi}{2\xi + \varepsilon_K + \Delta_K}, \tag{8.18}$$

where $\varepsilon_{min} = \hbar^2 \vec{K} k_F \cos\theta/2m^*$.

If the inequality $\varepsilon_c < \varepsilon_F^f$ is satisfied, then in Eq.(8.18) the integration with respect to $\xi$ may be performed by expanding the expression $\sqrt{\xi + \varepsilon_F^f}$ in powers of $\xi/\varepsilon_F^f$. Thus, at $2\varepsilon_c \gg \Delta_K$ and $K \to 0$, we obtain on integrating and after some algebraic manipulation the following expression for the binding energy of Cooper pairs:

$$\Delta_K = \Delta_0 - \frac{\hbar v_F \vec{K}}{2[1 - \Delta_0/4\varepsilon_F^f]} = \Delta_0 - \varepsilon(\vec{K}), \tag{8.19}$$

where $\varepsilon(\vec{K}) = \hbar v_F \vec{K}/2[1 - \Delta_0/4\varepsilon_F^f]$ is the excitation energy of Cooper pairs.

Consequently, the total energy of the Cooper pair in 3D systems is given by

$$E = 2\varepsilon_F^f - \Delta_K \tag{8.20}$$

We see that the energy of Cooper pairs $\varepsilon(\vec{K})$ in the weak coupling limit ($\Delta_0 << \varepsilon_F^f$) is given by the Eq. (8.19) [7, 50]

The linear dispersion relation for Cooper pairs in the 3D system is also obtained within the BCS approach [52]. Therefore, the excitation spectrum of Cooper pairs in the weak coupling limit satisfies the Landau criterion for superfluidity and the BCS condensate of quasi-fermionic Cooper pairs in the heavily overdoped cuprates just like in conventional superconductors is a SF Fermi-liquid. As mentioned before, the underdoped, optimally doped, and moderately overdoped doped cuprates fall in intermediate and strong electron-phonon coupling regimes and the pre-formed Cooper-like polaron pairs in these systems are composite bosonic particles and have the quadratic dispersion relation $\varepsilon(K) = \hbar^2 K^2 / 4m_p^*$ in the non-interacting particle approximation. The Landau criterion for superfluidity is not satisfied for an ideal Bose-gas of pre-formed (bosonic) Cooper pairs with the quadratic dispersion relation, so that Bose-Einstein condensate of such Cooper pairs is not SF condensate.

## 8.4. Superfluidity of Composite Bosonic Cooper Pairs in Unconventional High-$T_c$ Cuprate Superconductors

In unconventional high-$T_c$ cuprate superconductors the unpaired and paired Fermi particles exist (or coexist) below the Cooper-pair formation temperature $T^* (> T_c)$ as a mixed Fermi-Bose gas. The Hamiltonian of such a mixture of Fermi and Bose particles is written as

$$H = H_F + H_B + H_{FB} \qquad (8.21)$$

where $H_F$ and $H_B$ are the Hamiltonians of Fermi and Bose subsystems and the interaction between them is denoted by $H_{FB}$.

The diagonalization of the Hamiltonian (8.21) and its subsequent investigation are very complicated problem. Therefore, there are two different approaches to this problem. First of these approaches has been proposed in [53], where only fermion-boson interaction $H_{FB}$ is taken into account without interfermion and interboson interactions in $H_F$ and $H_B$. This approach allows to obtain the modified BCS-like excitation spectrum of Fermi-liquid which is combined with the BEC of an ideal Bose gas of $r$-space pairs. Another approach was proposed in Refs. [12, 13, 14] in which the fermion-fermion and boson-boson interactions are taken into account without fermion-boson interaction. Because the number of unpaired fermions below $T^*$ (e.g., at $T \simeq 0.9T^*$ or at even $T \simeq 0.95T^*$) determined from the equation

$$n_p^* = 2\sum_k u_k f(k) = \frac{\sqrt{2m_{ab}^2 m_c}}{2\pi^2 \hbar^3} \int\limits_{-\varepsilon_A}^{\varepsilon_A} \left(1 + \frac{\xi}{E}\right) \frac{(\xi+\mu)^{1/2}}{\exp[E/k_B T]+1} d\xi \qquad (8.22)$$

becomes rather small in comparison with $n_c$ and the fermion-boson interaction should be weak. Actually, when the density of unpaired fermions decreases rapidly and the spatial separation between pre-formed Cooper pairs and extra (i.e., unpaired) fermions is large, the Pauli blocking effect loses its efficiency in destroying the tightly-bound Cooper pairs. According to Eq. (8.22), the number of composite bosonic Cooper pairs $n_c$ somewhat below $T^*$ becomes much larger than $n_p^*$ and remains almost unchanged when the temperature decreases down to $T_c$. Thus, the fermions and composite bosonic particles are essentially decoupled just like the phase separation in a $^3$He-$^4$He mixture [54] or the spin-charge separation in RVB model [21, 22, 55]. Hence, the fermion-fermion and boson-boson attractive interactions without fermion-boson interaction (which can be safely neglected) might be responsible for the novel two-stage FBL scenario of superconductivity in high-$T_c$ cuprates. The two-stage FBL model proposed in Refs. [12, 13, 14] seems to be a more realistic approach to the problem of unconventional superconductivity in high-$T_c$ cuprates and other related materials. The treatment of tightly-bound Cooper pairs as composite bosonic particles has been justified because it does correctly describe the critical behavior of these superconductors (see Refs. [12, 13, 14, 56]). We believe that in unconventional superconductors the SC phase transition can be considered as a two-stage process: the precursor Cooper pairing above $T_c$ and the subsequent transitions of composite bosonic Cooper pairs to the SF Bose-liquid states at their attractive PC at $T_c$ and SPC at $T_c^* < T_c$. Our view, which we discuss in the rest of the book is that the unconventional superconductivity in high-$T_c$ cuprates and other systems is actually driven by the PC and SPC condensation of composite bosonic Cooper pairs and described by the mean-field theory of boson pairing similar to the BCS pairing theory of fermions [7]. Unlike the BCS condensate (i.e., Fermi superfluids), the pair and single-particle condensates of attracting pre-formed Cooper pairs are Bose superfluids, so that the extension of the theory of a SF Bose liquid to the bosonic subsystems of high-$T_c$ cuprates and other unconventional superconductors describes their novel superconductivity in the BCS-like pseudogap (PG) state naturally.

### 8.4.1.  Ground State of a Bose-liquid

Let us now discuss the possible SF states of a nonideal boson gas of both composite bosons (e.g., Cooper pairs) and non-composite ones such as $^4$He atoms or hypothetical holons in RVB model. First, we make a brief survey of the existing theories of SF Bose systems. Then we present the new microscopic theories of 3D and two-dimensional (2D) Bose superfluids. Landau [6] developed a simple phenomenological theory of superfluidity which explains reasonably well the behavior of a SF Bose-liquid of $^4$He at low temperatures not close to the $\lambda$-point. At that time the understanding of the SF state of $^4$He on a microscopic level was based on the BEC state of an ideal Bose gas [1]. As mentioned previously, the BEC of an ideal Bose gas cannot serve as a microscopic model for studying the SF properties of $^4$He (see also, Ref. [57]) and SC properties of electronic liquids in superconductors.

Bogoliubov [58] took an important step towards a theoretical understanding of the SF state of $^4$He and proposed a microscopic theory of superfluidity, which seeks to justify the Landau excitation spectrum and is based on the so-called $c$-number condensate of a repulsive Bose gas. Later, the Bogoliubov approximation has been discussed by other authors [59, 60, 61]. However, it turned out that the theory of a repulsive Bose-gas is unsuitable for studying the SF properties of $^4$He [62, 63]. Because the theory of repulsive Bose liquids or $c$-number-condensate theory [61] cannot explain a number of SF properties of $^4$He, such as the observed half-integral values of circulation [64], deviation of the specific heat from the phonon-like dependence [65] and the $\lambda$-like transition [54, 62], the condensate fraction $n_{B0} = N_{B0}/N_B$ (e.g., $c$-number theory predicts $n_{B0} > 1$ which is unphysical [63, 66]), and the depletion of the zero-momentum $k = 0$ state, where $N_{B0}$ is the number of Bose particles with $k = 0$ (here and further, for convenience, the CMM $\vec{K}$ of composite bosons is also replaced by $\vec{k}$), $N_B$ is the total number of Bose particles. Similar incorrect results are also predicted by the pair condensate theories of Girardeau and Arnowitt and others (see Ref. [66]). These inconsistencies in the theory of repulsive Bose liquids are caused by using the unnecessary Bogoliubov approximation (it was emphasized first by Luban [62], and then by Evans and Imry [63]) replacing the zero-momentum creation and annihilation operators by $c$-numbers. Moreover, there (with the exception [63, 67, 68] the important attractive part of the interboson interaction is ignored.

The next steps towards a microscopic theory of a nonideal Bose gas were made by Valatin and Butler [60], Luban [62], and Evans and Imry [63]; without using the Bogoliubov approximation. Although the approaches to the problem of SF condensation in a nonideal Bose gas proposed in Refs. [60, 62] are different from the $c$-number condensate theory of Bogoliubov, these approaches led to the Bogoliubov result in the case of a predominantly repulsive interaction. Also, the treatment of the zero-momentum ($\vec{k} = 0$) terms in the Valatin-Butler theory [60] led to the inconsistencies as pointed out by Evans and Imry [63]. The Luban's theory of superfluidity is tenable near $T_c$ which is redefined temperature $T_{BEC}$ of an ideal Bose gas (with the renormalized mass of bosons). In this theory, the nature of the $\lambda$-transition remains unknown. It is important to note that the Luban's theory at $T \geq T_c$ is the boson analog of Landau's Fermi-liquid theory. A more consistent numerical approach to the theory of a Bose-liquid was developed in Refs. [63] and [68] by taking into account both the repulsive and the attractive parts of interboson interaction. This pairing theory of the Bose superfluid is developed by analogy with the BCS pairing theory of fermions and is based on the concept of the PC of an attracting Bose gas. Further, a more general approach to the theory of a SF Bose-liquid was proposed by Dorre et al. [61]. This approach combines both the $c$-number condensate theory [58, 59] and boson pairing theory [63, 68] (i.e., the boson analog of the BCS theory). However, the pair BEC into the $k = 0$ state described in the pairing theories of bosons [61, 63, 68] are unphysical (as also argued in Ref. [69]). The validity of the $c$-number condensate theory [61] is controversial as it was noted by the authors themselves, and by Evans [70]. Moreover, Dorre et al. [61] assert that their (including also Evans and co-workers [63, 68]) pairing theory is also irrelevant to the SF state of $^4$He. It seems that the basic results of Ref. [61], such as the coexistence of the BEC-type and BEC-less pair states of attracting bosons, the order of the phase transition from the normal state to the SF state, the gapless energy spectrum up to $T_c$, the large condensate fraction $n_{B0} \simeq 0.93 - 0.96$ (see also Ref. [70]) are contradictory and at variance with the observed behavior of SF $^4$He. On the other hand, in the alternative models the so-called SPC and PC in an interacting Bose-gas have been studied at $T = 0$. Such models of a Bose-liquid with the interboson interaction potential, which has both repulsive and attractive parts, have been proposed in Refs. [67, 71], whereas the possibility of SPC and PC in a purely attractive Bose gas has been discussed in Ref. [69]. In these models, the possibility of SPC and PC of attracting bosons has not been explored for the important temperature range $0 < T \leq T_c$. Although some of the previously mentioned theories of a SF 3D Bose liquid [58, 62, 63, 71] were successful in explaining the Landau excitation spectrum, they were inadequate for the description of many observed SF properties of $^4$He.

After the discovery of the layered high-$T_c$ cuprate superconductors, a 2D model of an interacting Bose gas adapted to a 2D boson-like holon gas has been discussed in Refs. [72,

73], where, however, the PC (or SC transition) temperature $T_c$ of such exotic bosons was obtained in the weak coupling limit. From what has been already stated, it follows that the possible SF states and basic SF properties of Bose liquids were not established as functions of interboson interaction strength or coupling constant and temperature for the complete range $0 \leq T \leq T_c$, and the existing microscopic theories were not in a satisfactory state for understanding all the SF properties of $^4$He and other Bose-liquids. In this respect, more consistent and pertinent microscopic theories of SF Bose liquids describing the BEC-like SPC and BEC-less PC both in an interacting 3D Bose gas and in an interacting 2D Bose gas have been developed in Refs. [12, 13, 14, 47]. In these theories, the pair boson Hamiltonian and realistic BCS-like (i.e., with abandon the numerical pseudopotential) approximation for the interboson interaction potential are used to solve the self-consistent set of integral equations not only for $T = 0$ and weak interboson coupling, but also for the temperature range $0 < T \leq T_c$ and arbitrary interboson coupling strengths. In the next sections, we describe the essentials of such complete and detailed microscopic theories of SF states of 3D and 2D Bose liquids.

### 8.4.2. The Pair Hamiltonian Model

We consider a system of $N_B$ particles of mass $m_B$ and density $\rho_B$, contained in volume, $\Omega$, and start from the so-called pair Hamiltonian [12, 13, 14, 74] (see also Refs. [60, 63, 67]) which is the boson analog of the BCS pair Hamiltonian. In this Hamiltonian model, we take explicitly into account both the short-range repulsive (preventing collapse of an attractive Bose system) and long-range attractive interboson interactions. After the diagonalization of such a Hamiltonian by using the Bogoliubov transformations of Bose operators, we use the Evans and Imry's [63] elimination procedure of the $k = 0$ terms in the summations of the obtained equations and the boson analog of the BCS-like approximation for the interboson interaction potential [12, 13, 14, 74] which allows us to find thoroughly the analytical (including also numerical) solutions of the integral equations.

The Hamiltonian of the interacting Bose system, with the pair interaction between Bose particles has the form of Eq. (7.6) only by the absence of spin indices. The linearized part of this Hamiltonian (i.e., model Hamiltonian) may be written as

$$H = \sum_k \left[ \tilde{\varepsilon}_B(k) c_k^\dagger c_k + \frac{1}{2} \Delta_B(k) (c_{-k}^\dagger c_k^\dagger + c_k c_{-k}) \right] \tag{8.23}$$

where $\tilde{\varepsilon}(k) = \varepsilon(k) - \mu_B + V_B(0)\rho_B + \chi_B(k)$ is the Hartree-Fock quasiparticle energy, $\varepsilon(k) = \hbar^2 k^2 / 2m_B$ (here and further, for convenience, we replace $M_c^*$ by $m_B$), $\chi_B(k) = (1/\Omega) \sum_{k'} V_B(k - k') n_B(k)$, $\Delta_B(k) = (1/\Omega) \sum_{k'} V_B(k - k') \langle c_{-k'} c_{k'} \rangle$ is the coherence parameter, $n_B(k) = \langle c_k^\dagger c_k \rangle$ is the particle number operator, $\rho_B = (1/\Omega) \sum_{k'} n_B(k)$, $\mu_B$ is the chemical potential of a nonideal Bose gas, $c_k^\dagger (c_k)$ the creation (annihilation) operators of bosons with the wave vector $k$, $V_B(k - k')$ is the interboson interaction potential.

The Hamiltonian (8.23) is diagonalized by using the Bogoliubov transformations of Bose operators [75]

$$c_k = u_k \alpha_k + v_k \alpha_{-k}^+, \quad c_k^+ = u_k \alpha_k^+ + v_k \alpha_{-k}, \tag{8.24}$$

where $\alpha_k$ and $\alpha_k^+$ are new Bose operators which satisfy the Bose commutation rules, $u_k$ and $v_k$ are functions which satisfy the condition $u_k^2 - v_k^2 = 1$. Substituting Eq. (8.24) into Eq. (8.23), and neglecting the terms with three and four boson operators, we obtain the diagonalized Hamiltonian

$$H = E_0 + \sum_k E_B(k)\alpha_k^+\alpha_k, \tag{8.25}$$

where $E_0 = \frac{1}{2}\sum_k[E_B(k) - \tilde{\varepsilon}_B(k)]$ is the ground-state energy of a Bose-liquid and $E_B(k)$ is the excitation spectrum of interacting bosons given by

$$E_B(k) = \sqrt{\tilde{\varepsilon}_B^2(k) - \Delta_B^2(k)}, \tag{8.26}$$

The parameters $\Delta_B(k)$, $\mu_B$ and $\chi_B(k)$ in Eq. (8.26) are determined from simultaneous equations

$$\Delta_B(k) = -\frac{1}{\Omega}\sum_{k'} V_B(k-k')\frac{\Delta_B(k')}{2E_B(k')}\coth\frac{E_B(k')}{2k_BT} \tag{8.27}$$

$$N_B = \sum_k n_B(k) = \sum_{k'}\left[\frac{\tilde{\varepsilon}_B(k)}{2E_B(k)}\coth\frac{E_B(k)}{2k_BT} - \frac{1}{2}\right] \tag{8.28}$$

$$\chi_B(k) = \frac{1}{\Omega}\sum_{k'} V_B(k-k')\left[\frac{\tilde{\varepsilon}_B(k')}{2E_B(k')}\coth\frac{E_B(k')}{2k_BT} - \frac{1}{2}\right] \tag{8.29}$$

by means of their self-consistent solution.

As is well known, the BCS-like excitation spectrum of interacting fermions has a gap for all $\vec{k}$ in the case of s-wave pairing and is gapless only at some isolated points or lines on the Fermi surface in the cases of p- and d-wave pairing. The excitation spectrum of a SF Bose-liquid is rather different from that of a BCS-like Fermi-liquid. As seen from (8.26), if $|\tilde{\mu}_B| = -\mu_B + V_B(0)\rho_B + \chi_B(0) = |\Delta_B(0)|$, then the excitation spectrum of interacting bosons becomes gapless for $k = 0$ and $k' = 0$. Therefore, for obtaining the self-consistent solutions of Eqs. (8.27)-(8.29) the $k = 0$ and $k' = 0$ terms in the summation of these equations should be considered separately according to the procedure proposed in [63] as

$$\Delta_B(k) = -V_B(k)\rho_{B0}sign(\Delta_B(0))$$
$$-\frac{1}{\Omega}\sum_{k'}' V_B(k-k')\frac{\Delta_B(k')}{2E_B(k')}\coth\frac{E_B(k')}{2k_BT} \tag{8.30}$$

$$N_B = N_{B0} + \sum_{k'}'\left[\frac{\tilde{\varepsilon}_B(k)}{2E_B(k)}\coth\frac{E_B(k)}{2k_BT} - \frac{1}{2}\right] \tag{8.31}$$

$$\chi_B(k) = V_B(k)\rho_{B0} + \frac{1}{\Omega}\sum_{k'}' V_B(k-k')\left[\frac{\tilde{\varepsilon}_B(k)}{2E_B(k')}\coth\frac{E_B(k')}{2k_BT} - \frac{1}{2}\right], \tag{8.32}$$

where $\rho_{B0} = N_{B0}/\Omega$ is the density of Bose particles with $k = 0$.

### 8.4.3. Choice of the Pair Interaction Model Potential

Let us choose now a model pair interaction potential which has repulsive $V_{BR}$ and attractive $V_{BA}$ parts. In order to simplify the solutions of the equations for $\Delta_B(k)$, $N_B$, and $\chi_B(k)$, the pair interboson interaction potential may be chosen in a simple separable form as is done in the BCS-like pairing theory [13, 14, 74]

$$
V_B(k - k') = \begin{cases} V_{BR} - V_{BA} & \text{if } 0 \leq \varepsilon(k), \varepsilon(k') < \xi_{BA}, \\ V_{BR} & \text{if } \xi_{BA} \leq \varepsilon(k) \text{ or } \varepsilon(k') < \xi_{BR}, \\ 0 & \text{if } \varepsilon(k), \varepsilon(k') > \xi_{BR}, \end{cases} \tag{8.33}
$$

where $\xi_{BA}$ and $\xi_{BR}$ are the cutoff energies for attractive and repulsive parts of the $V_B(k - k')$, respectively.

This approximation allows us to carry out the calculation thoroughly and so it gives us a new insight to the problem of condensation (i.e., on the possible properties of a SF Bose-liquid). Further, we assume $\xi_{BR} >> \xi_{BA} >> |\tilde{\mu}_B| = -\mu_B + V_B(0)\rho + \chi_B(k_A) \sim \Delta_B \sim T_c$ (here and further, for convenience, we take $k_B = 1$), where $T_c$ is the mean-field temperature characterizing the appearance of the order parameter $\Delta_B$ of a SF Bose condensate. The cutoff parameter $\xi_{BA}$ characterizes the thickness of the condensation layer including almost all Bose particles. Therefore, the main contribution to the sums in Eqs. (8.27)–(8.29) comes from those values of $k$ less than $k_A$, whereas the large values of $k > k_A$ give small corrections that may be neglected. Before discussing the solutions of Eqs. (8.30)–(8.32), let us consider the formation of a boson pair in a dilute Bose gas taking into account only the interaction between two bosons. In the present case, we are dealing with the problem of the Cooper pairing in a dilute Bose system [14, 74]. In order to solve this problem, we use the model potential (8.33). Then the binding energy $E_b$ of two Bose particles is determined from the following Cooper-type equation:

$$
\tilde{V}_B \sum_{k=0}^{k_A} \frac{1}{2\varepsilon(k) - E_b} = 1, \tag{8.34}
$$

where $\tilde{V}_B = V_{BA} - V_{BR}[1 + V_{BR}I_R]^{-1}$, $I_B = \sum_{k=k_A}^{k_R}(2\varepsilon(k) - E_b)^{-1}$. The sum over the momenta can be expressed as an integral over the energies in terms of DOS $D_B(\varepsilon)$. At $\xi_{BA} >> E_b$, we obtain $I_B = \frac{1}{2}D_B\ln(\xi_{BR}/\xi_{BA})$, $D_B = m_B/2\pi\hbar^2$ and $I_B \simeq D_B[\sqrt{\xi_{BR}} - \sqrt{\xi_{BA}}]$, $D_B = \sqrt{2}m_B^{3/2}/2\pi^2\hbar^3$ for 2D and 3D Bose systems, respectively. Moreover, from (8.34), we obtain the following equation for determination of the binding energy $E_b$ of a isolated boson pair in a dilute 3D Bose gas:

$$
y\arctan\left(\frac{1}{y}\right) = \frac{\gamma_B - 1}{\gamma_B}, \tag{8.35}
$$

where $y = \sqrt{|E_b|/2\xi_{BA}}$, $\gamma_B = \tilde{V}_B D_B \sqrt{\xi_{BA}}$ is the coupling constant of the interboson interaction.

### 8.4.4. Superfluid Single Particle and Pair Condensation in an Interacting Three-dimensional Bose Gas

Let us first consider the case $T = 0$. Replacing the summation in Eqs. (8.27)–(8.29) over $k$ and $k'$ by an integration over $\varepsilon$ and making elementary transformations, we obtain the following equations for determination of the critical values of $\rho_B$ and $|\tilde{\mu}_B|$ at which the BEC-like SPC of interacting bosons sets in due to the vanishing of the energy gap $E_B(0) = \sqrt{\tilde{\mu}_B^2 - \Delta_B^2}$ in their excitation spectrum (see Appendix B):

$$\rho_B = \frac{D_B \xi_{BA}^{3/2}}{48} \left( \frac{\gamma_B^2 - 1}{\gamma_B} \right)^3 \tag{8.36}$$

$$|\tilde{\mu}_B| = \frac{\xi_{BA}}{2} \left( \frac{\gamma_B^2 - 1}{2\gamma_B} \right)^2, \tag{8.37}$$

As one can see from (8.35), the formation of the bound state of an isolated boson pair is possible only at $\gamma_B > \gamma_B^* = 1$ that coincides with the critical value of $\gamma_B^*$ determined from (8.36) in a dilute Bose system ($\rho_B \to 0$, $\Delta_B = 0$). In the dilute limit, we have $E_b = 2|\tilde{\mu}_B|$. Indeed, such a situation corresponding to the picture of isolated or incoherent boson pairs can arise only at a certain strong enough attraction between two bosons in the dilute phase as discussed before in Ref. [69]. However, at finite densities of bosons the energy gap $E_B(0) = \Delta_{SF}$ (which, in our context, may be called as the "SF gap" for the excitation of pair condensate) vanishes even for stronger couplings. According to (8.36), this means that the SF pair condensation of bosons sets in at $\gamma > \gamma_B^* > 1$ and the binding energy $2\Delta_{SF}$ of the boson pairs in their interacting collective (i.e., in the undilute case) decreases and becomes smaller than $2|\tilde{\mu}_B|$. Whereas the SPC of bosons sets in at $\gamma_B = \gamma_B^* > 1$ at which the gap $\Delta_{SF}$ closes. At this point, the Cooper-like boson pairs overlap strongly and loose their identity. The SF pair condensate disappears at $\gamma_B \leq \gamma_B^*$. The value of $|\tilde{\mu}_B|$ at $\gamma_B = \gamma_B^*$ is equal to [14, 74] (see Appendix B)

$$|\tilde{\mu}_B| = |\Delta_B| = 2.88 T_{BEC}. \tag{8.38}$$

¿From Eqs. (8.37) and (8.38), it follows that the critical value of $\gamma_B$ at which the phase transitions SPC⇔PC in the undilute phase of a Bose gas take place is equal to

$$\gamma_B^* = 2.404 \sqrt{\frac{T_{BEC}}{\xi_{BA}}} + \sqrt{1 + \frac{5.779 T_{BEC}}{\xi_{BA}}}. \tag{8.39}$$

For $\gamma_B \leq \gamma_B^*$ and $T_c \lesssim 3 T_{BEC}$, we obtain

$$g_B = \frac{2\Delta_B}{T_c} \lesssim 1.92. \tag{8.40}$$

For $\gamma_B < \gamma_B^*$ the fraction of condensed bosons in the zero-momentum state $n_{B0} = \rho_{B0}/\rho_B$ is determined as a function of $\gamma_B$ from the equations [14] (see Appendix B)

$$3(\rho_B - \rho_{B0}) = \sqrt{2}|\tilde{\mu}_B|^{3/2} D_B, \tag{8.41}$$

$$\rho_{B0} = \frac{D_B |\tilde{\mu}_B| \sqrt{\xi_{BA}}}{\gamma_B} \left[ 1 - \gamma_B \left( \sqrt{1 + \frac{2|\tilde{\mu}_B|}{\xi_{BA}}} - \sqrt{\frac{2|\tilde{\mu}_B|}{\xi_{BA}}} \right) \right], \tag{8.42}$$

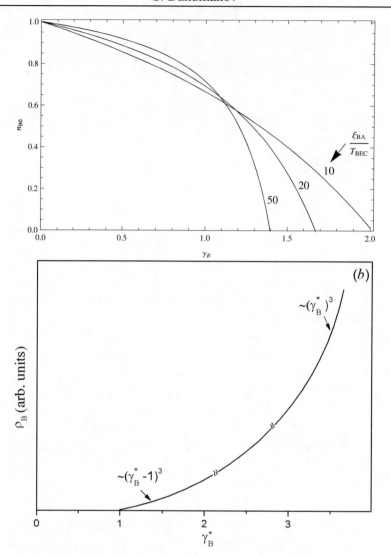

Figure 8.1. Variation of condensate fraction (a) and boson concentration (b) in a SF 3D Bose-liquid with coupling constant $\gamma_B$ for $T = 0$ and $\xi_{BA}/T_{BEC} = 10$, 20 and 50.

where $\rho_{B0} = N_{B0}/\Omega$ is the density of Bose particles with $k = 0$.

The dependence of the condensate fraction $n_{B0}$ and boson concentration $\rho_B$ on the coupling constant $\gamma_B$ in a SF 3D Bose-liquid at $T = 0$ and $\xi_{BA}/T_{BEC} = 10$, 20, and 50 is shown in Fig. 8.1. We now examine the numerical and analytical solutions of Eqs. (8.27) – (8.29) obtained using the model potential (8.33) for the case $T \neq 0$. In particular, the numerical solutions of these equations for $\gamma_B > \gamma_B^*$ exhibit only a second-order phase transition (i.e., PC) in an interacting Bose gas at $T = T_c$ without any feature of the order parameter $\Delta_B(T)$ below $T_c$ (see Fig. 8.2a). Such solutions of Eqs. (8.27) – (8.29) for $\gamma_B < \gamma_B^*$ exhibit two successive phase transitions with decreasing $T$, such as a second-order phase transition at $T = T_c$ and a first-order phase transition (i.e., SPC) in an interacting Bose gas at $T = T_c^*$ at which the energy gap $\Delta_{SF}$ vanishes and the order parameter $\Delta_B(T)$ shows the pronounced (at $\gamma_B << \gamma_B^*$) and in some cases not very pronounced (at $\gamma_B < \gamma_B^*$) kink-like behavior (see Figs. 8.2b and 8.2c). For $\gamma_B < \gamma_B^*$ the first-order phase transitions SPC $\Leftrightarrow$ PC takes place at $T = T_c^* << T_c$ in strongly interacting Bose gas. However, for $\gamma_B << \gamma_B^*$ such phase transitions occur at $T \geq 0.5T_c$ or somewhat below $T_c$ in weakly interacting Bose gas [14]. The numerical and analytical solutions of Eqs. (8.27) – (8.29) with using the separable interaction model (8.33) show that for $\gamma_B < \gamma_B^*$ the energy gap $\Delta_{SF}$ in $E_B(k)$ vanishes at $T = T_c^* << T_c$, whereas such a gap closes somewhat below $T_c$ or even near $T_c$ for $\gamma_B << \gamma_B^*$ [14]. In limit cases, the solutions of Eqs. (8.27) – (8.29) may be obtained also analytically. Indeed, for $\gamma_B < \gamma_B^*$ and $T \leq T_c^* << T_c$, we can assume $|\tilde{\mu}_B| = \Delta_B$ and use Eqs. (8.30) – (8.32) to study the behavior of $n_{B0}(T)$ and $|\tilde{\mu}_B(T)| = \Delta_B(T)$. From these equations it follows [14, 74] (see Appendix C) that

$$3(\rho_B - \rho_{B0}) \simeq D_B \left[ \sqrt{2}|\tilde{\mu}_B|^{3/2} + \frac{(\pi T)^2}{2\sqrt{2}|\tilde{\mu}_B|} \right] \tag{8.43}$$

$$-\rho_{B0} \simeq \left[ \sqrt{\xi_{BA} + 2|\tilde{\mu}_B|} - \sqrt{2}|\tilde{\mu}_B| + \frac{(\pi T)^2}{6\sqrt{2}|\tilde{\mu}_B|^{3/2}} - \frac{\sqrt{\xi_{BA}}}{\gamma_B} \right] D_B \tilde{\mu}_B. \tag{8.44}$$

The values of $T_c^*(\gamma_B)$ and $n_{B0}(T)$ can be obtained from Eqs. (8.43) and (8.44). At $T < T_c^* << T_c$, we obtain the following expression for $n_{B0}(T)$:

$$n_{B0}(T) = n_{B0}(0)[1 - gT^2], \tag{8.45}$$

where $g = m_B/12\rho_{B0}\hbar^2 v_s$, $v_s = \sqrt{|\tilde{\mu}_B|/m_B}$ is the sound velocity. Such an expression for $n_{B0}(T)$ was also obtained in the framework of the phenomenological approach [76]; where, however, instead of $\rho_{B0}(0)$ stands $\rho_B$ that correspond to the BEC of an ideal Bose gas. On the other hand, $n_{B0}(T)$ near $T_c^* (<< T_c)$ is proportional to $T_c^* - T$. Now, we consider the other limit case $\gamma_B << \gamma_B^*$ at which $\Delta_B << T_c$, $|\tilde{\mu}_B| << T_c$. In this case, the solution of Eqs. (8.27) – (8.29) may be found analytically, and, upon approaching $T_c$ we obtain (see Appendix C)

$$2.612\sqrt{\pi}T_{BEC}^{3/2} \simeq \sqrt{\pi}T^{3/2} \left[ 2.612 - 2\sqrt{\frac{\pi|\tilde{\mu}_B|}{T}} \left( 1 - \frac{\Delta_B^2}{8|\tilde{\mu}_B|^2} \right) \right], \tag{8.46}$$

$$\frac{1}{\gamma_B} \simeq \frac{\pi T}{2\sqrt{|\tilde{\mu}_B|\xi_{BA}}} \left( 1 + \frac{\Delta_B^2}{8|\tilde{\mu}_B|^2} \right), \tag{8.47}$$

from which at $T = T_c$ and $\Delta_B = 0$ it follows that

$$x^{3/2} - 2.13\gamma_B x^2 \sqrt{\frac{T_{BEC}}{\xi_{BA}}} = 1, \tag{8.48}$$

where $x = T_c/T_{BEC}$

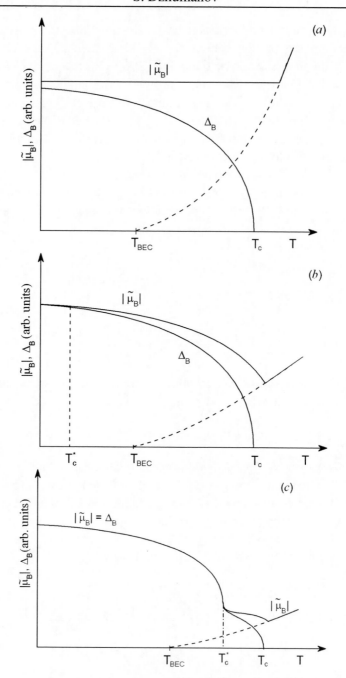

Figure 8.2. Temperature dependences of the chemical potential $\tilde{\mu}_B$ and order parameter $\Delta_B$ for an interacting 3D Bose gas (solid curves), for different coupling constants $\gamma_B$: (a) for $\gamma_B > \gamma_B^*$; (b) for $\gamma_B < \gamma_B^*$ and (c) for $\gamma_B \ll \gamma_B^*$. Dashed curves indicate temperature dependences of the chemical potential of an ideal 3D Bose gas.

If $\gamma_B \ll 1$, then we obtain from Eqs. (8.47) and Eqs. (8.48)

$$2.612\sqrt{\pi}T_c^{3/2} = 2.612\sqrt{\pi}T_{BEC}^{3/2} + \pi^2\gamma_B T_c^{3/2}\sqrt{T_c/\xi_{BA}} \qquad (8.49)$$

At $\gamma_B \to 0$, $T_c \to T_{BEC}$, and therefore, $T_c$ on the right-hand side of Eq. (8.49) can be replaced by $T_{BEC}$. Thus, at $\gamma_B << 1$ , we have

$$T_c \simeq T_{BEC} \left[1 + c\gamma_B \sqrt{T_{BEC}/\xi_{BA}}\right], \tag{8.50}$$

where $c = \pi^{3/2}/3.912$.

According to Eqs. (8.47) and (8.48), the temperature dependences of $\Delta_B$ and $|\tilde{\mu}_B|$ near the temperature $T_c$ of the second-order SF phase transition in an interacting 3D Bose gas are defined as [14, 74] (see Appendix C)

$$|\tilde{\mu}_B|(T) \simeq |\tilde{\mu}_B|(T_c) \left[1 + a \left(\frac{T_c - T}{T_c}\right)^{0.5}\right], \tag{8.51}$$

$$\Delta_B \simeq 2|\tilde{\mu}_B(T_c)| \sqrt{a} \left(\frac{T_c - T}{T_c}\right)^{0.25}, \tag{8.52}$$

where $a = 2(c\gamma_B)^{-0.5}(\xi_{BA}/T_c^*)^{0.25}$.

In the case $T \to T_c^*$ and $|\tilde{\mu}_B(T_c^*)| << T_c^* \le T_c$, the solutions of Eqs. (8.30) – (8.32) are obtained analogous to the solutions of Eqs. (8.27) - (8.29) at $T \to T_c$. Then the temperature dependences of $\tilde{\mu}_B$ (or $\Delta_B$) and $n_{B0}$ near the temperature $T_c^* < T_c$ of the first-order SF phase transition in an interacting 3D Bose gas are determined from the relations [14] (see Appendix C)

$$|\tilde{\mu}_B|(T) \simeq |\tilde{\mu}_B|(T_c^*) \left[1 + b \left[\frac{T_c^* - T}{T_c^*}\right]^{0.5}\right], \tag{8.53}$$

$$n_{B0}(T) \simeq \frac{b\gamma_B D_B (\pi T_c^*)^2}{2\rho_B \sqrt{2\xi_{BA}}} \left(\frac{T_c^* - T}{T_c^*}\right)^{0.5}, \tag{8.54}$$

where $b = (c\gamma_B)^{-0.5}(\xi_{BA}/T_c^*)^{0.25}$.

One can see that for $\gamma_B << \gamma_B^*$ the chemical potential $|\tilde{\mu}_B|$ and order parameter $\Delta_B$ have the kink-like temperature dependences around $T_c^*(< T_c)$. From Eq. (8.47) (at $\Delta_B = 0$) and the left side of Eq. (C.18) in Appendix C, it follows that for $1 < (|\tilde{\mu}_B(T_c^*)|/|\tilde{\mu}_B(T_c)|) \le 2$, $T/\sqrt{2} \le T_c^* \le T_c$. Whereas the condition $T_c^* > T_{BEC}$ follows from the left side of Eq. (C.18) (that is roughly equal to $2.612 T_{BEC}^{3/2}$ at $T = T_c^*$) in Appendix C. It is easy to show that the gap energy $\Delta_{SF}$ in $E_B(k)$ for $\gamma_B << \gamma_B^*$ will appear somewhat below $T_c$ and its magnitude is determined from

$$\Delta_{SF}(T) = |\tilde{\mu}_B|(T_c) \left[1 - a \left(1 - \frac{T}{T_c}\right)^{0.5}\right] \tag{8.55}$$

The values of $\gamma_B^*$ in interacting 3D Bose systems are approximately equal to 2.0, 1.7, and 1.4 for $\xi_{BA}/T_{BEC} = 10, 20$ and $50$. In the limit cases $\gamma_B < \gamma_B^*$ and $\gamma_B << \gamma_B^*$, the characteristic

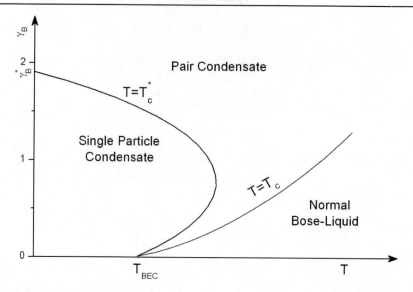

Figure 8.3. Phase diagram of an interacting 3D Bose gas for $\xi_{BA}/T_{BEC} = 10$, (illustrating the possible successive) phase transitions with decreasing $T$ and $\gamma_B$, such as normal Bose-liquid→ SF pair condensate →SF single particle condensate transitions at $\gamma_B < \gamma_B^*$, SF pair condensate → normal Bose-liquid transition at $T > 1.4T_{BEC}$, SF pair condensate → SF single particle condensate → SF pair condensate → normal Bose liquid transitions at $T > T_{BEC}$ and SF pair condensate → SF single particle condensate at $T < T_c^*$. Second order and first-order phase transition lines meet at the critical point, i.e., at $T = T_{BEC}$.

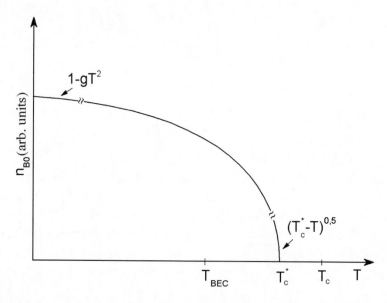

Figure 8.4. Temperature dependence of condensate fraction $n_{B0}$ in a SF 3D Bose-liquid.

temperatures $T_c^*$ of the first order SF phase transitions corresponding to these cases are close to $T = 0$ and $T = T_c$, respectively. The obtained results, in particular, the phase diagram of an interacting 3D Bose gas is presented in Fig. 8.3 and the temperature dependence of $n_{B0}$ is shown in Fig. 8.4. There are three different phases, namely, the normal Bose-liquid, SF pair condensate, and SF single particle condensate phases. Thus, there are two characteristic temperatures on the phase diagram, $T_c^*$ an $T_c$, denoting the critical temperatures for the onset of SPC⇔PC transition and for the onset of superfluidity in an interacting Bose gas, respectively.

### 8.4.5. Superfluid Single Particle and Pair Condensation in an Interacting Two-dimensional Bose-gas

Let us now consider the case of an interacting 2D Bose gas at $T = 0$. Replacing the summation in Eqs. (8.27) – (8.29) by an integration, we can find the critical values of $\gamma_B$ and $\tilde{\mu}_B$ at which the gap energy $\Delta_{SF}$ vanishes in the excitation spectrum of a SF 2D Bose-liquid. This critical value of $\gamma_B$ is determined from the relation [72]

$$\gamma_B^* = \frac{1}{Ar\sinh\sqrt{[\xi_{BA}/4T_0]}} \tag{8.56}$$

that corresponds to the value of $|\tilde{\mu}_B| = 2T_0$, where $T_0 = 2\pi\hbar^2\rho_B/m_B$.

The binding energy of isolated boson pairs in a dilute 2D Bose gas is determined from (8.34) just as the binding energy of isolated fermion pairs above the Fermi sea in metals and bound boson pairs is formed at weak interboson interaction (i.e., at $\gamma_B > 0$). In the case of a dilute 2D Bose gas ($\Delta_B = 0$), the boson pairs are formed with the binding energy $E_B = 2|\tilde{\mu}_B|$. At $\gamma_B > \gamma_B^*$, the boson pairs in a non-dilute 2D Bose gas are formed with the binding energy $E_B = 2\Delta_{SF} < 2|\tilde{\mu}_B|$. The binding energy of a boson pair $E_b$ in a dilute 2D Bose gas determined from Eq. (8.34) is given by

$$E_b = 2\xi_{BA}\exp(-1/\gamma_B), \tag{8.57}$$

where $\gamma_B = \tilde{V}_B D_B$.

The value of $\rho_{B0}$ is determined from the simultaneous equations [14] (see Appendix B)

$$2(\rho_B - \rho_{B0}) \simeq D_B|\tilde{\mu}_B|, \tag{8.58}$$

$$\rho_{B0} = \frac{D_B|\tilde{\mu}_B|}{\gamma_B}\left[1 - \frac{\gamma_B}{2}\ln\left(\frac{\sqrt{\xi_{BA}^2 + 2|\tilde{\mu}_B|\xi_{BA}} + (\xi_{BA} + |\tilde{\mu}_B|)}{|\tilde{\mu}_B|}\right)\right]. \tag{8.59}$$

The dependences of the condensate fraction $n_{B0}$ and boson concentration $\rho_B$ on the coupling constant $\gamma_B$ in a SF 2D Bose-liquid at $T = 0$ and $\xi_{BA}/T_0 = 5$, 10, and 30 are presented in Fig. 8.5.

Let us turn next to the case $T \neq 0$. In this case, the energy gap

$$\Delta_{SF} = -2T\ln\left[\frac{1}{2}\left(\sqrt{4 + \eta^2} - \eta\right)\right] \tag{8.60}$$

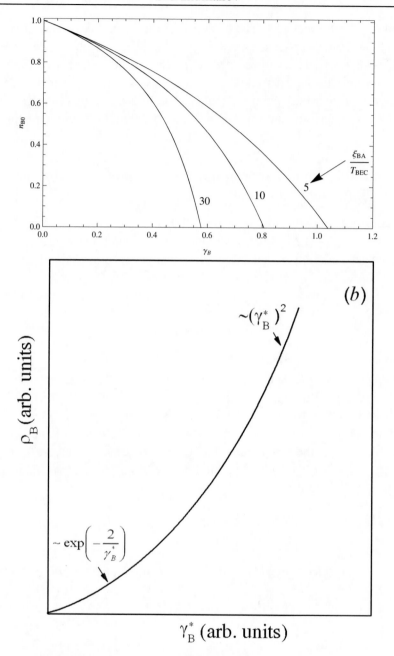

Figure 8.5. Variation of condensate fraction (a) and boson concentration (b) in a SF 2D Bose-liquid with coupling constant $\gamma_B$ for $T = 0$ and $\xi_{BA}/T_0 = 5$, 10, and 30.

always exists in $E_B(k)$, [72], where $\eta = \exp[(|\tilde{\mu}_B| - 2T_0)/2T]$. At low temperatures the temperature dependence of $\Delta_B$ has the form [14] (see Appendix C)

$$\Delta_B(T) \simeq \frac{Z}{2}T + \sqrt{\Delta_B^2(0) + \frac{Z-4}{4Z}(ZT)^2}, \tag{8.61}$$

where

$$Z = \frac{\exp(4/\gamma_B)}{[1+\exp(2/(\gamma_B)/2)^2]}, \quad \Delta_B(0) \simeq \frac{\xi_{BA}+|\tilde{\mu}_B|}{\sqrt{1+(\exp(2/\gamma_B)/2)^2}}.$$

¿From (8.61), we see that $\Delta_B$ decreases with increasing temperature and the temperature dependence of $\Delta_B$ and $|\tilde{\mu}_B|$ near $T_c$ can be written as [14] (see Appendix C)

$$\Delta_B(T) = (2+\gamma_B)T_c \left[ \left( \frac{T}{T_c} \right)^{2-q} - \frac{T}{T_c} \right] \tag{8.62}$$

and

$$|\tilde{\mu}_B|(T) = \sqrt{\Delta_B^2(T) + (2T_c)^2 \left( \frac{\gamma_B}{2+\gamma_B} \right)^2 \left( \frac{T}{T_c} \right)^{2q}}. \tag{8.63}$$

where the value of $q$ must be determined for the given values of $\gamma_B$ and $T/T_c$ by means of the self-consistent solution of (8.60), (8.62) and (8.63). The temperature dependences of $\Delta_B$ and $|\tilde{\mu}_B|$ are shown in Fig. 8.6.

It is important to go beyond the weak coupling limit and to derive a simple and more general expression for $T_c$, which should be valid not only for $\gamma_B << 1$ but also for $\gamma_B \leq 1$. Such an expression for $T_c$ can now be derived by equating the chemical potential of an ideal 2D Bose gas

$$|\tilde{\mu}_B|(T_c) = T_c \ln \left[ 1 - \exp \left( -\frac{T_0}{T_c} \right) \right] \tag{8.64}$$

with the expression (8.63) at $T = T_c$ (see dashed and solid curves in Figs. 8.6a and 8.6b). In so doing, we find the following expression for $T_c$:

$$T_c = -\frac{T_0}{\ln[1-\exp(-2\gamma_B/(2+\gamma_B))]} \tag{8.65}$$

from which at a particular case $\gamma_B << 1$ follows the result [72]. The phase diagram of an interacting 2D Bose gas is presented in Fig. 8.7.

## 8.4.6.  Concentration Dependences of the Superfluid Transition Temperatures in Nonideal 3D and 2D Bose Gases

In sections 8.4.4 and 8.4.5, the expressions for the SF transition temperatures in interacting 3D and 2D Bose gases are derived without taking into account the concentration dependences of $T_c$ and these expressions are valid for comparatively low concentrations of bosons. Therefore, we present now more correct expressions for $T_c$ obtained taking into account the dependence of $T_c$ on boson concentration entering the modified effective mass $m_B^*$ of interacting bosons within the applicability of this model. In order to find of the effective mass $m_B^*$ of the interacting bosons, there is no necessity to use the approximation (8.33) for the interboson interaction potential $V_B(k-k')$.

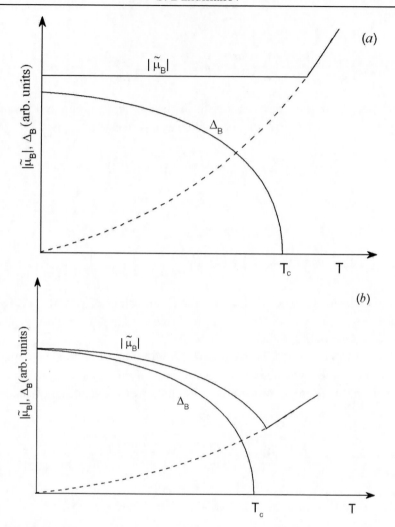

Figure 8.6. Temperature dependences of the chemical potential $\tilde{\mu}_B$ and order parameter $\Delta_B$ for an interacting 2D Bose gas (solid curves), for different coupling constants $\gamma_B$: (a) for $\gamma_B > \gamma_B^*$ and (b) for $\gamma_B < \gamma_B^*$. Dashed curves indicate temperature dependences of the chemical potential of an ideal 2D Bose gas.

Let us consider first the question of the concentration dependence of $T_c$ in an interacting 3D Bose gas. For this purpose, the desired expression for $\tilde{\varepsilon}_B(k)$ can be obtained using the effective mass approximation proposed in Ref. [62]. According to Ref. [62], the Fourier transform of $V_B(r)$ is given by

$$V_B(r) = \frac{4\pi W R^3}{kR} \int\limits_0^\infty dx x \Phi(x) \sin kRx \qquad (8.66)$$

where $W$ and $R$ are the energy and range parameters, respectively, $x = r/R$. After expanding the $V_B(r)$ in a Taylor series around $kR = 0$ (with a radius of convergence not smaller than

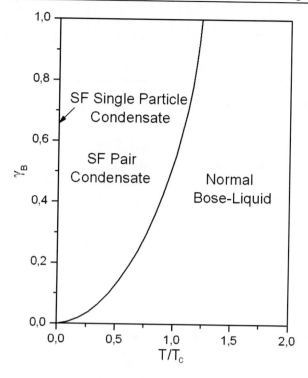

Figure 8.7. The phase diagram of an interacting 2D Bose gas for $\gamma_B \leq 1$, illustrating the possible SF single particle condensate (at $T = 0$), SF pair condensate (at $T > 0$) and normal (at $T > T_c$) states of a 2D Bose-liquid.

$kR = 1$ for $\Phi(x) = e^{-x}/x$) and some algebraic transformations [62], one obtains

$$\tilde{\varepsilon}_B(k) = \tilde{\varepsilon}_B(0) + \frac{\hbar^2 k^2}{2m_B^*}, \qquad 0 \leq k \leq k_A \tag{8.67}$$

where $k_A = \sqrt{2m_B \xi_{BA}}/\hbar \simeq (10R)^{-1}$ and $m_B^*$ satisfies

$$\frac{1}{m_B^*} = \frac{1}{m_B} - \frac{V_B(0)}{\pi^2 \hbar^2 k_R^2} \int_0^{k_A} dk k^2 \frac{1}{\exp[(\tilde{\varepsilon}_B(0) + \hbar^2 k^2/2m_B^*)/T] - 1}, \tag{8.68}$$

where $k_R = \sqrt{2m_B \xi_{BR}} \hbar$. Further, the density of Bose particles can be defined as

$$\rho_B = \int_0^{k_A} dk k^2 \frac{1}{\exp[(\tilde{\varepsilon}_B(0) + \hbar^2 k^2/2m_B^*)/T] - 1} \tag{8.69}$$

Comparing Eq. (8.68) with Eq. (8.69), we conclude that the effective mass of interacting bosons is

$$m_B^* = m_B \left[1 - \frac{\rho_B V_B(0)}{\xi_{BR}}\right]^{-1} \tag{8.70}$$

Then, the BEC temperature of an ideal 3D Bose gas with such renormalized mass of bosons is defined as [14] (see also Ref. [62])

$$T^*_{BEC}(\rho_B, m^*_B) = T_{BEC}(\rho_B, m_B)\left[1 - \frac{\rho_B V_B(0)}{\xi_{BR}}\right] \tag{8.71}$$

Accordingly, the BEC temperature $T_{BEC}$ of free bosons in Eqs. (8.48) and (8.50) should be replaced by $T^*_{BEC}$. Therefore, the behavior of $T_c(\rho_B)$ is now controlled by the behavior of $T^*_{BEC}(\rho_B, m^*_B)$. In this case, one can expect that $T_c$ first rises nearly as $\sim \rho_B^{2/3}$, and then goes through a maximum (at some $\rho_B = \rho_B^*$ determined from $\partial T^*_{BEC}(\rho_B, m^*_B)/\partial \rho_B = 0$), after that starts to decrease (Fig. 8.8). The description of the subsequent decreasing trend of $T_c$ within the present model is impossible. A similar result has also been obtained for the concentration dependence of $T_c$ in an interacting 2D Bose gas [14]. In this case, the Fourier transform of $V_B(r)$ is given by

$$V_B(k) = 2\pi \int_0^\infty dr V_B(r) J_0(kr) r, \tag{8.72}$$

where $J_0(kr)$ is the zero-order Bessel function.

Further, the potential $V_B(r)$ may be approximated just as in the case of a 3D Bose gas as $V_B(r) = W\Phi(x)$. Then we have

$$V_B(k) = 2\pi W R^2 \int_0^\infty dx x \Phi(x) J_0(kRx). \tag{8.73}$$

After expanding $V_B(k)$ in a Taylor series around $kR = 0$ (with a radius of convergence not smaller than $kR = \sqrt{2}$ for $\Phi(x) = e^{-x}/x$) and some algebraic transformations (see Appendix D), we obtain the equations, which are analogous to Eqs. (8.67) – (8.70). As mentioned before, the chemical potential of bosons with the effective mass $m^*_B$ at $T = T_c$ should be equal to the chemical potential of an ideal Bose gas of such bosons, i.e.,

$$\tilde{\mu}_B(T_c(m^*_B)) = T_c(m^*_B)\ln\left[1 - \frac{\exp(-T_0(m^*_B))}{T_c(m^*_B)}\right]. \tag{8.74}$$

The analogous relation may be written for the free bosons with the mass $m_B$

$$\tilde{\mu}_B(T_c(m_B)) = T_c(m_B)\ln\left[1 - \frac{\exp(-T_0(m_B))}{T_c(m_B)}\right]. \tag{8.75}$$

¿From Eqs. (8.74) and (8.75), we have (see Appendix D)

$$T_c(m^*_B) = \frac{m_B}{m^*_B} T_c(m_B) \tag{8.76}$$

Further, using Eq. (8.65), we find [14]

$$T_c(\rho_B) = -\frac{T_0(m_B)[1 - \rho_B V_B(0)/\xi_{BR}]}{\ln[1 - \exp(-2\gamma_B/(2 + \gamma_B))]} \tag{8.77}$$

from which it follows that at $\rho_B = \rho_B^* = \xi_{BR}/2V_B(0)$, $\partial T_c/\partial \rho_B = 0$ and $\partial^2 T_c/\partial \rho_B^2 < 0$. This means that $T_c$ first increases nearly as $\sim \rho_B$ and then goes through a maximum at $\rho_B = \rho_B^*$, after that will decrease just as in the case of a 3D Bose gas.

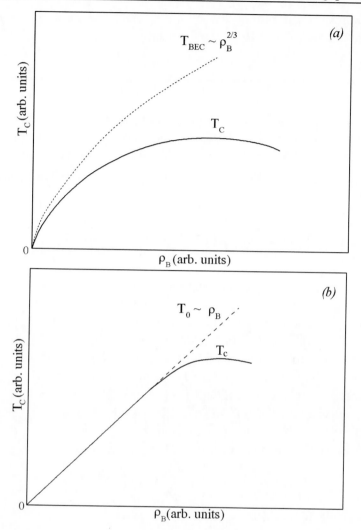

Figure 8.8. Concentration dependence of the BEC temperature for an ideal 3D Bose gas of free bosons (dashed curve) and the SF condensation temperatures for 3D and 2D nonideal Bose gases with attractive interaction between bosons given by Eq. (8.50) (where $T_{BEC}$ is replaced by $T_{BEC}^*$) and Eq. (8.77), respectively (solid curve).

## 8.4.7.   Specific Heat of a Superfluid Bose-liquid

The specific heat of a SF Bose-liquid is determined from relation [14]

$$c_v(T) = \frac{2}{T^2} \sum_k n_B(k)[1 + n_B(k)] \left\{ E_B^2(k) - T \left[ \varepsilon \frac{\partial |\tilde{\mu}_B|}{\partial T} + \frac{1}{2} \frac{\partial}{\partial T} \Delta_{SF}^2 \right] \right\}. \qquad (8.78)$$

At low temperatures, we can assume $T << |\tilde{\mu}_B|$, $\Delta_B$ and $\Delta_B \approx const$, $|\tilde{\mu}_B| \approx const$. Therefore, the specific heat of a SF 3D Bose gas is given by

$$C_v(T) \simeq \frac{\Omega D_B}{2T^2} \int_0^\infty \sqrt{\varepsilon} \frac{d\varepsilon}{\sinh^2[E_B(\varepsilon)/2T]} E_B^2(\varepsilon). \qquad (8.79)$$

At $\gamma_B > \gamma_B^*$ and $\Delta_{SF} > 2T$ the function $\sinh[E_B(\varepsilon)/2T]$ under the integral in Eq. (8.79) can be replaced by $(1/2)\exp[E_B(\varepsilon)/2T]$. Further, taking into account that the main contribution to the integral in Eq. (8.79) comes from the small values of $\varepsilon$, we can replace $E_B(\varepsilon)$ by $\sqrt{2|\tilde{\mu}_B|\varepsilon + \Delta_{SF}^2} \simeq \Delta_{SF} + |\tilde{\mu}_B|\varepsilon/\Delta_{SF}$ and use the Taylor expansion in the exponent $\sqrt{2|\tilde{\mu}_B|\varepsilon + \Delta_{SF}^2} \approx \Delta_{SF} + |\tilde{\mu}_B|\varepsilon/\Delta_{SF}$. Then integrating Eq. (8.79), we get

$$C_v(T) \simeq \frac{3\Omega D_B \Delta_B^{5/2}}{|\tilde{\mu}_B|^{3/2}} \sqrt{\pi T} \left[1 + \frac{4}{3}\sqrt{\frac{2}{\pi}}\frac{\Delta_{SF}}{T}\right] \exp\left(-\frac{\Delta_{SF}}{T}\right). \qquad (8.80)$$

However, for $\gamma_B < \gamma_B^*$ and $T \le T_c^*$ the excitation spectrum of a SF 3D Bose-liquid at small values of $k$ is phonon-like $E_B(k) \sim \sqrt{|\tilde{\mu}_B|/m_B}\hbar k$, and therefore, $C_v(T) \sim T^3$. For $\gamma_B << \gamma_B^*$, according to the expression (8.53), the specific heat of a SF 3D Bose-liquid varies as $C_v(T) \sim const/(T_c^* - T)^{0.5}$ near $T_c^*$ (where $\Delta_B << T_c^*$ and $|\tilde{\mu}_B| << T_c^*$) and will exhibit a $\lambda$ - like anomaly at $T_c^*$. Similarly, according to the expressions (8.51) and (8.52), the law $C_v(T) \sim const/(T_c - T)^{0.5}$ is also valid near $T_c$ and the behavior of $C_v(T)$ at $T_c$ is similar to that of $^4He$. These critical behaviors of $C_v(T)$ near $T_c^*$ and $T_c$ are shown in Fig. 8.9. Clearly, $C_v(T)$ shows a temperature behavior $\sim T^{3/2}$ for $T > T_c$ [14]. For a SF 2D Bose-liquid, the temperature dependence of $C_v(T)$ at low temperatures can be estimated in the same manner using these above-mentioned approximations. Then, at $\Delta_{SF} > 2T$ we have

$$C_v(T) \simeq \frac{4\Omega D_B \Delta_{SF}}{|\tilde{\mu}_B|} \left[1 + \frac{\Delta_{SF}}{2T}\right] \exp\left(-\frac{\Delta_{SF}}{T}\right). \qquad (8.81)$$

For $\Delta_{SF} < 2T$, we obtain (see Appendix C)

$$C_v(T) \simeq \frac{4\Omega D_B T^2}{\Delta_B} \sqrt{\pi T} \left[1 - \frac{\Delta_{SF}}{2T} + 19\exp(-2)\right]. \qquad (8.82)$$

Thus, at small $\Delta_{SF}$ the temperature dependence of $C_v(T)$ in a SF 2D Bose-liquid is also very close to phonon-like one.

## 8.4.8.  Entropy of a SF Bose-liquid

The entropy of a Bose-liquid is given by

$$S = \sum_k [(n_B(k,T)+1)\ln|(n_B(k,T)+1)| - n_B(k,T)\ln|n_B(k,T)|]. \qquad (8.83)$$

Making some transformation in Eq. (8.83), we have

$$S = \sum_k \left[ \frac{1}{(1-\exp(-E_B(k))/T)} \ln\left| \frac{1}{1-\exp(-E_B(k)/T)} \right| \right.$$
$$\left. - \frac{\exp(-E_B(k)/T)}{1-\exp(-E_B(k)/T)} \ln\left| \frac{\exp(-E_B(k)/T)}{1-\exp(-E_B(k)/T)} \right| \right] \qquad (8.84)$$

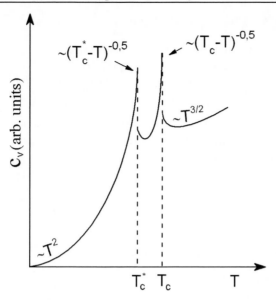

Figure 8.9. Temperature dependence of the specific heat of a SF 3D Bose-liquid for $\gamma_B \ll \gamma_B^*$ showing the existence of two $\lambda$-like anomalies near the temperatures $T_c^*$ and $T_c$, which are the first- and second-order SF phase transition temperatures, respectively.

At $\Delta_{SF} \neq 0$, using the expansion of the expressions

$$\frac{1}{1 - \exp(-E_B(k)/T)}, \quad \ln|\exp(-E_B(k)/T)|, \quad \ln|[1 - \exp(-E_B(k)/T)]|$$

in Taylor series, we find

$$S \simeq \sum_k \left[ 3\exp\left(-\frac{E_B(k)}{T}\right) - \exp\left(-\frac{3E_B(k)}{T}\right) \right]$$

$$\simeq 3\sum_k \exp\left(-\frac{E_B(k)}{T}\right) \tag{8.85}$$

Replacing the summation in Eq. (8.85) by an integration, we obtain

$$S \simeq 3\Omega D_B \int\limits_0^\infty \sqrt{\varepsilon}\exp\left[-\frac{E_B(\varepsilon)}{T}\right] d\varepsilon \tag{8.86}$$

for an interacting 3D Bose gas.

The main contribution to the integral in Eq. (8.86) comes from the small values of $\varepsilon$. In this case, we can write $E_B(\varepsilon) \simeq \sqrt{\varepsilon^2 + 2\varepsilon\tilde{\mu}_B + \Delta_{SF}^2} \simeq \sqrt{2\varepsilon\tilde{\mu}_B}$ at $\Delta_{SF} \to 0$. Then integrating Eq. (8.86), we find

$$S \simeq \frac{3\sqrt{2}\Omega D_B (T_c^*)^2}{\tilde{\mu}_B} \tag{8.87}$$

From (8.87), it follows that the entropy just like $\tilde{\mu}_B$ changes abruptly near $T = T_c^*$. Such behaviors of $S$ and $\tilde{\mu}_B$ near $T_c^*$ are manifested as the first-order phase transitions SPC$\Leftrightarrow$PC in an interacting 3D Bose gas.

### 8.4.9. Stability of Attractive Bose Systems

For attractive Bose systems the problem of their stability relative to spontaneous collapse can arise in the study of SPC and PC of attracting bosons in these systems. The SPC and PC in a 3D-Bose gas with pure interboson attraction that leads to the inevitable collapse of the system were studied in Ref. [69]. In order to avoid collapse in an attractive 2D Bose gas of holons, the strong Hartree-Fock repulsion, which ensures a positive compressibility, has been considered in Ref. [72]. Here, we briefly discuss the stability of attractive 3D and 2D Bose systems in these two limiting cases using a separable interaction model (8.33).

In the weak coupling limit ($\gamma_B \ll 1$) the SPC in an attracting 3D Bose gas with $\rho_B \sim \rho_{B0}$ is expected in a wide temperature range from $T = 0$ to $T_c^* < T_c$. In this limiting case, one obtains $\Delta_B \simeq \rho_B \tilde{V}_B$ [74], and $\tilde{\mu}_B \simeq 2\rho_B(V_{BR} - \frac{3}{2}V_{BA})$, so that the compressibility just as in the case of an attractive 2D Bose gas of holons [72] is given by

$$K = \rho_B^2 \frac{\partial \tilde{\mu}_B}{\partial \rho_B} \simeq 2\rho_B^2 \left( V_{BR} - \frac{3}{2}V_{BA} \right), \qquad (8.88)$$

which is essentially positive. This means that a nonideal 3D Bose gas with the attractive and repulsive interboson interactions is stable.

Let us turn now to the strong coupling limit. For $\gamma_B > \gamma_B^*$ (or $\tilde{\mu}_B > \Delta_B$) we deal with PC in attractive Bose gases with $n_{B0}(0) = 0$. Especially, for $\gamma_B \gg \gamma_B^*$ the behavior of such attractive Bose systems seems to be very close to a dilute gas limit. In this case, the quantities $\tilde{\mu}_B$ and $K$ both for a 3D Bose system and for a 2D Bose system are determined from the relations

$$\tilde{\mu}_B = 2\rho_B(V_{BR} - V_{BA}) - \frac{E_b}{2}, \qquad (8.89)$$

$$K = 2\rho_B^2(V_{BR} - V_{BA}). \qquad (8.90)$$

One can see that in the strong coupling limit the PC of attracting bosons leads to the formation of $N_B/2$ boson molecules or their clusters. As is well known, such fermion molecules are also formed in attractive Fermi systems in the dilute limit [16]. Thus, the attractive 3D and 2D Bose systems undergoing the SPC and PC are stable for $V_{BR} \gg V_{BA}$.

## 8.5. Novel Superconductivity of Charged Composite Bosons in the Pseudogap State of High-$T_c$ Cuprates

As discussed in chapter 7 and section 8.2, polaronic effects play a dominant role in unconventional Cooper pairing and in formation of pre-formed (bosonic) Cooper pairs and normal-state pseudogap (PG) in high-$T_c$ cuprates in which the SC state is as anomalous as the normal one (see section 8.1). Various experiments [8, 9, 18, 20, 22, 78] strongly suggest that underdoped, optimally doped, and even overdoped cuprates may not be BCS superconductors. Strong deviations from the conventional Fermi-liquid behavior in the normal state and from the BCS-liquid behavior in the SC state are indicative of the new normal and SC states in these high-$T_c$ materials. One can assume that unconventional cuprate superconductors are in the bosonic limit of pre-formed Cooper pairs and the SC state requires the SF condensation of composite bosons. In these polar materials the degenerate pola-ronic Fermi gas transforms first into a BCS-like Fermi-liquid above $T_c$ and then into a SF Bose-liquid. Here, we encounter a novel SC state of matter, which is a SF Bose liquid of composite bosonic Cooper pairs and qualitatively different from the Landau Fermi liq-uid and from the BCS-type SF Fermi liquid. It is therefore important to go beyond the BCS-type condensation and BEC schemes for unconventional superconductivity in high-$T_c$ cuprates. We believe that unconventional high-$T_c$ superconductivity in these systems is the result of the precursor Cooper pairing of carriers above $T_c$ and the subsequent SPC and PC of pre-formed Cooper pairs into a SF Bose-liquid state described by the previously stated mean-field theory of interacting composite bosons.

## 8.5.1. Gap-like Features of Bosonic Superconductor

In BCS superconductors, the superconductivity and a non-zero BCS gap $\Delta = \Delta_F$ (which serves as the SC order parameter) appear simultaneously at $T = T^* = T_c$ (Fig. 8.10a). According to the two-stage FBL scenario [12, 13, 14, 47], superconductivity in bosonic superconductors appears under the coexistence of two distinct order parameters: one of them $\Delta_F$ (which is BCS-like order parameter) characterizes the bond strength of bound fermion pairs and the other $\Delta_B$ defines the bond strength of all condensed composite bosons (e.g., the collective of such bosons in a SF Bose-liquid does not allow their partner to leave the SF condensate). In this scenario, the order parameter $\Delta_F$ becomes non-SC gap or PG and the existence of the SF phase (or SC state) in high-$T_c$ cuprates is associated with a nonzero coherence parameter $\Delta_B$, so that the order parameter $\Delta_B$ serves as the SC order parameter. Whereas the energy gap $\Delta_{SF}$ characterizes the binding energy of a single bound boson pair in the SF condensate of composite bosons. In unconventional cuprate superconductors, the superconductivity is the result of two distinct quantum phenomena; namely, BCS-like pairing of carriers leading to the formation of Cooper pairs above $T_c$ and the subsequent transition of these pre-formed Cooper pairs to a SF Bose-liquid state at $T_c$. In other words, the phase transition to the SC state in these systems is the result of two distinct successive phase transitions, such as the BCS-like transition at $T^* > T_c$ and the $\lambda$-like SC transition at $T_c$. In bosonic superconductors (Figs. 8.10b and 8.10c), the disappearance of the coherence parameter $\Delta_B$ or SF condensate of composite bosonic Cooper pairs at $T = T_c$ is not accompanied yet by the destruction of such Cooper pairs which disappear at higher temperatures (i.e., at $T = T^* > T_c$ or even $T = T^* >> T_c$). One can expect that in unconventional superconductors the new gap-like features associated with the coherence parameter $\Delta_B$ and energy gap $\Delta_{SF}$ will appear inside the BCS-like gap $\Delta_F$ without a sharp maximum of DOS. In particular, at $\gamma_B < \gamma_B^*$ and $T \leq T_c^*$ the non-zero DOS must exist near the bottom of the energy gap $\Delta_F$ (that is displayed as a peak in the DOS not only in the SC state but also in the normal state). The existence of a finite DOS inside the assumed BCS-like gap $\Delta_F$ was observed in high-$T_c$ cuprates [24, 25, 26]. The energy gap (or often called as the small PG [22, 78]) unknown nature observed in underdoped and optimally doped cuprates is the BCS-like gap $\Delta_F$ and it bears no relation to the SC order parameter $\Delta_{SC}$ since such a gap exists also in the normal state [79, 80]. In these high-$T_c$ materials, the BCS-like phase transition in electronic subsystem having an effect on the lattice state must occur at $T = T^* > T_c$. In all probability, the nature of the phase transitions unknown origin

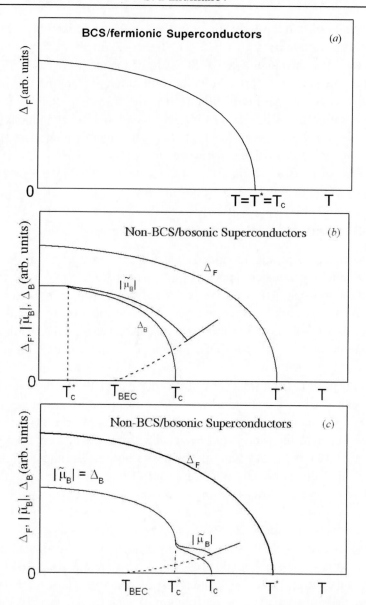

Figure 8.10. (a) Temperature dependence of the SC order parameter $\Delta_{SC} = \Delta_F$ in BCS (fermionic) superconductors. (b) Temperature dependences of the BCS-like PG $\Delta_F$ and the SC order parameter $\Delta_{SC} = \Delta_B$ at $\gamma_B < \gamma_B^*$ in non-BCS (bosonic) superconductors, where $\tilde{\mu}_B$ is the chemical potential of an interacting Bose gas of pre-formed Cooper pairs. (c) Temperature dependence of the BCS-like PG $\Delta_F$ and the SC order parameter $\Delta_{SC} = \Delta_B$ at $\gamma_B << \gamma_B^*$ in non-BCS (bosonic) superconductors.

observed in YBa$_2$Cu$_3$O$_{7-\delta}$ at ~150K and ~ 230K [8, 81] are the same and are caused by the destruction of Cooper pairs at $T = T^* >> T_c$. In high-$T_c$ superconductors, the existence of the BCS-like gap (or PG) both in the SC state and in the normal state with a disappearance temperature $T^* > T_c$ or even $T^* >> T_c$ without a break at $T_c$ was first predicted theoretically in Refs. [12, 13, 14] and then was observed experimentally [82, 83, 84]. Indeed, the gap-like feature (i.e., PG) observed in the underdoped cuprates [82, 83, 84] develops in the normal-state well above $T_c$ and persists into the SC state with no sign of an anomaly near $T_c$. Later, such a PG was also observed in underdoped, optimally doped and even overdoped cuprates by many other authors (see Refs. [22, 78, 80]). On the one hand, some researchers believe that the PG is caused by the SC fluctuations and connects smoothly with the SC gap below $T_c$ [48, 83]. On the other hand, various experiments (see, e.g., Refs. [85, 86]) have rather convincingly confirmed the coexistence of the distinct SC order parameter and small PG below $T_c$ predicted long before these experimental observations within a two-stage FBL (i.e., a two-gap) scenario [12, 13, 14]. In our opinion, the SC order parameter $\Delta_{SC}$ is best identified with the coherence parameter $\Delta_B$ rather than with the small PG $\Delta_F$ which becomes non-SC gap in bosonic superconductors both above $T_c$ and below $T_c$. Therefore, the SC order parameter $\Delta_{SC}$ in underdoped, optimally doped, and moderately overdoped cuprates should not be confused with the BCS-like paring PG $\Delta_F$. Since the identification of $\Delta_{SC}$ and $\Delta_F$ in the current literature is rather misleading and the determination of the reduced SC gap $g_{SC}$ from the BCS-like expressions for $\Delta_F$ and $T_c$ in bosonic superconductors is not correct. We believe that the strong deviation of the reduced SC gap defined as $g_{SC} = 2\Delta_F/T_c$ (which varies from 8 to 28 [87, 88]) from its BCS value 3.52 is the result of such a misunderstanding identification of $\Delta_{SC}$ and $\Delta_F$. In the present case, the reduced SC gap $g_{SC}$ should be defined as $g_{SC} = 2\Delta_{SC}(=\Delta_B)/T_c$ and not as $g_{SC} = 2\Delta_{SC}(=\Delta_F)/T_c$ that leads to non-real large value of $g_{SC}$ in comparison with its BCS value since the experimental value of $T_c$ in high-$T_c$ cuprates is not corresponding to $T^*$. The large values of $g_{SC} = 5 - 28$ Refs. [24, 25, 26, 87, 88] in these materials are caused by these circumstances. So, according to (8.38) and (8.49) or (8.50), the reduced SC gap in the 3D bosonic superconductors at $T_c \gtrsim T_{BEC}$ is approximately equal to [14]

$$g_{SC} = 2\Delta_{SC}(=\Delta_B)/T_c \leq 5.76 T_{BEC}/T_c. \tag{8.91}$$

In the 2D bosonic superconductors, this reduced SC gap at $\gamma_B \leq \gamma_B^*$ is determined from the relation [12, 14] (see Appendix C)

$$g_{SC} = 8\exp(-2/\gamma_B). \tag{8.92}$$

For 3D bosonic superconductors, after replacing the summation in Eqs. (8.27)–(8.29) by an integration, we solve self-consistently these equations for $\gamma_B = \gamma_B^*$ with the model potential (8.33) and find $T_c/T_{BEC} \simeq 3$. Then, from Eq. (8.91), we have $g_{SC} \simeq 1.9$. Similarly, for $\gamma_B < \gamma_B^*$, we obtain $g_{SC} \lesssim 1.7$ (Fig. 8.11). These values of $g_{SC}$ agree well with the observed values of the reduced SC gap in high-$T_c$ cuprates [25, 26, 89]. Whereas the above experimental values of $g_{SC}$=5–28 reported for these systems have been determined using the irrelevant BCS scheme as $g_{SC} = 2\Delta_{SC}(=\Delta_F)/T_c$. Perhaps the experimental values of $g_{SC} \simeq 0.14 - 2.12$ reported in Ref. [90] for high-$T_c$ cuprates for the temperature range $0.2 \leq T/T_c \leq 0.7$ is obtained by identification of the SC order parameter $\Delta_{SC}$ with the energy gap $\Delta_{SF}$. In unconventional (non-BCS) superconductors, the curves of the temperature dependences of $\Delta_{SC}$ and $\Delta_{SF}$ with increasing temperature must shift to meeting each other and cross at $T = T^* < T_c$ (Fig. 8.12). These gap-like features were also observed in high-$T_c$ cuprates [91, 92].

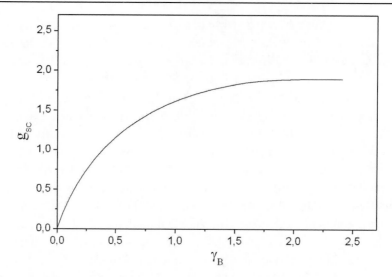

Figure 8.11. Variation of reduced SC gap in 3D boson superconductors with coupling constant $\gamma_B$.

### 8.5.2. Gapless Superconductivity and Kink-like Behavior of the Superconducting Order Parameter

At present the gapless superconductivity as well as the power-law dependence of specific heat. London penetration depth, etc. are explained only in terms of the BCS-like $s$-, $p$-, and $d$- wave pairing scenarios [19, 20, 93, 94, 95]. However, we argue that in unconventional superconductors other possible mechanisms of gapless superconductivity can exist and the theory of a SF 3D Bose-liquid (section 8.4) is well applicable to this phenomenon. Actually, the gapless superconductivity in high-$T_c$ cuprates and other unconventional superconductors should be caused by the SPC of an interacting 3D Bose of pre-formed Cooper pairs or by the absence of the gap $\Delta_{SF}$ in their excitation spectrum $E_B(k)$ at $T \leq T_c^*$ [13, 14] and could not be explicable by the presence of the point or line nodes of the BCS-like gap $\Delta_F$ [19, 20, 93, 94, 95]. Indeed, the experimental results are indicative of the absence of the BCS-like gap nodes responsible for gapless superconductivity in high-$T_c$ cuprates [24, 25, 96, 97]. Therefore, the presence of the DOS near the bottom of the BCS-like gap $\Delta_F$ can be considered as one of the direct evidence for the existence of gapless superconductivity. According to the theory of a SF 3D Bose-liquid [13, 14] (see section 8.4), the gapless superconductivity in bosonic superconductors can exist only in the temperature range $0 < T < T_c^*$ (which can be observed experimentally). The possibility of such a gapless superconductivity in high-$T_c$ cuprates predicted in Refs. [13, 14] is supported by the experimental observations. In particular, thermal conductivity measurements [98] have convincingly confirmed the absence of the energy gap in the excitation spectrum of high-$T_c$ cuprate at $T << T_c$. This means that for $\gamma_B < \gamma_B^*$ the energy gap $\Delta_{SF}$ closes at $T = T_c^* << T_c$ (Fig. 8.10b). In addition, the photoemission measurements [99] show that such an energy gap vanishes in the cuprates at $T \lesssim T_c/2$ in accordance with the predictions of the theory of a SF 3D Bose-liquid for $\gamma_B << \gamma_B^*$ for which the energy gap $\Delta_{SF}$ vanishes at $T \sim T_c/2$ or

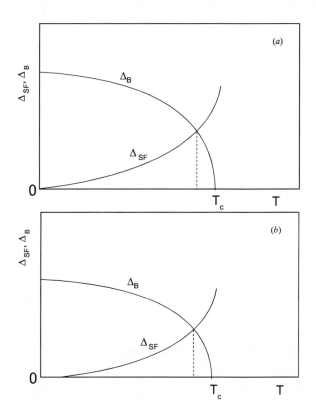

Figure 8.12. Temperature dependences of the SC order parameter $\Delta_{SC}(=\Delta_B)$ and energy gap $\Delta_{SF}$ (a) in 2D boson superconductors for $\gamma_B = \gamma_B^*$ and (b) in 3D boson superconductors for $\gamma_B < \gamma_B^*$.

even at $T \lesssim (0.6 - 0.7)T_c$ (see Fig.8.10c).

In bosonic superconductors the temperature dependence of the SC order parameter $\Delta_{SC} = \Delta_B$ is unusual and has a kink-like feature near $T = T_c^* < T_c$ for $\gamma_B << \gamma_B^*$ (Fig. 8.13). This kink-like feature in the temperature dependence of $\Delta_{SC}(T)$ caused by the first order PC-to-SPC transition of composite bosonic Cooper pairs at $T = T_c^*$ is less pronounced for $\gamma_B < \gamma_B^*$ but it is very pronounced for $\gamma_B << \gamma_B^*$. Such a kink-like behavior of $\Delta_{SC}(T)$ well below $T_c$ or somewhat below $T_c$ leads to the radical changes of other SC parameters (e.g., critical magnetic fields and current, etc.) of 3D bosonic superconductors. We believe that the kink-like behavior of the SC order parameter $\Delta_{SC}(=\Delta_B)$ predicted in Refs. [13, 14] seems to be quite plausible for high-$T_c$ cuprates and other unconventional superconductors. Indeed, the temperature dependence of $\Delta_{SC}(T)$ observed in the high-$T_c$ cuprate superconductors at $T \sim 0.6 - 0.7T_c$ [32, 33] is essentially different from the BCS-dependence and closely resembles kink-like behavior of $\Delta_{SC}(T)$ in bosonic superconductors at $\gamma_B << \gamma_B^*$

(cf. Fig. 8.13 with Fig. 3 of Ref. [32] and with the experimental results for Bi2212 and Bi2223 presented by Tsuda et al. in Fig. 2 of Ref. [33]) . This key question needs special experimental investigation.

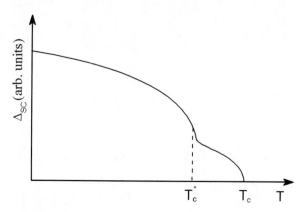

Figure 8.13. Temperature dependence of the SC order parameter $\Delta_{SC}$ shows the existence of the kink-like anomaly at $T_c^*$ in 3D boson superconductors for $\gamma_B << \gamma_B^*$.

### 8.5.3.   Specific Heat and λ-like SC Phase Transition in High-$T_c$ Cuprates

The experimental facts concerning the high-$T_c$ cuprate superconductors [8, 37, 100, 101] indicate that the electronic specific heat $C_e$ in these materials is proportional to $T^2$ or $T^3$ at low temperatures and has a linear $T$ term and a clear λ-like anomaly not only at $T_c$ but also somewhat below $T_c$. The observed low-temperature power laws for the electronic specific heat are quite different from the exponential dependence of $C_e(T)$ presented by BCS theory. The origin of the linear term in the electronic specific heat $C_e$ might be associated with the presence of normal (unpaired) carriers below $T_c$ [102], impurity phases (see Ref. [103]), double-well potentials or two-level-systems [102, 104]. The existence of the linear term in $C_e$ in some high-$T_c$ cuprates and its absence in other cuprates [24, 103] can be explained by the presence or absence of unpaired carriers in these materials. Indeed, the presence of unpaired carriers below $T_c$ predicted earlier in Refs. [14, 102] was observed in Ref. [105]. We believe that the electronic specific heat of high-$T_c$ cuprates is best described by the theory of a SF Bose-liquid (section 8.4) and not by the BCS-like $d$-wave pairing model since at $\Delta_{SF} < \Delta_{SC}$ and especially at $\Delta_{SF} << \Delta_{SC}$ (or $\Delta_{SF} = 0$) the main contribution to $C_e(T)$ in the cuprates comes from the excitation of composite bosonic Cooper pairs and not from the excitation of their Fermi components. At $\Delta_{SF} = 0$ the power law (i.e., phonon-like) temperature dependences of $C_e(T) \sim T^3$ and $\sim T^2$ in 3D and 2D cuprate superconductors predicted by this theory [13, 14] were actually observed experimentally in high-$T_c$ cuprates. Further, the expression for the electronic specific heat in 3D bosonic superconductors show the following temperature behaviors: $C_e(T) \sim (T_c - T)^{-0.5}$ near $T_c$ and $C_e(T) \sim (T_c^* - T)^{-0.5}$ near $T_c^*$. One can expect that $C_e(T)$ in high-$T_c$ cuprates diverges at $T \to T_c$ and at $T \to T_c^*$ just like the specific heat of SF $^4$He diverges near the λ-like transition. It follows that the 3D Bose-liquids in unconventional superconductors may undergo two successive

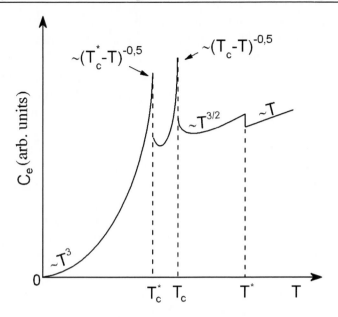

Figure 8.14. Possible anomalies of the electronic specific heat in bosonic superconductors that indicate the successive phase transitions, such as the second-order BCS-like phase transition at $T^*$, the second-order $\lambda$-like SC transition at $T_c$ and the first-order $\lambda$-like phase transition at $T_c^*$ below $T_c$.

phase transitions with decreasing $T$, such as a second-order phase transition at $T_c$ and a first-order phase transition at $T_c^* < T_c$, and they exhibit the $\lambda$-like anomalies in their specific heat near $T_c^*$ and $T_c$. Whereas the SF Fermi liquids like BCS superconductors show a step-like second-order phase transition accompanied by a finite jump in their specific heat at $T_c$. The $\lambda$-like anomalies in $C_e(T)$ near $T_c$ and $T_c^*$ have been observed in high-$T_c$ cuprates [8, 9, 37]. Further, a small BCS-like jump of $C_e(T)$ observed in these high-$T_c$ materials above $T_c$ or well above $T_c$ [8, 81] is associated with the second-order BCS-like phase transitions at $T = T^* > T_c$ or $T = T^* >> T_c$ (see Fig. 8.14) in their electronic subsystem as discussed in chapter 7.

### 8.5.4. Integer and Half-integer Magnetic Flux Quantization Effects

The unusual gap-like features observed in high-$T_c$ cuprates and the observed $\lambda$ - like anomalies in their specific heat indicate that the Cooper pairs in these superconductors are composite bosons that obey Bose-Einstein statistics and keep one's identity. So, the pre-formed Cooper pairs in the cuprates do not overlap strongly. The strong overlapping of such a Cooper pairs may take place only near $T^*$ where $\Delta_F \to 0$. However, the binding energy $2\Delta_F$ of these pairs will increase when the temperature decreases and their overlapping becomes weak enough or even impossible. For boson pairs the opposite situation is realized. Since the binding energy of such pairs in their interacting collective decreases below $T_c$ and becomes equal to zero at $\gamma_B < \gamma_B^*$ and $T = T_c^*$ at which the Cooper-like boson pairs begin to overlap strongly, so that such strongly overlapping boson pairs lose their identity at $\Delta_{SF} = 0$. These distinctive features for composite boson pairs are visually displayed in the magnetic flux quantization effects in high-$T_c$ cuprates. We believe that the integer and half-integer magnetic flux quantizations in units of $\hbar/2e$ and $\hbar/4e$ should be expected in the cuprates for $\Delta_{SF} = 0$ and $\Delta_{SF} > 0$, respectively. The energy gap opening in the excitation spectrum of a SF 2D Bose-liquid at $T > 0$ is larger than such a gap opening in the excitation spectrum of a SF 3D Bose-liquid at $T > T_c^*$. For this reason, the half-integer $h/4e$ magnetic flux quantization is rather best manifested in the 3D→2D crossover region than in the 3D region. Hence, in high-$T_c$ cuprates, the pre-formed Cooper pairs (composite bosons) would undergo SPC (with the integer $h/2e$ magnetic flux quantization) in the bulk and PC (with the half-integer $h/4e$ magnetic flux quantization) most probably at the 2D grain boundaries. Indeed, such magnetic flux quantization in units of $\hbar/4e$ predicted first within the microscopic theory of novel superconductivity [13, 14] has been discovered experimentally at the grain boundaries and in thin films of some high-$T_c$ cuprates [106] (see also Ref. [43]). However, authors of Refs. [43, 106] claim that the half-integer magnetic flux quantum effect in high-$T_c$ materials is associated with the BCS-like $d$-wave pairing symmetry. It seems that such an interpretation and other alternative points of view (see Refs. [43, 106]) are not very convincing. In our opinion, the half-integer magnetic flux quantum effect observed in grain boundary junction experiments [43] is due to the PC (or SPC-to-PC transition) of Cooper pairs in the 3D-to-2D crossover region and not due to the $d$-wave symmetry of Cooper pairs. Although some experimental observations advocate in favor of a $d$-wave pairing symmetry [43, 107], many other experiments closely trace a $s$-wave pairing symmetry [108] and are incompatible with a $d$-wave pairing symmetry. According to the PC theory of an interacting Bose gas of pre-formed Cooper pairs (section 8.4), the half-integer $\hbar/4e$ magnetic flux quantum effect in purely 2D bosonic superconductors exists in the temperature range $0 < T < T_c$. Remarkably, this prediction was experimentally confirmed by Kirtley et al. [109] providing compelling evidence for the existence of such a magnetic flux quantum effect in a thin film of $YBa_2Cu_3O_{7-\delta}$ in the temperature range $0.5K < T < T_c$. Further, in 3D bosonic superconductors the magnetic flux quantizations in units of $\hbar/2e$ and $\hbar/4e$ should take place in the temperature ranges $0 \le T \le T_c^*$ and $T_c^* < T < T_c$, respectively. Indeed, the integer ($\hbar/2e$) magnetic flux quantum effect at low temperatures has been observed experimentally in the bulk of high-$T_c$ cuprates [110]. In general, the existence of both the integer and the half-integer magnetic flux quantization effect in the bulk of high-$T_c$ cuprates is quite possible. The experimental observation of the half-integer magnetic flux quantization effect in 3D high-$T_c$ cuprates in the temperature range $T_c^* < T < T_c$ will therefore be of great interest.

### 8.5.5.   London Penetration Depth

In BCS-like pairing theories, the magnetic field penetration into the superconductor or the London penetration depth $\lambda_L(T)$ is determined within the two Fermi-liquid model. However, in bosonic superconductors the temperature dependence of the London penetration depth $\lambda_L(T)$ should be determined within the two Bose-liquid model [2, 3, 14] (in the case of 2D-holon superconductors this question was studied in Ref. [72]) from the relation

$$\frac{\lambda_L(T)}{\lambda_L(0)} = \left[1 - \frac{\rho_{Bn}(T)}{\rho_B}\right]^{-1/2}, \tag{8.93}$$

where $\lambda_L(0) = (m_B c^2 / 4\pi\rho_B e^2)^{1/2}$, $c$ is the light velocity, $\rho_B = \rho_{Bs} + \rho_{Bn}$, $\rho_{Bs}$ and $\rho_{Bn}$ are the densities of the so-called "SF" (nonexcited) and "normal" (excited) Bose-liquid. In a 3D Bose-liquid, $\Delta_{SF}$ for $T \leq T_c^*$ becomes zero and $\rho_{Bn}(T) \sim T^4$. Then, Eq. (8.93) yields [14]

$$\frac{\lambda_L(T)}{\lambda_L(0)} = \left[ 1 - \left(\frac{T}{T_c}\right)^4 \right]^{-1/2}, \tag{8.94}$$

which has been obtained earlier only empirically. When $T_c^* < T \leq T_c$, and $\Delta_{SF} > 0$, Eq. (8.93) takes the following form:

$$\frac{\lambda_L(T)}{\lambda_L(0)} = \left[ 1 - \left(\frac{\Delta_{SF}(T)}{|\tilde{\mu}_B(T)|}\right)^{5/2} \left(\frac{T}{T_c}\right)^{3/2} \exp\left(-\frac{\Delta_{SF}(T)}{T}\left(1 - \frac{T}{T_c}\right)\right) \right]^{-1/2}. \tag{8.95}$$

At $\Delta_{SF} < 2T$ the density of a normal 2D Bose-liquid varies approximately as $\rho_{Bn} \sim T^3$. Then Eq. (8.93) becomes

$$\frac{\lambda_L(T)}{\lambda_L(0)} = \left[ 1 - \left(\frac{T}{T_c}\right)^3 \right]^{-1/2}. \tag{8.96}$$

For the case $\Delta_{SF} > 2T$, we obtain

$$\frac{\lambda_L(T)}{\lambda_L(0)} = \left[ 1 - \left(\frac{\Delta_{SF}(T)}{\tilde{\mu}_B(T)}\right)^2 \left(\frac{T}{T_c}\right) \exp\left(-\frac{\Delta_{SF}(T)}{T}\left(1 - \frac{T}{T_c}\right)\right) \right]^{-1/2}. \tag{8.97}$$

At $\Delta_{SF}(T \to T_c) \to \tilde{\mu}_B(T_c)$, Eqs. (8.95) and (8.97) predict the power law dependences $\lambda_L(T)/\lambda_L(0) \sim (T/T_c)^{3/2}$ and $\sim T/T_c$, respectively. At $\Delta_{SF}(T \to T_c^*) \to 0$, the relations (8.95) and (8.97) are close to the the power law dependences (8.94) and (8.96), respectively. Hence, at $T > T_c^*$ we may approximate $\lambda_L(T)/\lambda_L(0)$ by the power law dependence $\lambda_L(T)/\lambda_L(0) \sim (T/T_c)^n$ with $n \simeq 1.5 - 4$ for 3D bosonic superconductors. Similarly, for 2D bosonic superconductors we can approximate $\lambda_L(T)/\lambda_L(0)$ by the power law dependence $\lambda_L(T)/\lambda_L(0) \sim (T/T_c)^n$ with $n \simeq 1 - 3$ in the temperature range $0 \leq T \leq T_c$.

We now turn to the experimental evidence for $\lambda_L(T)$ in high-$T_c$ cuprates. Experimental results on the London penetration depth in high-$T_c$ cuprates [40, 111, 112] are in well agreement with Eq. (8.94) and at variance with exponential dependence of the BCS theory. Some experimental data [94, 113] speak well for the power law dependences $\lambda_L(T)/\lambda_L(0) \sim (T/T_c)^{3/2}$ and $\sim (T/T_c)$. Further, in high-$T_c$ cuprates the power law dependence $\lambda_L(T) \sim T^2$ is also observed [40, 94, 114]. Such a behavior of $\lambda_L(T)$ also follows from the relation (8.95). In addition, in some experiments [115] the power law dependence $\lambda_L(T)/\lambda_L(0) \sim (T/T)^n$ with $n = 1.3 - 3.2$ were observed in accordance with these theoretical predictions.

### 8.5.6. Critical Magnetic Fields

In the case of bosonic superconductors, the thermodynamic critical magnetic field is determined from the difference of the free energies of normal and SF Bose-liquids

$$F_{nB} - F_{sB} = \frac{H_c^2}{8\pi}. \tag{8.98}$$

The expression for the free energy of a SF Bose-liquid with the chemical potential $\tilde{\mu}_B$ is given by [46, 74]

$$F_{sB}(T,\Delta) = U_B(T,\Delta_B) - TS$$
$$= -|\tilde{\mu}_B|N_B + T\sum_k \ln[1 - \exp(-E_B(k)/T)] + \frac{1}{2}\sum_k [E_B(k) - \tilde{\epsilon}_B(k)], \qquad (8.99)$$

where $U_B(T,\Delta_B)$ is the total energy of a SF Bose-liquid, S is the entropy of this Bose-liquid.

At $T = 0$, the chemical potential of a normal Bose gas is equal to zero (see Fig. 8.2) and the critical magnetic field $H_c$ is determined from the relation

$$\frac{H_c^2}{8\pi} = U_B(0,0) - U_B(0,\Delta_B) = |\tilde{\mu}_B|N_B - \frac{1}{2}\sum_k [E_B(k) - \tilde{\epsilon}_B(k)]. \qquad (8.100)$$

Further, we consider a 3D bosonic superconductor. After replacing the sum in Eq. (8.100) by the integral and taking into account that $\Delta_{SF} = 0$ for $\gamma_B < \gamma_B^*$, we obtain the following expression for $H_c$ (see Appendix E):

$$H_c(0) = 2\sqrt{2\pi\rho_B\Delta_B\Omega + \pi D_B\Delta_B^2\Omega\sqrt{\xi_{BA}}}. \qquad (8.101)$$

In the weak coupling limit $\gamma_B << 1$, we have $\Delta_B \simeq \rho_B V_{BA}$.

Let us consider now the case $T << T_c$. For $\gamma_B < \gamma_B^*$, the energy gap $\Delta_{SF}$ in the excitation spectrum of 3D bosonic superconductors vanishes at $T = T_c^* << T_c$. Taking into account that the main contribution to the second sum in Eq. (8.99) comes from small values of $k$, we replace $E_B(k) = \sqrt{\epsilon^2(k) + 2|\tilde{\mu}_B|\epsilon(k)}$ by $\sqrt{2\Delta_B\epsilon(k)}$. Then, after replacing the summation in Eq. (8.99) by an integration, we obtain

$$F_{sB}(T,\Delta_B) = -|\tilde{\mu}_B|N_B + \Omega D_B T \int_0^\infty \sqrt{\epsilon}\ln\left[1 - \exp(\sqrt{2\epsilon\Delta_B}/T)\right]d\epsilon$$
$$+ \frac{D_B}{2}\Omega \int_0^{\xi_{BA}} \sqrt{\epsilon}[\sqrt{\epsilon^2 + 2\Delta_B\epsilon} - (\epsilon + \Delta_B)]d\epsilon$$
$$= -\Delta_B N_B - \frac{\Omega D_B\Delta_B^2\sqrt{\xi_{BA}}}{2} - (\pi T)^4 \frac{\sqrt{2D_B}\Omega}{90\Delta_B^{3/2}}. \qquad (8.102)$$

The free energy of a Bose-gas in the normal state $(|\tilde{\mu}_B| = 0)$ is

$$F_{nB}(T,0) = D_B\Omega T \int_0^\infty \sqrt{\epsilon} \ln[1 - \exp(-\epsilon/T)]d\epsilon$$
$$= -\frac{2}{3}D_B\Omega T^{5/2}\Gamma\left(\frac{5}{2}\right)\xi\left(\frac{5}{2}\right) \simeq -0.67\sqrt{\pi}D_B\Omega T^{5/2}. \qquad (8.103)$$

¿From Eqs. (8.102) and (8.103), we have

$$\frac{H_c^2(T << T_c)}{8\pi} = F_{nB}(T,0) - F_{sB}(T,\Delta_B) \simeq \frac{H_c^2(0)}{8\pi} - 0.67\sqrt{\pi}D_B\Omega T^{5/2},$$

$$(8.104)$$

or

$$H_c(T) \simeq H_c(0)\sqrt{1-A(T/T_c)^{2.5}}, \tag{8.105}$$

where

$$A = \frac{0.678\pi\sqrt{\pi}D_B\Omega}{H_c^2(0)}T_c^{5/2}.$$

Now we analyze the case $T \to T_c^* < T_c$ (for $\gamma_B << \gamma_B^*$). In this case, $T_c^* > T_{BEC}$ and $|\tilde{\mu}_B| \sim \Delta_B << T$. The free energy of a Bose gas with non-zero chemical potential $\tilde{\mu}_{Bn} < 0$ in the normal state is determined from the relation (see Appendix F)

$$F_{nB}(T,0) \simeq -|\tilde{\mu}_{Bn}|N_B + \sqrt{\pi}D_B\Omega T^{5/2}\left[-0.67 + 1.306\frac{|\tilde{\mu}_{Bn}|}{T}\right] \tag{8.106}$$

Using Eq. (8.99), we obtain (see Appendix G)

$$F_{sB}(T,\Delta_B) \quad \simeq -\Delta_B N_B - D_B\Omega\sqrt{\xi_{BA}}\frac{\Delta_B^2}{2}$$
$$+\sqrt{\pi}D_B\Omega T^{5/2}\left[-0.67 + 1.306\frac{\Delta_B}{T}\right]. \tag{8.107}$$

¿From Eqs. (8.106) and (8.107), we have

$$\frac{H_c^*(T \to T_c^*)}{8\pi\Omega} \quad \simeq \rho_B(\Delta_B - |\tilde{\mu}_{Bn}|) + \frac{D_B\sqrt{\xi_{BA}}\Delta_B^2}{2}$$
$$-1.306\sqrt{\pi}D_B T^{3/2}(\Delta_B - |\tilde{\mu}_{Bn}|). \tag{8.108}$$

One can see that the first term in Eq. (8.108) would be the order of the third term. As a result, we have

$$H_c(T \to T_c^*) \approx \sqrt{4\pi D_B\xi^{1/2}\Omega}\Delta_B(T \to T_c^*), \tag{8.109}$$

where $\Delta_B(T) = \Delta_{SC}(T)$.

At weak interboson coupling ($\gamma_B << \gamma_B^*$) the temperature dependence of $H_c$ is shown in Fig. 8.15. As seen from Fig. 8.15, the behavior of $H_c(T)$ is very unusual in bosonic superconductors since $H_c(T)$ has a kink-like temperature dependence around $T_c^*$ due to a kink in the temperature dependence of SC order parameter $\Delta_{SC}(T) = \Delta_B(T)$ around $T_c^*$ and shows the root-like behavior in the vicinity of $T_c$ due to the root-like temperature dependence of $\Delta_{SC}(T)$ near $T_c$. Interestingly, such a temperature dependence of $H_c(T)$ with the kink-like feature near $T_c^* \simeq 75-85$K was unambiguously observed in high-$T_c$ cuprates [116] (see also inset of Fig. 8.15).

The lower and upper critical magnetic fields $H_{c1}(T)$ and $H_{c2}$ are determined from the well known relations

$$H_{c1} = (\ln\chi/\sqrt{2}\chi)H_c(T) \tag{8.110}$$

and

$$H_{c2} = \sqrt{2}\chi H_c(T), \tag{8.111}$$

where $\chi = \lambda_L/\xi_B$ is the Ginzburg-Landau parameter, which is nearly constant and equal to $\lambda_L(0)/\xi_B(0)$ (see Ref. [117]), $\xi_B \simeq \hbar/\sqrt{2m_B\Delta_B}$ is the coherence length of boson pairs.

From (8.109), (8.110), and (8.111), it follows that the temperature dependences of $H_{c1}$, $H_c$, and $H_{c2}$, are determined by the temperature dependence of the SC order parameter of a bosonic superconductor ($\Delta_{SC} = \Delta_B$). Therefore, for $\gamma_B < \gamma_B^*$ and especially for $\gamma_B \ll \gamma_B^*$ the critical magnetic fields $H_{c1}(T)$ and $H_{c2}(T)$ just like $H_c(T)$ in 3D-bosonic superconductors exhibit crossover or kink-like behaviors near $T_c^*$ (Fig. 8.16). The crossover or kink-like features of $H_{c1}(T)$, $H_c(T)$, and $H_{c2}(T)$, correspond to the first-order phase transitions SPC⇔PC in a interacting 3D Bose gas of composite bosons near $T_c^* < T_c$. The characteristic temperature $T_c^*$ lies very close to $T_c$ for $\gamma_B \ll \gamma_B^*$ (e.g., for $\gamma_B \sim 1$ and 0.5, we have $T_c^* \leq 0.7T_c$ and $T_c^* \simeq 0.9T_c$, respectively). The critical magnetic fields $H_{c1}(T)$, $H_c(T)$, and $H_{c2}(T)$, just like $\Delta_B(T)$ increases abruptly near $T_c^*$ with decreasing $T$ and they manifest wide-spreading positive (or upward) curvature in the temperature range $T_c^* \leq T \leq T_c$ [14, 46]. Further, for $\gamma_B \ll \gamma_B^*$ the behavior of $\Delta_{SC}(T)$ near $T_c$ [13, 14] determines the extremely high negative slope and root-like temperature dependence of $H_{c2}$ in the vicinity of $T_c$. Indeed, all these features of $H_{c1}(T)$, $H_c(T)$, and $H_{c2}(T)$ were observed in high-$T_c$ cuprates [27, 28, 29, 34, 35, 116, 118, 119] in accordance with the predictions of the theory of a SF 3D Bose-liquid.

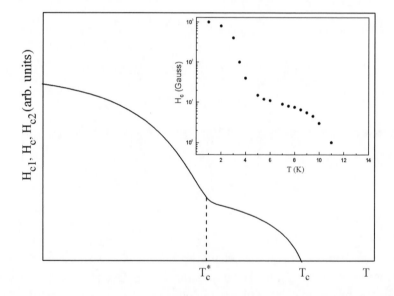

Figure 8.15. Temperature dependence for the thermodynamic critical magnetic field $H_c$ that shows the existence of the kink-like anomaly near $T_c^* < T_c$ in 3D boson superconductors for $\gamma_B \ll \gamma_B^*$. The inset shows the kink-like temperature dependence of $H_c$ near $T = T_c^* \sim 5$K observed in Bi2201 [119].

The Meissner effect in bosonic superconductors is determined by superfluidity of a Bose-liquid. One can show the absence of the paramagnetic part of current for a SF Bose-liquid in a similar manner as it was done for a SF Fermi-liquid one in BCS theory.

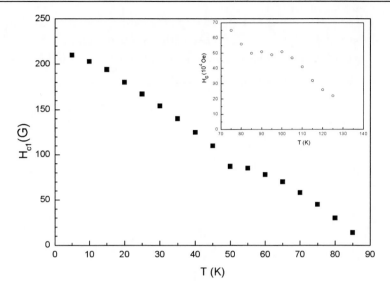

Figure 8.16. Temperature dependence of the lower critical magnetic field $H_{c1}$ that shows the kink-like behavior near $T_c^* \simeq 45K$ below $T_c \simeq 92K$ observed by Umezawa et al. in $YBa_2Cu_3O_{7-\delta}$ [27]. The inset shows the kink-like temperature dependence of the upper critical magnetic field $H_{c2}$ near $T_c^* \simeq 85K$ below $T_c \simeq 133K$ observed by Schilling et al. in $HgBa_2Ca_2Cu_3O_8$ [29].

### 8.5.7. Critical Current, Sound Velocity and Superfluid Density

The critical current destroying superconductivity (superfluidity) in boson superconductors is determined microscopically by [14]

$$I_c = 2e\rho_B v_c \qquad (8.112)$$

where $v_c$ is the critical velocity of SF carriers. The quantity of $v_c$ in unconventional high-$T_c$ cuprate superconductors (which are boson superconductors), should be determined within the above SF Bose-liquid theory (section 8.4) and not within the Fermi-liquid one (as it accepted in BCS-like pairing theory). We now estimate the value of $I_c$ in high-$T_c$ cuprates within the SF Bose-liquid model. One can assume that the relevant charge carriers in high-$T_c$ cuprates are large polarons and Cooper-like polaron pairs. In these high-$T_c$ materials, the values of the effective mass of large polarons are $m_p \simeq (2-4)m_e$ [51, 84, 120]. Using the values of $g_{SC} \sim 1$ for $YBa_2Cu_3O_{7-\delta}$ (YBCO) ($T_c \simeq 90K$), we find $\Delta_{SC}(= \Delta_B) \simeq 3.9 \times 10^{-3}eV$. For $T \leq T_c^*$, the theory of a SF Bose-liquid applied to the high-$T_c$ cuprates predicts that the excitation spectrum $E_B(k)$ of these 3D bosonic superconductors becomes gapless ($\Delta_{SF} = 0$) and phonon-like (at small $k$) in the temperature range $0 \leq T \leq T_c^*$. Then, according to the Landau criterion for superfluidity the critical velocity of SF carriers is $v_c = \sqrt{\Delta_B/m_B}$. Therefore, the critical velocity $v_c$ and current $I_c$, calculated with the values of $m_p \simeq 3m_e$, $m_B = 2m_p$, and $\rho_B \sim 10^{21}cm^{-3}$ are $v_c \simeq 1.074 \times 10^6 cm/s$ and $I_c \approx 3.45 \times 10^8 A/cm^2$. If we take $m_p = 2m_e$ [51] and $m_B = 2m_p$ we find $v_c \simeq 1.31 \times 10^6 cm/s$ and $I_c \simeq 4.2 \times 10^8 A/cm^2$. Now, using the value of $g_{SC} = 1$, we find $\Delta_{SC} = 1.726 \times 10^{-3}$ eV for La-based cuprates with $T_c \simeq 40K$. By taking $m_p \simeq 2m_e$, $m_B = 2m_p$, and $\rho_B = 0.4 \times 10^{21} cm^{-3}$ for these systems, we obtain $v_c \simeq 8.7 \times 10^5 cm/s$ and $I_c \simeq 1.12 \times 10^8 A/cm^2$. These values of $I_c$ are in good agreement with the observed experimental values of $I_c \simeq 10^6 - 10^9 A/cm^2$ in high-$T_c$ cuprates [115, 121]. Further, the unusual

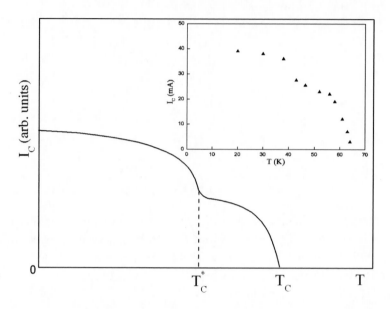

Figure 8.17. Temperature dependence of the critical current $I_c$ shows the existence of the kink-like anomaly near $T_c^* < T_c$ in 3D boson superconductors for $\gamma_B << \gamma_B^*$. The inset shows the kink-like temperature dependence of $I_c$ near $T_c^* \simeq 45K$ observed in $(Bi, Pb)_2 Sr_2 CaCu_2 O_y$ [30].

upward increase of $I_c$ in high-$T_c$ cuprates was observed below $T = (0.4 - 0.9)T_c$ (see inset of Fig. 8.17) [30, 122]. For $\gamma_B < \gamma_B^*$, and especially for $\gamma_B << \gamma_B^*$, the anomalous kink-like behavior of $I_c$ (Fig. 8.17) can be also explained by the predicted kink-like behavior of $\Delta_{SC}(T)$ below $T = T_c^* = (0.4 - 0.9)T_c$ in bosonic superconductors. The critical velocity for the creation of phonons or sound velocity in bosonic superconductors is equal to $v_s = v_c$. As a result, this sound velocity just like the SC order parameter $\Delta_{SC}(= \Delta_B)$ has the kink-like temperature dependence around $T_c^* < T_c$. For $\gamma_B << \gamma_B^*$, the characteristic temperature $T_c^*$ is very close to $T_c$ and the kink-like anomaly in $v_s(T)$ is expected slightly below $T_c$ as observed experimentally in high-$T_c$ cuprates YBCO (see Ref. [31]).

There are also the following experimental facts: (i) the small value of the entropy (or the large fraction of single particle condensate $n_{B0}$) observed in high-$T_c$ cuprates at $T < T_c$ [123] in comparison with its value expected for an ideal 3D Bose gas; and (ii) the change of SF density according to the law $n_S(t) = n_S(0)[1 - (T/T_c)^4]$ (with $n_{S0} = 4n_S(0)$ which corresponds to our $n_{B0}(0) = 0.25$ and $\gamma_B \simeq 1.4$ at $\xi_{BA}/T_{BEC} = 20$) in high-$T_c$ cuprates [124]. These observations are also confirmed the validity of the microscopic theory of novel superconductivity driven by SPC and PC of pre-formed Cooper pairs in high-$T_c$ cuprates.

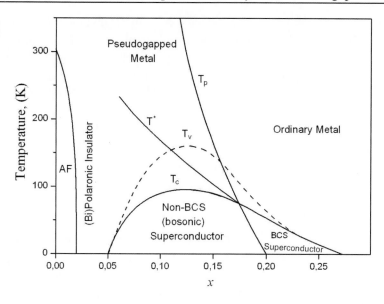

Figure 8.18. Generic phase diagram of high-$T_c$ cuprate superconductors as a function of temperature and doping level.

### 8.5.8.  Electronic Phase Diagram of High-$T_c$ Cuprate Superconductors

In this section, we discuss the existence of the possible normal and SC phases of high-$T_c$ cuprate superconductors at different temperatures and doping levels in terms of the large polaron theory, the BCS-like pairing theory of large polarons and the theory of a SF Bose-liquid of pre-formed Cooper pairs. As discussed in chapters 6and 7, polaronic effects control the essential physics of high-$T_c$ cuprates and are responsible for the formation of the new insulating, metallic and SC states in these polar materials. It seems likely, however, that polaronic effects are absent in the heavily overdoped cuprates, which are in the BCS (fermionic) limit due to the strong overlapping of loosely bound Cooper pairs (see section 8.2). In contrast, the underdoped, optimally doped and moderately overdoped cuprates are close to the bosonic limit due to the presence of polaronic effects and non-overlapping Cooper pairs. We believe that the BCS-like phase transition is actually SC transition in heavily overdoped cuprates where the Cooper pairing and superfluidity of Cooper pairs take place simultaneously at the mean-field temperature $T^* = T_c$. However, such a BCS-like phase transition might be non-SC transition taking place in the normal state of underdoped, optimally doped, and moderately overdoped cuprates, where the polaronic effects play a crucial role in the precursor Cooper pairing and in the formation of the PG state at $T^* > T_c$. One of the basic principles of unconventional superconductivity in high-$T_c$ cuprates is that the separation between the two temperatures $T^*$ (the onset of the BCS-like transition) and $T_c$ (the $\lambda$-like SC transition) occurs due to the polaronic effects. In these systems, the Cooper-pair formation and the condensation of pre-formed Cooper pairs into a SF Bose-liquid state would occur at different mean-field temperatures [12, 13, 14], so that the mean-field temperature $T^*$ determined from the BCS-like equations (7.16) or (7.20) is not a mean-field $T_c$.

It follows that the concentration dependences of $T_c$ in 3D and 2D bosonic superconductors (i.e., in underdoped, optimally doped, and moderately overdoped cuprates) are determined by the dependences $T_c(\rho_B)$ presented in section 8.4 for 3D and 2D SF Bose-liquids of composite bosons. Here and further, for convenience $\rho_B$ is replaced by the dimensionless carrier concentration $x = \rho_B/\rho_a = 0.5\rho_F/\rho_a$, where $\rho_a = 1/V_a$ is the density of the host lattice atoms, $V_a$ is the volume per $CuO_2$ unit in the cuprates. According to Eqs. (8.50), (8.71), and (8.77), $T_c$ first increases nearly as $T_c \sim x^{2/3}$ (in the 3D case) and $T_c \sim x$ (in the 2D case) and goes through a maximum with saturation at optimal doping and then decreases with increasing $x$. As discussed in chapter 7, the BCS-like PG temperature $T^*$ in high-$T_c$ cuprates determined from the relation (7.20) decreases exponentially when the carrier concentration $x$ increases (i.e., concentration of large polarons). Another characteristic PG temperature $T_p$ (chapter 7) corresponding to the thermal dissociation of large polarons is also decreased when the concentration of large polarons increases. Thus, $T^*$ ($T_p$ also) and $T_c$ have opposite doping dependences up to some optimal doping level $x = x_0$. The two curves $T_c(x)$ and $T^*(x)$ meet at some point $x > x_0$, corresponding to the moderately overdoped level at which the polaronic effects disappear and high-$T_c$ cuprates become BCS superconductors with $T_c(x) = T^*(x)$ and without PG in the normal state. The resulting electronic phase diagram of high-$T_c$ cuprates determined within the large polaron theory (chapter 6 and 7), the precursor BCS-like pairing theory of large polarons (chapter 7) and the theory of a SF Bose-liquid of pre-formed Cooper-like polaron pairs (section 8.4) is presented in Fig. 8.18. In this phase diagram, the curve $T_p(x)$ crossing the curve $T_c(x)$ and ending at the zero-temperature polaronic quantum critical point (QCP) $x_p > x_0$ separates two types of SC phases (below $T_c$) and two types of metallic phases (above $T_c$) [47]. The polaronic QCP separates the Landau Fermi-liquid (normal metal phase) from the normal Bose-liquid at $T_c \to 0$ (e.g., at the applied magnetic field $H = H_c$), and this QCP separates the SF Bose and Fermi liquids at $T_c > 0$. The curve $T_p(x)$ below $T_c$ becomes boundary between the so-called bosonic and fermionic superconductors. The normal metal and pseudogapped polaronic metal phases separated by this curve exist above $T_c$. There are three crossover temperatures on the electronic phase diagram of bosonic superconductors, $T_c$, $T^*$, and $T_p$. The curve $T^*(x)$ separates two pseudogapped metal phases of high-$T_c$ superconductors, namely, pseudogapped polaronic and BCS-like metal phases. In the case of heavily overdoped cuprates, we deal with the BCS superconductors that has only one crossover temperature $T_c$ on their electronic phase diagram. Whereas the lightly doped cuprates at $x < 0.02$ and $x > 0.02$ are antiferromagnetic and (bi)polaronic insulators, respectively, [125] (see also chapter 6). Indeed, all these predicted insulating, metallic, and SC phases were observed experimentally in high-$T_c$ cuprates.

We now estimate the possible values of $T_c$ in bosonic high-$T_c$ cuprate superconductors. In 3D high-$T_c$ cuprates with $m_p \simeq 4m_e$, $m_B = 2m_p$, $m_B^* = m_B[1 - \rho_B V_B(0)/\xi_{BR}]^{-1} = 2m_B$ and $\rho_B \simeq 0.6 \times 10^{21} cm^{-3}$, Eq. (8.71) predicts $T_{BEC}^* = 130K$. For 2D high-$T_c$ cuprates, using the values of $m_p = 7m_e$, $m_B = 2m_p$, $m_B^* = m_B[1 - \rho_B V_B(0)/\xi_{BR}]^{-1} \simeq 1.5m_B$ and $\rho_B \simeq 1.3 \times 10^{14} cm^{-2}$, from Eq. (8.77), we obtain $T_0^* = 2\pi\hbar^2\rho_B/k_B m_B^* \simeq 344K$. Then, according to Eqs. (8.71) and (8.77) the SC transition temperatures $T_c$ in 3D and 2D high-$T_c$ cuprates are given by

$$T_c^{3D} \simeq T_{BEC}^*[1 + 1.423c\gamma_B\sqrt{T_{BEC}^*/\xi_{BA}}] \qquad (8.113)$$

and

$$T_c^{2D} \simeq -\frac{T_0^*}{\ln[1 - \exp(-2\gamma_B/(2+\gamma_B))]}, \tag{8.114}$$

respectively.

If we take $\gamma_B = 0.2$ and $T_{BEC}^*/\xi_{BA} \simeq 0.06$, we find $T_c^{3D} \simeq 1.07 T_{BEC}^* \simeq 139K$ for 3D high-$T_c$ cuprates. By taking $\gamma_B = 0.15$ for 2D high-$T_c$ cuprates, we obtain $T_c^{2D} \simeq T_0^*/2.04 \simeq 167K$. These results for $T_c^{3D}$ and $T_c^{2D}$ show that the SC transition temperature of pre-formed Cooper pairs at 2D grain boundaries in high-$T_c$ cuprates becomes higher than their SC transition temperature in the bulk (when $\rho_B \gtrsim 1.3 \times 10^{14} cm^{-3}$ and $m_p \lesssim 8m_e$ for the 2D case). Therefore, we can identify $T_c^{2D}$ as the highest SC transition temperature in these superconductors. We believe that such a SC transition temperature might be manifested as a new crossover temperature $T_v = T_c^{2D}$ in the phase diagram of some high-$T_c$ cuprates (Fig. 8.18) and the SC dome is divided into a part in which the 3D superconductivity and the 2D superconductivity coexist below the bulk SC transition temperature $T_c^{3D}$. In a part in which the 2D superconductivity persists in the temperature range $T_c^{3D} < T < T_c^{2D}(= T_v)$ at the grain boundaries. It follows that the transition between 3D and 2D SC phases is accompanied by the destruction of the bulk superconductivity in the 3D-to-2D crossover region and by the formation of the vortex-like excitations. The experimental results presented in Ref. [126] agree with these theoretical predictions. Actually, the vortex-like Nernst signals observed in high-$T_c$ cuprates (see Ref. [45]) in the temperature regime between $T_c(= T_c^{3D})$ and $T_v(> T_c^{3D})$ are rather associated with the destruction of the bulk superconductivity in the 3D-to-2D crossover region (where 2D superconductivity persists at the grain boundaries) than with the PG state assumed in the SC fluctuation scenario [48], i.e., Nernst effects due to vortex-like excitations are not related to the SC fluctuations (see also Refs. [127, 128])

## 8.6.   Basic Principles of Conventional and Unconventional Superconductivity

Let us now formulate the basic principles of conventional superconductivity and novel (unconventional) superconductivity (in the PG state):

1.  Conventional superconductivity is the result of the Cooper pairing of quasi-free carriers accompanied simultaneously by the BCS condensation of weakly bound Cooper pairs into a SF Fermi-liquid state at the mean-field temperature $T_c$ in the so-called fermionic superconductors due to the absence of the polaronic effects.

2.  The excitation spectrum of the center-of-mass of Cooper pairs in BCS (fermionic) superconductors is phonon-like and the Landau criterion for superfluidity applied to such a spectrum is well satisfied.

3.  Ordinary metals and heavily overdoped cuprates are the BCS (fermionic) superconductors.

4.  Novel (unconventional) superconductivity as a rule is also result of two distinct quantum phenomena such as the precursor BCS-type pairing of self-trapped carriers with

the formation of pre-formed (composite bosonic) Cooper pairs at a characteristic mean-field temperature $T^*$ above $T_c$ and the subsequent condensation of Cooper pairs into a SF Bose-liquid state at $T_c$ in the so-called bosonic superconductors.

5. The separation between the BCS-like transition temperature $T^*$ and the SC transition temperature $T_c$ occurs due to the polaronic effects in bosonic high-$T_c$ cuprate superconductors.

6. The excitation spectrum of an interacting Bose gas of pre-formed (bosonic) Cooper pairs is phonon-like and satisfies the Landau criterion for superfluidity, whereas the BEC of an ideal Bose gas of pre-formed Cooper pairs is not their SF (or SC) state.

7. The underdoped, optimally doped, and moderately overdoped cuprates are the non-BCS (bosonic) superconductors.

8. Unconventional superconductivity in any Fermi systems results from the coexistence of the BCS-like pairing gap or PG $\Delta_F$ and the coherence parameter $\Delta_{SC} = \Delta_B$, which characterize the bond strength of pre-formed Cooper pairs and the bond strength of all condensed composite bosonic Cooper pairs, respectively.

9. The SF single particle and pair condensations of pre-formed Cooper pairs in unconventional superconductors result in the formation of two new SC states below $T_c$, which are quite different from the BCS condensation state and the BEC state of an ideal Bose gas of pre-formed Cooper pairs.

## 8.7.  Unconventional Superconductivity and Superfluidity in Other Systems

The ideas and methods of the standard theory of superconductivity and superfluidity based on the BCS pairing model of fermions is widely adopted to other fields of modern physics, such as organic and heavy-fermion superconductors [10, 11, 19], liquid $^3$He [3, 5, 54], nuclear and neutron star matter physics [3, 129, 130, 131, 132, 133], cosmology [134, 135, 136, 137], etc. However, the mechanisms of superconductivity and superfluidity in these systems might be different from the BCS condensation of quasi-fermionic Cooper pairs. In this connection, we briefly discuss the validity of the novel two-stage FBL scenarios for superfluidity and superconductivity in other Fermi systems and the validity of the theory of a SF Bose-liquid in liquid $^4$He.

## 8.8.  Novel Superconductivity in Organic and Heavy-Fermion Superconductors

The phenomenology of superconductivity in organic and heavy-fermion superconductor just like in high-$T_c$ cuprate superconductors is unconventional in many respects. There are important similarities in SC properties of these superconductors. Therefore, we believe that the theory of a SF Bose-liquid presented in section 8.4 will provide a new insight into the basic SC properties of the organic and heavy-fermion superconductors. In these super-conductors, the reduced gap $2\Delta/k_B T_c$ and the specific heat jump $\Delta C/\gamma T_c$ are considerably larger than in the BCS theory [19, 20]. Such deviations from the BCS theory of supercon-ductivity are indicative of the separation between the BCS-like transition temperature $T^*$ and the SC transition temperature $T_c$ due to the bosonic character of the pre-formed Cooper pairs in organic and heavy-fermion superconductors. A full understanding of unconven-tional superconductivity in these systems needs a new theoretical approach just like the novel two-stage FBL model (section 8.5) which accomplished the fusion of the BCS-like pairing theory of carriers with a proper theory of the SF condensation of composite bosonic Cooper pairs. A more microscopic consideration shows that a genuine phase transition into a SC state is $\lambda$-like transition driven by the SF condensation of pre-formed Cooper pairs at $T_c$ and is not related to a BCS-type phase transition. Indeed, experimental obser-vations show that organic superconductors and heavy-fermion superconductors exhibit the following power-law behaviors in specific heat and London penetration depth at $T \ll T_c$ [11, 19, 20, 42, 123, 138, 139]: $C_e(T) \sim T^2, T^3$, and $\lambda_L(T) \sim T^2, T^3$, and $T^4$, which can be explained by the absence or smallness of the energy gap $\Delta_{SF}$ in the excitation spectrum of a SF 3D Bose-liquid of pre-formed Cooper pairs. Whereas the origin of a $T$-linear term in the electronic specific heat of these superconductors may be associated with the presence of unpaired carriers below $T_c$. The specific heat of organic and heavy-fermion supercon-ductors near $T_c$ has a striking resemblance with the $\lambda$-like specific heat anomaly in liquid $^4$He. According to the theory of a SF 3D Bose-liquid, such a behavior of $C_e(T)$ in these un-conventional superconductors can be explained by the law $C_e(T) \sim (T - T_c)^{-1/2}$, whereas the second anomaly in the electronic specific heat of heavy-fermion superconductors ob-served near $T_c^*$ somewhat below $T_c$ (see Refs. [38, 140]) is fairly explained by the law $C_e(T) \sim (T_c^* - T)^{-1/2}$. Moreover, anomalous temperature dependence of the lower criti-cal magnetic field $H_{c1}$ was observed in these superconductors just like in high-$T_c$ cuprates near $T_c^*$ below which $H_{c1}(T)$ suddenly increases. This means that the SC order parameter in heavy-fermion superconductors has also a kink-like feature near $T_c^*$. Another striking behavior of the upper critical magnetic field $H_{c2}(T)$ unknown from conventional supercon-ductors has been observed in heavy-fermion superconductors where $H_{c2}(T)$ has a root-like behavior near $T_c$ with the large negative slope, which decreases very rapidly in magnitude as one goes away from $T_c$ [20, 35]. Further, the upward curvature of $H_{c2}(T)$ was observed at a lower temperature range. We argue that all these anomalous features of $H_{c2}(T)$ might be due to the anomalous temperature dependence of the SC order parameter $\Delta_{SC}(= \Delta_B)$ near $T_c$ and $T_c^*$ predicted by the theory of a SF 3D Bose-liquid of pre-formed Cooper pairs.

## 8.9.   Superfluidity of $^4$He

According to the SF Bose-liquid theory, the excitation spectrum $E_B(k)$ of $^4$He at $\gamma_B < \gamma_B^*$ and small $k$ becomes gapless and phonon-like in the temperature range $0 \leq T \leq T_c^*$. For $T > T_c^*$, the gap $\Delta_{SF}$ in $E_B(k)$ appears being responsible for the half-integer value of the circulation [64] and for the departure of the specific heat $C_v(T)$ from the phonon-like $T^3$ dependence observed in SF $^4$He [141]. Depletion of the zero-momentum state (or often named as condensate) of an interacting 3D Bose gas at $T = 0$ and $0 < T \leq T_c^*$ as a function of $\gamma_B$ (Fig. 8.1) and temperature (Fig. 8.4), as well as its complete absence in the range $T_c^* < T \leq T_c$ are also in good agreement with the experimental data available for $^4$He [66, 76].

The experimental dependence $n_{B0}(T)$ has a feature such as a noticeable increasing the fraction of the bosons condensed into the zero-momentum state $n_{B0}$ below $\simeq 1K$ [76]. The features of the velocity circulation quantum, $C_v(T)$ and $n_{B0}(T)$ are indicative of the appearance of the gap $\Delta_{SF}$ in the excitation spectrum of SF $^4$He at $T \geq 1.1$ (i.e., at $T_c^* \sim 1.1K$). Further the experimental values of $n_{B0} = 0.10 - 0.14$ (at $T = 0$) in $^4$He [76] correspond to the values of $\gamma_B \simeq 1.5 - 1.6$ for $T_{BEC}/\xi_{BA} = 0.05$. This means that the interaction in liquid $^4$He is strong enough. Hence, the formation of the SF single particle condensate (with $k = 0$ and circulation quantum $\hbar/m_4$) and pair condensate (with $k \neq 0$ and circulation quantum $\hbar/2m_4$) in $^4$He are quite possible in the temperature ranges $0 \leq T \leq T_c^*$ and $T_c^* < T < T_c$, respectively. The first signs of these phenomena was observed by Whitmore and Zimmerman and other authors [64]. Apparently, the existence of the condensate-less pair solutions of Eqs. (8.30) - (8.32) in the complete range $0 \leq T \leq T_c$ (at $\gamma_B > \gamma_B^*$) are not appropriate for the SF $^4$He. The experimental situation in SF $^4$He is very close to the previously mentioned situation (for $1 < \gamma_B < \gamma_B^*$). It seems that the numerical studies [61, 63] predict nonrealistic (for $^4$He) condensate fractions $n_{B0} \simeq 0.75$ and $\simeq 0.93$. However, some numerical results of Ref. [61] (see Figs. 3(b) and 3(c) of Ref. [61]) resemble our results obtained for $\gamma_B > \gamma_B^*$ (Fig. 8.2(a)) and $1 < \gamma_B < \gamma_B^*$ (Fig. 8.2(b)) but with the essential distinctions (cf. e.g., Fig. 3(c) in Ref. [61] and Fig. 8.2(b) in this chapter). Our numerical and analytical solutions of Eqs. (8.27) - (8.29) for $\gamma_B < \gamma_B^*$ and $\gamma_B << \gamma_B^*$ taking into account the approximation (8.33) are original and there are no analogs in Refs. [61] and [68]. We now estimate the lower $v_{c1} = (\hbar/2m_Bl_0)ln(l/l_0)$ and upper $v_{c2} = \sqrt{\Delta_B/m_B}$ critical velocities. If we assume that the interatomic distance is $l_0 \simeq 4\text{Å}$ and the coherence length is of order $l \simeq \pi\hbar/\sqrt{2m_B\Delta_B} \simeq 7.33\text{Å}$ (at $2\Delta_B/T_c \sim \gamma_B \sim 1$ and $T_c \sim 2.2K$), we obtain $v_{c1} \simeq 64cm/s$ and $v_{c2} \simeq 48cm/s$ which are consistent with the experimental data [3, 142, 143, 144]. The temperature dependence of $v_{c1}$ and $v_{c2}$ are also in good agreement with the observations [143, 144]. If the momentum dependence of $\chi_B$ at $\Delta_{SF} = 0$ is taken into account in a simple form $\chi_B(k) = A' - B'k$ (where $A'$ and $B'$ are constant parameters) just like it is done in the Bogoliubov theory [145] for an interboson interaction potential, then one can obtain the Landau's phonon-roton energy spectrum. Further, at $\gamma_B < \gamma_B^*$ or $\gamma_B < 1$ we obtain the relation $n_{B0}(T) \sim (T_c^* - T)^{(2-\beta)/3}$ (that have been derived earlier only in the framework of a phenomenological approach [76, 146] for $^4$He with $\beta \geq 0$ and $T_c$ instead of $T_c^*$ corresponding to the case of the BEC of an ideal Bose gas) with $\beta \geq -1$ and $\beta \leq 0.5$, respectively. It means that for $0 < \gamma_B < \gamma_B^*$ the critical index $\beta$ will change from -1 to 0.5. Therefore, near $T_c^* < T_c$ jump of $C_v(T)$ may be expected at weak ($\gamma_B << 1$) and intermediate ($\gamma_B \leq 1$) couplings. However, at strong couplings ($\gamma_B > 1$), instead of such jump only peculiarity may be displayed in $C_v(T)$ as was observed, for example, in $^4$He [65]. The observed low temperature heat capacity $C_v(T) \sim T^2$ of a 2D Bose-liquid of $^4$He in mesopores [147] is also consistent with the predictions of the theory of a SF 2D Bose-liquid. Whereas the shift of the SF frequency observed there (with the anomaly at $T \simeq (0.7 - 0.8)T_C$) as a function of the temperature closely resembles the kink-like behavior of the order parameter $\Delta_B$ of a SF 3D-Bose-liquid. Perhaps the $^4$He adatoms in mesopores manifest both 2D- and 3D-superfluidity one of them will display in the heat capacity and another will display in the SF frequency shifts.

## 8.9.1.  Superfluidity of $^3$He

It is widely believed that in liquid $^3$He the triplet Cooper pairing of $^3$He atoms with angular momentum $l = 1$ described by the BCS-like pairing theories is responsible for superfluidity of this quantum liquid [93, 148] (see chapter 7). However, the BCS-like pairing theories cannot explain many SF properties of $^3$He observed below the critical temperature $T_c$ (e.g., the origin of the first-order transition between the $A$- and $B$-phases at $T \simeq T_{AB} \simeq 0.7T_c$) and the half-integer flux quantum $\hbar/4m_3$, where $m_3$ is the mass of $^3$He atoms [149, 150]. One can assume that in liquid $^3$He the small fraction of atoms may take part in Cooper pairing and $\rho_B/\rho_F << 1$ (where $\rho_F$ is the density of $^3$He atoms in unit volume). At $\rho_F \sim 10^{22} cm^{-3}$ and $\rho_B/\rho_F \sim 10^{-3}$, we obtain $T_c > T_{BEC} \simeq 2.63 \times 10^{-3} K$ that is very close to the observed value of $T_c$ in $^3$He. When the number of $^3$He atoms taking part in Cooper pairing is small enough and the spatial separation between Cooper pairs and other unpaired $^3$He atoms is large, the Pauli blocking loses its efficiency in hindering the bosonization of Cooper pairs. If the interatomic interaction in liquid $^3$He is not very weak, the precursor Cooper pairing of $^3$He atoms occurs at $T^* > T_c$ and leads to the formation of pre-formed Cooper pairs which may behave like composite bosons and undergo the PC at $T_c$ and SPC at $T_c^* < T_c$. In the two-stage FBL scenario (section 8.5), the genuine SF state is described by the order parameter $\Delta_B$ in an interacting Bose gas of pre-formed Cooper pairs. Apparently, the interatomic interaction in liquid $^3$He is comparatively weaker ($\gamma_B < 1$) than such an interaction in $^4$He. Therefore the condensate fraction in $^3$He must be larger (see Fig. 8.1a) than in SF $^4$He. Indeed, the condensate fraction in liquid $^3$He-$^4$He mixtures was found to be $n_{B0} \simeq 0.18$ [151] much larger than $n_{B0} \simeq 0.10$ in pure liquid $^4$He [76]. It seems that the gap $\Delta_{SF}$ in $E_B(k)$ vanishes at $T = T_c^* \simeq 0.7T_c$ (for $\gamma_B \leq 1$) at which some features of the physical properties of $^3$He must be displayed. Such features are actually observed in the SF phase of $^3$He as jump-like increasing of the critical current velocity $v_c$ three times under pressure and as the abrupt change of the SF density at $T \simeq (0.6 - 0.7)T_c$ [148, 150].

This jump-like increase of $v_c$ and SF density is caused by the sharp increase of $\Delta_B$ (or $v_c = \sqrt{\Delta_B/m_B}$) at $T = T_c^*$ when $\gamma_B << \gamma_B^*$ (Fig. 8.13). We believe that the increase of the interaction strength between composite bosons occurs under pressure or rotation and it is accompanied by appearance of the gap $\Delta_{SF}$ in $E_B(k)$ at more lower temperatures. Then, the splitting of the so-called $B$-phase into two phases $B1$ and $B2$, as well as the transition between them observed at $T \sim 0.6T_c$ [152] might be caused by these circumstances (i.e., the $B1$ phase should be expanded region of the $A$-phase under rotation). Since both the transition between $B1$ and $B2$ phases [150] and the transition between $B$ and $A$ phases [148, 149] are first-order phase transitions, so that the origins of the $A$- and $B$-phases, as well as the nature of the transition between these phases in $^3$He at $T \sim 0.7T_c$ [148] (cf. the value of $T_c^* \geq 0.7T_c$) are caused by the first-order $SPC \Leftrightarrow PC$ phase transitions in an interacting Bose gas of pre-formed Cooper pairs and the line $T_{AB}$ in the SF $^3$He phase diagram corresponds to these phase transitions. The jump-like increase of the SF density observed in $^3$He [148, 150] just at the phase transition $A \rightarrow B$ is in favor in this assumption. Further, the influence of the external magnetic field $H$ on this phase transition can be taken into account through the chemical potential of interacting composite bosons $\tilde{\mu}_B$ (i.e., in the presence of the magnetic field $H$, $\tilde{\mu}_B$ should be replaced by $\sim \tilde{\mu}_B + \mu_0 H$, where $\mu_0$, is the Bohr magneton) in Eqs. (8.41) and (8.42) from which follows the increase of $\gamma_B$ (see Fig.

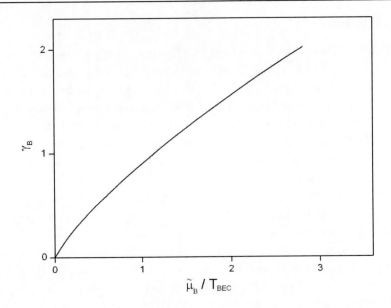

Figure 8.19. The dependence of $\gamma_B$ on $\tilde{\mu}_B/T_{BEC}$ for a SF 3D Bose-liquid.

8.19) and it is accompanied by the decrease of $n_{B0}$ and $T_c^*$. This prediction of the theory of a SF 3D Bose-liquid of pre-formed Cooper pairs is also in good agreement with the observed decrease of the transition temperature $T_{AB}$ in $^3$He under external magnetic field [153]. We argue that the power law dependence of the specific heat $C_v(T) \sim T^3$ observed in SF $^3$He [148] is associated with the absence of the gap $\Delta_{SF}$ in $E_B(k)$ at $T \leq T_c^*$ or with the smallness of $\Delta_{SF} << T$ at $T > T_c^*$ (section 8.6). The specific heat jump at $T = T_c$ in $^3$He has some resemblance with the $\lambda$-like transition [154].

### 8.9.2.   Superfluidity of Nuclear Matter

The low-, intermediate- and high-density nuclear systems are similar to the underdoped, optimally doped, and overdoped high-$T_c$ cuprate superconductors. Therefore, the two-stage FBL scenario for superconductivity and superfluidity can be applied to the description of the precursor Cooper pairing of nucleons and the condensation of nucleon Cooper pairs in the SF state within the nuclei. When the residual interaction between the nucleons becomes sufficiently strong, the BCS-like pair correlation leads to the formation of nucleon Cooper pairs at $T^*$ above the critical temperature $T_c$ of SF transition and these pre-formed Cooper pairs may behave like composite bosons [14]. With decreasing temperature, the bosonic deuteron-like Cooper pairs undergo a SF condensation with the corresponding critical temperature $T_c$ in low- and intermediate-density nuclear systems, which exhibit the PG phenomena above $T_c$ [14, 155]. The cold nuclear matter can be in a SF Bose-liquid state. Actually, such nuclear systems have a new SF state that is different from the BCS condensation state of quasi-fermion Cooper pairs. At the high density limit, $T_c$ follows the BCS result and coincides with the Cooper-pair formation temperature, but at low and intermediate densities, the SF transition temperature $T_c$ deviates from the BCS prediction and does not coincide with the PG formation temperature $T^*$. Hence, the situations corresponding to the fermionic and bosonic superconductors are also realized in high- and low-density nuclear systems, respectively.

In an interacting Bose gas of deuteron-like Cooper pairs, the order parameter $\Delta_B$ characterizes the nuclear binding energy per one bound nucleon pairs (then the nuclear binding energy per one nucleon is $\simeq \Delta_B/2$). In particular, for intermediate interboson coupling (e.g., $\gamma_B \simeq 1.2$ which corresponds to the dense heavy nuclei), we find from (8.50) $T_c = 2.4 T_{BEC}$ (at $T_{BEC}/\xi_{BA} \simeq 0.034$). Then, for nuclei with the nucleon number $A = 200$ and radius $R_0 = 1.3 \times A^{1/3} 10^{-13} cm$, we obtain $\rho_B \simeq 5.46 \times 10^{37} cm^{-3}$, $T_{BEC} \simeq 10 MeV$ and $\Delta_B \simeq 14.4 MeV$ at $2\Delta_B/T_c \simeq \gamma_B$. However, a dilute nuclear matter (perhaps light nuclei and outer layer of heavy nuclei are the same) might be in the strong coupling regime ($\gamma_B > \gamma_B^*$ with $\Delta_{SF} \neq 0$ and $\Delta_B > 2.88 T_{BEC}$). In this case, if we take $R_0 = 1.6 \times 10^{-13} A^{1/3}$ and $A = 64$, we obtain $\rho_B \simeq 3 \times 10^{37} cm^{-3}$, $T_{BEC} \simeq 6.25 MeV$, and $\Delta_B \simeq 18.8 MeV$. These values of $\Delta_B$ (or rather $\Delta_B/2$) agrees with the nuclear binding energies determined by the mass defect. At $\gamma_B > \gamma_B^*$, we deal with a dilute Bose gas and with the PC of attracting deuteron-like bosons leading to the $\alpha$-clustering in the light nuclei and in the outer layer of heavy nuclei in accordance with the observations [156]. Subsequently, the $\alpha$-particles as the composite bosons may undergo the PC with the formation of nuclear molecules (cf. Ref. [157]). From Fig. 8.1a, it follows that the increase of $\gamma_B$ is accompanied by the smearing or depletion of the SF condensate of deuteron-like bosonic Cooper pairs, $\alpha$-particles and other composite bosons over their broadening condensation layer with the characteristic thickness $\xi_{BA}$.

Further, the theory of a SF Bose-liquid of pre-formed nucleon Cooper pairs explains other observed experimental facts in the following way: (i) double-proton, alpha, and cluster decay of nuclei are caused by the strong depletion of the SF single particle condensate of deuteron-like Cooper pairs, alpha particles and cluster bosons at the strong interboson coupling $\gamma_B > 1$; (ii) presence of the phonon-like or gapless excitations is the result of the absence of the gap $\Delta_{SF}$ in $E_B(k)$; (iii) zero angular momentum of the nuclei in the ground state is due to the presence of the single particle condensate of deuteron-like Cooper pairs at $\gamma_B < 1$; (iv) low lying excited state in comparison with BCS-like pairing energy $2\Delta_F$ [129] is associated with the existence of the small energy gap $\Delta_{SF} << \Delta_F$ and SF order parameter $\Delta_B < \Delta_F$ for $\gamma_B \approx \gamma_B^*$; (v) presence of the exotic light nuclei with a large neutron halos or dilute neutron skins extended to large radii [158] is the result of the strong smearing of the SF condensate of neutron pairs for $1 < \gamma_B \leq \gamma_B^*$; (vi) staggering effect in some superdeformed nuclei [159] is associated with the formation of vortical motions in rotating SF nuclei just like in rotating SF $^4He$; (vii) high stability of magic and twice magic nuclei is associated with the SPC and PC of nucleon pairs both in proton and in neutron subsystems at $\gamma_B << \gamma_B^*$; (viii) fission of the nuclei is the result of the nucleation and growing of the vortical motion due to the presence of inpaired nucleons led to the pulsation and fission of nuclei at the angular velocity $\Omega_a > \Omega_{c1}$ and $\Omega_a = \Omega_{c2}$, respectively, where

$$\Omega_{c1} = \frac{\hbar}{2 M_n R_0^2} \ln \left( \frac{R_0}{r_0} \right) \quad (R_0 >> r_0) \tag{8.115}$$

and

$$\Omega_{c2} = \frac{\hbar}{5.5536 M_n R_0^2} \tag{8.116}$$

are the first and second critical angular velocities of a SF nucleonic Bose-liquid, respectively, $M_n$ is the mass of nucleons. In case of $^4$He, the quantity of $r_0$ is nearly equal to atomic size and it is equal to internucleon distance in nuclei. Then, for $A \sim 200$, $R_0 \simeq 8.2 \times 10^{-13} cm$ $r_0 \sim 2 \times 10^{-13} cm$ we find $\Omega_{c1} \sim 6.6 \times 10^{20} c^{-1}$ (this corresponds to the beta decay with the energy $\simeq 0.435 MeV$ (see Ref. [160])) and $\Omega_{c2} \simeq (0.625 - 1.35) \times 10^{21} c^{-1}$ at which the nuclear fission take place. So, for $\Omega_{c1} < \Omega_a < \Omega_{c2}$, the nuclear conversions, such as beta, alpha, and gamma emission are expected. The strong depletion of the single particle condensate of composite Bose particles in nuclei at $\gamma_B < \gamma_B^*$ are rather responsible for the observed double-proton, and cluster radioactivity [160, 161] than the tunneling effect which becomes unlikely for heavy particles.

### 8.9.3. Superfluidity of the Neutron Star Matter

The formation of the bound singlet or triplet nucleon Cooper pairs is quite possible in the neutron star matter just like in SF $^3$He and nuclei. It was argued [14] that the precursor Cooper pairing of nucleons with the formation of deuteron-like Cooper pairs should also occur at a certain temperature $T^*$ above $T_c$ in the low- and intermediate-density regions of the outer crust of a neutron star just like in underdoped and optimally doped cuprates. These deuteron-like Cooper pairs may behave like composite bosons and condense into a SF nucleonic Bose-liquid state. Hence, the normal and SF properties of such neutron star matter are described by the BCS-like energy gap $\Delta_F$ and by the gap $\Delta_{SF}$ and order parameter $\Delta_B$. The energy gap $\Delta_F$ depending on the nuclear matter density in the neutron stars may be small (in the inner crust of a neutron star) and large (in the outer crust of a neutron star) [133]. So the situation in the inner crust of neutron stars closely resembles the situation in heavily overdoped cuprates which are BCS (fermionic) superconductors. Therefore, the parameters of the SF inner crust of neutron stars can be determined according to the BCS-like pairing theory of nucleons (chapter 7). In particular, $T_c$ coincides with the Cooper pair formation temperature $T^*$ at the high density limit corresponding to the inner crust of neutron stars. Whereas the parameters of the SF outer crust of neutron stars with low- and intermediate nuclear matter densities are determined according to the theory of a SF Bose-liquid presented in section 8.4. We now estimate the values of $T_c \simeq T_{BEC}$, $\Omega_{c1}$, and $\Omega_{c2}$ for the outer crust of a neutron star. For the mass density of neutron star matter $\rho_M \sim 10^{11} - 10^{14} g/cm^3$ [3, 162] and the concentration of deuteron-like Cooper pairs $\rho_B \sim \rho_M/2M_n \sim 3 \times (10^{34} - 10^{37}) cm^{-3}$, we find $T_{BEC} \simeq 5.3 \times (10^8 - 10^{10}) K$. Then, at $\gamma_B \simeq 0.3$ and $T_{BEC}/\xi_{BA} \sim 0.1$, we obtain from Eq. (8.50) $T_c \sim 6 \times (10^8 - 10^{10}) K$. The quantity of $\Omega_{c1}$ is determined from (8.115). The parameter $r_0$ is the same as in nuclei, but $R_0$ is the distance between vortices and has a macroscopic size just like in $^4$He. Then, by taking $R_0 \sim 10^{-2} - 10^{-1} cm$ [3, 142] and $r_0 \simeq 2 \times 10^{-13} cm$ for the neutron stars, we obtain $\Omega_{c1} \sim 0.8 - 60 c^{-1}$ which agree well with the observed periods of neutron star pulsation [3, 162]. Using this value of $R_0$ we find $\Omega_{c2} \simeq (0.55 - 1.47) \times 10^{21} cm^{-1}$. If the angular velocity $\Omega_a$ of neutron stars exceeds the value of $\Omega_{c1}$, then the formation of a mixed state (by analogy with the type II superconductors) and partial destruction of a SF condensate with the formation of several spatially separated SF nucleonic liquids which are weakly linked with each other like weak links or so-called SNS intergranular Josephson junctions between SC grains in high-$T_c$ cuprates is quite possible. Perhaps two-fold pulsing neutron stars [163, 164] are the same. If that is the case, then multi-fold pulsing neutron stars may be

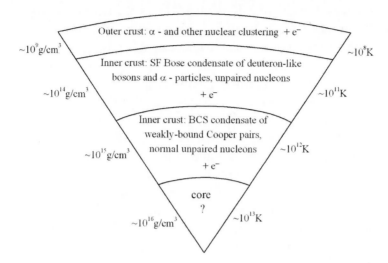

Figure 8.20. The assumed internal structure of a neutron star.

also observed. It seems likely that the interstellar Josephson junctions serve as the accretion channels for the two-fold and multi-fold star systems. The nucleons in the inner crust of a neutron star joining with its core (see Fig. 8.20) should be unpaired fermions like unpaired quasi-free carriers in the heavily overdoped cuprates. In this inner crust joining with outer crust of neutron stars, the BCS-like pairing of nucleons leads to the formation of deuteron-like bosonic Cooper pairs at $T^* > T_c$ and then these composite bosons undergo the PC and SPC at $T_c$ and $T_c^*$, respectively, for $\gamma_B < \gamma_B^*$. In a dilute outer crust of a neutron star, the PC of attracting deuteron-like bosons, $\alpha$-particles and other composite bosons at $\gamma_B > \gamma_B^*$ leads to their clustering with the formation of various nuclear systems (which are rather light nuclei). The situation in this outer crust of neutron stars is very similar to the situation in the underdoped high-$T_c$ cuprates. In the inner crust of a neutron star joining with its outer crust the situation $T_c^* < T < T_c$ seems to be more realistic and almost all deuteron-like bosons will undergo PC with the formation of $\alpha$-particles in the temperature range $T_c^* < T < T_c$, whereas the negligible fraction of excited (i.e., over-condensate) deuteron-like bosons may form deuterium after explosion of neutron stars. The gravitation contraction of the massive neutron stars leads to the increasing of the temperature (which approaches to $T_c$) and vortex number. Therefore, at $\Omega_a \sim \Omega_{c2}$ (once again by analogy with the type II superconductors) the complete destruction of a SF condensate of nuclear matter takes place just like the standard Big Bang and it is accompanied either by complete scattering of a neutron star matter or by throw off the inner and outer crusts of a neutron star with the formation of moderately small neutron stars, ordinary stars (sometimes with the planet systems) which have low nuclear densities and temperatures (e.g., $T \sim 10^6 - 10^9$K), and other small objects.

### 8.9.4. Nucleosynthesis in the Early Universe

It is most likely that the formation of different neutron stars corresponds to the early but not latter stage of the universe evolution after its creation by the standard Big Band scenario. We believe that in the expanding and cooling in early stages of the universe (when its mass density and temperature decreases down to $\rho_M \sim 10^{14} g/cm^3$ and $T \sim 10^{11}$K) the formation of different neutron stars under the vortical motions in a dense SF matter is quite possible. Then a dilute Bose gas of deuteron-like bosons at $\gamma_B > \gamma_B^*$ formed in interstellar sites and the subsequent PC of these composite bosons led to the formation of $\alpha$-particles which somewhat later turn into $^4$He atoms, i.e., the subsequent Cooper-like pairing of composite bosons (e.g., deuterons, $\alpha$-particles, etc.) leads to the formation of more heavy elements in interstellar sites (where the part of excited or over-condensate deuterons will form deuterium and their other part form $^3$He atoms at the collisions with unpaired nucleons). So, the main nucleosynthesis in expanding universe takes place first in neutron stars and between these stars and then in ordinary stars. Since at $T \rightarrow T_c$ and $\Omega_a \rightarrow \Omega_{c2}$ the vortical motion involves almost all neutron star matter and the mixing of deuterons and unpaired nucleons at the condensate explosion leads to the conversion of some part of over-condensate deuterons into $^3$He. The vortical motions of the scattering SF fragments of neutron stars may also retain after the condensate explosion. This caused the formation of the different cosmic objects with their circular and rotational motions. In particular, such an explosion of neutron stars led to the conversion of their nuclear matter into the observed now hydrogen H($\sim$ 75%), $^4$He($\sim$ 25%) and other light elements ($\leq$ 1%) in the ordinary stars, planets and interstellar sites [164, 165, 166, 167, 168, 169]. The small fraction ($\sim 10^{-4} - 10^{-5}$) of the deuterium and $^3$He in the universe [168] and sun [166] may be also indicative of this scenario for nucleosynthesis in the early universe. One can assume that the explosion of neutron stars as a supernova is the latest stage of the non-standard (i.e., Planck's epoch) Big Bang scenario. Then the standard Big Bang nucleosynthesis takes place in such neutron stars and interstellar sites in the early universe.

# References

[1] F. London, *Superfluids*, V. 2 (John Wiley and Sons, Inc, New York, 1954).

[2] E. M. Lifshitz and L. P. Pitaevskii, *Statistical Physics*. Part 2 (Nauka, Moscow, 1978).

[3] D. R. Tilley and J. Tilley, *Superfluidity and Superconductivity* (Adam Hilger, Bristol, 1990).

[4] V. Z. Kresin and S. A. Wolf, *Fundamentals of Superconductivity* (Plenum Press, New York, 1990).

[5] D. M. Lee, *Rev. Mod. Phys.* 69, 645 (1997); J. R. Schriffer and M. Tinkham, *Rev. Mod. Phys.* 71, S313 (1999).

[6] L. D. Landau, *J. Phys. (Moscow)* 5, 71 (1941); 11, 91 (1947).

[7] J. Bardeen, L. N. Cooper, and J. R. Schrieffer, *Phys. Rev.* 108, 1175 (1957).

[8] S. E.Inderhees, M. B. Salamon, N. Goldfeld, J. P. Rice, B. G. Pazol, D. M. Ginsberg, J. Z. Liu, and G. W. Crabtree, *Phys. Rev. Lett.* 60, 1178 (1988); K. Fossheim, O. M. Nes, T. Legreid, C. N. W. Darlington, D. A. O'Connor, and C. E. Gough, *Int. J. Mod. Phys.* B1, 1171 (1988); M. B. Salamon, S. E. Inderhees, J. P. Rice, and D. M. Ginsberg, *Physica* A168, 283 (1990); T. Matsuzaki, M. Ido, N. Momono, R. M. Dipasupil, T. Nagata, A. Sakai, and M. Oda, *J. Phys. Chem. Solids* 62, 29 (2001).

[9] M. B. Salamon, in: *Physical Properties of High Temperature Superconductors I*, ed., D. M. Ginsberg (Mir, Moscow, 1990), chapter 2

[10] D. Jerome and H. J. Schulz, *Adv. Phys.* 31, 299 (1982); H. Mori, *Int. J. Mod. Phys.* B8, 1 (1994).

[11] M. B. Maple, *Physics Today. March*, 72 (1986); R. Caspary, P. Hellmann, M. Keller, G. Sparn, C. Wassilew, R. Köhler, C. Geibel, C. Schank, F. Steglich, and N. E. Phillips, *Phys. Rev. Lett.* 71, 2146 (1993).

[12] S. Dzhumanov and P. K. Khabibullaev, *Izv. Akad. Nauk Uzb. SSR, Ser. Fiz. Math. Nauk* 1, 47 (1990); S. Dzhumanov, *Int. Conf. on High Temperature Superconductivity and Localization Phenomena*, Moscow, USSR, 11-15 May (1991), p. T22; S. Dzhumanov, P. J. Baimatov, and N. I. Rahmatov, *Abstract 2nd Liquid Matter Conf.* (Firenze, Italy, 1993).

[13] S. Dzhumanov, *Physica* C235-240, 2269 (1994); S. Dzhumanov, P. J. Baimatov, A. A. Baratov, and N. I. Rahmatov, *Physica* C235-240, 2339 (1994); S. Dzhumanov, *Superlattices and Microstructure* 21, 363 (1997).

[14] S. Dzhumanov, P. J. Baimatov, and P. K. Khabibullaev, *Uzb. Zh. Phys.* 6, 24 (1992); S. Dzhumanov and P. K. Khabibullaev, *Pramana J. Phys.* 45, 385 (1995); S. Dzhumanov, A. A. Baratov, and S. Abboudy, *Phys. Rev.* B54, 13121 (1996-II); S. Dzhumanov, *Int. J. Mod. Phys.* B12, 2151 (1998).

[15] J. F. Phillips, *Physics of high-$T_c$ Superconductors* (Academic Press, San Diego, 1989); A. S. Davidov, *Phys. Rep.* 190, 193 (1990).

[16] R. Micnas, J. Ranninger, and S. Robaszhkiewicz, *Rev. Mod. Phys.* 62, 113 (1990); J. Ranninger, *Physica* C235-240, 277 (1994); R. Friedberg, and T. D. Lee, *Phys. Lett.* A138, 423 (1989).

[17] J. R. Schriffer, *Physica C185-189*, 17 (1991); J. Schmalian, D. Pines, and B. Stojkovic, *Phys. Rev.* B60, 667 (1999).

[18] A. S. Alexsandrov, *Theory of Superconductivity from Weak to Strong Coupling* (IOP Publishing, Bristol and Philadelfia, 2003).

[19] D. Rainer, *Phys. Scr.* T23, 103 (1988).

[20] B. H. Brandow, *Int. J. Mod. Phys.* B8, 3859 (1994).

[21] P. W. Anderson, *The Theory of Superconductivity in the High-$T_c$ Cuprates* (Princeton University Press, Princeton, 1997).

[22] P. A. Lee, N. Nagaosa, and X.-G. Wen, *Rev. Mod. Phys.* 78, 17 (2006).

[23] V. Z. Kresin and S. A. Wolf, *Rev. Mod. Phys.* 81, 481 (2009).

[24] D. M. Ginsberg, in: *Physical Properties of HIgh Temperature Superconductors I*, ed., D. M. Ginsberg (Mir, Moscow, 1990), chapter 1.

[25] Ch. Thomsen and M. Cardona, in: *Physical Properties of High Temperature Superconductors I*, ed., D. M. Ginsberg (Mir, Moscow, 1990), chapter 8.

[26] N. V. Zavaritskii, *Usp. Fiz. Nauk* 160, 177 (1990); Ch. Renner and Ö. Fischer, *Physica* C235-240, 53 (1994).

[27] H. Adrian, W. Assmus, and A. Höhr, J. Kowalewski, H. Spille, and F. Steglich, *Physica* C162-164, 329 (1989); A. Umezava, G. W. Crabtree, K. G. Vandervoort, U. Welp, W. K. Kwok, and J. Z. Liu, *Physica* C162-164, 733 (1989).

[28] A. Schilling, R. Jin, H. R. Ott, and Th. Wolf, *Physica* C235-240, 2741 (1994); C. J. Van der Beek, B. Schmidt, M. Konczykowski, V. M. Vinokur, and G. W. Crabtree, *Physica* C235-240, 2813 (1994); M. Lang, F. Steglich, N. Toyota, and T. Sasaki, *Physica* C235-240, 2469 (1994).

[29] H. R. Ott, *Int. J. Mod. Phys.* B6, 473 (1992); A. Schilling, O. Jeandupeux, S. Büchi, H. R. Ott, and C. Rossel, *Physica* C235-240, 229 (1994); I. Ukrainczyk and A. Dulcic, *Physica* C235-240, 2001 (1994); A. Sidorenco, C. Sürgers, T. Trappmann, and H. V. Löhneysen, *Physica* C235-240, 2615 (1994).

[30] G. Oya, M. Aoyama, S. Kishida, and H. Tokutaka, *Physica* C185-189, 2453 (1991); P. Müller, *Physica* C235-240, 289 (1994); D. Hu, V. Brabers, and W. J. M. de Jonge, *Physica* C235-240, 951 (1994).

[31] V. Müller, C. Hucho, K. de Groot, D. Winea, D. Maurer, and K. H. Rieder, *Solid State Commun.* 72, 997 (1989); J. Ranninger, *Z. Phys.* B84, 167 (1991).

[32] M. A. Izbizky, M. Nunez Regueiro, P. Esquinazi, and C. Fainstein, *Phys. Rev.* B38, 9220 (1988); M. D. Nunez Regueiro and D. Castello, *Int. J. Mod. Phys.* B5, 2003 (1991).

[33] N. Tsuda, D. Shimada, and N. Miyakawa, *Physica* C185-189, 1903 (1991).

[34] M. Ledvij, D. Davidovic, and L. Dobrosavljevic-Grujic, *Physica* C165-166, 1119 (1990); M. Ledvij and L. Dobrosavljevic-Grujic, *Mod. Phys. Lett.* B4, 471 (1990).

[35] H. R. Brand, H. Pleiner, and M. M. Doria, *Physyca* C162-164, 251 (1989); L. I. Burllachkov and L. I. Glazman, *Physica* C166, 75 (1990).

[36] J. M. Barbut, D. Bourgault, N. Schopohl, A. Subpice, and R. Tournie, *Physica* C235-240, 2855 (1994); T. Ishida, K. Okuda, A. I. Rykov, S. Tajima, and I. Terasaki, *Phys. Rev.* B58, 5222 (1998-I); M. T. Beal-Monod, *Phys. Rev.* B58, 8830 (1998-I).

[37] J. E. Gordon, S. Prigge, S. J. Collocott, and R. Driver, *Physica* C185-189, 1351 (1991).

[38] H. R. Ott, H. Rudigier, Z. Fisk, and J. L. Smith, *Phys. Rev.* B31, 1651 (1985); R. A. Fisher, S. Kim, B. F. Woodfield, N. E. Phillips, L. Taillefer, K. Hasselbach, J. Flouquet, A. L. Giorgi, and J. L. Smith, *Phys. Rev. Lett.* 62, 1411 (1989); T. Trappmann, H. V. Löhneysen, and L. Taillefer, *Phys. Rev.* B43, 13714 (1991).

[39] D. R. Harshmann, G. Aeppli, E. J. Ansaldo, B. Batlog, J. H. Brewer, J. F. Carolan, R. J. Cava, M. Ceilo, A. C. D. Chaklader, W. N. Hardy, S. R. Kreitzmann, G. M. Luke, D. R. Noakes, and M. Senba, *Phys. Rev.* B36, 2386 (1987); J. Carini, L. Drabeck, and G. Gruner, *Mod. Phys. Lett.* B3, 5 (1989); B. Pümpin, H. Keller, W. Kündig, W. Odermatt, I. M. Savic, J. W. Schneider, H. Simmler, and P. Zimmermann, *Phys. Rev.* B42, 8019 (1990).

[40] G. Deutscher, *Physica Scripta* T29, 9 (1989).

[41] J. R. Cooper, C. T. Chu, L. W. Zhou, B. Dunn, and G. Gruner, *Phys. Rev.* B37, 638 (1987); J. Annett, N. Goldenfeld, and S. R. Renn, *Phys. Rev.* B43, 2778 (1991); W. Hardy, D. A. Bonn, D.C. Morgan, R. Liang, and K. Zhang, *Phys. Rev. Lett.* 70, 399 (1993).

[42] A. I. Sokolov, *Superconductivity: Physica, Chemistry, Technika* 5, 1794 (1992).

[43] C. C. Tsuei and J. R. Kirtley, *Rev. Mod. Phys.* 72, 969 (2000).

[44] K. Kawabata, S. Tsukui, Y. Shono, O. Michikami, H. Sasakura, K. Yoshiara, Y. Kakehi, and T. Yotsuya, *Phys. Rev.* B58, 2458 (1998-I); I. Iguchi, T. Yamaguchi, A. Sugimoto, *Nature* 412, 420 (2001).

[45] Z.A . Xu, E. Ahmed, Z. W. Zhu, J. Q. Shen, and X. Yao, *Physica* C460-462, 833 (2007).

[46] S. Dzhumanov, S. Kuchkarov, and B. Hamdamov, *Superlattices and Microstructures* 21, Suppl. A, 19 (1997).

[47] S. Dzhumanov, *Solid State Commun.* 115, 155 (2000); *Physica* C341-348, 159 (2000); *Physica* C460-462, 1131 (2007).

[48] V. J. Emery and S. A. Kivelson, *Nature* 374, 434 (1995).

[49] V. L. Ginzburg, *Usp. Fiz. Nauk* 167, 429 (1997).

[50] S. Fujita, *J. Superconduct.* 5, 83 (1992); V. V. Tolmachev, *Phys. Lett.* A266, 400 (2000).

[51] M. A. Kastner, R. J. Birgeneau, G. Shirane, and Y. Endoh, *Rev. Mod. Phys.* 70, 897 (1998).

[52] M. Fortes, M. Solis, M. de Llano and V. V. Tolmachev, *Physica* C364-365, 95 (2001).

[53] J. Ranninger and S. Robaszkiewicz, *Physica* B135, 468 (1985); R. Friedberg and T. D. Lee, *Phys. Lett.* A138, 423 (1989).

[54] J. Wilks, *The Properties of Liquid and Solid Helium* (Clarendon Press, Oxford, 1967); W. E. Keller, *Helium-3 and Helium-4* (Plenum Press, New York, 1969); V. J. Emery, in: *Quantum Fluids*, eds., N. Wiser and D. I. Anit (Gordon and Breach Science Publishers, Inc., New York, 1970).

[55] V. J. Emery, S. A. Kivelson, and O. Zachar, *Phys. Rev.* B56, 6120 (1997); S. Maekaw and T. Tohyama, *Rep. Prog. Phys.* 64, 383 (2001).

[56] A. M. Goldman and N. Marković, *Phys. Today, November*, 39 (1998).

[57] N. N. Bogolubov, V.V. Tolmachev, and D. V. Shirkov, *A New Method in the Theory of Superconductivity* (Izd. Akad. Nauk SSSR, Moscow, 1958).

[58] N. N. Bogolubov, *J. Phys. USSR* 11, 23 (1947).

[59] S. T. Buliaev, *Sov. Phys. JETP* 7, 289 (1958); P. Hohenberg, and P. C. Martin, *Ann. Phys.* 34, 291 (1965).

[60] J. C. Valatin and D. Butler, *Nuovo Cimento* 10, 37 (1958).

[61]  P. Dorre, H. Haug, and D. B. Tran Thoai, *J. Low Temp. Phys.* 35, 465 (1979).

[62]  M. Luban, *Phys. Rev.* 128, 965 (1962); M. Luban, in: *Quantum Fluids*, eds., N. Wiser and D. I. Amit (Gordon and Breach Science Publishers, Inc., New York, 1970) p. 117.

[63]  W. A. B. Evans and Y. Imry, *Nuovo Cimento* B63, 155 (1969).

[64]  S. C. Whitmore and W. Zimmerman, *Phys. Rev. Lett.* 15, 389 (1965); A. W. Steyert, R. D. Taylor, and T. A. Kitchens, *Phys. Rev. Lett.* 15, 546 (1965).

[65]  R. Hasting and J. W. Halley, *Phys. Rev.* B12, 267 (1975).

[66]  R. A. Cowley and A. D. B. Woods, *Can. J. Phys.* 49, 177 (1971).

[67]  A. Coniglio, F. Mancini, and M. Mturi, *Nuovo Cimento* B63, 227 (1969).

[68]  W. A. B. Evans and C. G. Harris, *J. Phys. Colloq. (Paris)* C6, 39, 237 (1978).

[69]  P. Nozieres and D. Saint James, *J. Phys. (Paris)* 43, 1133 (1982).

[70]  W. A. B. Evans, *Physica* B165-166, 513 (1990).

[71]  E. A. Pashitskii, S. V. Mashkevich, and S. I. Vilchynskyy, *Phys. Rev. Lett.* 89, 075301 (2002).

[72]  M. J. Rice and Y. R. Wang, *Phys. Rev.* B37, 5893 (1988).

[73]  J. M. Wheatley, T. C. Hsu, and P. W. Anderson, *Phys. Rev.* B37, 5897 (1988).

[74]  P. J. Baimatov, *Ph.D. Thesis Department of Thermal Physics, Uzbek Akademy of Sciences* (Tashkent, 1995).

[75]  N. N. Bogoliubov, *J. Phys. USSR* 11, 23 (1947); *Zh. Eksp. Teor. Fiz.* 34, 58 (1958) [*Sov. Phys. JETP* 7, 41 (1958)].

[76]  I. V. Bogoyavlensky, L. V. Kamatsevich, G. A. Kozlow, and A. V. Puchkov, *Fiz. Nisk. Temp.* 16, 139 (1990).

[77]  G. B. Dvait, *Integral Table and Other Mathematic Formulas* (Nauka, Moscow, 1978).

[78]  A. Damascelli, Z. Hussain, and Z.-X. Shen, *Rev. Mod. Phys.* 75, 473 (2003); T. Matsuzaki, M. Ido, N. Momono, R. M. Dipasupil, T. Nagata, A. Sakai, and M. Oda, *J. Phys. Chem. Solids* 62, 29 (2001).

[79]  B. N. J. Persson and J. E. Demuth, *Phys. Rev.* B42, 8057 (1990); M. Boekholt, M. Hoffmann, and G. Guntherodt, *Physica* C175, 127 (1991).

[80]  Ch. Renner, B. Revaz, J.-Y. Genoud, K. Kadowaki, and Ö. Fischer, *Phys. Rev. Lett.* 80, 149 (1998); S. Rast, B. H. Frazer, M. Onellion, T. Schmauder, M. Abrecht, O. Touzalet, H. Berger, G. Margaritonda, and D. Pavina, *Europhys. Lett.* 51, 103 (2000).

[81]  V. N. Morgun, N. N. Chebotarev, and A. V. Bondarchenko, *Fiz. Nisk. Temp.* 16, 264 (1990).

[82] C. C. Homes, T. Timusk, R. Liang, D. A. Bonn, and W. N. Hardy, *Phys. Rev. Lett.* 71, 1645 (1993); C. C. Homes, T. Timusk, D. A. Bonn, R. Liang, and W. N. Hardy, *Physica* C254, 265 (1995); A. C. Loeser, Z.-X. Shen, D. Desau, D. Marshall, C. Park, P. Fournier, and A. Kapitulnic, *Science* 273, 325 (1996).

[83] H. Ding T. Yokoya, J. C. Campuzano, T. Takahashi, M. Randeria, M. R. Norman, T. Mochiku, K. Kadowaki, and J. Giapintzakis, *Nature* 382, 51 (1996); M. R. Norman, H. Ding, M. Randeria, J. Campuzano, T. Yokoya, T. Takeuchi, T. Takahashi, T. Michiku, K. Kadovaki, P. Guptasarma, and D. Hinks, *Nature* 392, 157 (1998).

[84] A. V. Puchkov, D. N. Basov, and T. Timusk, *J. Phys.: Condens. Matter* 8, 10049 (1996).

[85] G. Deutscher, *Nature* 397, 410 (1999); J. L. Tallon, J. W. Loram, J. R. Cooper, C. Panagopoulos, and C. Bernhard, *Phys. Rev.* 68, 180501 (2003); W. S. Lee, I. M. Vishik, K. Tanaka, D. H. Lu, T. Sasagawa, N. Nagaosa, T. P. Devereaux, Z. Hussain, and Z. X. Shen, *Nature* 450, 81 (2007); J. L. Tallon and J. G. Storey, arXiv:0908.4430.

[86] S. Hüfner, M. A. Damaselli, and G. A. Sawatzky, *Rep. Prog. Phys.* 71, 062501 (2008).

[87] Z. Schlesinger, L. D. Rotter, R. T. Collins, F. Holtzberg, C. Feild, U. Welp, G. W. Crabtree, J. Z. Liu, Y. Fang, and K. G. Vandervoort, *Physica* C185-189, 57 (1991).

[88] Ø. Fischer, M. Kugler, I. Maggio-Aprile, and C. Berthod, *Rev. Mod. Phys.* 79, 353 (2007).

[89] Th. Timusk and D. B. Tanner, *Physical properties of high temperature superconductors I*, ed., D. M. Ginsberg (World Scientific: Singapore, 1989) chapter 7.

[90] W. L. Kennedy and S. Sridhar, *Solid State Commun.* 68, 71 (1988).

[91] M. Lee, M. Naito, A. Kapitulnik, and M. R. Beasley, *Solid. State. Commun.* 70, 449 (1989).

[92] A. Pashitsky, A. E. Pashitsky, and A. V. Semenov, *Pis'ma v ZhETF* 54, 36 (1991).

[93] G. F. Annet, *Adv. Phys.* 39, 83 (1990).

[94] D. J. Scalapino, *Physica* C235-240, 107 (1994); D. Pines, *Physica* C235-240, 113 (1994).

[95] V. P. Mineev and K. V. Samokhin, *Introduction to Unconventional Superconductivity* (Gordon and Breach Science Publishers, Amsterdam, 1999).

[96] M. Granath, V. Oganesyan, S. A. Kivelson, E. Fradkin, and V. J. Emery, *Phys. Rev. Lett.* 87, 167011 (2001).

[97] G. Iadonisi, V. Cataudella, D. Ninno, and M. L. Chiafalo, *Phys. Lett.* A196, 359 (1995); I. L. Landau and L. Rinderer, in: *Abstracts 5 th World Congress of Superconductivity*, Budapest, July 7-11, 1996, p. 128.

[98] M. Chiao, R. W. Hill, Ch. Lupien, L. Taillefer, P. Lambert, R. Gagnon, and P. Fournier, *Phys. Rev.* B62, 3554 (2000).

[99] T. Valla, A. V. Fedorov, P. D. Johnson, B. O. Wells, S. L. Hubert, Q. Li, G. D. Gu, and N. Koshizuka, *Science* 285, 2110 (1999).

[100] B. D. Dunlap, M. V. Nevitt, M. Slaski, T. E. Klippert, Z. Sungaila, A. G. McKale, D. W. Capone, R. B. Poeppel, and B. K. Flandermeyer, *Phys. Rev.* B35, 7210 (1987); P. C. W. Fung and W. Y. Kwok, *J. Superconduct.* 4, 67 (1991); Y. Zhang, N. P. Ong, Z. A. Xu, K. Krishana, R. Gagnon, and L. Taillefer, *Phys. Rev. Lett.* 84, 2219, (2000).

[101] N. Momono, M. Ido, T. Nakano, M. Oda, Y. Okajima, and K. Yamaya, *Physica* C235-240, 1739 (1994); N. Momono and M. Ido, *Physica* C246, 311, (1996); K. A. Moler, D. J. Baar, J. S. Urbach, R. Liang, W. N. Hardy, and A. Kapitulnic, *Physica* C235-240, 1775 (1994).

[102] S. Dzhumanov, P. J. Baimatov, and P. K. Khabibullaev, *Uzb. Zh. Phys.* 4, 28 (1991).

[103] R. A. Fischer, S. Kim, S. E. Lacy, N. E. Phillips, D. E. Morris, A. G. Markeltz, J. Y. T. Wei, and D. S. Ginley, *Phys. Rev.* B38, 11942 (1988).

[104] B. Golding, N. O. Birge, W. H. Haemmerle, R. J. Cava, and E. A. Rietman, *Phys. Rev.* B36, 5606 (1987).

[105] J. Schützmann, S. Tajima, O. V. Misochko, S. Miyamoto, and S. Tanaka, *Physica* C235-240, 1109 (1999).

[106] C. C. Tsuei, J. R. Kirtley, C. C. Chi, L. S. Yu-Jahnes, A. Cupta, T. Shaw, J. Z. Sun, and M. B. Ketchen, *Phys. Rev. Lett.* 73, 593. (1994); C. C. Tsuei and J. R. Kirtley, Physica C282-287, 4 (1997).

[107] D. A. Wollman, D. J. Van Harlingen, J. Giapintzakis, and D. M. Ginsberg, *Phys. Rev. Lett.* 74, 797 (1995).

[108] A. G. Sun, D. A. Gajewski, M. B. Maple, and R. C. Dynes, *Phys. Rev. Lett.* 72, 2267 (1994); P. Chaudhari and S. Y. Lin, *Phys. Rev. Lett.* 72, 1084 (1994); A. Bussmann-Holder, H. Keller, A. R. Bishop, A. Simon, and K. A. Müller, *J. Supercond. Nov. Magn.* 21, 353 (2008).

[109] J. R. Kirtley, C. C. Tsuei, and K. A. Moler, *Science* 285, 1373 (1999).

[110] R. Kleiner, A. S. Katz, A. G. Sun, R. Summer, D. A. Gajewski, S. H. Han, S. I. Woods, E. Dantsker, B. Chen, K. Char, M. B. Maple, R. C. Dynes, and J. Clarke, *Phys. Rev. Lett.* 76, 2161 (1996).

[111] A. P. Malozemoff, in: *Physical Properties of High Temperature Superconductors I*, ed., D. M. Ginsberg (Mir, Moscow, 1990), chapter 3; B. Pümpin, H. Keller, W. Künding, W. Odermatt, I. M. Savic, J. W. Schneider, H. Simmler, P. Zimmermann, E. Kaldis, S. Rusiecki, Y. Maeno, and C. Rossel, *Phys. Rev.* B42, 8019 (1990).

[112] J. Carini, L. Drabeck, and G. Grüner, *Mod. Phys. Lett.* B3, 5 (1989).

[113] O. G. Vendik. A. B. Kozyrev, T. B. Sarnoilova, and A. Yu. Popov, in: *High Temperature Superconductivity*. Issue I (Mashinostroenie, Leningrad, 1990), p. 7.

[114] K. Kitazawa, *Science* 271, 261 (1996).

[115] E. B. Eom, J. Z. Sun, J. Z. Lairson, S. K. Streiffer, A. F. Marshall, K. Yamamoto, S. M. Anlage, J. C. Bravman, and T. H. Geballe, *Physica* C171, 354 (1990).

[116] A. K. Grover, N. Goyal, F. Iga, K. Ino, N. Aoki, Y. Yamaguchi, and Y. Nishihara, *Physica* C235-240, 3281 (1994); C. J. van der Beek, B. Schmidt, M. Kontzykowski, V. M. Vinokur, and G. W. Crabtree, *Physica* C235-240, 2813 (1994).

[117] E. A. Lynton, *Superconductivity* (Mir, Moscow, 1971).

[118] M. Ledvij, D. Davidovic, L. Dobrosavljevic-Grujic, *Physica* B165-166, 1119 (1990); M. Ledvij and L. Dobrosavljevic-Grujic, *Mod. Phys. Lett.* B4, 471 (1990).

[119] V. V. Moshchalkov, L. Gielen, C. Strunk, R. Jonckheere, X. Qiu, C. Van Haesendonck, and Y. Bruynseraede, *Physica* C235-240, 2513 (1994); A. Schilling, R. Jin, H. R. Ott, and Th. Wolf, *Physica* C235-240, 2741 (1994).

[120] A. Ino, C. Kim, M. Nokamura, T. Yoshida, T. Mizokawa, A. Fujimori, Z.-X. Shen, T. Kakeshita, H. Eisaki, and S. Uchida, *Phys. Rev.* B65, 094504 (2002).

[121] R. Griessen, *Phys. Rev. Lett.* 64, 1674 (1990); H. Jaeger, *Adv. Mater.* 3, 509 (1991).

[122] V. V. Metlushko, V. V. Moshchalkov, Y. Bruynseraede, G. Guntherodt, H. Thomas, and K. Winzer, *Physica* C235-240, 2793 (1994); Z. G. Ivanov, N. Fogel, P. A. Nilsson, E. A. Stepantsov, and A. Ya. Tzalenchuk, *Physica* C235-240, 3253 (1994).

[123] N. F. Mott, *Contemporary Physics* 31, 373 (1990); *Physica* C205, 191 (1993).

[124] A. Gold, *Physica* C190, 483 (1992); T. Schneider and H. Keller, *Int. J. Phys.* B8, 487 (1998).

[125] S. Dzhumanov, P. J. Baimatov, O. K. Ganiev, Z. S. Khudayberdiev, and B. V. Turimov, *J. Phys. Chem. Solids* 73, 484 (2012).

[126] G. Bridoux, P. Pedrazzini, F. De La Cruz, and G. Nieva, *Physica* C460-462, 841 (2007).

[127] A. S. Alexandrov and V. N. Zavaritsky, *Phys. Rev. Lett.* 93, 217002 (2004).

[128] H. Kitano, T. Ohashi, A. Maeda, and I. Tsukada, *Physica* C460-462, 904 (2007).

[129] V. G. Solovev, *Influence of the Superconducting Type Pair Correlation on the Property of the Nucleus* (Gosatorniiidat, Moskow, 1963).

[130] H. J. Lipkin, *Quantum Mechanics. New Approaches to Selected Topics* (Mir, Moscow, 1977).

[131] Yu. B. Sokolov, *Density of Levels of Atomic Nucleus* (Energoatomizdat, Moscow, 1990).

[132] H. Stein, A. Schenell, T. Aim, and G. Ropke, *Z. Phys.* A351, 295 (1995).

[133] G. Lazzari and F. V. De Blasio, *Z. Phys.* A348, 7 (1994).

[134] A. D. Linde, *Elementary Particle Physics and Inflationary Cosmology* (Nauka, Moscow, 1990).

[135] L. Parker and Y. Zhang, *Phys. Rev.* D47, 4l6 (1993).

[136] D. V. Semikoz and I. I. Tkachev, *Phys. Rev. Lett.* 74, 3093 (1995).

[137] P. V. Vorob'ev, A. I. Kabidze, and I. V. Kolokolov, *Jader. Fiz.* 58, 8S8 (1995).

[138] A. S. Davidov, *High Temperature Superconductivity* (Naukova Dumka, Kiev, 1990).

[139] K. Kanoda, K. Akiba, K. Suzuki, T. Takahashi, and G. Saito, *Phys. Rev. Lett.* 65, 1215 (1990); Y. Nakazawa and K. Kanoda, *Phys. Rev.* B55, R8670 (1997-II).

[140] D. S. Hirashima and T. Matsuura, *J. Phys. Soc. Jpn.* 59, 24 (1990).

[141] N. E. Phillips, C. C. Waterfield, and J. K. Hoffer, *Phys. Rev. Lett.* 25, 1260 (1970).

[142] R. P. Feynman, *Statistical Mechanics* (Mir, Moscow, 1978).

[143] E. B. Sonin, *Usp. Fiz. Nauk* 137, 267 (1982).

[144] S. Burkhart, M. Bernard, and O. Avenel, *Phys. Rev. Lett.* 72, 380 (1994).

[145] Yu. B. Rumer and M. Sh. Rivkin, *Thermodynamics, Statistical Physics and Kinetics* 3 (Nauka, Moscow, 1977).

[146] E. M. Lifshite and L. P. Pitaevskii, *Statistical Physics* (Nauka, Moscow, 1978).

[147] N. Wada. A. Inoue, H. Yano, and K. Torii, *Phys. Rev.* B52, 1167 (1995-II).

[148] J. C. Wheatley, *Physica* 69, 218 (1973).

[149] P. J. Hakonen, M. Krusins, M. M. Salomaa, and J. T. Simola, *Phys. Rev. Lett.* 54, 245 (1985).

[150] P. Hakonen and O. V. Lounasmaa, *Physics Today, February*, 70 (1987).

[151] Y. Wang and P. E. Sokol, *Phys. Rev. Lett.* 72, 1040 (1994).

[152] P. Schiffer, M. T. O'Keefe, M. D. Hildreth, H. Fukuyama, and D. D. Osheroff, *Phys. Rev. Lett.* 69, 120 (1992).

[153] N. D. Mermin and V. Ambegaokar, *Proc. 24th Novel Symp.* 1973 (Academic Press, New York-London, 1974), p. 97.

[154] E. R. Dobbs, *Helium Three* (Oxford University Press, Oxford, 2000).

[155] P. Bożek, arXiv:nucl-th/9902019; X.-G. Huang, arXiv:1002.0060 [nucl-th].

[156] P. E. Hodgson, *Z. Phys.* A349, 197 (1994).

[157] M. Brenner, *Z. Phys.* 349, 233 (1994).

[158] F. Poiigheon, *Z. Phys.* A349, 273 (1994); J. S. Vaagen, I. J. Thompson, J. M. Bang et al., *Z. Phys.* A349, 285 (1994).

[159] I. N. Mikhailow and P. Queutin, *Phys. Rev. Lett.* 74, 3336 (1995).

[160] B. M. Yavorakii and A. A. Detlaf, *Handbook on Physics* (Nauka, Moscow, 1968).

[161] D. N. Pnenaru, W. Creiner, E. Hounari, and M. Huseonnois, *Z. Phys.* A349, 307 (1994).

[162] V. M. Lipunov, *Astrophysics of Neutron Stars* (Nauka, Moscow, 1987).

[163] J. H. Teilor, *Usp. Fiz. Nauka.* 164, 757 (1994).

[164] R. Kippenhahn, *Hundred Million Suns. Birth, Life, and Death of Stars* (Mir, Moscow, 1990).

[165] S. Weinberg, *First Three Minutes. Modern View on the Origin of Universe* (Energoizdat, Moscow, 1981).

[166] B. M. Kuzhevakii, *Usp. Fiz. Nauk* 137, 237 (1982).

[167] P. Davies, Superforce. *The Search for a Grand Unified Theory of Nature* (Mir, Moscow, 1989).

[168] I. D. Novikov, *Evolution of Universe* (Nauka, Moscow, 1990).

[169] B. E. J. Pagel, *Physica Scripta* T36, 7 (1991).

# Conclusion

In this work, we have presented a consistent and more pertinent microscopic theory of novel (unconventional) superconductivity and superfluidity in various classes of superconductors, quantum liquids and condensed matter systems. We have developed a realistic and conceptually more consistent approach which enables to describe the novel superconductivity and superfluidity realized in the pseudogap state of unconventional superconductors, superfluid $^3$He, nuclear matter and neutron star matter by starting from the two-stage Fermi-Bose-liquid (FBL) model proposed previously beyond the standard BCS condensation (superfluid Fermi-liquid) and BEC theories, which were not very adequate for description of the SC and superfluid phase transitions in these condensed matter systems.

Now we conclude by summarizing the basic theoretical results and the main physical features that distinguish unconventional superconductors (including also superfluid $^3$He) from the BCS superconductors. This can serve as a guide for discriminating between SC materials that have usual BCS behavior and those which cannot be consistently explained by the BCS theory. From the above considerations and experimental evidences, it follows that the BCS theory is well applicable to weak coupling systems, such as ordinary metals and heavily overdoped cuprates, which are in the fermionic limit of weakly-bound Cooper pairs due to the absence of any dressing effects (i.e. dressing of carriers by the static lattice deformations). Depending on the strength of the attractive interaction between two pairing fermions, however, the physical properties of the SC state could be distinguishably altered. Therefore, to understand the new physics of the SC transition in high-$T_c$ cuprates and other related systems, the brilliantly successful BCS theory, which presumes that the SC state is a SF Fermi-liquid, must be radically modified. Since the dressing effects (which usually exist in the intermediate and strong coupling regimes) might be responsible for the BCS-like pairing correlations above the SC transition temperature $T_c$ and for the novel superconductivity in unconventional (high-$T_c$, heavy-fermion and organic) superconductors. In the case of such exotic superconductors, there are strong enough interactions which bind together the constituent Fermi particles of tightly-bound Cooper pair, creating a composite boson, whereas the residual interactions between the fermions which belong to different Cooper pairs are comparatively weak. Further, the strong interactions that cause dressing effects in liquid $^3$He, can also play an important role in precursor Cooper pairing and pseudogap formation above the superfluid transition temperature in such an interacting Fermi system. It seems likely that the pre-formed weakly overlapping Cooper pairs having the size $\zeta$ of the order of the intercooperon distance $d$, in contrast to the BCS regime (where $\zeta >> d$), behave sufficiently like composite bosons and undergo BEC. However, according to the Landau criterion for superfluidity, the BEC of tightly-bound (bosonic) Cooper pairs is not at all SC (or superfluid) transition. In order to approach the physics of the systems with the precursor Cooper pairing and a new SC transition, we have considered the two-stage FBL scenarios for superconductivity in unconventional superconductors and for superfluidity in liquid $^3$He. In doing so, we have assumed that these systems are close to the bosonic limit of pre-formed Cooper pairs. Such a FBL approach to the problem represents one of possible alternative and allows us to describe consistently the novel SC and superfluid states of high-$T_c$ cuprates and other systems from a unified position. We have argued that the BCS-like ($s$-,$p$- and $d$-wave) pairing of fermions as the first necessary stage of SC transition should take place not only below $T_c$ in so-called fermionic superconductors but also well above $T_c$ in bosonic superconductors manifesting itself as the onset of precursor Cooper pairing and pseudogap formation. Since the conventional BCS pairing picture is the particular case of a more general BCS-like one (i.e., BCS-like pairing of dressed carriers). Therefore, it is worthwhile to consider the phenomenon of unconventional superconductivity in the new classes of superconductors and superfluidity in liquid $^3$He and nuclear matter as the result of the successive two phase transitions which correspond to the formation of pre-formed (quasi-bosonic) Cooper pairs at a characteristic mean-field temperature $T^*$ above $T_c$ and the subsequent condensation of these Cooper pairs into a superfluid Bose-liquid state at $T_c$. Further, we have demonstrated that the novel superconductivity in high-$T_c$ cuprates and other condensed matter systems is actually driven by the PC and SPC of bosonic Cooper pairs and described by the mean-field theory of boson pairing similar to the BCS pairing theory of fermions. This phenomenon is quite different from conventional BCS superconductivity and occurs in the pseudogap state of the bosonic superconductors (e.g. the underdoped, optimally doped and moderately overdoped cuprates, heavy-fermion and organic superconductors belong to this class of superconductors). We believe that the unconventional superconductivity in bosonic superconductors results from the coexistence of two distinct order parameters: one of them $\Delta_F$ (which is the BCS-like order parameter) characterizes the bond strength of tightly-bound Cooper pairs and the other $\Delta_B$ characterizes the bond strength of all condensed composite bosons (i.e., the collective of such bosons in a SF Bose condensate does not allow their partner to leave the condensate). It is shown that various SC properties of high-$T_c$ cuprates and other unconventional superconductors and the basic SF properties of quantum liquids $^4$He and $^3$He are well described by the developed theory of a SF Bose-liquid of composite bosons. In contrast to the conventional BCS and BEC theories, the proposed microscopic theory of a SF Bose-liquid of bosonic Cooper pairs is able to explain many experimental findings for the unconventional superconductors, SF $^3$He and other SF condensed matter systems. In particular, the experimentally observed behavior of the underdoped, optimally doped and even moderately overdoped cuprates in their SC state does not resemble that of a fermionic system and strongly deviates from the BCS-type Fermi-liquid behavior. This is indicative of a new SC state in these high-$T_c$ cuprate superconductors, which is a SF Bose-liquid of composite bosonic Cooper pairs. Whereas the conventional superconductivity driven by the BCS-type condensation of weakly-bound Cooper pairs would occur in fermionic superconductors (in particular, the heavily overdoped cuprates and ordinary metals belong to that kind of superconductors) in which the Cooper-pair formation temperature $T^*$ coincides with the SC transition temperature of Cooper pairs. We have formulated the basic concepts and principles of conventional and unconventional superconductivity and superfluidity in high-$T_c$ cuprates and other condensed matter systems. We have discussed various applications of the theory of a SF Bose-liquid to high-$T_c$ cuprates, heavy-fermion and organic superconductors, SF quantum liquids $^4$He and $^3$He, nuclear matter, neutron star matter and nucleosynthesis in the early universe. Finally, it is worthwhile to enumerate some original predictions of the two-stage FBL model and the microscopic theory of a SF Bose-liquid of composite bosonic Cooper pairs (including composite bosonic $^4$He atoms), which were confirmed by the following experimental findings:

1. The precursor Cooper pairing of carriers at a mean-field temperature $T^*$ above $T_c$ and the existence of incoherent Cooper pairs as the Bose-type species with charge $2e$ were predicted theoretically and subsequently observed in the normal state of high-$T_c$ cuprates.

2. The coexistence of the BCS-like pairing pseudogap and the new SC order parameter below $T_c$ in high-$T_c$ cuprate superconductors were predicted theoretically and subsequently observed in these SC materials.

3. The existence of the so-called bosonic/non-BCS superconductors (with the normal-state pseudogap appearing at $T^* > T_c$ and the SC order parameter appearing at $T_c$) and fermionic/BCS superconductor (with the BCS order parameter $\Delta_F$ appearing as the SC gap below $T_c = T^*$) were predicted theoretically and then established experimentally as the unconventional high-$T_c$ cuprate superconductors (e.g., underdoped, optimally doped and slightly overdoped cuprates) with $T^* > T_c$ and as the BCS-type high-$T_c$ cuprate superconductors (i.e., overdoped cuprates) with $T_c = T^*$.

4. The half-integer ($\hbar/4e$) magnetic flux quantization in 3D and 2D high-$T_c$ cuprate superconductors caused by the PC of composite bosonic Cooper pairs were predicted theoretically and subsequently observed in the grain boundaries and in thin films of high-$T_c$ cuprates.

5. The existence of the first-order SC phase transition somewhat below $T_c$ (at $T = T_c^* < T_c$) or well below $T_c$ (at $T = T_c^* << T$) in high-$T_c$ cuprate superconductors and other unconventional superconductors were predicted theoretically and subsequently observed in high-$T_c$ cuprates near $T = 0.45T_c$ and in heavy-fermion superconductors near $T = 0.8T_c$.

6. The generic electronic phase diagram of high-$T_c$ cuprate superconductors with the BCS-like crossover temperature $T^* > T_c$ was independently proposed theoretically and confirmed experimentally.

7. The existence of a quantum critical point under the SC dome of the phase diagram of high-$T_c$ cuprates somewhat above optimal doping separating the conventional Fermi-liquid phase from a non-Fermi-liquid one or most likely separating the BCS-type SC phase from the non-BCS-type SC phase was predicted independently of its experimental observation.

8. The power-law temperature dependences of the electronic specific heat and the London penetration depth observed in high-$T_c$ cuprates and other unconventional superconductors are most probably associated with the gapless excitation spectrum of a SF

3D Bose-liquid of bosonic Cooper pairs rather than with the point or line nodes of the BCS-like gap assumed in some BCS-like $p$- or $d$-wave pairing theories.

9. The dependence of $T_c$ on carrier concentration $n$ for high-$T_c$ cuprate superconductors with $T_c \sim n^{2/3}$ and $\sim n$ predicted within the SF Bose condensation model was observed over a wide range of doping $n$.

10. Experimental observations of the $\lambda$-like SC transition at $T_c$ in high-$T_c$ cuprates and other unconventional superconductors lend support to the theory of a SF Bose-liquid of bosonic Cooper pairs rather than to the BCS theory.

11. The specific heat jump observed somewhat below $T_c$ (i.e, at $T_c^* < T_c$) in high-$T_c$ cuprates and other unconventional superconductors is strikingly similar to the predicted specific heat anomaly at the first-order phase transition temperature $T_c^*(< T_c)$ corresponding to the SPC→PC transition in an interacting 3D Bose gas of bosonic Cooper pairs.

12. The kink-like temperature dependences of the SC order parameter $\Delta_{SC}$, critical magnetic fields ($H_{c1}$, $H_c$ and $H_{c2}$) and current $I_c$ near $T_c^* < T_c$ or even near $T_c^* << T_c$ and the unusual upward increasing of these SC parameters with decreasing temperature in high-$T_c$ cuprates predicted by the theory of a SF 3D Bose-liquid were actually like the kink-like behaviors of $\Delta_{SC}(T)$, $H_{c1}(T)$, $H_c(T)$, $H_{c2}(T)$ and $I_c(T)$ seen in these superconductors in the temperature range $T = (0.35 - 0.90)T_c$.

13. The positive curvature of $H_{c1}(T)$, $H_c(T)$ and $H_{c2}(T)$, which persists over a wide temperature range $T_c^* < T < T_c$, and the large negative slope of these dependences and their root-like behaviors in the vicinity of $T_c$ observed in high-$T_c$ cuprates and heavy-fermion superconductors point towards a 3D superfluidity of quasi-bosonic Cooper pairs rather than to the BCS superconductivity of quasi-fermionic Cooper pairs.

14. The experimental observation of the vortex-like excitations (Nernst signals) in high-$T_c$ cuprates above the bulk SC transition temperature $T_c$ (i.e. in the temperature range $T_c \leq T \leq T_v$) is clear evidence for the destruction of the bulk superconductivity in the 3D-to-2D crossover region (where 2D superconductivity still survives up to $T = T_v > T_c$) rather than for the assumed SC fluctuation scenario.

15. The first-order transition between $A$- and $B$- phases at $T = T_c^* = T_{AB} \simeq (0.6 - 0.7)T_c$ and the half-integer flux quantum $\hbar/4m_3$ observed in SF $^3$He are strong evidences for the SPC↔PC transitions in a interacting Bose gas of bosonic Cooper pairs rather than for the transition between the $A$- and $B$- phases of SF $^3$He attributed to the Anderson-Brinkman-Morel (ABM) and the Balian-Werthamer (BW) states, respectively. Because both the transition to ABM state and the transition to BW state is the second-order BCS-like phase transition and not at all the first-order phase transition at $T = T_{AB}$

16. The gapless or phonon-like excitation spectrum of SF $^4$He and an appreciable increasing of the condensate fraction ($n_{B0} \approx 0.1$) in the temperature range $0 \leq T \leq T_c^*(\simeq 1K)$

below $T_c$, the departure of the specific heat from the phonon-like $T^3$ dependence, the strong depletion of the zero-momentum state (i.e. condensate) at $T < T_c^*$ and its complete absence in the temperature range $T_c^* < T < T_c(= T_\lambda)$, the half-integral value $(\hbar/2m_4)$ of the circulation and the $\lambda$-like specific heat anomaly at $T = T_c(= T_\lambda)$ observed in SF $^4$He are direct experimental evidences for the predictions of the theory of a SF Bose-liquid presented in chapter 8.

17. The phonon-like (or gapless) excitations and low-lying excited states in comparison with the BCS-like pairing energy, the $\alpha$ clustering (or condensation into $\alpha$ particles) favoured in the light nuclei and in the nuclear surface of heavy nuclei, the $\alpha$ and cluster emissions leading to excited states of nuclear, the staggering effect in some superdeformed nuclei, the cluster nucleosynthesis in the universe and the other experimentally observed SF properties of nuclear matter strongly support the concept of novel superfluidity of a nucleonic Bose-liquid.

# Appendix A

# Calculation of the Critical Superconducting Temperature in BCS Superconductors

For the Bogoliubov model potential (3.131) the gap function $\Delta(\vec{k})$ will be approximated as

$$\Delta(\vec{k}) = \begin{cases} \Delta_1, & \xi(\vec{k}) < \hbar\omega_D = \varepsilon_D \\ \Delta_2, & \hbar\omega_D < \xi(\vec{k}) < \hbar\omega_c = \varepsilon_F \\ 0, & \xi(\vec{k}) > \hbar\omega_c \end{cases} \tag{A.1}$$

Then the gap equation (3.80) is reduced to the two equations

$$\Delta_1 = -\frac{1}{2}D(0)(V_c - V_{ph}) \int_{-\hbar\omega_D}^{\hbar\omega_D} \frac{\Delta_1 d\xi}{\sqrt{\xi^2 + \Delta_1^2}} \left[1 - 2f\left(\sqrt{\xi^2 + \Delta_1^2}\right)\right]$$

$$-\frac{1}{2}D(0)V_c \left\{ \int_{-\hbar\omega_c}^{-\hbar\omega_D} \frac{\Delta_2 d\xi}{\sqrt{\xi^2 + \Delta_2^2}} \left[1 - 2f\left(\sqrt{\xi^2 + \Delta_2^2}\right)\right] \right.$$

$$\left. + \int_{\hbar\omega_D}^{\hbar\omega_c} \frac{\Delta_2 d\xi}{\sqrt{\xi^2 + \Delta_2^2}} \left[1 - 2f\left(\sqrt{\xi^2 + \Delta_2^2}\right)\right] \right\} \tag{A.2}$$

$$\Delta_2 = -\frac{1}{2}D(0)V_c \left\{ \int_{-\hbar\omega_D}^{\hbar\omega_D} \frac{\Delta_1 d\xi}{\sqrt{\xi^2 + \Delta_1^2}} \left[1 - 2f\left(\sqrt{\xi^2 + \Delta_1^2}\right)\right] \right.$$

$$+ \int_{-\hbar\omega_c}^{-\hbar\omega_D} \frac{\Delta_2 d\xi}{\sqrt{\xi^2 + \Delta_2^2}} \left[1 - 2f\left(\sqrt{\xi^2 + \Delta_2^2}\right)\right]$$

$$\left. + \int_{\hbar\omega_D}^{\hbar\omega_c} \frac{\Delta_2 d\xi}{\sqrt{\xi^2 + \Delta_2^2}} \left[1 - 2f\left(\sqrt{\xi^2 + \Delta_2^2}\right)\right] \right\}, \tag{A.3}$$

where $f\left(\sqrt{\xi^2+\Delta^2}\right) = \left[\exp\left(\sqrt{\xi^2+\Delta^2}/k_B T\right) + 1\right]^{-1}$.

These equations can be rewritten as

$$\Delta_1 = -D(0)(V_c - V_{ph})\int_0^{\hbar\omega_D} \frac{\Delta_1 d\xi}{\sqrt{\xi^2+\Delta_1^2}}\left[1 - 2f\left(\sqrt{\xi^2+\Delta_1^2}\right)\right]$$

$$-D(0)V_c \int_{\hbar\omega_D}^{\hbar\omega_c} \frac{\Delta_2 d\xi}{\sqrt{\xi^2+\Delta_2^2}}\left[1 - 2f\left(\sqrt{\xi^2+\Delta_2^2}\right)\right] \tag{A.4}$$

$$\Delta_2 = -D(0)V_c\left\{\int_0^{\hbar\omega_D} \frac{\Delta_1 d\xi}{\sqrt{\xi^2+\Delta_1^2}}\left[1 - 2f\left(\sqrt{\xi^2+\Delta_1^2}\right)\right]\right.$$

$$\left.+\int_{\hbar\omega_D}^{\hbar\omega_c} \frac{\Delta_2 d\xi}{\sqrt{\xi^2+\Delta_2^2}}\left[1 - 2f\left(\sqrt{\xi^2+\Delta_2^2}\right)\right]\right\} \tag{A.5}$$

At $T = 0$ and $\hbar\omega_D >> \Delta_1, \Delta_2$, we obtain from Eqs.(A.4) and (A.5)

$$\Delta_1 = -D(0)(V_c - V_{ph})\Delta_1 \ln(2\hbar\omega_D/\Delta_1) - D(0)V_c\Delta_2 \ln(\omega_c/\omega_D) \tag{A.6}$$

$$\Delta_2 = -D(0)V_c\Delta_1 \ln(2\hbar\omega_D/\Delta_1) - D(0)V_c\Delta_2 \ln(\omega_c/\omega_D) \tag{A.7}$$

¿From Eq.(A.7), we find

$$\Delta_2 = -\frac{D(0)V_c\Delta_1 \ln(2\hbar\omega_D/\Delta_1)}{1 + D(0)V_c\Delta_2 \ln(\omega_c/\omega_D)} \tag{A.8}$$

Substituting this expression into Eq.(A.6), we obtain

$$1 = D(0)\tilde{V}_A \ln(2\hbar\omega_D/\Delta_1), \tag{A.9}$$

where $\tilde{V}_A = V_{ph} - \frac{V_c}{1+D(0)V_c \ln(\omega_c/\omega_D)}$ is an effective attraction potential.

At $T \to T_c$, we have $\Delta_1 \to 0$, $\Delta_2 \to 0$. We may then evaluate the first integral in (A.4) and (A.5) as (see Eq. (3.90))

$$I_1 = \int_0^{\hbar\omega_D} \frac{d\xi}{\sqrt{\xi^2+\Delta_1^2}} \tanh\left[\frac{\sqrt{\xi^2+\Delta_1^2}}{2k_B T}\right]$$

$$\simeq \int_0^{\hbar\omega_D} \frac{d\xi}{\xi} \tanh\frac{\xi}{2k_B T} = \ln\left(\frac{2\gamma\hbar\omega_D}{\pi k_B T_c}\right) \tag{A.10}$$

The second integral in (A.4) and (A.5) is essentially logarithmic in the energy range $\hbar\omega_D < \xi < \hbar\omega_c$ and will be written

$$I_2 = \int_{\hbar\omega_D}^{\hbar\omega_c} \frac{d\xi}{\sqrt{\xi^2+\Delta_2^2}} \tanh\left[\frac{\sqrt{\xi^2+\Delta_2^2}}{2k_B T}\right] \simeq \int_{\hbar\omega_D}^{\hbar\omega_c} \frac{d\xi}{\xi} = \ln\left(\frac{\omega_c}{\omega_D}\right) \tag{A.11}$$

Then, Eqs. (A.4) and (A.5) are written as

$$\Delta_1 = -D(0)(V_c - V_{ph})\Delta_1 \ln\left(1.135\frac{\hbar\omega_D}{k_B T_c}\right) - D(0)V_c\Delta_2 \ln\left(\frac{\omega_c}{\omega_D}\right) \tag{A.12}$$

$$\Delta_2 = -D(0)(V_c)\Delta_1 \ln\left(1.135\frac{\hbar\omega_D}{k_B T_c}\right) - D(0)V_c\Delta_2 \ln\left(\frac{\omega_c}{\omega_D}\right) \tag{A.13}$$

from which we obtain the equation for $T_c$,

$$1 = D(0)\tilde{V}_A \ln\left(1.135\frac{\hbar\omega_D}{k_B T_c}\right) \tag{A.14}$$

¿From Eqs.(A.9) and (A.14), we see that the Bogoliubov approximations (3.131) and (A.1) become equivalent to the following BCS-like approximations

$$V(\vec{k} - \vec{k}') = \begin{cases} -\tilde{V}_A, & \xi(\vec{k}), \xi(\vec{k}') < \hbar\omega_D = \varepsilon_D, \\ 0, & \text{otherwise} \end{cases} \tag{A.15}$$

and

$$\Delta(\vec{k}) = \begin{cases} \Delta, & \xi(\vec{k}) < \hbar\omega_D \\ 0, & \xi(\vec{k}) > \hbar\omega_D \end{cases} \tag{A.16}$$

The BCS-like model potential (A.15) now contains the attractive component $V_{ph}$ and the reduced Coulomb interaction potential

$$\tilde{V}_c = \frac{V_c}{1 + D(0)V_c \ln(\omega_c/\omega_D)} \tag{A.17}$$

instead of the usual Coulomb potential $V_c$.

# Appendix B

# Calculation of the Basic Parameters of an Attractive Bose-Gas for $T = 0$

Using the Bogoliubov-like approximation (8.33), we obtain from (8.27)-(8.29)

$$\begin{cases} \Delta_{B1} = -(V_{BR} - V_{BA})\Delta_{B1}I_A - V_{BR}\Delta_{B2}I_R \\ \Delta_{B2} = -V_{BR}\Delta_{B1}I_A - V_{BR}\Delta_{B2}I_R \end{cases} \tag{B.1}$$

$$\chi_B = \rho_{B1}(V_{BR} - V_{BA}) + V_{BR}\rho_{B2} \tag{B.2}$$

where

$$\rho_{B1} = \frac{1}{\Omega}\sum_{k=0}^{k_A} n_B(k), \rho_{B2} = \frac{1}{\Omega}\sum_{k=k_A}^{k_B} n_B(k), n_B(k) = \frac{1}{\exp\left(E_B(k)/T\right) - 1},$$

$$\varepsilon(k_A) = \xi_{BA}, \varepsilon(k_R) = \xi_{BR}, I_A = \frac{1}{\Omega}\sum_{k'=0}^{k_A} \frac{(1 + 2n_B(k'))}{2E_B(k')},$$

$$I_B = \frac{1}{\Omega}\sum_{k'=k_A}^{k_B} \frac{(1 + 2n_B(k'))}{2E_B(k')}.$$

¿From Eq. (B.1), we obtain

$$\Delta_{B2} = -\frac{V_{BR}\Delta_{B1}I_A}{1 + V_{BR}I_R}, \quad I_A\tilde{V}_B = 1, \tag{B.3}$$

Let us assume that almost all Bose particles have energies smaller than $\xi_{BA}$. After replacing the summation over $k$ and $k'$ in these expressions for $\rho_B$, $I_A$, and $I_B$ by an integration on $\varepsilon$ we have

$$2\rho_B \simeq$$

$$\simeq D_B \int_0^{\xi_{BA}} \sqrt{\varepsilon}\left[\frac{\varepsilon + |\tilde{\mu}_B|}{\sqrt{(\varepsilon + |\tilde{\mu}_B|)^2 - \Delta_{B1}^2}}\coth\left(\frac{\sqrt{(\varepsilon + |\tilde{\mu}_B|)^2 - \Delta_{B1}^2}}{2T}\right) - 1\right]d\varepsilon \tag{B.4}$$

$$I_A = D_B \int_0^{\xi_{BA}} \sqrt{\varepsilon} \frac{\coth\left[\sqrt{(\varepsilon+|\tilde{\mu}_B|)^2 - \Delta_{B1}^2}/2T\right]}{2\sqrt{(\varepsilon+|\tilde{\mu}_B|)^2 - \Delta_{B1}^2}} d\varepsilon \tag{B.5}$$

$$I_R = D_B \int_{\xi_{BA}}^{\xi_{BR}} \sqrt{\varepsilon} \frac{\coth\left[\sqrt{(\varepsilon+|\tilde{\mu}_B|)^2 - \Delta_{B2}^2}/2T\right]}{2\sqrt{(\varepsilon+|\tilde{\mu}_B|)^2 - \Delta_{B2}^2}} d\varepsilon \tag{B.6}$$

At $\xi_{BA} \gg |\tilde{\mu}_B|, \Delta_{B1}, \Delta_{B2}, T$ we obtain from Eq. (B.6)

$$I_R \simeq D_B \int_{\xi_{BA}}^{\xi_{BR}} \sqrt{\varepsilon} \frac{d\varepsilon}{2\varepsilon} = D_B\left[\sqrt{\varepsilon_{BR}} - \sqrt{\varepsilon_{BA}}\right] \text{ and } I_R \simeq \frac{D_B}{2}\ln\frac{\varepsilon_{BR}}{\varepsilon_{BA}}, \tag{B.7}$$

for 3D and 2D Bose systems, respectively, For these systems, the latter expression in Eq. (B.3) can be rewritten as

$$\tilde{V}_B I_A = [V_{BA} - V_{BR}(1 + V_{BR}I_R)^{-1}]I_A = 1 \tag{B.8}$$

At $\rho_{B2} \ll \rho_{B1}$ the result of Eq. (B.2) together with Eq. (B.4) determines the value of $|\tilde{\mu}_B| = -\mu_B + 2\rho_B(V_{BR} - V_{BA})$, whereas the order (coherence) parameter $\Delta_B = \Delta_{B1}$ is determined from Eq. (B.8). So Eq. (8.33) is equivalent to the following simple BCS-like approximation

$$\begin{cases} V_B(k - k') = -\tilde{V}_B, & \text{if } \varepsilon(k), \varepsilon(k') < \xi_{BA} \\ 0, & \text{otherwise} \end{cases} \tag{B.9}$$

For a 3D Bose gas at $T = 0$ and $\xi_{BA} \gg |\tilde{\mu}_B| = \Delta_B$, we obtain from (B.4) and (B.8)

$$\frac{3\rho_B}{D_B} = \lim_{\xi_{BA} \to \infty}\left[\sqrt{\xi_{BA} + 2|\tilde{\mu}_B|}(\xi_{BA} - |\tilde{\mu}_B|) + |\tilde{\mu}_B|\sqrt{2|\tilde{\mu}_B|} - \xi_{BA}^{3/2}\right]$$
$$\simeq |\tilde{\mu}_B|\sqrt{2|\tilde{\mu}_B|}, \tag{B.10}$$

and

$$\frac{1}{D_B\tilde{V}_B} = \sqrt{\xi_{BA} + 2|\tilde{\mu}_B|} - \sqrt{2|\tilde{\mu}_B|}. \tag{B.11}$$

Equation (B.11) brings to the relation (8.37) and its substitution into Eq. (B.10) gives the relation (8.36). Further from Eq. (B.10) follows Eq. (8.38). Equations (8.30)-(8.32) can now be expressed as

$$\Delta_B(k) = -V_B(k)\rho_{B0}\frac{\Delta_B(0)}{|\Delta_B(0)|} - \frac{1}{\Omega}\sum_{k'\neq 0}V_B(k - k')\frac{\Delta_B(k')}{2E_B(k')}(1 + 2n_B(k')),$$

$$\rho_B = \rho_{B0} + \frac{1}{\Omega}\sum_{k=0}n_B(k), \chi_B(k)$$
$$= V_B(k)\rho_{B0} + \frac{1}{\Omega}\sum_{k'\neq 0}V_B(k - k')n_B(k'). \tag{B.12}$$

Replacing the summation in Eq. (B.12) by an integration and taking into account the approximation (B.9), we obtain

$$2(\rho_B - \rho_{B0}) = D_B \int_0^{\xi_{BA}} \sqrt{\varepsilon} \left[ \frac{\varepsilon + |\tilde{\mu}_B|}{\sqrt{\varepsilon^2 + 2|\tilde{\mu}_B|}} - 1 \right] d\varepsilon, \tag{B.13}$$

$$\tilde{V}_B \rho_{B0} = |\tilde{\mu}_B| \left[ 1 - \tilde{V}_B D_B \int_0^{\xi_{BA}} \sqrt{\varepsilon} \frac{d\varepsilon}{2\sqrt{\varepsilon^2 + 2|\tilde{\mu}_B|\varepsilon}} \right]. \tag{B.14}$$

¿From Eqs. (B.13) and (B.14), we obtain Eqs. (8.41) and (8.42), respectively. For a 2D-Bose gas the multiplier $\sqrt{\varepsilon}$ under the integrals in Eqs. (B.13) and (B.14) will be absent.

# Appendix C

# Calculation of the Basic Parameters of an Interacting Bose-Gas for $T \neq 0$

Equations (B.4) and (B.5) for the temperature range $0 < T \le T_c$ may be written as

$$\frac{2}{D_B \tilde{V}_B} = \int_0^{\xi_{BA}} \sqrt{\varepsilon} \frac{d\varepsilon}{\sqrt{(\varepsilon + |\tilde{\mu}_B|)^2 - \Delta_B^2}}$$

$$+ 2 \int_0^{\xi_{BA}} \sqrt{\varepsilon} \frac{d\varepsilon}{\sqrt{(\varepsilon + |\tilde{\mu}_B|)^2 - \Delta_B^2} [\exp(\sqrt{(\varepsilon + |\tilde{\mu}_B|)^2 - \Delta_B^2}/T) - 1]} \tag{C.1}$$

$$\frac{2\rho_B}{D_B} = \int_0^{\infty} \sqrt{\varepsilon} \left[ \frac{\varepsilon + |\tilde{\mu}_B|}{\sqrt{(\varepsilon + |\tilde{\mu}_B|)^2 - \Delta_B^2}} - 1 \right] d\varepsilon$$

$$+ 2 \int_0^{\infty} \sqrt{\varepsilon} \left[ \frac{(\varepsilon + |\tilde{\mu}_B|) d\varepsilon}{\sqrt{(\varepsilon + |\tilde{\mu}_B|)^2 - \Delta_B^2} [\exp(\sqrt{(\varepsilon + |\tilde{\mu}_B|)^2 - \Delta_B^2}/T) - 1]} \right] \tag{C.2}$$

The main contributions to the latter integrals in these equations come from small values of $\varepsilon$, so that for $T \ll T_c$ and $\tilde{\mu}_B = \Delta_B$ the latter integrals in Eqs. (C.1) and (C.2) are equal to $(\pi T)^2 / 3\sqrt{2}\tilde{\mu}_B^{3/2}$, and $(\pi T)^2 / 3\sqrt{2\tilde{\mu}_B}$, respectively. Further, according to Eq. (B.12) the terms $2\rho_{B0}/D_B$ and $2\rho_{B0}/\tilde{\mu}_B D_B$ in Eqs. (C.1) and (C.2) must be tolerated, respectively. Then, it is easy to obtain (8.43) and (8.44) taking into account Eqs. (B.10) and (B.11). In the case of $\Delta_{SF} \neq 0$ (or $\rho_{B0} = 0$), the first integral both in (C.1), and in (C.2) can be evaluated approximately using the Taylor expansion

$$\frac{1}{\sqrt{(\varepsilon + |\tilde{\mu}_B|)^2 - \Delta_B}} \simeq \frac{1}{\varepsilon + |\tilde{\mu}_B|} \left[ 1 + \frac{\Delta_B^2}{2(\varepsilon + |\tilde{\mu}_B|)^2} \right]. \tag{C.3}$$

Performing the integration and using also the expansion

$$\arctan \sqrt{\xi_{BA}/\tilde{\mu}_B} \simeq \frac{\pi}{2} - \sqrt{\frac{|\tilde{\mu}_B|}{\xi_{BA}}} + \frac{1}{3} \left( \frac{|\tilde{\mu}_B|}{\xi_{BA}} \right)^{3/2} - \cdots, \tag{C.4}$$

we obtain the following results for the previously mentioned integrals in Eqs. (C.1) and (C.2):

$$2\sqrt{\xi_{BA}}\left[1+\frac{3\pi}{32}\left(\frac{\Delta_B}{\tilde{\mu}_B}\right)^2\sqrt{\frac{|\tilde{\mu}_B|}{\xi_{AB}}}\right] \quad\text{and}\quad \frac{\pi\Delta_B^2}{4\sqrt{|\tilde{\mu}_B|}}, \tag{C.5}$$

respectively.

The latter integrals in Eqs.(C.1) and (C.2) can be evaluated near $T_c$ making the substitution $t=\sqrt{(\varepsilon/|\tilde{\mu}_B|)^2+2\varepsilon/|\tilde{\mu}_B|}$, $a_1^2t^2+a_2^2=[(\varepsilon+|\tilde{\mu}_B|)^2-\Delta_B^2]/T^2$ and using the method proposed in Ref. [62], where $a_1=|\tilde{\mu}_B|/T$, $a_2=\sqrt{|\tilde{\mu}_B|^2-\Delta_B^2}/T$. Then the second integral in Eq. (C.2) has the form

$$I_2=\tilde{\mu}_B^{3/2}\int_0^{\infty}\frac{\sqrt{\sqrt{t^2+1}-1}\,t\,dt}{\sqrt{t^2+(a_2/a_1)^2}\left[\exp(a_1\sqrt{t^2+(a_2/a_1)^2})-1\right]} \tag{C.6}$$

It is reasonable to assume that $a_1\ll 1$, $a_2\ll 1$, and $\Delta_B\ll\tilde{\mu}_B$ near $T_c$. Therefore, the integral $I_2$ may be calculated by using the previously mentioned method [62]. Here, we present the final result which has the form

$$I_2\simeq\frac{\sqrt{\pi}}{2}T^{3/2}\left[2.612-\sqrt{2\pi}\sqrt{\frac{|\tilde{\mu}_B|}{T}+\frac{\Delta_{SF}}{T}}+1.46\frac{|\tilde{\mu}_B|}{T}\cdots\right]$$

$$=\frac{\sqrt{\pi}}{2}T^{3/2}\left[2.612-\sqrt{2\pi}\sqrt{\frac{|\tilde{\mu}_B|}{T}+\frac{|\tilde{\mu}_B|}{T}\left(1-\frac{\Delta_B^2}{2\tilde{\mu}_B^2}\right)}+1.46\frac{|\tilde{\mu}_B|}{T}\right] \tag{C.7}$$

The second integral $I_2'$ in Eq. (C.1) is also evaluated in the same manner

$$I_2'\simeq\frac{\pi T}{\sqrt{2|\tilde{\mu}_B|}}\left[\frac{|\tilde{\mu}_B|}{|\tilde{\mu}_B|+\Delta_{SF}}-1.46\sqrt{\frac{2|\tilde{\mu}_B|}{\pi T}}+\cdots\right]$$

$$=\frac{\pi T}{2\sqrt{\tilde{\mu}_B}}\left[\frac{1}{1-\Delta_B^2/4\tilde{\mu}_B^2}-1.46\sqrt{2}\sqrt{\frac{2\tilde{\mu}_B}{\pi T}}\right] \tag{C.8}$$

By expanding the expressions

$$\sqrt{1-\Delta_B^2/4\tilde{\mu}_B^2}\quad\text{and}\quad\sqrt{\frac{1}{1-\Delta_B^2/4\tilde{\mu}_B^2}}$$

in powers of $\Delta_B/4\tilde{\mu}_B$ and replacing $1.46\sqrt{2}$ by 2, we obtain from (C.1), (C.2), (C.5), (C.7) and (C.8) (with an accurate to $\sim|\tilde{\mu}_B(T)|$)

$$\frac{1}{D_B\tilde{V}_B}\simeq\sqrt{\xi_{BA}}\left[1+\frac{3\pi}{32}\left(\frac{\Delta_B}{\tilde{\mu}_B}\right)^2\sqrt{\frac{|\tilde{\mu}_B|}{\xi_{BA}}}\right]$$

$$+\frac{\pi T}{2\sqrt{|\tilde{\mu}_B|}}\left[\left(1+\frac{\Delta_B^2}{8\tilde{\mu}_B^2}\right)-2\sqrt{\frac{2|\tilde{\mu}_B|}{\pi T}}\right] \tag{C.9}$$

$$\frac{2\rho_B}{D_B} \simeq \frac{\pi\Delta_B^2}{4\sqrt{\tilde{\mu}_B}} + \sqrt{\pi}T^{3/2}\left[2.612 - 2\sqrt{\pi\tilde{\mu}_B/T}\left(1 - \frac{\Delta_B^2}{8\tilde{\mu}_B^2}\right)\right] \tag{C.10}$$

For $T/\xi_{BA} << 1/2\pi$ the relation (8.47) follows from (C.9). Setting $2\rho_B/D_B = 2.612\sqrt{\pi}T_{BEC}^{3/2}$ [77] in Eq. (C.10) and making some transformations in this equation, we have

$$2.612\sqrt{\pi}T_{BEC}^{3/2} = \sqrt{\pi}T^{3/2}\left[\frac{\sqrt{\pi}}{4}\left(\frac{\Delta_B^2}{\tilde{\mu}_B}\right)^2\left(\frac{\tilde{\mu}_B}{T}\right)^{3/2}\right.$$

$$\left. + 2.612 - 2\sqrt{\frac{\pi\tilde{\mu}_B}{T}}\left(1 - \frac{\Delta_B^2}{8\tilde{\mu}_B^2}\right)\right] \tag{C.11}$$

from which follows (8.46). Now, the quantities $\tilde{\mu}_B(T)$ and $\Delta_B(T)$ near $T_c$ can be determined by eliminating $\Delta_B^2/8\tilde{\mu}_B^2$ from Eqs. (8.46) and (8.47). Thus, after some algebraic transformations, we have

$$\frac{2.612}{2\sqrt{\pi\tilde{\mu}_B(T)}}\left(\frac{T_c^{3/2} - T^{3/2}}{T}\right) + \sqrt{\frac{\tilde{\mu}_B(T_c)}{\tilde{\mu}_B(T)}}\frac{T_c}{T} = 1 - \frac{\Delta_B^2}{8\tilde{\mu}_B^2}$$

$$\sqrt{\frac{\tilde{\mu}_B(T)}{\tilde{\mu}_B(T_c)}}\frac{T_c}{T} = 1 + \frac{\Delta_B^2}{8\tilde{\mu}_B^2}$$

from which it follows that

$$\sqrt{\frac{\tilde{\mu}_B(T)}{\tilde{\mu}_B(T_c)}} + \sqrt{\frac{\tilde{\mu}_B(T_c)}{\tilde{\mu}_B(T)}} = \left[1 - \frac{1.306}{\sqrt{\pi\tilde{\mu}_B(T_c)}}\left(\frac{T_c^{3/2} - T^{3/2}}{T_c}\right)\right] - 2\frac{T}{T_c} = 0 \tag{C.12}$$

The solution of this equation has the form

$$\sqrt{\frac{\tilde{\mu}_B(T)}{\tilde{\mu}_B(T_c)}} = \frac{T}{T_c} + \sqrt{\left(\frac{T}{T_c}\right)^2 - 1 + \frac{1.306}{\sqrt{\pi\tilde{\mu}_B(T_c)}}\left(\frac{T_c^{3/2} - T^{3/2}}{T_c}\right)}$$

Further, taking into account that near $T_c$,

$$\frac{T_c^{3/2} - T^{3/2}}{T_c} \simeq \frac{T_c^3 - T^3}{2T_c^{5/2}} = \frac{(T_c - T)(T_c^2 + T_cT + T^2)}{2T_c^{5/2}} = \frac{3T_c^2(T_c - T)}{2T_c^{3/2}},$$

we obtain

$$\sqrt{\frac{\tilde{\mu}_B(T)}{\tilde{\mu}_B(T_c)}} = \frac{T}{T_c} + \sqrt{\left[\frac{3.918}{2\sqrt{\pi}}\sqrt{\frac{T_c}{\tilde{\mu}_B}} - 2\right]\frac{(T_c - T)}{T_c}}$$

from which after the determination of $\tilde{\mu}_B(T_c)$ from Eq. (8.47) at $T_c/\tilde{\mu}_B(T_c) >> 1$ follows approximately Eq. (8.51). The equation (8.47) near $T_c$ may be written as

$$\frac{\pi T_c}{2\sqrt{\tilde{\mu}_B(T)}\xi_{BA}} \simeq \frac{\pi T}{2\sqrt{\tilde{\mu}_B(T)}\xi_{BA}}\left(1 + \frac{\Delta_B^2(T)}{8\tilde{\mu}_B^2(T)}\right). \tag{C.13}$$

¿From Eqs. (C.13) and (8.51) we obtain Eq. (8.52).

Now we examine the behavior of $\tilde{\mu}_B(T)$ (or $\Delta_B(T)$) and $n_{B0}(T)$ near the SF transition temperature $T = T_c^* < T_c$ assuming $\tilde{\mu}_B(T)/T_c^* \ll 1$. By replacing the summation in Eq. (B.12) by an integration and taking into account the relations (C.7) and (C.8) at $\Delta_{SF} = 0$, we may write the equations determining the $\tilde{\mu}_B(T)$ and $\rho_{B0}(T)$ (or $n_{B0}(T)$) near $T_c^*$ as

$$\frac{2(\rho_B - \rho_{B0})}{D_B} \simeq \frac{2|\tilde{\mu}_B|^{3/2}}{3} + \sqrt{\pi}T^{3/2}\left[2.612 - \sqrt{\frac{2\pi|\tilde{\mu}_B|}{T}} + 1.46\frac{|\tilde{\mu}_B|}{T}\right] \tag{C.14}$$

$$\frac{1}{\gamma_B} \simeq \frac{\rho_{B0}}{D_B|\tilde{\mu}_B|\xi_{BA}} + \sqrt{1 + \frac{2|\tilde{\mu}_B|}{\xi_{BA}}} - \sqrt{\frac{2|\tilde{\mu}_B|}{\xi_{BA}}}$$
$$+ \frac{\pi T}{\sqrt{2|\tilde{\mu}_B|\xi_{BA}}}\left[1 - 1.46\sqrt{\frac{2|\tilde{\mu}_B|}{\pi T}}\right] \tag{C.15}$$

If $T = T_c^*$, $\rho_{B0} = 0$ (which corresponds to a complete depletion of the SPC condensate). For $|\tilde{\mu}_B|/T_c^* \ll 1$, Eqs. (C.14) and (C.15) can be then written as

$$\frac{2\rho_B}{D_B} \simeq \sqrt{\pi}(T_c^*)^{3/2}\left[2.612 - \sqrt{\frac{2\pi|\tilde{\mu}_B|}{T_c^*}} + 1.46\frac{|\tilde{\mu}_B|}{T_c^*}\right] \tag{C.16}$$

and

$$\frac{1}{\gamma_B} \simeq \frac{\pi T_c^*}{\sqrt{2|\tilde{\mu}_B|\xi_{BA}}} \tag{C.17}$$

Therefore, at $|\tilde{\mu}_B| \ll T_c^*$ Eqs. (C.14) and (C.15) near $T_c^*$ become

$$2.612\sqrt{\pi}(T_c^*)^{3/2} - \pi T_c^*\sqrt{2|\tilde{\mu}_B(T_c^*)|}$$
$$= \frac{2\rho_{B0}(T)}{D_B} + 2.612\sqrt{\pi}T^{3/2} - \pi T\sqrt{2|\tilde{\mu}_B(T)|} \tag{C.18}$$

and

$$\frac{\pi T_c^*}{\sqrt{2|\tilde{\mu}_B(T_c^*)|\xi_{BA}}} = \frac{\rho_{B0}(T)}{D_B|\tilde{\mu}_B(T)|\sqrt{\xi_{BA}}} + \frac{\pi T}{\sqrt{2|\tilde{\mu}_B(T)|\xi_{BA}}} \tag{C.19}$$

Solving these two equations and making some algebraic transformations, we obtain the equation for $|\tilde{\mu}_B(T)|$, which is similar to Eq. (C.12). The solution of this equation near $T_c^*$ leads to the expression (8.53). Further, substituting $|\tilde{\mu}_B(T)|/|\tilde{\mu}_B(T_c^*)|$ from Eq. (8.53) into Eq. (C.18), we obtain the relation (8.54).

In the case of a 2D Bose gas, Eq. (8.27) after replacing the sum by the integral and making the substitution $y = \sqrt{(\varepsilon + |\tilde{\mu}_B|)^2 - \Delta_B^2}/2T$ takes the following form [14]:

$$\frac{2}{\gamma_B} = \int_{y_1}^{y_2} \frac{\coth y \, dy}{\sqrt{y^2 + (\Delta_B^*)^2}} \tag{C.20}$$

where $y_1 = \Delta_{SF}/2T$, $y_2 = \sqrt{(\xi_{BA} + |\tilde{\mu}_B|)^2 - \Delta_B^2}/2T$, $\Delta_B^* = \Delta_B/2T$. In the intervals $y_1 < y < 1$ and $1 < y < y_2$, one can take $\coth y \approx 1/x$ and $\approx 1$, respectively. Then, integrating Eq. (C.20), we obtain

$$\frac{2}{\gamma_B} \simeq \ln \left\{ \left[ \frac{y_1 (\Delta_B^* + \sqrt{1 + (\Delta_B^*)^2})}{\Delta_B^* + \sqrt{y_1^2 + (\Delta_B^*)^2}} \right]^{-1/\Delta_B^*} \left[ \frac{y_2 + \sqrt{y_2^2 + (\Delta_B^*)^2}}{1 + \sqrt{1 + (\Delta_B^*)^2}} \right] \right\} \tag{C.21}$$

At low temperatures $\Delta_B^* \gg 1$, $y_2 \gg \Delta_B^*$ and $\Delta_B^* \gg y_1$. Hence, $\ln y_1$ is small and it can be neglected. Equation (C.21) can then be approximately written as

$$\frac{2}{\gamma_B} \simeq \left( \frac{2y_2}{1 + \Delta_B^*} \right) \tag{C.22}$$

from which after some algebra follows Eq. (8.61). At high temperatures close to $T_c$, $\Delta_B^* \ll 1$, and therefore, from Eq. (C.21), we have (with an accuracy to $\sim (\Delta_B^*)^2$)

$$\frac{2}{\gamma_B} \simeq -\frac{1}{\Delta_B^*} \ln \left| \frac{y_1 (1 + \Delta_B^*)}{y_1 + \Delta_B^*} \right| + \ln y_2 \tag{C.23}$$

Further, when taking into account $y_2^{\Delta_B^*} \simeq 1$ and $\Delta_B^*/\gamma_B \ll 1$, we obtain from Eq. (C.23)

$$\frac{1 + \Delta_B^*/y_1}{1 + \Delta_B^*} \simeq \exp \left( \frac{2\Delta_B^*}{\gamma_B} \right) \simeq 1 + \frac{2\Delta_B^*}{\gamma_B} + \cdots$$

from which it follows that

$$\Delta_B(T) = \gamma_B T \left[ \frac{2T}{\Delta_{SF}(T)} - \frac{\gamma_B + 2}{\gamma_B} \right] \tag{C.24}$$

Let us assume that $\Delta_{SF}(T)$ varies near $T_c$ as $\sim \alpha_0(2T)^q$, where $\alpha_0$ is determined at $T = T_c$ from the condition $\Delta_B(T_c) = 0$), $q$ is variable parameter. Then, $\Delta_B(T)$ and $|\tilde{\mu}_B(T)|$ are determined from Eqs. (8.62) and (8.63).

For a 2D Bose system, the multiplier $\sqrt{\varepsilon}$ under the integral in Eq. (8.79) will be absent. We now estimate this integral for $\Delta_{SF} < 2T$. Making the substitution $x = E_B(\varepsilon)/2T$ and taking into account that at $x < 1$ and $x > 1$ the function $\sinh x$ is approximately equal to $x$ and $(1/2 \exp(x))$, respectively, we obtain the following expression for the specific heat of a 2D Bose-liquid:

$$C_v(T) \simeq 4\Omega D_B T \left\{ \int_{y_1}^{1} \frac{x \, dx}{\sqrt{x^2 + (\Delta_B^*(T))^2}} + 4 \int_{1}^{\infty} \frac{x^3 \exp(-2x) \, dx}{\sqrt{x^2 + (\Delta_B^*(T))^2}} \right\} \tag{C.25}$$

The second integral can be approximately estimated taking into account $\sqrt{x^2 + (\Delta_B^*(T))^2} \simeq \Delta_B^*$ (at low temperatures) since the main contribution to this integral comes from a region near lower limit of the integral, where $x \ll \Delta_B^*$. Calculating the integrals in Eq. (C.25) with this approximation, we obtain Eq. (8.82).

Finally, at $T = 0$ and $\Delta_{SF} = 0$ the integral (C.20) is equal to

$$\frac{2}{\gamma_B} \simeq \ln \frac{2(\varepsilon + |\tilde{\mu}_B|)}{\Delta_B(0)} \tag{C.26}$$

Whereas at $T = T_c$ the approximate estimation of the integral in Eq. (C.20) according to the above scheme gives

$$\frac{2}{\gamma_B} \simeq \int_{y_1}^{1} \frac{dy}{y^2} + \int_{1}^{y_2} \frac{dy}{y} = \frac{2T_c}{|\tilde{\mu}_B|(T)} - 1 + \ln \frac{\xi_{BA}}{2T_c} \tag{C.27}$$

where $y_1 = \tilde{\mu}_B/2T$, $y_2 = (\xi_{BA} + \tilde{\mu}_B)/2T$. According to Eq. (8.63), we find $\tilde{\mu}_B(T_c) = 2T_c\gamma_B/(2 + \gamma_B)$ at $T = T_c$. Then, using Eqs. (C.26) and (C.27), we obtain Eq. (8.92).

# Appendix D

# Calculation of the Modified BEC-Like Temperature for a 2D Bose-Gas

In the case of a 2D Bose gas the expressions for $\tilde{\varepsilon}_B(k)$ (see section 8.4.2) and $\rho_B$ (see Appendix B) after replacing the summations by the integrals can be written as

$$\tilde{\varepsilon}_B(k) = \varepsilon(k) - \mu_B + V_B(0)\rho_B + 2\int\limits_0^{\infty} dk'k'V_B(k-k')\frac{1}{\exp[\tilde{\varepsilon}_B(k')/T]-1} \tag{D.1}$$

and

$$\rho_B = \frac{1}{2\pi}\int\limits_0^{\infty} dk'k'\frac{1}{\exp[\tilde{\varepsilon}_B(k')/T]-1} \tag{D.2}$$

where $V_B(k-k') = \frac{1}{2(2\pi)^2}\int\limits_0^{2\pi} d\psi V_B[(k^2+(k')^2-2kk'\cos\psi)^{1/2}]$.

Now, the function under the integral $J_0(kr)$ in Eq. (8.72) can be expanded in a Taylor series around $kR = 0$. Then from Eq. (8.73) we obtain

$$V_B(k) \simeq V_B(0)\left[\frac{1-k^2}{k_R^2}\right], \quad 0 \leq k \leq k_R \tag{D.3}$$

where $V_B(0) = 2\pi WR^2 I_1$, $k_R = 4I_1/I_3R^2$, $I_n = \int\limits_0^{\infty} dx x^n \Phi(x)$.

The subsequent analytical calculations are analogous to the case of a 3D Bose gas [62]. Therefore, we present only final results, i.e., for $\tilde{\varepsilon}_B(k)$, $m_B^*$ and $\rho_B$ we obtain the following equations:

$$\tilde{\varepsilon}_B(k) = \tilde{\varepsilon}_B(0) + \frac{\hbar^2 k^2}{2m_B^*} \tag{D.4}$$

$$\frac{1}{m_B^*} = \frac{1}{m_B} - \frac{V_B(0)}{\pi\hbar^2 k_R^2} \int\limits_0^{k_A} dk'k' \frac{1}{\exp[(\tilde{\varepsilon}(0) + \hbar^2 k^2/2m_B^*)/T] - 1} \tag{D.5}$$

$$\rho_B = \frac{1}{2\pi} \int\limits_0^{k_A} dk'k' \frac{1}{\exp[(\tilde{\varepsilon}(0) + \hbar^2 k^2/2m_B^*)/T] - 1} \tag{D.6}$$

from which follows also the relation (8.70).

Further, replacing $\tilde{\varepsilon}(0)$ by the chemical potential $\tilde{\mu}_B$ of a 2D ideal Bose gas at $T = T_c$ and using Eqs. (8.74) and (8.75), we obtain

$$T_0(m_B^*) - \tilde{\mu}_B(T_c(m_B^*)) = -T_c(m_B^*) \ln\left|\left\{\exp\left[\frac{\tilde{\mu}_B(T_c(m_B^*))}{T_c(m_B^*)}\right] - 1\right\}\right| \tag{D.7}$$

and

$$T_0(m_B) - \tilde{\mu}_B(T_c(m_B)) = -T_c(m_B) \ln\left|\left\{\exp\left[\frac{\tilde{\mu}_B(T_c(m_B))}{T_c(m_B)}\right] - 1\right\}\right|, \tag{D.8}$$

Equations (D.7) and (D.8) together with Eqs. (8.74) and (8.75) yield

$$\left\{1 - \exp\left[-\frac{T_0(m_B^*)}{T_c(m_B^*)}\right]\right\} = \left\{1 - \exp\left[-\frac{T_0(m_B)}{T_c(m_B)}\right]\right\} \tag{D.9}$$

from which follows the relations (8.76) and (8.77).

# Appendix E

# Calculation of the Thermodynamic Critical Magnetic Field at Low Temperatures

Replacing the sum in Eq. (8.100) by the integral, we have

$$
\begin{aligned}
\frac{H_c^2(0)}{8\pi\Omega} &= \Delta_B \rho_B + \frac{D_B}{2} \int_0^{\xi_{BA}} \sqrt{\varepsilon} \left[ \varepsilon + \Delta_B - \sqrt{\varepsilon^2 + 2\Delta_B \varepsilon} \right] d\varepsilon \\
&= \Delta_B \rho_B + \frac{D_B}{2} \left\{ \frac{2}{5} \left[ \xi_{BA}^{5/2} - (\xi_{BA} + 2\Delta_B)^{5/2} \right] - \frac{4}{15} (2\Delta_B)^{5/2} \right. \\
&\quad \left. + \frac{2\Delta_B}{3} \xi_{BA}^{5/2} + \frac{4\Delta_B}{3} (\xi_{BA} + 2\Delta_B)^{3/2} \right\}
\end{aligned}
\tag{E.1}
$$

At $\xi_{BA} \gg \Delta_B$, we use the Taylor expansion

$$
\begin{aligned}
(\xi_{BA} + 2\Delta_B)^{5/2} &= \xi_{BA}^{5/2} \left( 1 + 2\frac{\Delta_B}{\xi_{BA}} \right)^{5/2} \\
&\simeq \xi_{BA}^{5/2} \left[ 1 + \frac{5\Delta_B}{\xi_{BA}} + \frac{15}{2} \left( \frac{\Delta_B}{\xi_{BA}} \right)^2 + \frac{5}{2} \left( \frac{\Delta_B}{\xi_{BA}} \right)^3 - \cdots \right] \\
&= \xi_{BA}^{5/2} + 5\Delta_B \xi_{BA}^{3/2} + \frac{15}{2} \Delta_B^2 \xi_{BA}^{1/2} + \frac{5}{2} \Delta_B^3 / \xi_{BA}^{1/2} - \cdots
\end{aligned}
\tag{E.2}
$$

$$
\begin{aligned}
\frac{4\Delta_B}{3} (\xi_{BA} + 2\Delta_B)^{3/2} &= \frac{4\Delta_B}{3} \xi_{BA}^{3/2} \left( 1 + 2\frac{\Delta_B}{\xi_{BA}} \right)^{3/2} \\
&\simeq \frac{4\Delta_B}{3} \xi_{BA}^{3/2} \left[ 1 + \frac{3\Delta_B}{\xi_{BA}} + \frac{3}{2} \left( \frac{\Delta_B}{\xi_{BA}} \right)^2 - \cdots \right] \\
&= \frac{4\Delta_B}{3} \xi_{BA}^{3/2} + 4\Delta_B^2 \xi_{BA}^{1/2} + 2\Delta_B^3 / \xi_{BA}^{1/2} - \cdots
\end{aligned}
\tag{E.3}
$$

Substituting Eqs. (E.2) and (E.3) into Eq. (E.1), we get

$$
\begin{aligned}
\frac{H_c^2(0)}{8\pi\Omega} &= \Delta_B \rho_B + \frac{D_B}{2} \left\{ \frac{2}{5} \left[ \xi_{BA}^{5/2} - \xi_{BA}^{5/2} - 5\Delta_B \xi_{BA}^{3/2} - \frac{15}{2}\Delta_B^2 \xi_{BA}^{1/2} \right. \right. \\
&\quad \left. - \frac{5}{2}\Delta_B^3/\xi_{BA}^{1/2} + \cdots \right] - \left[ \frac{4}{15}(2\Delta_B)^{5/2} + \frac{2\Delta_B}{3}\xi_{BA}^{3/2} \right. \\
&\quad \left. \left. + \frac{4\Delta_B}{3}\xi_{BA}^{3/2} + 4\Delta_B^2 \xi_{BA}^{1/2} + 2\Delta_B^3/\xi_{BA}^{1/2} - \cdots \right] \right\} \\
&= \Delta_B \rho_B + \frac{D_B}{2} \left\{ -2\Delta_B \xi_{BA}^{3/2} - 3\Delta_B^2 \xi_{BA}^{1/2} - \Delta_B^3/\xi_{BA}^{1/2} - \frac{4}{15}(2\Delta_B)^{5/2} \right. \\
&\quad \left. + 2\Delta_B \xi_{BA}^{3/2} + 4\Delta_B^2 \xi_{BA}^{1/2} + 2\Delta_B^3/\xi_{BA}^{1/2} - \cdots \right\} \\
&= \Delta_B \rho_B + \frac{D_B}{2} \left\{ \Delta_B^2 \xi_{BA}^{1/2} + \Delta_B^3/\xi_{BA}^{1/2} - \frac{4}{15}(2\Delta_B)^{5/2} \right\} \\
&= \Delta_B \rho_B + \frac{D_B}{2}\Delta_B^2 \xi_{BA}^{1/2} \left\{ 1 + \frac{\Delta_B}{\xi_{BA}} - \frac{16\sqrt{2}}{15}\left(\frac{\Delta_B}{\xi_{BA}}\right)^{1/2} \right\}.
\end{aligned}
\tag{E.4}
$$

Neglecting the small terms in Eq. (E.4), we finally obtain (8.101).

# Appendix F

# Calculation of the Free Energy of a Bose Gas Near the Characteristic Temperature $T_c^*$

The free energy of a Bose gas in the normal state ($H \geq H_c$ and $\Delta_B = 0$) is determined from the relation

$$F_{nB}(T,0) = -|\tilde{\mu}_{Bn}|N_B + T \sum_k \ln[1 - \exp(-(\varepsilon(k) + |\tilde{\mu}_{Bn}|)/T)] \tag{F.1}$$

After replacing the sum in Eq. (F.1) by the integral, we have

$$F_{nB}(T,0) = -|\tilde{\mu}_{Bn}|N_B + D_B\Omega T \int_0^\infty \sqrt{\varepsilon}\ln[1 - \exp(-(\varepsilon + |\tilde{\mu}_{Bn}|)/T)] \tag{F.2}$$

At $|\tilde{\mu}_{Bn}|)/T) \ll 1$, we can use the Taylor expansion of the second term on the right-hand side in Eq. (F.2) (see Appendix G and Eq. (F.2)). As a result, we obtain Eq. (8.106)

# Appendix G

# Calculation of the Free Energy of a SF Bose-Liquid Near the Characteristic Temperature $T_c^*$

We consider the second term in Eq. (8.99) and write this term in the form

$$I = T \sum_k \ln[1 - \exp(E_B(k)/T)]$$

$$= D_B \Omega T \int_0^\infty \sqrt{\varepsilon} \ln[1 - \exp(-\sqrt{(\varepsilon + |\tilde{\mu}_B|)^2 - \Delta_B^2}/T)]d\varepsilon \qquad (G.1)$$

At $|\tilde{\mu}_B|/T \ll 1$ and $\Delta_{SF} = \sqrt{|\tilde{\mu}_B|^2 - \Delta_B^2} \to 0$, the integral in Eq. (G.1) can be evaluated using the analogous method of calculation presented in Ref. [62]

$$\int_0^\infty \sqrt{\varepsilon} \ln\left\{1 - \exp\left[-\sqrt{(\varepsilon + |\tilde{\mu}_B|)^2 - \Delta_B^2}/T\right]\right\} d\varepsilon$$

$$\simeq \frac{\sqrt{\pi}}{2} T^{3/2} \left\{ 1.341 + 2.612|\tilde{\mu}_B|/T - \frac{4}{3}\sqrt{2\pi}\sqrt{\left(|\tilde{\mu}_B| + \sqrt{|\tilde{\mu}_B|^2 - \Delta_B^2}\right)/T} \right.$$

$$\left. \times(|\tilde{\mu}_B|/T - \sqrt{|\tilde{\mu}_B|^2 - \Delta_B^2}/2T) + 1.46\frac{3}{2}(|\tilde{\mu}_B|/T)^2 - \cdots \right\}. \qquad (G.2)$$

At $T \leq T_c^*$ and $|\tilde{\mu}_B| = \Delta_B$, we obtain from (G.2)

$$I = D_B \Omega \sqrt{\pi} T^{5/2} \left\{ -0.67 + 1.306\frac{\Delta_B}{T} + \cdots \right\} \qquad (G.3)$$

The latter term in Eq. (8.99) was already evaluated (see Eqs. (E.1) and (8.101)). Substituting Eq. (G.3) into Eq. (8.99), we obtain Eq. (8.107).

# INDEX

## N

## O

## P

## Q